S0-BRZ-162

The Ghosts of Fredericksburg

. . . and nearby environs

by L. B. Taylor, Jr.

Photographs by the Author
Illustrations by Lisa M. R. Sullivan

Printed in U.S.A. by Progress Printing Co., Inc.

ISBN NO. 0-9628271-8-5

Contents

Acknowledgements

Many, many people gave generously of their time and knowledge in sharing the stories, history, vignettes and anecdotes of "The Ghosts of Fredericksburg." Their enthusiasm and encouragement greatly helped make the book possible. I am always somewhat reluctant to publish a list of those who were so gracious and helpful for fear that I may leave someone out. If I do, it is unintentional. Anyway, here goes. I am especially grateful to the following:

Mrs. Lynn Franklin at Fall Hill. . . Mrs. Bess Lanier and Lee Langston Harrison at Federal Hill, and Mrs. Harrison also at the James Monroe Museum. . . Tammy Cross at Chatham. . . Barbara Willis at the Willis House and in general. . . Evelyn Kealey, Ed Patton and Stacia Norman at Kenmore. . . Ann Rowe at St. George's Church. . . Jay Harrison for "The Headless Blue Lady". . . Joyce Ackerman and Lonnie Williams at Smythe's Cottage. . . Linda Mix at the Rising Sun Tavern. . . Mike Zitz for "The Case of the Confused Confederate". . . Gail Braxton at Mary Washington House. . . and Pierre Mouryard at Le Lafayette Restaurant (formerly the Chimneys).

Also: Boyd and Elizabeth Braden at Litchfield. . . Kathy Dunton at Verville. . . Polly Tayloe at Mt. Airy. . . Barbara Powell and Larry Toymako at Marmion. . . Peter Larson at Old Mansion . . . Ann Power in Fauquier County. . . William Wilbur at Loretto . . . Shiela Heath and Mrs. Mead Palmer at the Old Gaol in Warrenton. . . Anne Rumbough at Edgehill. . . Charles Gray at Longwood. . . Norman Siefferman at Lamb's Creek Church. . . Charles and Faye Joy at Fork Church. . . Mary Adams, Alan Ward, Stuart Womeldorph and Alice and Ron Steele at Scotchtown. . . Rhonda Lefever and John Pearce of the Preservation Club of Mary Washington College. . . Dwight Storke at Pope's Creek. . . Robert Siegrist at Ferry Farm. . . Judy Warsing of the Bell House. . . Margie McGrath, Jo Ann Boyer and the security guards at Stratford Hall. . . Edward Haile and Sandra Pounsberry at Linden. . . and Carl Flemer of Ingleside Plantation.

I am indebted to Lucy Paul for "disking" the manuscript and to Wes Seekamp for proofreading. Plus special thanks and love to my intrepid cousins, Vance Shook of Dahlgren and Jane Ward of Norfolk.

Author's Personal Note

To be honest, I hadn't really intended to write this book, or at least I hadn't intended to write it this soon after publication in late 1990 of my most ambitious book in this series — "The Ghosts of Tidewater." To be honest again, I had intended to rest for a while. It was five years between the "Ghosts of Richmond" and the Tidewater book. I'm not getting any younger. I have a granddaughter now (she's a princess!), and I needed to spend more time marketing my books. They seem to sell well once they get into the bookstores, but somebody has to go out and get them into the bookstores, and I have been terribly neglectful in doing that.

Why on earth would I want to write another book?

Well, the answer came to me — not from the great psychic beyond or anything like that — but from the waves of comments, conversations, phone calls and letters that I have received over the past year or so. Like most of us, I guess, authors tend to have rather sensitive egos despite what they may say to the contrary. I'm no different.

Frankly, I was pleasantly overwhelmed at the response my new book received; and, in fact, at the response my other ghost books have received. More out of curiosity than anything else, last December I took part in a Christmas craft show in Richmond. Hundreds of people stopped by my booth to chat; to share with me their psychic experiences; to compliment me on my writings; and, fortunately, to buy books. The experience was most gratifying. The same thing happened at autograph signings, and at speaking engagements.

And then there have been the letters. They came from as far away as Japan. A young woman in California wrote that she had read only two books all the way through in her life. One of them was "The Ghosts of Williamsburg." A couple wrote from Maryland, "Your latest book, 'The Ghosts of Tidewater,' arrived today. I had planned to work on some records for our income tax report this evening, but my husband said, 'oh, no, not tonight. We're going to start the new book.' " A 14 year old boy in Newport News said, "I bought your book and read it cover to cover many times. . .'The Ghosts of Williamsburg' is honestly the best book I have ever read." A librarian at the Henrico

County Library in Richmond ordered a number of new books, saying the six they had in circulation had been completely worn out.

A letter came from Carolyn Kim, executive secretary to Charles Thomas Cayce, President of the Association for Research and Enlightenment in Virginia Beach. "I feel," she said "besides being entertaining, that you are rendering a great service. It could only be to the advantage of all of us to be aware of the phenomena. Who knows how many ways we could help these poor souls if we were only more open to their existence, and could feel free to share our knowledge and experiences."

And so I began to realize the prophetic words of Margaret DuPont Lee which she included in the introduction of her second book on ghosts 60 years ago. She wrote: "The very generous words of approval accorded my little edition of 'Virginia Ghosts' by friends, and particularly the many gracious testimonials from strangers, renders the adventuring after yet further evidence of spirit return a happy quest."

And then there was the call I got one night from a nurse at the Medical College of Virginia in Richmond. She told me of a young boy who was critically ill in New Mexico, and who came to MCV twice a year for treatment of a rare disease. She said they had asked him what he wanted on his next trip to the hospital. He said he wanted two things. One, he wanted to ride on some long rides at an amusement park, so the nurse said they would take him to King's Dominion and to Busch Gardens. He said the other thing he would like most was a copy of "The Ghosts of Richmond."

There was my answer.

Introduction

It could be said, arguably, that Fredericksburg is America's most historic city. Certainly, it is one of the most historic. It has been written that no other similar area in the world, if you include the immediate surrounding regions, produced so many great men in so short a time. Even a partial listing is impressive: George Washington, George Mason, Richard Henry, Lighthorse Harry and Robert E. Lee, James Monroe, James Madison, John Paul Jones, Matthew Fontaine Maury...

Named for Crown Prince Frederick of England, the town was founded in 1727, and became a colonial center for commerce and trade. Throughout the next two and a half centuries Fredericksburg persevered. It was virtually burned to the ground in 1807. It has been inundated by floods. During the Civil War it changed hands between the Union and Confederate forces seven times. Fredericksburg and the surrounding area provided the sites for four major battles during the conflict. Seventeen thousand Civil War soldiers lie buried in regional cemeteries. One historian summed it up thusly: "Fredericksburg and the country immediately about it was fought over, marched over, shelled, ravaged and desolated. Under its streets and in yards, hundreds of dead were buried to be, now and again, in after years, unearthed. No other American city ever suffered as did this formerly prosperous town."

Is it no wonder then, that Fredericksburg and nearby environs has more than its share of ghostly haunts?

Authors of psychic phenomena have called it the nation's most haunted city for its size. One report said: "Nearly every building in Fredericksburg boasts an apparition or two. The townspeople no longer attempt to refute their ghosts. They have learned to co-exist with them. And they will not hesitate to speak of such controversial topics as ancestral ghosts and spirit return with friendly strangers."

Indeed, the local Visitor's Center once put out a brochure on the subject. A Garden Club once promoted its annual tour of homes in the area by calling it "Grandeur, Gardens and Ghosts." And the Preservation Club of Mary Washington College holds an annual Ghost Walk each Halloween. A Fredericksburg psychic has been quoted as saying: "This is a very, very active area. There has been a lot of death here . . . a lot of violent death. Many homes in the Fredericksburg area have ghosts, which are usually benign."

In a letter to the editor, published in the local newspaper a few years ago, one resident wrote: "Many people in this area have first-hand knowledge about spirits and hauntings or they know someone who has experienced a paranormal event. It is my contention that if the *Free Lance Star* printed all the stories people could relate about every ghost in the Fredericksburg area alone, the newspaper would be running a ghost story every day for weeks on end."

"Nearby Environs" takes in some literary license so as to include areas rich in both history and psychic phenomena. Several stories emanated from the Fauquier County region and Warrenton, north of Fredericksburg. To the east, I have included sites extending the length of the Northern Neck, from King George in the north to Kilmarnock in the south. And to the southeast, I have added some rich tales from Essex County and the Tappahannock area. To the south, coverage extends to Patrick Henry's 1770s home, Scotchtown, northwest of Ashland and about halfway between Fredericksburg and Richmond. And directly west, there are tales originating in Orange and Culpeper Counties. All sites are within easy commuting distance of Fredericksburg.

What are ghosts? Does anyone really know? There have been many attempted definitions. "A disembodied soul. . . . the soul of a dead person believed to be the inhabitant of the unseen world, or to appear to the living in bodily likeness. . . . a surviving emotional memory or someone who has died traumatically, and usually tragically, but is unaware of his or her death. . . . something from human personality that exists after death. . . . a form of psychic energy which manifests itself over a period of time, most often in one place. . . ."

Are ghosts real? It is a time honored question. Are the reports of mysterious footsteps, rappings, moans, smells, cold drafts of air, and sightings of apparitions real or imagined? Certainly, as skeptics point out, a great many of such manifestations can be explained by rational means. Nevertheless, there appears to be a certain percentage of cases that remain inexplicable.

Those recorded in this book belong in this category. The one thing I have no doubt of is the honesty and sincerity of those people who were good enough to share their stories with me. I believe that they believe.

And anyway, as I have said many times, my task is not to make converts to the believability of ghosts. It is merely to entertain; to pass along the fascinating accounts I have heard. As the great television magician of another era, Dunninger, once said: "To those who believe, no explanation is necessary. To those who do not believe, no explanation is possible."

So whatever your persuasion is or isn't, I hope you will find the following accounts readable, interesting and entertaining.

Enjoy!

* * * * *

On a personal note, I am still searching for my first elusive encounter with the ethereal. Maybe I have too much journalistic objectivity to be sensitive enough to accept psychic activity. I did try, though. I arranged to spend the night in the haunted bedroom of a haunted 300-year-old house — "Old Mansion," in Bowling Green, a half hour's drive south of Fredericksburg. There, gracious host Peter Larson told me of the multiple-manifestation history of the place, and I eagerly anticipated the possibility of a ghostly experience that night.

I arrived after dark with a lady friend of mine who was a good enough sport to join me in this little adventure, and I must admit when I parked at the end of the long entryway to the house and got out of the car in the pitch blackness, I was startled. Alas, it was not from anything supernatural — Peter's dog had leaped up to greet me. As we approached the porch we saw a figure fleetingly pass by a window, and after repeated knocks on the front door proved to no avail, my friend suggested we leave for perhaps the more familiar trappings of a Holiday Inn. But I persisted. I opened the unlocked door and called several times. Finally, Peter emerged from the back of the house and greeted us.

He gave us a little history of Old Mansion, and after a brief tour we went upstairs to retire. I filled my friend in further on the apparitions sighted there, including strange premonitions of death that they carried as sort of spiritual messengers. And then my puckish sense of humor got the best of me, and I nearly lost a friend. I had gone downstairs to look through a book I had seen on the history of the county, and when I came back upstairs, I circled around and went through the bathroom. As I reentered the bedroom, my friend was standing with her back to me, facing a closet door through which, it is alleged, some of the ghosts periodically appeared. I did a terrible thing. I snuck up on my friend, grabbed her, and uttered a loud "boo." I scared the hell out of her! She was not amused. And, rightfully, she didn't speak to me for the rest of the evening — after she had told me what she thought of my ill-timed prank.

The rest of the evening was spent uneventfully. I was tired from a full day of ghost-tracking, and I slept like a log. I didn't see, hear, feel or otherwise experience anything supernatural. Fortunately, I was able to repair the friendship the next morning, as Peter prepared one of his famous breakfasts. Following orange juice, coffee, and granola cereal, he whipped up a concoction which he referred to as — from Shakespeare — "Eye of the frog, toe of the newt." He said, "Remember the witches brew in the caldron," from MacBeth, I think. Anyway, it was fried apples, sliced sausage, walnuts, and brown sugar, and it was delicious.

Peter told us how other guests at the house — it is open to the public as a Bed and Breakfast, which I highly recommend — had experienced various forms of phantasmal visitations in the night. But to me, it was not to be. I did leave the house with a certain amount of apprehension, however. I know my friend will one day devise a plot to get even with me. The thought of such retribution can be frightening in itself!

Therefore, it is with self-preservation in mind, that I would like to dedicate this book to her — Brenda Goens.

WASHINGTON
WARRENTON
CHANCELLORSVILLE
FREDERICKSBURG
SPOTSYLVANIA
RAPPAHANNOCK RIVER
COLONIAL BEACH
GEORGE WASHINGTON'S BIRTHPLACE
STRATFORD HALL
POTOMAC RIVER
BOWLING GREEN
TAPPAHANNOCK
WARSAW
SCOTCHTOWN
HOME OF PATRICK HENRY
RAPPAHANNOCK RIVER
KILMARNOCK
RICHMOND

CHAPTER 1

Caring Katina of Fall Hill

Mrs. Lynn W. Franklin, born February 28, 1899, is both a delightful and a remarkable person. She is today still an active woman with a lucid, sharp mind who can rattle off historic dates, names and places with the rapidity and accuracy of a serious student in American history prepping for final exams. She is a direct descendent of Alexander Spotswood's wife (he was a highly respected colonial Virginia governor), and she has lived in the magnificent hilltop plantation called Fall Hill near Fredericksburg since 1908.

She has lived there these past eight decades plus, she says, with a long-time resident ghost. But she harbors no fear. "I doubt that you would ever find a more friendly spirit than the one we have here," Mrs. Franklin smiles. "In a way, it's actually a comfort to have her here. This house is surrounded by 100 acres of woods, and it's good to have a ghost with me so no mortals bother us."

Exactly when the house, or rather houses, at Fall Hill were built is still somewhat debatable. "Oh, I guess there's an argument about that," Mrs. Franklin says. It is, however, generally accepted that ever since the first Francis Thornton arrived in this country from England in 1673, his descendents have lived within thousands of acres of scenic land at the site with a majestic view overlooking the picturesque Rappahannock River on the outskirts of Fredericksburg.

One account says he built an "interesting old house" about 1680, and named it "The Falls," since the falls of the river thundered nearby. A later Francis Thornton — there were a number of them in a direct line of descendency — put up a "cottage" or summer residence somewhere in the 1738 to 1740 time frame.

According to the Virginia Landmarks Register, the present house, which includes eight rooms and, says the current owner, "an enormous attic and basement," probably was built for Francis Thornton V, sometime around 1790. Mrs. Franklin disagrees. "The house certainly was here before 1790, she contends. "I believe it was started in 1763."

At any rate, the designer was Richard Taliaferro who has been described as being the most skillful architect in the colonies. Mrs. Franklin says he was instrumental in the design of the Palace and of the Wythe House in Williamsburg, for example, and that he pioneered such innovations as square and corner fireplaces. When was the house finished? Mrs. Franklin laughs, and says, "Oh, it's not finished yet."

The legend of the benevolent spirit which sometimes surfaces at Fall Hill had its origins in Williamsburg, when a young Indian girl — some have said she was a Sioux princess — was captured and given to then-governor Spotswood. Her name was Katina. When this venerable gentleman retired from active public life in 1720, and moved to his palace in the wilderness at Germanna, near Fredericksburg, he took the Indian maiden with him, and she became the nurse, or nanny, for his four children. Her services were excellent, and she was treated like one of the family. William Byrd was so impressed with her during a visit, it is said he gave her the "largest tip" ever received by a servant.

After Spotswood died in 1740, Katina went to work for the Thorntons at Fall Hill, where she helped raise three generations of children. "But she was much more than a servant," says Mrs. Franklin. She was "the essence of dedication and devotion to the young ones she loved, and they loved her." Recalled as being small, dark and lithesome, Katina taught the young Thorntons the ways of the Indian, and how best to appreciate nature's most beautiful secrets.

She died in 1777, and was buried in the garden, "beside a little stream, with great boulders of granite gathered from her native hills marking the spot. . . . this Indian sleeps her last sleep beneath a tree, up and over which climbs a wild grape vine. . . ."

"When I first came to Fall Hill to live, I was nine years old," Mrs. Franklin says. "My grandfather took me by the hand one day and told me, quite solemnly, 'I'm going to show you the grave of our old family nurse, Katina.' We knelt beside a little grave covered by a granite stone. But nothing was written on it. Katina was a slave and the family was very careful not to discriminate or show partiality by engraving her stone.

Mrs. Lynn W. Franklin at Fall Hill

"My grandfather then told me that when his great-grandfather lived, she brought him up and taught him to speak Indian. She was a very old woman then, and when she died, he was inconsolable. He wept and said he'd lost his best friend."

Exactly when Katina first reappeared at Fall Hill, allegedly to make sure that young descendents of the Thornton family were being properly cared for, is not certain, though recorded reports of her sightings go back to the early years of this century. When Mrs. Bessie Taylor Robinson lived in the house in the 1920s, she said that "many persons. . . have spoken of seeing her walking about the plantation as though looking for her companions of long ago."

Mrs. Franklin says one of the first occurrences she remembers was when two boys were home from school on vacation and were sleeping in the nursery. The next morning one of the youngsters came downstairs, "appearing quite pale," and asked Mrs. Robinson if she had come in their room the previous night to cover them. She told them no, and inquired why he asked. He told her that "an old woman with long black braids" had come in during the night and then disappeared through the wall at the head of the bed!

Mrs. Franklin says that in 1938 a New York journalist named Alice Dickson came to Fall Hill as a guest of her mother. "One afternoon she was taking a nap upstairs. She awoke around five o'clock and started to get up when, she said, a young boy dressed in knee britches walked through the open door. He had his hair tied back and was attired in colonial period clothes. Then she said that behind him followed a little Indian woman with long black braided hair."

Mrs. Franklin says the woman thought the children in the house had dressed up to amuse her. But when she addressed them, they didn't answer. They just disappeared! "There were no children in the house at the time. She'd seen the ghost of Katina!"

In 1969, a newspaper reporter named Linda Raymond was invited to spend a night at Fall Hill by Mrs. Franklin. She wanted to do an article on Katina. She started her resulting story by saying, "She'd been dead for more than 200 years (actually 192), but she was there that night close beside me, as near and thick a presence as fog in a river bottom." Ms. Raymond also said, "I could feel the ghost's presence all around us. The only thing that seemed strange was that we couldn't see her when she was so close."

On yet another occasion, Mrs. Robinson saw the apparition. She came home late one night from a meeting in town and as she stood in the downstairs hall, she witnessed "a figure" come out of the room where her younger son was sleeping. Upon examination, Mrs. Robinson found every other member of the family sound asleep and all the doors and windows were locked shut. She told friends she had no doubt she had seen Katina, still checking on the youngsters in the house.

And, finally, a few years ago, Mrs. Franklin herself had an ethereal experience in her bedroom. "I had been away for awhile and I was in bed, wide awake, reading. I had my little granddaughter in the house with me. We'd just recently lost her father, and it was a period of considerable stress, as you can imagine.

"I had never seen a ghost of any description before, although, of course, I was well aware of the stories about Katina. I never thought I would see her, and to be truthful, I was never quite convinced that anyone had ever seen her. Imagination can do a lot of things, you know. But I definitely wasn't dreaming. I was alert. Then, at the foot of my bed there appeared this darkly beautiful face. She just looked at me with those dark Indian eyes. Her expression never changed, but it seemed like she had a look of great concern. I interpreted it to mean that I had better take good care of my granddaughter. She was there just for an instant, and then she was gone. But I have no question that she was real."

There is a curious footnote to the appearances and disappearances of Katina over the years at Fall Hill. Mrs. Franklin says that those who claimed to have seen the Indian ghost say that she most often has been seen near the top of the stairs, where she vanishes from sight by apparently walking through a bedroom wall.

"Years ago, we stripped off the old wallpaper in that room," Mrs. Franklin notes. "We discovered that during the 1800s there were some alterations made in the house. At the spot where Katina appears to walk through the wall, there was, under the wallpaper, an old sealed-up doorway. It was a second door to that bedroom. I believe it was once the nursery!"

More recently, a towering oak tree that has been standing guard over Katina's grave, crashed to earth one night during a fierce storm and completely covered her burial site. Mrs. Franklin says she has not had the tree removed because of the fear that vandals might think about digging the body up to search for old Indian relics.

Perhaps it is nothing more than pure coincidence that Katina's ghost has not been seen since.

CHAPTER 2

The Mystery Man at Smythe's Cottage

If you are lucky — or if you are unlucky, depending upon how you view such things — there is a chance you can have dinner in Old Town Fredericksburg and possibly see or sense a ghost at the same time. But even if no spirits arise, you can enjoy a good old-fashioned home cooked meal and learn about the colorful history of Smythe's Cottage at 303 Fauquier Street, about half way between the Rising Sun Tavern and the Mary Washington house.

Owner-host Lonnie Williams and his crew will be happy to serve up a variety of soups, salads and sandwiches for lunch, and at dinner time it is, in his words, "a little bit of everything," including roast pork, Virginia ham, chicken pot pie and stuffed quail among other entrees. Sixty can be seated in the two rooms downstairs, complete with bar, and in the summer another 40 can dine outside.

It is not exactly certain when the cottage, located at 1210 Princess Anne Street, was built. Former owner Joyce Ackerman, who used to serve a mean turkey hash there, believes it dates back to the 1830s, and originally was a blacksmith shop, hence the name. Lonnie, however, says tax records on the building go back to the 1850s, and he's not sure beyond that. He has heard that it may even have served for a time as a bordello during Civil War days.

In any event, both Joyce and Lonnie have not only heard others tell of unusual activities in the cottage, but they have had experiences of their own. In addition, there is a ghostly legend associated with an old house directly across the street.

Joyce vividly remembers the day, a few years ago, when a tourist approached her and asked why the old lady in that house was so rude. He told her he had gone up to the front door and knocked, and said he could see an old woman through a window just staring at him. She then turned away and started crawling up the stairs on her hands and knees. Joyce said she just laughed and told the tourist, "that's just Tootie. She's been dead a year and a half!"

The tourist had apparently seen the apparition of a woman named Tootie Ninde, an eccentric town character. "She had been ill when I first bought Smythe's Cottage in 1975," says Joyce. "I think she had cancer and emphysema. And she did have to crawl up the stairs. Her room faced my place and I used to see her light go out at night. Then a curious thing happened. About two years after she died, I saw the light on in her room and then it went out. I didn't think anything about it at the time, because I just thought a relative or someone was in the house. But when I saw one of her relatives later and asked about it, he or she said no. Another time I walked over to the front porch and I saw someone inside at the foot of the stairs. It was like a figure, and it just sort of drifted away."

William Doyle Butzner, now dead, who bought the house in the 1970s, told a newspaper reporter in 1984 that he and several of his friends had heard someone climbing the stairs at night, and they, too, thought it was the ghost of Tootie. Butzner had another spooky encounter around Christmas 1983. He and several guests were rudely awakened late one night by the sounds of music, voices and the tinkling of glasses coming from downstairs. It sounded like a party, he said. A search of the house revealed nothing, but the sounds continued until about 4 in the morning.

The same phenomena reoccurred early in 1984, and Butzner theorized that it might have something to do with Civil War spirits. The reason: while unearthing a cistern in the yard, he once found more than 100 champagne bottlenecks and various other remnants from the War Between the States.

Joyce Ackerman says similar happenings took place at Smythe's Cottage when she owned it. "I had a little office upstairs, and on more than one occasion when I was up there working, I would hear noises downstairs, annoying noises. It sounded like a group having a conversation, like they were holding a meeting. But when I walked down, there was never anyone there."

Equally mysterious at the cottage was the periodic appearance of a tall man in a long black jacket with long black hair and a loose, western-style tie. Joyce saw him at least twice on the

outdoor patio and she spoke to him both times and said he just "drifted away." Once, after closing up for the night, Joyce's cook was getting in her truck when she saw the man and she admitted it scared her to death. On another occasion, one of the kitchen helpers saw the vision and went after it with a knife, but it disappeared.

"I personally have never seen him," says Lonnie Williams, "but we have had customers ask us who the strange man was on the patio. They had seen him. We have had some odd things happen since we've been running the restaurant. I've seen shadows moving now and then and heard voices and footsteps when no one else was around. We've found the water running when we opened up in the morning — things like that. We have an old clock that Joyce told us hadn't worked in years. It has started up on occasion, keeping the right time, as if someone had just wound it."

"I can tell you this," Lonnie adds, "we had a waiter here once who claimed he used to see a young girl upstairs. He made up a story about her, telling customers that she had been a prostitute in the house. Everytime he told that story, the candle on the table would crack. I can't explain that.

"But I guess the strangest thing was the time two or three years ago when one of our waitresses said she heard the door open and she turned a corner and ran into somebody — who wasn't there! She said there was somebody there, but there wasn't anybody there. That's how she explained it. She screamed and ran and got me. I was only a couple of steps from the doorway and when I entered the room there was no one there. She was terrified. She ran out the front door and never came back!"

CHAPTER 3

The Mystery Woman of Marmion

Virginia historic marker J 63, on Route 3 two miles west of King George and a few miles east of Fredericksburg, says of Marmion: "Probably built by John Fitzhugh early in the 18th century and later named for Scott's poem. About 1785 it passed from Philip Fitzhugh to George Washington Lewis, Washington's favorite nephew, who died there.... The richly decorated interior is one of the best in Virginia."

Indeed, says the Virginia Landmarks Register: "Although it (Marmion) appears plain and unrefined in contrast to the brick mansions of the James River, its paneled drawing room, now exhibited in the Metropolitan Museum of Art, is one of the most elegant of the surviving colonial interiors."

There are a number of legends surrounding this grand old house, and one of them involves the interior design. It is said that at the end of the Revolutionary War, Philip Fitzhugh found a Hessian soldier near death on the banks of the Potomac River, a mile and a half distant. The man was nursed back to health, and, as it turned out, was a highly skilled artisan. In appreciation for the kindness shown him, he decorated the walls of the parlor as one historian phrased it, "in lovely landscapes and cornucopias filled with flowers, making from Virginia clay and plants the paints he used — clear and beautiful after the passing of 150 years!"

Also inside are two intriguing secret rooms, built one on top of the other in a huge chimney, doubtless as hideouts from marauding Indians. Outbuildings flanking the main house include a kitchen, office, dairy and smokehouse. At one time there was a formal garden to the east. And there are still cannonballs embedded in the brick walls leading from the mansion — relics of wars long ago.

A second legend involves alleged buried treasure. There have been stories, circulating for generations, about a "chest of valuables" that was hidden somewhere on the grounds, but no one seems to know if it ever was recovered. Mrs. Lucy Lewis Grymes, who lived in the house early in the 20th century, and who is a direct descendent of Betty Washington of Kenmore, George Washington's only sister, did uncover some long-lost money sometime in the 1920s, but it would hardly qualify as a king's ransom. She found a roll of colonial bills in the attic of the office outbuilding.

The third legend swirls around the ghost or ghosts at Marmion. "I'm not a believer in ghosts and I don't know much about it, but a woman is supposed to appear in the house at times," says Jay Powell, great nephew of Lucy Lewis Grymes, and a former owner of the property. Jay's wife, Barbara, sheds more light on the subject.

"The only thing I know is that it was supposed to be the appearance of a young girl dressed in white, but no one knew who she was or why she was there," Barbara says. "I know that many times when she was alive, Lucy said that while sitting at her desk she felt a presence so strong that she 'could reach out and touch someone'."

Lucy, Barbara says, had heard house guests speak of a "lovely young girl" since her childhood, and she once confided

that on more than one occasion she felt "someone" in the room with her, but she had never seen anything. One visitor who did, however, was Edmonia Goode. In the summer of 1928, she was lying down on her bed resting, when, she said, the door opened and a "very beautiful young girl" came in and proceeded to open the wardrobe. Miss Goode greeted her and said she hadn't known there was another guest in the house. The girl turned and stared straight at her. Miss Goode then became startled as she realized she wasn't looking at a mortal being. When she got up from bed and approached the girl, the figure vanished!

"There was another time when there was a party at Marmion, and one lady claimed she saw the girl in white descending the stairs," Barbara says. "The lady went through every photo album in the house to see if the apparition matched anyone but she had no luck.

"The only thing I can remember that happened to us while we lived in the house," Barbara continues, "was an experience my daughter had one evening when she was about 10 or 12 years old. She had walked down the hill to the mail box and had a vision of some hunters. She said they walked up the road towards her and then disappeared before her eyes. She ran back to the house and was as white as a sheet. Jay went out to look for the hunters, but he couldn't find a trace."

Barbara says the strangest thing she heard during the time Lucy Lewis Grymes lived at Marmion was the so-called mysterious dinner party. Barbara recalls the account as it was passed on to her: "One evening, Lucy and her husband, Carter, were in bed when they heard a commotion in the dining room. They both got up to investigate, and when they entered the room they saw that all the chairs had been pulled away from the table. Lucy said it was as if people were sitting there! She and Carter pushed the chairs back under the table and went back to bed. Then they heard the noise again and when they went downstairs the second time, all the chairs had been pulled out again! Carter searched the entire house, but found nothing. This time they let the chairs stay where they were and there was no more ruckus. I always thought it was odd, too, that the Grymes had what was described as a 'ferocious' dog. A real watchdog. Yet both times when they went downstairs that night, the dog would not enter the dining room. It cowered at the doorway."

While the identity of the phantom diners may never be

known, there is a possible clue as to who the lady in white may have been. The current owners of Marmion are David Newhall and Larry Toymako. Larry found a reference in an old book to a woman named Kate Pollock, who lived in the house in the 1800s. She died in child birth at age 22 on October 24, 1821, as did the infant. They are buried on the grounds. It is perhaps she who periodically roams about searching for a happiness denied her so long ago.

CHAPTER 4

Kindred Spirits of Kenmore

One of the truly unsung heroes of the American Revolutionary War was an aristocratic gentleman not necessarily noted for his physical appearance but more so for his courtly bearing and great dignity. Though his name may be unfamiliar to high school history students, he was a close and respected associate of such noble patriots as Edmund Pendleton, Francis Lightfoot Lee, Richard Henry Lee, George Wythe and many others. He also was a lifelong intimate friend and brother-in-law of George Washington. His name was Fielding Lewis.

Born in Gloucester County in 1725, Lewis moved north to the Fredericksburg area as a young man, where it is said his natural leadership abilities and distinguished connections quickly won him a position of prominence in the community. Biographers have described him as an efficient man of affairs with polished manners who was widely recognized as a gentleman of wealth and integrity.

Perhaps his greatest measurable contribution to the cause of American freedom was the sacrifice of his personal wealth — and possibly of his health as well — to launch and operate a gun manufactory during the war, which provided arms for the colonial troops. He literally gave everything he had, materially, physically and otherwise, to keep this factory going during the darkest years of the fighting. And when the war ended with no proper compensation, as promised, from the Continental Congress, Lewis went broke. With less patriotic creditors pressing him, he suffered serious lung trouble — then called consumption — and died after a lingering illness in December 1781.

Among his other notable accomplishments was the building of a mansion and estate in Fredericksburg which came to be known as Kenmore. After his first wife died in February 1750, Lewis married Betty Washington, the only sister of the first President of the United States, in May of that year. Shortly after that he reportedly asked his new brother-in-law to advise him in the selection of a favorable site for the home he proposed to build. The site was chosen near the corner of what is now Lewis Street and Washington Avenue, on a green slope which fell away towards the Rappahannock River. The grounds then were surrounded by orchards and woods full of gum, hickory and red, white and black oak trees.

Construction of the house began in 1752 and evolved into what architects consider to be one of the most beautiful colonial mansions in America. The walls of the elegantly simple exterior of Kenmore are two feet thick, fashioned of Flemish bond brick. Inside is an exceptionally elaborate interior containing what the Virginia Landmarks Register calls "the finest 18th century plasterwork and chimneypieces in the country."

Following Fielding Lewis' death in 1781, Betty Lewis maintained the 1,100 acre estate, raising her three youngest sons, for 15 years before moving to a farm south of town. The mansion passed through the ownership of several families during the 19th century and into the 20th, and after suffering relatively little damage through the Civil War, fell on hard times by the 1920s. When plans were announced to subdivide the property and dismantle the great house, a movement began to save it. This led to the formation of the Kenmore Association and fostered a nationwide preservation effort which, as any visitor to the site today will readily attest, has been highly successful.

It is now a museum open to the public, complete with period furniture, a beautifully restored garden, a gift shop, and a kitchen dependency in which old fashioned gingerbread is served. The recipe is said to be the same as that used by Mary Ball Washington, George Washington's mother. There are many special exhibits illustrating the history of Kenmore and the colonial period, and the Association calls it a house that "belongs to the nation."

It also has been said that when in the mansion one becomes conscious of the "brooding presence" of Fielding Lewis. And there are many people — both tourists and Association employees and volunteers alike — who have sworn they have seen and heard the ghost of this refined gentleman at Kenmore. The most common manifestation is the sound of his heavy tread in an upstairs bedroom as he paces back and forth.

He has been sighted a number of times, too, and the descriptions vary little. Often in broad daylight, witnesses have reported seeing a man with a "worried expression" on his face dressed in clothes of the Revolutionary War period. Some have claimed to have seen him poring over a sheaf of papers, which they have speculated were the bills of creditors he could not pay.

At times, the Kenmore Association hostesses have tried to discourage the stories of psychic experiences in the house, saying, appropriately, that the beauty and history of Kenmore are far more interesting. Still, the legends abound. Door knobs turn when no one is at the door. Doors have stuck shut for days at a time, but when a carpenter is called, they mysteriously open. Guests have felt inexplicable cold drafts "blowing on their heads" in the dead of summer. A visitor standing in the Betty Washington Lewis chamber with two friends in the 1920s remarked, "I think this is a haunted room." As she did, to their astonishment, they heard a "click" and the wardrobe door slowly swung open.

In October 1971 — just five days before Halloween — an "official" seance was held at Kenmore. It was requested by Adi-

Kent Thomas Jeffrey, a Pennsylvania writer and psychic investigator. The session was conducted by a woman named Grace Walker of Yardley, Pennsylvania, a member of the International General Assembly of Spiritualists, and a self-described "born clairvoyant." Mrs. Jeffrey apparently had asked for such a meeting a year after she had observed closet doors in the house swinging open and shut by themselves.

Among those present, aside from Mrs. Jeffrey and Ms. Walker, were then-Kenmore director, Col. Robert Burhans, Susie Hallberg, then-director of the Fredericksburg Information Center, two friends of Mrs. Jeffrey, three members of a Washington radio station there to record the event, and a newspaper reporter. Also present were two Kenmore hostesses, Ann Cunningham and Claire Barnard.

Mrs. Walker said the "vibrations were good" in the children's room, but she felt "utter confusion and sadness" there, so the seance instead was held in the master bedroom where the doors supposedly swung open and shut on occasion. The participants were then seated in a circle and asked to place their feet on the floor, to uncross their arms, and to relax and be silent. The Lord's Prayer was recited.

Mrs. Walker sat on a folding chair with her hands on her lap, the palms turned upward. Her eyes were half closed. After some initial conversation with members of the circle, she said she envisioned the spirit of an older man, "tired and weary of life." He was dressed in a collarless shirt and his hair was "threaded with gray." She placed the time of his "era" as being shortly after the Revolutionary War.

Immediately, the other members of the party thought of Kenmore's master, Fielding Lewis, who probably was at this most troubled period at that time, worn down with physical illness and the heavy burden of his debts. The medium said the man she was "communicating with" from the beyond was "not very pleasant and was inclined to be snappish." Indeed, Lewis was known to be a no-nonsense man of business who exhibited little humor in his affairs. Mrs. Walker added that this "soul" had appeared to her because he did not rest at peace; he was unhappy and was doomed to "always wander."

Beyond this, she indicated that there was a second spirit in the house responsible for the swinging doors. She said it was a young man who caused this manifestation periodically, more as a prank than anything else, "just to let you know he is present and around the house." During the seance a door was shut to see if it would open, but nothing happened. Mrs. Jeffrey explained this inactivity by saying psychic phenomena rarely happened "on command." With that, the seance closed, conclusively or inconclusively, depending upon your point of view.

Twenty years later, Ann Cunningham says she hasn't seen anything happen at Kenmore. "I guess you can't see what didn't happen," she acknowledges. "I think I'm just too practical a person." Yet she admitted there were many tales of "things" occurring in the house. "There is a lot of hearsay," says another hostess who asked not to be identified by name. "People hear things here. We've found beds puffed up. Lights flicker at times and windows sometimes seem to open by themselves.

"I did hear one story," the hostess continued, "about a lady who once stayed here as a guest with her mother. They were in a front bedroom, and each night they would hear footsteps, so they would get up and close the door. The next morning when they awoke the door would be wide open. So one night they pushed a heavy table across the room and shoved it against the door. They said the next morning the table was back where it had been the night before and the door was open again." On another occasion, a student at Mary Washington College claimed she got a "ghostly image" in photos she took at the house.

One person who has had a number of psychic encounters at Kenmore over the past couple of years is a young lady named Evelyn Kealey, a volunteer who works on the archeological digs that take place on the mansion's grounds. "I definitely think I have more psychic powers than the average person," she says. "That may explain why I was the only one who saw some of the things I did."

Several of the "occurrences" take place around Labor Day and in the fall and winter, when Evelyn and her associates spend a lot of time in the basement sifting through, cleaning and cataloguing the artifacts found in the diggings. These have included animal bones and teeth, apothecary weights, Civil War buttons, shards of 18th century ceramic and glass, nails and other items. "I've said the more they dig, the more it will stir up the restless spirits," she laughs. She may be right.

Evelyn says some of the more common manifestations have included "someone fooling with the light. You have to flip the lights on and off or trip the circuit box," she points out. "The lights have gone out for no reason on more than one occasion, and no one working in the basement was anywhere near the switch. We joke about it. We just say it's Fielding. We think he likes to play pranks sometimes just to let us know he's around."

"Sometimes he, or it, locks the door to the basement. Again, you would have to latch it, or lock it with a key, and sometimes when we try to get through the door, it's like someone is holding it, and then all of a sudden it releases." On another occasion, Evelyn set a pail of silty water down to open the door. She was taking it outside to dump the water which had been used to wash off the artifacts. She opened the door and turned back to get the pail only to find that it had been "knocked over" by unseen hands or feet, and the water spilled down the stairs. "I had to clean it up," she says. "I wasn't very happy with Fielding about that."

Evelyn also has seen two apparitions in the basement, although she doesn't know if it was the same entity or two different ones. "Once, I saw a big willowy outline of a person move from one room to another. It had a cloudy, billowy shape. I had had the feeling that day that something was going to happen. I don't know why but I did. There was not a whole lot of shape to what I saw, but it definitely was moving. Shortly after that, the lights went out."

The second sighting proved to be more frightening. "It was about four in the afternoon in the fall, and I was taking a bucket of water out to empty it. I felt very strange. I was getting spooked out. As I got to the area I call 'mortuary wall,' I stopped. Against the wall I saw a dark outline. This is the darkest part of the basement, but I saw a tall figure that I estimated to be about six feet tall, draped with a cape around its shoulders.

"It was just standing there looking at me. I assumed it was a man, possibly a military officer in some kind of uniform. I could see the outline of his head, neck and shoulders, but when I looked down, I couldn't see any boots or footwear.

I just stood there. I froze. I was stunned. I could feel goose bumps. I know there was no way what I was looking at was mortal! Nor could it have been my shadow. The sun doesn't get to this part of the basement. When I couldn't see his feet or legs, a thought struck me that maybe they had been amputated. Kenmore had been used as a hospital during the Civil War and I had a

Fielding Lewis

theory that when any soldiers died, they stacked them up against this particular wall, because it is the coolest place in the entire house in the summer.

"Anyway, I stood there for what seemed like an eternity. I guess it was only a few seconds. Then I went outside and dumped the water and when I came in again, the figure was gone. It was very eerie. No one else has seen anything like it, but as I said, I believe I am more psychically sensitive than most. I can tell you this, though. There are people who work here who won't come into the basement. They are afraid. It doesn't really bother me in that respect. I know there is some kind of presence down there. But I say it adds character."

Another person who has had unusual experiences at Kenmore — although he doesn't claim to be psychically sensitive in the least — is Ed Patton, who worked at the mansion as a part-time security guard for more than 15 years. Ed, now retired, is 83, but he remembers his encounters as if they happened yesterday, although he is in no way afraid of ghosts.

"Actually, there were three separate things that happened to me at different times, and I can't really explain any of them," Ed says. "One was the night I got a call at home from the police at two in the morning saying that a burglar alarm had been set off at Kenmore and that I should go check it out. Well, when I got there I didn't see anything out of the ordinary, but when I got up on the second floor and was walking down the hall, checking things out, a very strange thing occurred.

"I heard someone, or something, calling out my name. I heard it three times. It said, 'Eddie, Eddie, Eddie.' It was very distinct. I know I wasn't imagining it. I looked up and down the hall and in the nearby rooms. I saw nothing. Then I looked out the windows onto the grounds. There was no one there. It never happened again, only that once."

Ed continued his story. The second time, I was outside the house at night and looked down toward the gate. There was a lady there. She had on a veil, which I thought was a little odd. It looked like a mosquito net to me. I watched as she crossed the brick walkway, and when she got to the other side — well, the thing is, and I don't know quite how to explain it — she never got to the other side! She disappeared right in front of me. I never figured that out."

Ed says that many times when he was in the basement of the mansion he heard footsteps on the floor above, when no one should have been in the house. Everytime that he went to investigate, he found nothing amiss. "Sometimes, these things can play on your imagination, you know what I mean," he notes. "But I never made a big deal out of it. It never scared me. I always thought I was safer in the house with a ghost than I was out in the streets with a crowd."

The third specific episode at Kenmore took place one night when Ed was alone in the gift shop, eating a sandwich. To most people, this particular manifestation might have been the scariest of all — as the scene has been done and redone in chiller movies — but Ed, as usual, took it in stride. "I was just sitting there minding my own business, when I heard this screeching noise," he recalls. "Sounded a little like what a mouse would make. I turned around to the door where it was coming from and saw that the door knob was turning. It was turning real slow like, and making a slight screeching sound. Now this was one time I know I wasn't imagining things. I was sitting right there and I saw it. After I watched it for a minute or two, I got up and opened the door. There was no one on the other side. You explain it. I can't."

Fielding Lewis was not known to have had a sharp sense of humor during his lifetime. He is better remembered as a brooder, a worrier, and those who have claimed to have seen his apparition say that's the way he appeared to them. But maybe he did have a lighter side, too, and maybe that could account for some of the more prankish manifestations which have taken place over the years — and still occur — at historic Kenmore.

CHAPTER 5

The Gentle Ghost of St. George's

It is fortunate that there is a ghost story related to beautiful old St. George's Church on Princess Anne Street at George Street in Fredericksburg, because the parish of St. George, founded in 1720, has such a long and colorful history. The present house of worship is the third one to be built on the site. The first, a small wooden church, was erected in 1732, just five years after the town was laid out. It was enlarged several times, but construction couldn't keep up with the growth of the congregation, and a second, larger structure was put up in 1816.

In the 18th century, parishioners were required by law to attend church at least once a month, and both this and the fact that some of the early clergymen at times took matters into their own hands, literally, to assure attendance — led to some interesting anecdotes. Spotsylvania County records, for example, early in the 18th century, cite a John Diggs "for absenting himself from the place of Divine worship." He was subsequently fined ten shillings, or 100 pounds of tobacco, or "must receive corporal punishment in lieu thereof, as the law directs."

There is, too, reference pointing out that some of the sermons were bone-jarring tough, and critics were physically intimidated. It is recorded that on one occasion a parson "of gigantic size and strength had a rough and tumble fight with members of his vestry, in which the laymen were knocked out." The following Sunday the parson preached, "And I contended with them, and cursed them, and smote certain of them, and plucked off their hair." Small wonder that it was written, "In the main, the character and manner of living of the early ministers of the Church of England here were not in accord with the dignity of their mission."

Margaret DuPont Lee, who sketched the history of the church in her book "Virginia Ghosts" in 1930, told of three Baptist preachers who were seized by the county sheriff in 1768 for "preaching the gospel contrary to law." They were summarily thrown in the clink whereupon they preached from the jail windows "to the crowd gathered below." They finally were

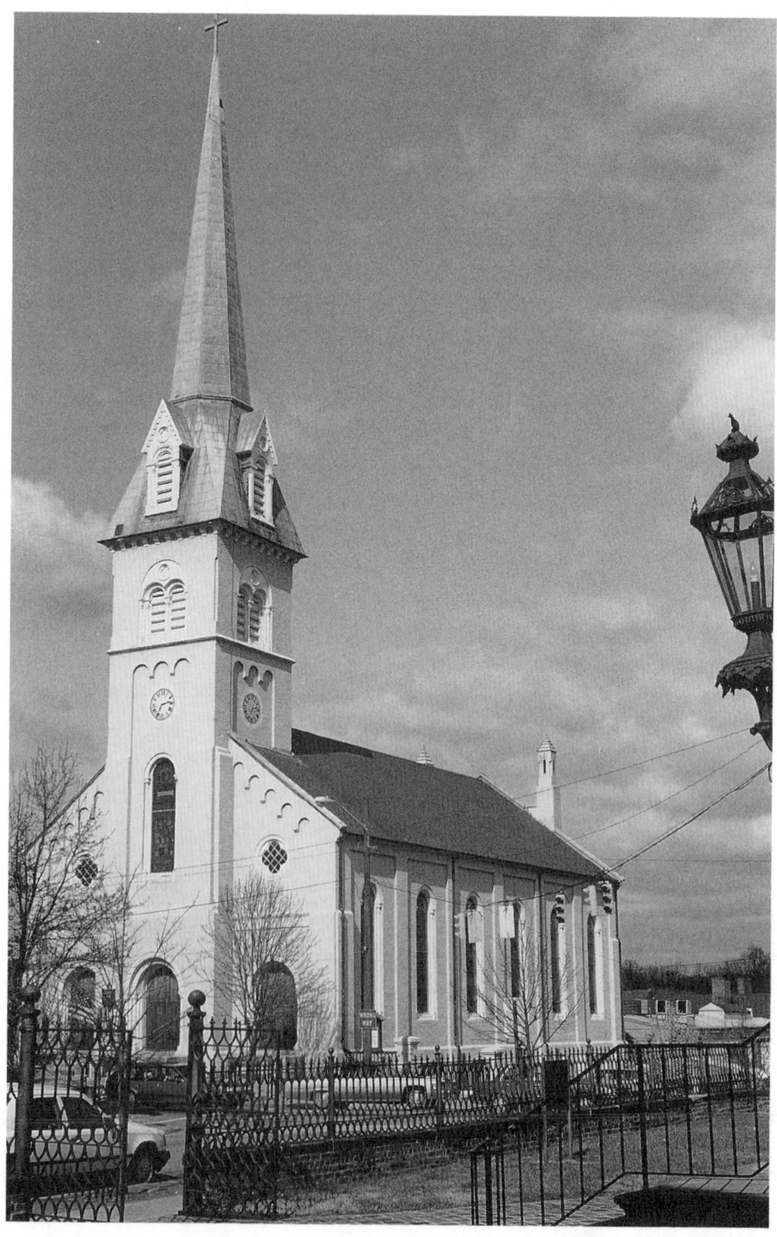

released after the great Patrick Henry pleaded their cause. Interestingly, the second rector of St. George's was also a Patrick Henry, uncle of the famous orator.

Mary Ball and Augustine Washington, George Washington's parents, attended the church after they moved to Ferry Farm, and, earlier this century the Daughters of the American Revolution placed a beautiful window in the church in memory of the first president's mother. George himself was said to be in attendance one Sunday in the first little frame church when the roof allegedly threatened to collapse "causing the people to leave by the doors and windows!"

Many Virginia notables are permanently at rest in an adjacent cemetery. The oldest existing gravestone is that of "John Jones, 1752." Colonel John Dandridge, father of Martha Washington, and William Paul, brother of John Paul Jones, also are buried here. Colonel Fielding Lewis of Kenmore, and his three infant grandchildren, lie beneath the old stone steps of the present church, which was built in 1849. A year later the town clock, still maintained by the city, was installed in the church tower.

The present building is in the Romanesque or Roman Revival style. Box pews survived both the ravages of the Civil War and a fire and are still in use, although the original windows of clear diamond-shaped glass panes have been replaced by stained glass. The "Handbook of Historic Fredericksburg" calls the church's three Tiffany windows "priceless," and "the Mary Ball Washington window is also a fine example of stained glass art."

St. George's was badly damaged during the battle of Fredericksburg, but a year later, in 1863, General Robert E. Lee's troops held religious revival meetings there. It was turned into a hospital during the Battle of the Wilderness. Curiously, according to the handbook, the silver communion set, stolen in 1862, "was recovered piece by piece over a span of 70 years."

The ghostly sighting at St. George's occurred just before the Civil War, in 1858, and was experienced by Mary Ella McCarty, the great grandmother of Ann Rowe, a long-time resident of Fredericksburg. Ironically, Ann first learned of the story by reading about it in a church bulletin some years ago, although she says her mother had been told about the incident many times.

Ella McCarty married Hugh M.D. Martin and was described as "devoted to St. George's." She sang in the choir, and later, in

1862, was "refuged" during the Battle of Fredericksburg. And she was said to be "not the type person to see things."

Ann Rowe says that one night in 1858, Ella and a young man went to the church for choir practice, and when they arrived it was dark except for a dim light burning in the choir loft. The young man was met by the organist and they both set out to get a sexton and more lamps, leaving Ella alone. She ascended the stairs to the loft, and sat facing the altar rail, which in those days was closer to the loft, when, suddenly, down in the vestibule, she saw a woman dressed in white with a veil over her face, kneeling at the rail. Ann says it was about dusk, and Ella watched the figure for several minutes before realizing that what she was seeing was not mortal! The figure then rose, turned, and looked up at Ella with what she later said was a "sad expression." As Ella started to call out to the woman, she evaporated!

CHAPTER 6

Terror in the Aquia Belfry

What is it about an old house or building reputed to be haunted that fascinates people? Elmwood in Essex County near Tappahannock quickly comes to mind. When newspaper accounts of haunting activities there were published more than a half a century ago, hundreds of people tramped through the woods every time the moon was full to see for themselves what eerie happenings might unfold in the then-vacant mansion. Literally thousands of curious onlookers have braved many a cold and damp night on the railroad tracks near West Point to catch a glimpse of the mysterious train light that is said to appear and disappear on occasion. And in Portsmouth, years ago, so many people clustered around a small frame house after it was reported there was a resident poltergeist inside, that the police had to barricade the place to protect its mortal occupants.

Aquia Church in Stafford County, about 20 miles north of Fredericksburg is such a place. It has held generations of area youngsters spellbound with the oft-told tales of its haunting past. In fact, this venerable, two-and-one-half century old structure has to be guarded around the clock every Halloween because so many teenagers otherwise would descend upon it, as they did in years past, occasionally rendering it harm.

Could it be the element of danger that is so intriguing, particularly in the case of Aquia Church? One must wonder about the sanity of those who want to explore its ghostly interior to prove their manhood, so to speak, because it was on just such a venture, a long time ago, that a young man allegedly lost his life!

The church itself, according to the Virginia Landmarks Register, is a "good illustration of rural Virginia's use of ecclesiastical architecture endowed with urbanity and sophistication." The Register adds that its "elegant classicism contrasts with its isolated woodland setting." Is that not a perfect setting for ethereal happenings?

Ill winds swirled about the church even before its completion. Begun in 1751, it was seriously damaged by fire on February 17, 1754 — three days before construction was to be finished! It was rebuilt within the walls over the next three years. The interior preserves "a unique three-tiered pulpit as well as the original Ionic reredos, west gallery, and pews — all excellent examples of colonial joinery. Three times in the history of the church, its precious silver, including an old dish, chalice, cup and paten, have been buried for safekeeping — during the Revolutionary War, the War of 1812, and the Civil War.

The hauntings at Aquia stem from a night of horror in the church more than 200 years ago, probably during the time of the American Revolution. A young woman was murdered in the chapel by a highwayman or men, apparently after a violent struggle. Her body was hidden in the belfry, and, as the church was not in use during this period, it was years later before her skeletal remains were found, with her golden hair still intact.

It is said, too, that the bloodstains from where the woman was slain were clearly visible for more than 100 years, until early in the 20th century when a new cement floor was laid. Not only was this physical evidence present, but there also has been, through the years, a continuous stream of scary psychic phenomena, so much so, in fact, that reportedly, through most of the 18th century, even the parishioners were afraid to go into Aquia Church at night.

The most prominent and persistent manifestations are said to be recreated by the victim. They include, with only slight variations, the sound of feet running up and down the stairs to the belfry, heavy noises of a struggle, and the apparition of a terrified woman standing at one of the windows.

While this oft-repeated phenomenon is the most common occurrence, it is by no means the only one. There is, for example, the popular tale of the prominent socialite who spent her summers in Stafford County in the 1920s, and who became interested in the church through the spectral stories related to her by her maids. She decided to see the spirits herself, but couldn't get any of the strapping men in the area to accompany her. They all politely, but forcefully backed off when they learned she was going at night. Undaunted, she recruited two "scientists" — likely early 20th century ghost-busters — from Washington.

They entered Aquia Church on a dark night, led by the determined socialite. But just after she walked through the door, an unseen hand slapped her sharply across the face. The two men

ran inside and searched everywhere, but they found nothing, and had no rational explanation for what happened. But that it did happen was evident in the fact that the mark on the lady's face remained for several days!

There is, too, a time-honored story of a "whistling spirit" at Aquia who saved the lives of two Confederate soldiers during the Civil War. It has been passed along for generations. The originator was a William Fitzhugh, who during a scouting mission in 1862 or 63, stopped off in the church with a comrade to rest. They had heard about the hauntings there, but they were too tired to care. They promptly went to sleep in the square pews.

Sometime during the night they were roused by what Fitzhugh described as "unmistakable footsteps at the rear of the church on some stone flagging." Then they heard someone or something whistling the tune, "The Campbells are Coming." Frightened out of their wits, they jumped up and struck a light, but saw nothing. Then they went to the door and looked out. A troop of Yankee soldiers was advancing along the road heading directly for the church. They raced to the back of the building, leaped out of a window and escaped. Fitzhugh later attributed the whistling ghost to saving his and his friend's lives.

Was it the spirit of the murdered girl? Or is it her apparition that Robert Frazier and his son have seen flitting among the tombstones in the Aquia cemetery? Frazier, a former caretaker there, told two reporters about 15 years ago that he has often sighted "things" running through the graveyards. He said they appeared "blurred and funny." He added that they were white but not transparent. He couldn't see through them. The sightings were all at night, and when Frazier and his son went over to see what or who it was that was darting about, the figures disappeared. "They just fade away, kinda slow like," he told the journalists. He said he couldn't tell if they were men or women because they were too blurry. But he was convinced he knew what they were. "Everybody says there's ghosts up here. Me and my son seen 'em. They're here!"

The death caused by the ghost or ghosts of Aquia Church supposedly occurred more than 100 years ago. Supposedly, because while the story has been told and retold with relish and enthusiasm enough so as to defy disbelief, there is no documented record of who the victim was or when the event took place.

What is told is that in the days when everyone was afraid to approach the church at night, one young man — perhaps taunted by a dare — declared that no ghost could get the best of him. He said he would go inside, in the dark of night, and even climb to the haunted belfry. Those he made the boast to, however, were skeptical, so they gave him a hammer and a nail and told him to drive the nail into the wall, so they could tell for sure later whether or not he had lived up to his word.

Alone, he set out through the woods toward the old church. When the young man had not returned, hours later, his friends became worried and went to the church to find out what had happened. They found him in the belfry — dead! In the darkness, he had hammered the nail into the wall through his coat! When he turned to leave, he was held fast. Evidently thinking he was in the grasp of an evil spirit, it is said he died of fright!

CHAPTER 7

Historic Rendezvous in a Time Warp

There are perhaps only a few people in the long history of the country — probably less than a single handful, if that — who could write a more impressive and powerful resume than James Monroe, a native of Westmoreland County, and fifth President of the United States. It has been said that Westmoreland is "distinguished above all other counties in Virginia as the birthplace of genius," including such notables as George Washington, Richard Henry Lee, Francis Lightfoot Lee, and Robert E. Lee, among others.

It also has been written that Monroe progressed to "more high public offices, elective and appointive, than have ever been bestowed on any other American, before or since." A college student at William and Mary at age 16, he became a Revolutionary War hero in 1777 at the Battle of Trenton. He was 19. Five years later he was chosen to the Virginia Assembly, then to the Confederation Congress of the U.S. He became: a United States senator; a minister to France during Washington's administration; governor of Virginia (four times); Secretary of State and Secretary of War during James Madison's administration; and, in 1817, President. He fathered the Monroe Doctrine, and was instrumental in America's purchases of the Louisiana Territory and Florida.

In 1780, Monroe began studying law under the man-genius who was to become his lifelong friend and ardent supporter — Thomas Jefferson of Albermarle County. (Forty-five years later, in 1825, Monroe served on the board of visitors of the University of Virginia with Jefferson and Madison.)

In 1786, Monroe settled in Fredericksburg and took up the practice of law in offices at 908 Charles Street. He was there only three years, but aside from his legal work he also managed to be chosen to the city council, became a vestry man of St. George's Church, and served as a trustee of the Fredericksburg Academy. He was, to say the least, a most energetic man.

The site where Monroe began his professional career is today a shrine, encompassing his law office, a museum and a memorial library. Here, for a nominal fee, one can see the magnificent Louis XVI furniture bought in France in the 1790s and later used in the White House. The desk is the one on which he signed his historic message to Congress in 1823, a portion of which became known as the Monroe Doctrine. Here, too, are: the statesman's green cut velvet suit with heavily embroidered waistcoat, and sword and sash, worn at the Court of Napoleon; duelling pistols heavily inlaid with silver; his Revolutionary War gun; his wife's exquisite jewelry and court gowns; the dispatch box in which he carried the Louisiana Purchase papers and many other fascinating mementoes. On one wall hangs the priceless portrait of Monroe painted in the White House by Rembrandt Peale. Thousands of books and historical manuscripts and documents are amassed in the library, a haven for Monroe scholars. Outside, a splendid bust of the Virginian by Margaret French Cresson overlooks the walled, old-fashioned garden, where, upon special occasions, Mrs. Monroe's julep is served.

Unquestionably, the man most responsible for the painstaking preservation of this shrine-museum was a rather eccentric character-about-town named Laurence G. Hoes (pronounced Hoos). He was the great, great, great grandson of James Monroe. He has been described, alternately, as highly imaginative, gruff, gregarious, demonstrative, demanding, determined, blustery, irritating and commanding. Apparently, there was little middle ground with Hoes, townspeople either liked him, ignored him, or, in the words of one resident, "hated his guts."

Whatever, Hoes is credited with almost single-handedly saving the Monroe building from being demolished earlier in this century. He and his mother bought it in 1927. She died in 1933, but for more than 50 years, Laurence Hoes devoted his life not only to preserving Monroe's law offices in Fredericksburg, but to faithfully perpetuating the fifth President's memory and long list of notable achievements.

He coaxed, cajoled and commanded distant relatives and others to donate "Monroeabilia" to the museum. The quest became an all-consuming passion. That he was able to keep things going through the great depression and World War II is a tribute to his determination and endurance.

It therefore seems justly fitting that Hoes should be the one person to have experienced an extraordinary psychic event at the site in the late 1960s, about 10 years before he died. It is, to the best of the author's knowledge, the first time this rare and fascinating occurrence has been published.

It was told one blustery, rainy January day by Mrs. Lee Langston Harrison, the museum curator. She had collected it from some of the long-time guides at the building, some of whom have worked there for more than 40 years, and are reluctant, to this day, to repeat it. Here is what Mrs. Harrison said:

"Mr. Hoes was walking to the museum one winter's day. We think it was in the late 1960s. He was walking down Charles Street, and when he got adjacent to the Masonic Cemetery, which is next door, he saw two men standing at the front door of the museum. Apparently, he became excited at the thought of two prospective paying customers during the slow off season, because he shouted at them to go on into the building.

"The men, both tall, appeared to be having a lively animated discussion, possibly an argument, and when Mr. Hoes shouted, they both turned to face him. It was then that he noticed their dress. They were in 18th century attire, each with silk knee britches, silk stockings, knee buckles, low quarter shoes fashioned with buckles, embroidered waistcoats and long jackets! Mr. Hoes then realized that the two men, still engaged in their heated discussion with occasional raised voices, looked strangely familiar. The taller one had distinctly red hair, and the other brown hair."

It was at this instant, Mrs. Harrison believes, that the revelation struck Hoes. He was looking squarely at James Monroe and Thomas Jefferson!

As Hoes neared the entrance, the two men turned to him again, and the one with brown hair — allegedly Monroe — waved at him. Then the two turned back toward the front door and walked through it! Breathless, Hoes reached the door seconds later, but he couldn't open the door. It appeared to be stuck. He pounded on it and shouted for the guides inside to open it. When they finally did, Hoes screamed at them, asking where the two men had gone.

They told him that no one had come in. They hadn't seen anyone. Hoes became agitated. He thought they were playing a joke on him; that they had seen the "visitors," but weren't telling him. He ranted at them. At this point, the guides, seeing how excited and serious Hoes was, joined him in room-to-room search of the building. It yielded no sign of the two gentlemen.

So far as Mrs. Harrison can determine, neither Hoes nor any of the guides ever saw or heard of any such incident afterwards. Hoes died in 1978. He was not a drinking man. How then, does one explain his incredible experience on that cold wintry day? In the psychic realm there is a phenomenon called a "time warp," in which a person or persons in the present somehow is given a view of something that may have occurred in the distant past.

There have been reports of such happenings although they are extremely rare, psychic experts say. One apparently took place early on Sunday morning in 1971 near the old colonial-era church on Jamestown Island when a troup of men, women and children, clad in "settler-style" clothing marched past two tourist-witnesses. The difference here was the tourists said the group appeared to be talking and laughing, but they heard no sounds. Hoes adamantly declared he heard his two "visions" arguing, at times in loud voices.

Could the time-warp theory possibly explain Hoes' experience? Did Jefferson ever visit his former law student at Monroe's Fredericksburg law office? And if they went inside, where did they go and why didn't anyone else see them? Did Hoes have a sensitivity the others in the building didn't? Intriguing ques-

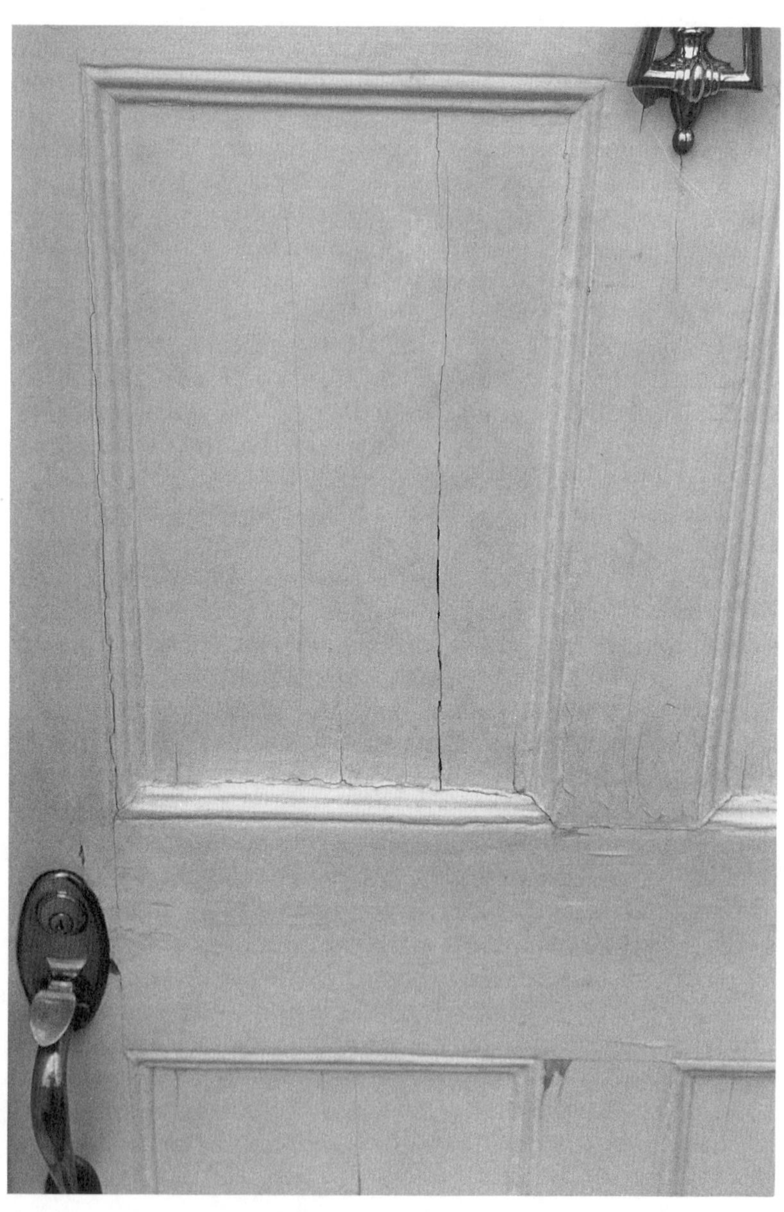

Crack in the Monroe Law Office door

tions, yes, but it is likely they never will be answered. Any hope of an explanation undoubtedly went to the grave with Laurence Hoes.

And finally, there is a curious footnote to this ghostly episode. Today, at the James Monroe museum, there is a long and wide crack in the warped front door. Guides who have worked there for 30 and 40 years or more swear that the crack appeared the same day Hoes saw the apparent apparitions of two of Virginia's most famous sons!

CHAPTER 8

The Lost Little Girl of Litchfield

Sometimes an old house just gives the perception of being haunted. Take Litchfield, for example. It is a rustic, two-story, six room structure a mile or so back from the intersection of state roads 206 and 218, in King George County, about 20 miles east of Fredericksburg. According to dates in its chimney, it was built in 1802 by "the Dades," a well-known family in the area linked to the Washingtons, the Townsends, and other well-connected clans.

Litchfield once served as a rectory for St. Paul's Episcopal Church nearby — one of the oldest houses of worship in Virginia, dating to 1766. It is believed that several ministers may have lived here down through the years. But it is the appearance more than anything else that gives the old house its eerie reputation. For one thing, it sits all alone atop a hill half a mile from the nearest neighbor. It kind of broods on the hill like the weathered Bates' house did in Alfred Hitchcock's classic thriller, "Psycho."

"Of course, the fact that Litchfield stood vacant for a number of years probably contributed to it's haunting legend," says current owner Boyd Braden. "But I think the main reason for the perception is because the house faces due north and south, and when the sun sets it makes the old glass windows shine with an uncanny brightness. Sometimes it looks like it's on fire."

Surely, then, the appearance of Litchfield — and its isolation — (can you imagine its effect in the moonlight?) might strike fear into more than the faint-hearted. The case with this house, however, goes much deeper than perception or run-away imagination.

Litchfield, you see, really is haunted! There have been frequent recurrences of at least three different and striking forms of psychic phenomena over the nearly two centuries of its existence.

"We knew nothing of any of this when we first moved into the house in 1959," says Elizabeth Braden, Boyd's wife. "We hadn't heard any of the ghost stories then, and we were pretty busy. There was a lot of fixing up to do. But even before we heard the background, there were many times, especially late at night, when you almost felt as if something was here with you in the house. I don't know quite how to describe it. It was eerie, weird. One of the first times we had a baby sitter over, she told us she felt some kind of presence," Elizabeth says.

"Then one day, an elderly lady who lived down the road, a Mrs. Green, came to pay us a visit. But she wouldn't come inside. She stayed in her car. We thought that a little strange. She asked us if we liked living in the house, and she did it with a subtle smile on her face, you know, like she knew something we didn't and was gently probing."

It didn't take the Bradens long to find the hidden meaning in the old woman's question. Boyd tells what happened: "One night not long after we moved in, there was a terrible noise downstairs. It sounded like it was coming from the dining room, which was the original kitchen in the house. It was a loud banging noise, like someone beating on wood, or banging chairs around. I got my gun and started downstairs. I thought some kind of varmint had gotten inside. Either that, or we had some unwelcome visitors.

"But when I got down there and turned on the lights, there was nothing. Then, I heard singing. It sounded like that of a little girl singing to herself. I searched the whole first floor of the house, but found nothing. I started back upstairs, and the singing started up again. I came back and looked around again, but never did see anything."

That was the Braden's introduction to the ghost of a young girl they believe to have been about eight years old. "I've never seen her myself," Boyd says, scratching his head. "But a lot of other people have. Our children saw her. Once she appeared and seemed to be trying to say something to our son, Bryan. She opened her mouth, but no sound came out. She wasn't scary, or anything like that. Our kids were never afraid of her.

"One time my mother was visiting us, and she was in the living room, playing the organ. It's an old fashioned organ. All of a sudden she stopped playing and ran into the kitchen where we were. She was all excited. She had seen the little girl. At first, she thought it was a friend of Ginny Kay's, our daughter. But then, Mom noticed how she was dressed. She had old button-up shoes and a dress that looked like the Civil War era. She had long brown hair, but other than that she looked just like a normal person. I mean my mother said you couldn't see through her or anything. She wasn't transparent. Mom said she was excited, but not afraid."

Boyd said on another occasion he and his brother-in-law were walking to the front gate outside, when they heard the singing of the girl in the attic. "He turned to me and asked what that was, because our children weren't in the house," Boyd recounts. "I said, I don't know how to tell you this, but I think that's our resident ghost!"

As time went on, many guests at the house, some of whom had either lived or visited there in years past, asked about the girl. "I remember once when the Price sisters came here," Elizabeth says. "They asked about the girl and then described her perfectly, just as our children and Boyd's mother had described her. Other people who have come here have asked about her, too."

Besides the night of the slamming and banging in the dining room, and the periodic appearance and singing of the young girl, there is another distinct manifestation that had reoccurred many times over the years at Litchfield. Again, Boyd describes it: "It's always the same. It doesn't matter if it's day or night. Very clearly, you hear wheels roll up in the driveway. It's like the sound of carriage wheels on gravel. Then you hear sounds like doors slamming shut. Dogs bark whenever it happens, and the horses come up from the pasture. But everytime we go out to see who's there, there is nothing! And this had happened many times, some recently."

Adds Elizabeth: "We had a group of people over one day and one lady said, 'does the wagon still drive up at night?' We just looked at each other. The lady was in her seventies and she had lived in the house as a little girl. She brought it up unsolicited. We hadn't mentioned it. So this must have been happening for at least 60 or 70 years or more."

Boyd and Elizabeth have tried to find some rational answers for the phantom carriage, the banging noises, and the periodic appearances of the little girl, but they have been unsuccessful. They have found nothing in the written history of Litchfield to explain the phenomena.

"We've talked about it a great deal with many people, some

of whom lived in the house a generation or two ago," Boyd says. "It has been suggested that the girl may have been 'hidden away' in the house, maybe locked in the attic. They think maybe she had what then was called 'water on the brain,' or that she may have been mentally deranged. But we have never found any proof of this. She has appeared to all who have seen her as a perfectly normal girl."

Is the arrival of the mystery carriage tied to her? Could it have been someone coming to take her away? Does she reappear, singing, because she was happy in the house? Intriguing questions, yes, but the answers appear lost in the mists of time.

The one thing that is certain is that there is more than just a haunting perception at Litchfield!

CHAPTER 9

The Lost Yankee at Willis House

If John Allan, the Scottish merchant who built a small house at 1106 Princess Anne Street — considered to be the second house built in Fredericksburg (circa 1740s) — were to transcend time and come back today to view his abode, he doubtless would not recognize it. Two extra stories, an entire new wing and a spacious back porch have been added over the past 200 years. However, he probably would be pleased at the loving care successive owners have given it, including thorough renovations and the addition of handsome period furniture, antiques and family heirlooms.

It is called the Willis house today, and is presently owned by Judge Jere Willis and his wife, Barbara. It has been in the Willis family for more than a century. Flanked by no less than seven chimneys, the house features a large dining room, living room, music room, foyer, one bedroom and kitchen. From the sheltered porch, which the Willis family added, there is a pleasant view across a half-acre garden with old brick walls and a patio built with millstones found on the property. A pecan tree, dogwoods, daffodils, tulips and azaleas add color, fragrance and spice.

Remarkably, the house withstood ferocious Union army shelling, preceding the great battle of Fredericksburg during the bitter winter of 1862. It is remarkable because 181 guns, spaced along Stafford Heights from the Washington farm to Falmouth, opened up at dawn on December 11th, and all the fire was concentrated on the town. At times during the bombardment, 100 guns a minute were fired — round shot, case shot and shell. As John Goolrick, author of the book, "Historic Fredericksburg," published in 1922, wrote of the shelling. . . "walls toppled, fires sprang up and chaos reigned." One survivor described the scene: "Men, women and children were driven from town. Hundreds of ladies and children were wandering homeless over the frozen highways, with bare feet and thin clothing."

Soon after came one of the fiercest fights of the entire war. The Willis House stood directly in the line of fire as the Federals and Confederates battled through the old town's streets and alleys.

Although the story is not as well known as are those of Kenmore, Chatham, Fall Hill, Federal Hill, and a few other area buildings — there is, or to be more precise, was a resident ghost at the Willis House.

Barbara Willis tells the story: "Our house is directly opposite to where the Union Army crossed the Rappahannock River on pontoon bridges, and there was house-to-house combat. Apparently, a young Union soldier was in the house, and was standing behind one of the double doors in the back hall, using the doors as a shield. A bullet ripped a splinter through the door at chest-high level, killing the soldier, and leaving blood stains on the floor. He was buried in the garden. The door was never fully repaired. It was plugged, and the plug remains there to this day. In the 1920s, a Mrs. Marian "Carrie" Willis was living in the house and she had a cook named Nannie. Carrie used to call the Union soldier 'Yip the Yank.' According to the legend that has been passed down, Nannie saw a young man come into the house by the side porch door, dressed in a Union uniform of the Civil War era. He went upstairs. She thought it might be Carrie's younger brother, and she told Carrie about it. But when they went upstairs to investigate, they found no one there."

This must have happened on more than one occasion, Barbara says, because Nannie finally said one day that she was going to "lay his soul to rest." She went out in the garden, kneeled, and said something over his grave. There have been no sightings of the apparition since. It appears that even though the Yankee soldier died far from home, Nannie persuaded him that Fredericksburg wasn't such a bad resting place after all.

CHAPTER 10

The Case of the Confused Confederate

Most ghost stories are kind of fun. Some may be a bit scary, but generally the spirits are friendly, and in more than a few cases even mischievous — ethereal pranksters so to speak. But rarely is anyone harmed in the process, and even then it most often is accidental. There was, for example, an incident at the Norfolk Naval Shipyard several years ago where a person — frightened by the apparition of a long-dead seaman — fell down a flight of stairs and broke his leg. But that was not intentioned. Occasionally, poltergeist activity will surface. In Poquoson, Virginia, a mother whose teenage daughters didn't mind her in life came back after death to physically taunt them with slaps, pinches and pulled hair. But such reports are few and far between.

That is why the psychic events which surrounded a home in the Lake Acres section of Spotsylvania County during a brief period in November 1986 seem to be so unusual. First of all it happened in a modern house, not an old one full of history. Secondly, it appeared that in this case the ghost involved "freaked out" and went on a tantrum throwing spree, which although it didn't cause any physical harm, did scare the bejabbers out of the resident family. And finally there was a rather nasty aftermath to the episode that left a bad taste in the mouths of community residents for a long time.

The story broke November 11, 1986, when the Fredericksburg *Free Lance-Star* ran a long article by reporter Mike Zitz which chronicled a wide variety of psychic phenomena that allegedly occurred in the house over a hectic, three-week period. It began one day in late October when Sheliajean Colosimo, who lived in the house with her husband, Richard, and their 11-year-old daughter, was entertaining a neighbor, Sherry Chewning.

When Mrs. Chewning commented on how cold it seemed to be in one of the bedrooms, Mrs. Colosimo told her that it had always been chilly in that room, even during the hottest days of summer. She had, in fact, moved her daughter out of that bedroom because of the strange cold. Mrs. Chewning then asked for a cross and she was given a rosary. Clutching the crucifix, she walked around the room repeating the phrase "Leave this room." Both women later said the temperature in the room seemed to rise immediately. They left the rosary hung on a wall.

A short time later the women's children, playing outside, told their mothers they were frightened by something they described as being "big and red" they said they saw in the window of the room. Mrs. Colosimo and Mrs. Chewning then went back up to the room to check, but, oddly, it was locked from the inside. They jimmied the lock and, inside, found the room "icy cold." The rosary cross, they said, was imbedded in the wall opposite the one they had hung it on.

Next followed a sequence of events which sounded like it had been taken from the script of the book and movie, "The Amityville Horror." The women went to St. Mary's Church in Fredericksburg and spoke to a priest, explaining the situation. He gave them some holy water to sprinkle in and around the house. He later said, "Holy water is used very often in places where there is a spirit."

But over the next few days the mysterious events continued, understandably unnerving the Colosimos who often were jarred awake late at night. Each time this happened they would find the room's door locked, and once they got inside things would be in disarray. The couple said the manifestations included:

** Books sailing off a shelf.

** A door which inexplicably flew off its hinges twice and "flung" the pins from the hinges with such force that they were driven into a wall like nails.

** Handprints without fingerprints which appeared on window panes in the room, and smudges, seemingly made by hands, showed up on the walls.

At the family's request, another priest, from St. Patrick Catholic Church in Spotsylvania, visited the house and blessed it. Next, a friend of the Colosimos contacted a local psychic. According to the newspaper account, the psychic, after viewing snapshots which appeared to show a "blurry image" in a room, reportedly said the image was an "evil druid."

Rumors then began circulating in the neighborhood that the Catholic Church was going to perform an exorcism in the house, but clergymen denied this. Father Dominic Irace of St. Mary's was quoted as saying, "I've never dealt with anything like this. In this Diocese we've never had anything really serious like that happen. . .I tell people that it's almost like voodoo in a way. If you don't believe in it, it can't hurt you."

But the Colosimos took little comfort in that. They previously had not believed in ghosts. "Before all this happened I thought it was all hocus pocus about the supernatural," Sheliajean Colosimo said. Now they were terrified, and so, too, apparently were some neighbors who began spreading salt around their houses to ward off "evil spirits."

Eventually, on the advice of a friend, the family called in another "expert" — a woman who claimed to be a "psychic advisor, clairvoyant, tarot reader and witch." When she first arrived at the house, she immediately went to the room where all the activity had taken place and said she sensed "a lot of energy" emanating from it.

Then she explained the cause. She said she saw the apparition of a young Confederate soldier. She described him as being only 16 or 17 years old. He had blond hair, was in uniform, and had been grievously wounded. His arm and leg were bandaged and he had a homemade crutch. The psychic said the lad had been "fatally wounded" in the war and died near there. His spirit had been hiding in the closet from Union soldiers because he believed the war was still going on.

"He was very confused. Scared. He needed some help," the psychic was quoted as saying. She added that the spirits of those who have died sudden and violent deaths often linger on near the scene, uncertain of what has happened. The psychic then had a "conversation" with the ghost during a half hour session with an Ouija board. Mrs. Colosimo said the board seemed to move by itself, and that there was so much static electricity in the room that both her and her husband's scalps were tingling. The psychic said that during the conversational exchange she told the young man that no one was trying to harm him. Reporter Zitz quoted her as saying, "I told him that the light was beautiful, it was where his friends were, and where he should be." She added that the ghost had become "frightened and confused" by the rosary, the Holy water and the commands to leave the house.

The psychic's soothing apparently had a positive effect. The manifestations stopped. Mrs. Colosimo said she and her husband were convinced that the woman's analysis was correct and that she had been successful in sending the ghost to the great beyond. "In my opinion, yes, there was a soul here, and yes, it was a young boy."

But while the supernatural activities ceased, the Colosimos' fears did not. The family began getting ugly and obscene phone calls. Someone threatened to burn their house to the ground. A vandal smashed a 20 ounce bottle of ketchup just above the front door of the home. Insulting articles appeared in the newspaper's letters to the editor section.

Sheliajean Colosimo responded with a letter of her own. "There are many things that happen to us in our lives that we don't understand," she wrote. "Nor can we just explain them away with simple science or logic. Such an event happened in my home. I gained nothing by telling the truth. My family and I never really thought about the supernatural. But I now feel what happened to us can happen to anyone, anytime, for no apparent reason.

"Yes, there was a ghost in my home. And yes we were living in fear. And we really don't care who does or doesn't believe us. We know the truth. A good conscience is a continual Christmas. I hope this letter can mollify the skeptics, the pranksters, the obscene callers and the vandals. Please leave me and my family alone."

The newspaper, too, was criticized for running the story which subsequently was picked up and published nationally by the Associated Press. Skeptics claimed reporter Mike Zitz had been "used" and "taken in." The paper said, "Reporting on news of interest to our readers doesn't mean that we, as a newspaper, endorse the views of those we quote . . . We feel we did a responsible job of reporting a variety of viewpoints."

Zitz today shakes his head at the storm on criticism and controversy the incident and its publication caused. While he is not convinced about the authenticity of everything the psychics said, he believes firmly that the Colosimos fears were real. "I believe them," he says. "They were concerned. It was genuine. They really believed. They were very upset. They were stressed out. And strange things did happen."

As a postscript, Zitz interviewed Erlendus Haraldsson of the University of Iceland, who then was a visiting scholar at the University of Virginia's Department of Parapsychology. He is a psychologist who specializes in psychic phenomena. He told Zitz that reports of violent paranormal activity — such as was occurred in the Colosimo's home — were very unusual.

"These cases come up now and then and I think quite often you find normal explanations, but there are cases never fully explained. If it seems that when those who investigate the case no longer find a normal explanation, these cases are often termed poltergeist cases," Haraldsson said.

CHAPTER 11

Rustling Skirts at Washington House

It is not entirely surprising that Mary Ball Washington has "returned" to her house in Fredericksburg on occasion, perhaps to see if custodians today are keeping it up in good taste, or possibly just waiting for her famous son to pay her another visit. It is not surprising because she was a domineering and shrewish spirit in life, so if, in fact, it is she who has scared the wits out of hostesses at the great white house on the corner of Charles and Lewis streets, it would well fit her psychological profile.

The daughter of an illiterate mother and a father who died when she was just three, Mary Ball demonstrated unusual independence from an early age. Nor was she destitute. Her father left her 400 acres of land near the falls of the Rappahannock, three slaves, 15 head of cattle, and "all the feathers in the kitchen loft, to be put in a bed for her." By the time she married Augustine Washington, at the then-considered ripe old age of 23 or 25, depending upon which source you subscribe to, she had come into a comfortable estate of her own through the deaths of other relatives.

Biographers have described her as "an extremely self-willed woman," and "a termagant (overbearing) mother." When she joined the Washington household on the banks of Pope's Creek, she immediately took over the supervision of Augustine's motherless children, and, on February 22, 1732, she gave birth to her first — and favorite — child. Six weeks later he was christened George.

In 1738 Mary and Augustine and five children moved to Ferry Farm across the river from Fredericksburg, and five years later, at age 35, she was widowed. Young George, then 11, became the man of the house and the passion of her life. It was, it is said, a very possessive passion. In his award winning book, "Washington - The Indispensable Man," author James Thomas Flexner noted that, "Even when he was Commander in Chief, even when he was President, she objected to his occupations, complaining violently that he was ungratefully neglecting his duties to her."

Her smothering demands and devotion may well have been among the reasons he left home at such an early age, first as a surveyor and later as an Indian fighter. One wonders. Nevertheless, he remained loyal to her throughout life and visited her as often as his arduous schedule allowed. In 1772, when she was 64, and he was worried that she no longer could manage Ferry Farm by herself, he bought her a three room cottage with a kitchen, for about $800, in downtown Fredericksburg. He chose it because it was just behind his sister Betty's mansion at Kenmore, and his youngest brother, Charles, lived only two blocks away. She brought with her two horses, one cow, one dog and six servants. An entrance hall, parlor, porch and a guest bedroom, where George frequently stayed, were added.

Here, Mary Ball Washington held court for the last 17 years of her life. An avid gardener, she lined a brick walk from her backyard to Kenmore with fine English boxwood. Many of her son's most famous and influential friends stopped off at her home on their travels to pay their respects. Lafayette came several times and was offered mint juleps and slices of her renowned ginger bread.

In March 1789, George stopped by to visit his mother and get her blessings just before he was to inaugurated as the first President of the United States. It was the last time he saw her. She died of breast cancer at the age of 81 five months later. At her request, she was buried several blocks away at her favorite spot in town, Meditation Rock.

A century later her house was scheduled to be dismantled and taken to the Chicago World's Fair for exhibition, when a group of concerned local women arranged for the home to be bought and preserved by the Association for the Preservation of Virginia Antiquities.

While there have been persistent reports over the years of Mary Washington's spirit reappearing in and around the house, Gail Braxton, who manages the property today for the APVA, is not convinced. "We haven't seen her," she says. "Oh, every now and then something funny happens in the house, but nothing more than that. It would be wonderful to have her, but she hasn't shown herself."

The New York Times, however, in an article published more than two decades ago, claimed that there had been "recurring reports over the years of a shadowy figure moving along the boxwood path leading from Mary's home to Kenmore." It was further noted that caretakers said they had even tried to "tone down" the ghost stories for fear of scaring off the help.

A number of other townspeople, some of whom preferred not to have their names mentioned, have told of strange sightings and goings on in the house's kitchen dependency. One person who experienced psychic phenomena in the house was a former hostess — the home is open to the public — named Gertrude Sawyer, now deceased. She told of one time when she heard doors opening and closing and then the rustle of skirts. "I was so scared," she told a newspaper reporter. "I ran out of the house and spent the night with a friend."

She eventually went back, but confided to friends that she knew Mary Washington's ghost was around, and although she hadn't seen it yet, she expected to any night.

Some have speculated that Mrs. Washington "returns" to the house not only to assure that it is cared for in the proper style, but also in anticipation of a final visit from her famous son.

CHAPTER 12

A Lover's Lonely Vigil at Chatham

Of all the places in America where George Washington allegedly slept, dined, and was entertained, none apparently surpassed the hospitality of a magnificent Georgian mansion sitting high on a bluff just across the Rappahannock River from Fredericksburg. It is called Chatham — named by its builder, William Fitzhugh, for a friend and former classmate of his at Eton and Oxford — William Pitt, Earl of Chatham.

Washington was a frequent visitor here following the Revolutionary War — so much so, in fact, that he once wrote Fitzhugh, saying: "I have put my legs oftener under your mahogany at Chatham than anywhere else in the world, and have enjoyed your good dinners, good wine, and good company more than any other." Many other notables also visited Chatham during these years, including the Marquis de Lafayette, and an assortment of Randolphs, Lees and additional friends and relatives. The mansion became sort of a "free tavern" for the sophisticated gentry traveling north or south.

There was an early sadness associated with the great house, too. There is a sampler adorning the wall of an empty room there today. It was started by Patsy, the third daughter of the Fitzhugh family, as a memorial to her two older sisters who died at a very early age. In embroidery, it says:

"Here Innocence and Beauty lie, whose Breath
Was snatch'd by early, not untimely Death
Hence. . ."

At this point, Patsy, aged seven, died. The sampler was then completed by another sister, Molly:

". . . . did they go, just as they did begin
Sorrow to know, before they knew to Sin.
Death that does Sin and Sorrow thus prevent,
Is the next Blessing to a Life well Spent."

Because of the steady stream of "tourists," and possibly

because of the sad memories of the lost children, Fitzhugh, ailing in health and plagued with debt, called himself a slave in his own house, and, reluctantly, decided to sell Chatham, his dream home, which he had built in 1768-1771. So, in 1797, he advertised, calling it "a brick house delightfully situated and containing nine commodious rooms, exclusive of a spacious hall or entry, two pairs of stairs, convenient passages, and good dry cellars." The grounds, he added, comprised pleasure and kitchen gardens, interspersed with scarce trees, choice flowers and flowering shrubs, fruit trees and berries. Adjacent were orchards of peaches, apples and pears. Features of the grounds were turfed slopes "created by great labor and expense."

And there was more. Detached from the mansion itself were various offices, kitchen and larder, housekeeper's rooms and laundry, storehouse and smokehouse, a dairy and springhouse, coach houses for four coaches, stables for 30 horses, a cow house with stalls for 36 head of cattle, a large farmyard with barns and granary, a variety of sheds, an overseer's house, a blacksmith shop, and quarters for more than 50 slaves!

It was, in short, a splendid estate of which a National Park Service brochure (The Park Service manages Chatham today) once said: "(with) its various outbuildings and dependencies, and the historic ground which surrounds it. . . Chatham represents a small preserve in which the entire scope of Virginia heritage can be understood and appreciated."

Following a succession of owners, the mansion came into historic renown again during the Civil War when it was then the property of Major J. Horace Lacy, C.S.A. It served for a time as headquarters for Union generals Irwin McDowell, Ambrose Burnside, Rufus King, Edwin Sumner and John Gibbon. It also suffered "wanton vandalism" according to the National Park Service. Yankee soldiers "removed original panelling to burn for firewood, pencilled graffiti on exposed plaster, rode horses through the mansion, and generally left Chatham a victim of the Civil War, as were countless other homes in the vanquished South."

One gentleman who had the opportunity to further inflict damage upon the mansion, but chose not to, was the redoubtable leader of the Confederate Army, Robert E. Lee. During the fighting at Fredericksburg, when General Ambrose Burnside was using Chatham as his headquarters, Major Lacy, owner of the house, rode up to Lee and said, "General, there are a group of Yankee officers on my porch. I do not want my house spared. I ask permission to give orders to shell it." Lee is said to have smiled, and replied, "Major, I do not want to shell your fine old house. Besides, it has tender memories for me. I courted my bride under its trees."

Abraham Lincoln visited Chatham at least twice during the early years of the war and may well have been treated to "a gourmet lunch," as General McDowell had two French chefs on the premises. More importantly, as "men, horses and guns swarmed over the Lacy plateau," the house became a field hospital for wounded Union troops after the battle of Fredericksburg. The famous nurse and later founder of the American Red Cross, Clara Barton, courageously tended to the sick and the lame here, as did the great American poet, Walt Whitman, who came to check on his wounded younger brother.

At the time, Chatham was described as being "crammed with wounded and dying covering all available space of every room and even, (as Miss Barton never forgot) "the floors of the frigid porches."

In his book, "The Wound Dresser," Whitman described the scene at Chatham: "It (the house) is used as a hospital since the battle, and it seems to have received only the worst cases. Outdoors, at the foot of a catalpa tree, within ten yards of the front of the house, I noticed a heap of amputated feet, legs, arms, hands, etc. — about a load for a one-horse cart. Several dead bodies lie nearby, each covered with its brown woolen blanket. In the dooryard, toward the river, are some graves, mostly of officers, their names on crosses of barrel staves or broken board, stuck in the dirt.

"The house is quite crowded, everything impromptu, no system, all bad enough, but I have no doubt the best that can be done; all the wounds pretty bad, some frightful, the men in their old clothes, unclean and bloody. . . Some of the men are dying."

Following the war, the 12,000-square-foot mansion was carefully restored to its former elegance, and regained its status as one of the most beautiful 18th century homes in the state. The last private owner, industrialist John Lee Pratt decreed in his will that Chatham be preserved for the "enjoyment of this and future generations," and deeded the house and grounds to the National Park Service.

Oddly, the ghostly legend at Chatham is not associated with the Civil War, although so much agony and death pervaded the house and grounds in the 1860s. One hundred and thirty three Union soldiers once lay buried under the front lawn, although 130 of these bodies were later reinterred. Psychics who have visited the house immediately sensed "blood" when they walked into the right wing room where so many amputations took place.

The ghost, instead, is a lady who lived in George Washington's day, although she did not make her haunting presence known until the 20th century. The National Park Service says Chatham "has been granted a Lady-in-White who first materialized in this century. A lonely periodic walker, she has not been seen for some time. Other ghosts, however, abound at all times. Though these spirits have not a body like man (or woman), a perceptive soul can sense their permeation of house and grounds."

Tammy Cross, a National Park Service employee at Chatham, tells visitors this version of the story of "the Lady in White:" "One of the first persons to see the lady was Mrs. Randolph Howard. She lived in the house from 1909 to 1914. She reported seeing the apparition while looking out from one of the front windows on the west side. The date was June 21st. She said she just saw a flowing white figure walking up and down the front lawn, actually in the colonial carriage lane. The place where she saw the lady came to be known as the 'ghost walk.'

"Mrs. Howard was apprehensive about mentioning what she saw to the servants and to her family members. She was afraid it might scare the servants, and that her family might think she was 'seeing things.' She was the only one to have seen this and it was in the afternoon. But she was intrigued and wanted to find out more about it.

"Years later, a woman magazine writer researching some material in a library in Newark, New Jersey, came across a book about ghosts written in French in the early 19th century. She found references to a Lady in White at Chatham. She then wrote an article about the references, which Mrs. Howard read. She then invited the writer to visit her in Fredericksburg, and they discussed the ghost over tea or lunch."

(Author's note: It should be mentioned that while Tammy says it was a woman writer who found the reference to the Lady

in White at Chatham, other versions say it was: a man writer; a French scholar and/or a friend of Mrs. Howard. Whatever, Tammy continues the story.)

"Apparently, the Frenchman who wrote the book had been told the story of the Lady in White while he had been visiting Chatham sometime early in the 1800s." Tammy Cross didn't say it, but Mrs. Howard must have been delighted to find some confirmation of her sighting. Tammy did say that when she began work at the house, she was instructed not to bring the subject up unless asked directly about it, because there had been no reoccurrences of the apparition since the Park Service took over the house in 1976.

But there have been others who claim to have seen her this century — always on the same date, June 21st, and always in seven year intervals. There also have been a number of articles written about the Lady in White over the past 80 years.

The legend goes that sometime in the last quarter of the 18th century, an Englishman who has been described only as "a distinguished man of letters," came to this country and brought his beautiful young daughter with him. One of the reasons for his travel to America was to disengage his daughter from a flaming romance she was carrying on in England with a drysalter

— a dealer in dry chemicals, dyes and salted food products. She had met him when her beloved pet, a talking parrot had died, and he was called in to preserve the bird. Her father, however, felt the young man was unworthy of the family's prominent social status.

So the father and disconsolate daughter made the rounds, visiting many friends in this country. At some point, they were invited by William Fitzhugh to stay at Chatham. Unbeknownst to the father, the drysalter had somehow managed to follow his love across the ocean, and, with the help of a servant, he managed to get a message to his sweetheart at the mansion. They exchanged notes, and had a secret meeting. They planned an elopement.

Alas, the father got word of the plan and locked the girl in her room nightly. But the determined young man got a message to her that he would call for her on a specific night. She was to lower herself from her room by means of a rope ladder. Word of this plan was passed around the servants' quarters, and someone told it to the man-servant of George Washington, who happened to also be a guest of Fitzhugh at the time. He told the general, who had the drysalter detained by his men.

And, at the appointed hour, when the girl descended the rope ladder, she landed in the arms not of her lover but of George Washington! It is said he bore her with a "stout grip" into her father's room.

This was enough for the Englishman. He hurried her back to England and arranged her marriage with someone more suitable to her status. Resigned to her fate, she had ten children, but she never forgot her lost love at Chatham. She vowed on her deathbed that she would return to the great house on the Rappahannock on the anniversary of her death to walk up and down the garden path and search for the young man.

It is the vision of this love-struck young woman who Mrs. Howard allegedly saw early in the 1900s, and who others have claimed to have seen in the years since — always on the same date, June 21st. Her last "scheduled" visit, since she has been reported seen only once every seven years, was in 1986. Tammy Cross says several Park Service employees held a vigil at the house on that date that year until midnight, but no one saw anything.

Three questions come to mind. Tammy asks one of them.

"Why didn't the lady have a name? I've always wondered that. It kind of adds an air of mystery."

The second question is why did the lady not reappear on the expected date in 1986? One day a year or so ago, a group of Fredericksburg third graders visited the house and Tammy told them the ghost story. A nine-year-old girl piped up: "Maybe she hasn't returned because she finally found who she was looking for." Adds Tammy: "I don't know why I had never thought of that. It seems so simple."

And, lastly, what was the significance of June 21st? Here, there may be a plausible explanation. That was the precise date, in 1790, on which the Lady in White died!

CHAPTER 13

The Happy Host of Federal Hill

If there is a ghost at Federal Hill in Fredericksburg — the house owner, Mrs. Bess Lanier, doesn't happen to believe in such things, although she readily admits many others have claimed to have seen apparitions there — then it may well be the jolliest specter in all of Virginia. He allegedly is none other than Alexander Spotswood, former governor of the colony, explorer, military expert, aristocrat and bon vivant. He is said to appear, to those who have seen him, standing by the dining room sideboard, smiling, and mixing his favorite liquid concoctions. On occasion, he has even lifted a glass in a toast — either to startled onlookers, or to his own portrait which hangs on a nearby wall. No one is really quite sure. In fact, people at the Fredericksburg Visitor Center have called Spotswood a "ghostly spirit full of spirits."

This colorful Scotsman, who was born in 1676, is said by some biographers and historians to have administered one of the most notable terms in the entire colonial era when he was Virginia's chief executive from 1710 to 1722. He pursued a more enlightened and humane policy toward the Indians. He had a low tolerance for outlaws, and is the man responsible for the death of the notorious pirate Edward Teach, better known as Blackbeard. Williamsburg flourished under his ruling guidance. One colonial scholar summed up Spotswood's career by writing: "The 12 years of his governorship were full of energy, and much was done for the betterment of the colony."

He also was noted as being somewhat of an adventurer, and he never turned down an invitation to a good party. It was Alexander Spotswood, who, in 1716, gathered up a group of "convivial gentlemen" and set out to explore the Blue Ridge Mountains. The expedition — the first such attempted by Englishmen — included 63 men, 74 horses, an assortment of dogs and a "vast quantity of alcoholic beverages." They fought off hornets and rattlesnakes, shot bear and deer for their suppers and generally had a good old time.

After reaching what they perceived to be the top of the mountains, they came down into the valley, camped beside a river, and decided it was time to celebrate their accomplishment. A description of this event was duly recorded by John Fontaine, a member of the group. He wrote the following:

"We had a good dinner, and after we got the men together, and loaded all their arms, and we drank the King's health in champagne and fired a volley, and all the rest of the Royal Family and fired a volley — the Princess' health in Burgundy, and fired a volley, and all the rest of the Royal family in claret and fired a volley. We drank the Governor's health, and fired another volley. We had several sorts of liquors, viz., Virginia red wine and white, Irish usquebaugh, brandy, shrub, two sorts of rum, champagne, canary, cherry, punch, water, cider, &c."

Is it any wonder where Spotswood got his reputation for having a good time? Upon their return home, the governor presented each of his companions with a golden horseshoe "covered with valuable stones resembling heads of nails, and they all became known in history as the Knights of the Golden Horseshoe."

In his later years, Spotswood migrated to the Fredericksburg area. He lived in Germanna for awhile, and owned considerable property in Spotsylvania, Orange and Culpeper counties. It is along here where the story gets a little — well —spotty. According to some accounts, including a 1931 edition of "Homes and Gardens in Virginia," and the 1930 publication of Margaret DuPont Lee's "Virginia Ghosts," Federal Hill either was built by or for the now ex-governor.

However, according to the third edition of the Virginia Landmarks Register, printed in 1987, Federal Hill "is a late 18th century architecturally formal dwelling which illustrates the dignity that could be achieved with wood-frame construction. It was built ca. 1795 for Robert Brooke, governor of Virginia 1794-96." Now if that is the case, Spotswood couldn't have lived, or even visited there, because he died in 1740! Maybe, if he didn't live there, he came back in spirit form because he liked the house and what went on in it.

In any event, it appears that Governor Brooke did buy the house at some point, whether it was built for him, Spotswood, or someone else, and he renamed it Federal Hill after the Federalist

Party of which he was one of the founders. It is, nevertheless, a large, two-story frame house with walls of solid brick beneath the white clapboard. The interior has been described as "elegant," and contains "exquisitely carved woodwork of great dignity." The ballroom, occupying the entire north end of the first floor, has woodwork similar to that from the ballroom of Gadsby's Tavern in Alexandria, which is now displayed in the Metropolitan Museum of Art. A rare early summerhouse with louvered sides and ogee-domed roof (whatever that is) stands in the garden.

The legends of the reappearance of Spotswood at the house date back to early in the 20th century. Mrs. Henry Theodora Wight bought the property around 1910. According to at least one version, there were two sideboards in the dining room, because "in olden times huge hunt breakfasts were often given by Governor Spotswood and his lady." The smaller sideboard was used for the bowls of apple-toddy, eggnog, hot grog, etc., the customary drinks of the day.

It is here that a number of people through several generations have claimed to have seen the Governor. And the recollections of the sightings all have a strikingly similar ring, although many of those who witnessed the apparition were not aware that others had, too. The consensus is that Spotswood suddenly just appears, in front of the small sideboard, dressed in a pink coat and hunting breeches, "pleasantly engaged in mixing drinks."

In one fairly credible account, very early this century, Mrs. Wight had invited Mrs. Margaret Halsey Weir to dine with her at Federal Hill. But when she arrived, Mrs. Wight had to apologize that her cook and waitress had suddenly disappeared. She then explained that the cook's young daughter had told them she had seen "an old gentleman, with boy's pants, with a white plait down the back, tied with a black string" standing by the sideboard. The girl then said, "He had a silver cup histed (hoisted) to de picture of a old gentleman on wall." She then indicated that the gentleman she saw and the portrait on the wall were one and the same man. Mrs. Wight concluded that the child was too young to have invented such a story. Anyway, it was certain that the girl's mother and the waitress believed her, because they packed their belongings and left!

Mrs. Wight herself experienced the same phenomena, although with somewhat different details, about a year later. She was drafting some business correspondence at her desk in the library about dusk one evening when the "same old gentleman" appeared to her, complete with boy's pants and pink coat and plait, but minus the silver cup. He lingered there a "long minute," she said, "and then faded gently into the twilight, much as though a curtain of gauze shut him from sight!"

In the intervening years, others have reported similar sensations in the dining room at Federal Hill. When the author first called Mrs. Lanier, the present owner, and asked her about the ghost stories associated with the house, she laughed a hearty laugh.

"If I did believe in ghosts, I guess I would be scared to death, because if there ever was a house that could be haunted this would be it." Mrs. Lanier and her late husband bought Federal Hill in 1947, and later began extensive renovations. "You wouldn't believe all the things we found here," she says. "We found great numbers of Civil War bullets, cannonballs, and hand-made nails." Indeed, the house was in the direct line of fire during the battle of Fredericksburg in 1862, and the old trenches still extend across the back lawn and terrace. It is said that Confederate general T. R. Cobb was killed in battle while facing the mansion, and a fragment of the shell can be seen beneath the northwest window of the drawing room that was turned into an operating room. "As I said," Mrs. Lanier noted, "if there were such things as ghosts, I'm sure they would be here."

Ironically, although Mrs. Lanier doesn't believe in haunting spirits, she and her husband had the house exorcised from ghosts in 1949, before they moved in! "We had some friends over to look at the inside of the house while the repairs were being made," she says. It was a Captain and Mrs. Porter. Mrs. Porter had psychic sensitivities, and she and her husband had their house, Colby, on the Potomac near Alexandria, exorcised, because there supposedly was a ghost in residence there.

"I remember that the house was just a shell then," said Mrs. Lanier. "Everything had been stripped down in preparation for the renovations. We walked into the library and Mrs. Porter said she had a strong sensation that there was a 'presence' in the room. Because of this and the fact that there were so many stories associated with the house, she suggested that we have it 'done' too."

"So we talked to the minister at St. George's Church, and he

said the bishop would be in town the following week." House exorcisms, it should be noted, are not taken lightly by the clergy. It helps, of course, to have a thorough understanding of what is involved, and the rites are performed in a very serious manner.

In this case, apparently nothing dramatic happened, as it did in the movie versions of "The Exorcist," and "The Amityville Horror," when priests were attacked, and in one instance killed. Mrs. Lanier says the bishop and the rector at St. George's came over one day, and as best she can recall they walked around on the first floor carrying prayer books and blessed the house. She doesn't remember them sprinkling any Holy water, or anything like that. She did say, however, that they didn't go upstairs, because it was in such "a shambles."

Mrs. Lee Langston Harrison, curator of the James Monroe museum says that while the Laniers had the house exorcised, the upstairs and the attic definitely were not covered in the ministrations. She should know, because she lived in an attic room for a brief period when she first moved to Fredericksburg.

"It is a big, haunting house, there's no doubt about that," Mrs. Harrison says today. "When it was used as an army hospital during the Civil War, bodies had been stored in the basement, or ice house. I can remember hearing the story that one servant wouldn't go in the house until it had been exorcised because she told everyone who would listen that she wasn't going to 'be around no hants'.

"I moved into a 'turret' room — the house has lots of turrets and gables — in the late spring of 1986. Shortly after I had been there a few nights, I was awakened in the pre-dawn hours with a start. A table against one of the gables was banging against the wall. At first, I thought it might be noise made by one of the other tenants in the house. There was an aerobics instructor living downstairs. But this specific banging kept occurring, always late at night, for two weeks straight," Mrs. Harrison says.

"I started sleeping with a hall light on. But every night I kept getting waked up out of a dead sleep about two or three in the morning. I started getting really scared. A young girl in the house who was really interested in psychic phenomena asked if she could sleep in my room one night, and she did, but nothing happened. Then one night I was roused at about 2:30 a.m., and the room was filled with what I can only describe as TV snow. You know, what it looks like when the cable goes out, or the station signs off for the night. The whole room was filled with this, and there was some sort of swooshing sound.

"I had a feeling of absolute terror. I sat up and screamed. And then I told the ghost, or whatever it was that was causing all this, if they would leave me alone I would be out of the house within a few days.

"Shortly after this, another young girl, who had psychic sensitivities examined the room. She said she found much 'activity' all along one wall in the room, and that there was a spirit who was not malevolent in the closet behind my wall on the same floor as the attic. She said this area had been used as a surgery room during the War Between the States, and that many soldiers had died both from the surgery and from the lack of it. I certainly didn't doubt her, and I couldn't wait to get out of the house, which I did soon after."

Thus, it seems, colorful legends of a most mysterious nature abound at venerable old Federal Hill. Alexander Spotswood would have loved it. Undoubtedly, he would raise a glass to toast his haunting companions!

CHAPTER 14

The Headless Blue Lady of Charlotte Street

Within a literal stone's throw of Federal Hill are three houses on Charlotte Street in Fredericksburg in and around which a storm of inexplicable psychic phenomena swirled during one week in May 1974 that still has neighbors talking and shaking their heads in disbelief whenever the subject is brought up. There had been no previous history of spiritual manifestations at these sites, and there has been none since. Nor is there any indication of the significance of that particular time period.

"We don't know why it happened and we don't know whether or not it all is related, although two of the incidents involved the same apparition," says Jay Harrison, a local archeologist and historian. The order of sequence of the events isn't clear either.

One was experienced by Mrs. Ruth Walker Heflin, Jay's maternal grandmother, who lived at 507 Charlotte Street. "She lived three doors up from our house on the same side of the street," Jay says. "One afternoon she was washing dishes when she heard the screen door open, and then the front door opened. She thought it was me, or my brother, Scot, and she called out to us. When she didn't get any answer, she walked into the living room to see who had come in. There was no one there.

"She went back to her dishes, then she distinctly heard the front door open again, and the screen door open after it. She went back to see if someone was going out, but again saw nothing. To this day, we haven't a clue as to who her mystery visitor was or what their purpose might have been."

The second and third occurrences happened to Mrs. Virginia McGrath, a next door neighbor to the Harrisons, who lived at 511 Charlotte Street. Jay remembers the scene vividly. "I was just a kid then, and one evening there were several police cars in front of her house," he says. "We learned later that something very mystifying had occurred. Mrs. McGrath worked for the FBI and she had kept some semi-classified papers and documents in file cabinets in an upstairs room. She always kept that room locked from the outside.

"On this particular evening, when she unlocked the door to this room, it looked like a cyclone had hit it. Every file cabinet had been knocked over and every file drawer had been emptied with the contents strewn all over. Someone or something had com-

pletely ransacked it, yet no papers were missing. But the curious thing — and neither Mrs. McGrath nor the police ever came up with a satisfactory answer — was how anyone or anything got into the room. The door had been locked from the outside and there was no sign of entry or escape from any window! It defied explanation."

During that same week Mrs. McGrath told Jay's family that she was home one night when she happened to be in the pantry and looked out the back window of her house, which, like the houses of the Harrisons and Mrs. Heflin, border on the Federal Hill property. "She told us she saw an amorphous form with a bluish cast at the foot of Federal Hill," Jay says. "She described it as a 'concentration of bluish light' that was 'floating above the ground' moving toward the old mansion. She said it had the form of a woman, but was headless!"

Jay believes she may have seen this vision the same night his father at 513 Charlotte Street had his frightening encounter with what residents in the area came to call "the Blue Lady." "My father, James G. Harrison, Jr., who died in May 1990, was watching television in the sun porch of our house late one night, again in May 1974," Jay recalls.

"He got up out of his chair and was going to switch stations, when something caught his attention. He turned to his right and saw someone standing at the doorway watching him. He said it was the form of a woman with a bluish cast about her, and she had no head. She appeared to be dressed in mid-19th century style.

"He stared at her for what he thought was an eternity, but actually probably was only a few seconds. Then he said she took the hemline of her dress and wrapped it around her as if in disgust or haste, swished by him, moved quickly through the dining room and vanished! My father looked through a kitchen window and said he saw what he called 'a glow' moving up toward the old bell house in the garden at Federal Hill.

"This tremendously unnerved him. For a moment, he thought that maybe my mother, Shirley, had come down to see if he had fallen asleep watching TV. He raced upstairs and found her sound asleep. He was so excited he jumped up and down on the bed until she woke up.

"I have never seen my father so frightened when he told us about it," Jay says. "You could see the fear in his eyes. Later on, he laughed about it, and joked that maybe she would come back one day, but she never did. But I can tell you this. He was really shaken, and he was not a man who got upset easily.

"All of this took place during that one week, and to this day, none of us know why she appeared, who she was, or what caused all of the flurry of psychic activity."

CHAPTER 15

Spirited Diners at Le Lafayette

"Come on up, anytime, and visit me. Yes, I'll be happy to talk to you about the ghost. I can't promise you if you'll see or hear anything, but you never know. Maybe it will make its presence known. Several of our customers have told me about experiences they have had, and we've had a waitress or two who could tell you some stories. . . ."

Pierre Mouryard is talking about the spirit or spirits which reside in his colorful establishment — Le LaFayette Restaurant at 623 Caroline Street, directly across from the Fredericksburg Visitors Center. It is billed as serving "Virginia-French-American regional cuisine," and even if no psychic manifestations materialize, the food is good and the hospitality warm.

The flavor of the restaurant is French with strong Virginian and Southwestern accents. "We might serve you an oven-roasted salmon with Pinoir sauce, or a bourbon marinated tenderloin," says sous chef Dan Cornish, who works with executive chef Greg Hancock. Most everything is smoked, and the variety is mouth watering: roasted pork loin with honey mustard glaze; smoked chicken "Old South" stuffed with a cornbread-apple dressing; or blackened mahi mahi with mango puree. There is an assortment of French pates and liver mousses, and fresh desserts are made daily and may include a classic Belgium sacher torte, a frozen Grand Marnier souffle, several types of cheesecake, or a white chocolate raspberry truffle mousse.

Another reason for a visit is the history and interesting architecture of the structure. It was built circa 1769-1771 as a magnificent Georgian town house for John Glassell, a Scottish merchant, and is noted as one of Fredericksburg's most important colonial dwellings. It is distinguished, and one might even say dominated by its massive exterior chimneys. In fact, it is still known today to many townspeople simply as "The Chimneys." Architecturally, it features unusually elaborate woodwork in the southwest parlor section, complete with carved swages and

garlands on the chimneypiece and lattice-work friezes on the window and door frames. At the rear of the restaurant are remnants of a terraced garden leading toward the river.

No one knows for sure who it is who haunts the house-restaurant, although the "happenings" have been going on for 100 years or more and occasionally still are heard or felt. "I haven't experienced anything personally," says Cornish, "but others have told me they have. Usually, it's late at night. People say they hear things like a chair moving across the room, a rocking chair rocking, or someone walking upstairs when no one else is in the place."

"Quite a few of our guests have told me about hearing strange noises," adds Mouryard. "Workmen have reported the sound of glass crashing to the floor, but they never have found anything broken. I, too, have heard the sound of footsteps and of chairs moving upstairs." Rhonda LeFever, who directs the annual Preservation Club's ghost walk tour of the town, says that "Things seem to happen in one room upstairs, and the ghost of a little boy has been seen." Others cite doorknobs mysteriously turning, doors opening and closing, and impressions being made on beds, as if by unseen nappers.

Yet no one has tied any of the events to the original owner. John Glassell himself was described as a "merchant of large enterprises and fortune," but he didn't live there long. A Royalist, he decided to return to his native Scotland when the Revolutionary War began. Through the years, the house has been owned by many families, and was the childhood residence of Nell Arthur, wife of Chester A. Arthur, 21st President of the United States.

How far back the psychic phenomena go also is unknown, although there is reference to a Dr. Brodie Herndon, who owned The Chimneys sometime in the mid-19th century, and frequently declared the house to be haunted. A clue to the ghost of a little boy may come from an account, more than a half century ago, of a mother who went into her son's bedroom upstairs to place a blanket on his bed. She reportedly was astonished to find another boy asleep with her son. Assuming it to be a neighborhood friend, she didn't rouse them. But the next morning there was no trace of the mystery guest, and her son swore that no one had slept with him.

It also is speculated that the ghost or ghosts may either be musically inclined, or at least appreciative of music. Margaret DuPont Lee, in her book "Virginia Ghosts" told of "a singer of long ago" who "returns to listen to the strains of some familiar melody played in the old parlor today."

And, finally, there was the encounter of the pianist who had an invisible accompanist, as told in a Fredericksburg tourist brochure and elsewhere. According to this legend, a young girl was alone in the house one evening and was softly singing and playing the piano when she heard the front door open. Footsteps then resounded across the hall and into the room. As the girl was singing, "The light of others days is faded, and all their glories past," she felt someone sit down beside her on the piano bench and touch her on the shoulder. She looked around but could see no one. She immediately fled the house.

One of Pierre Mouryard's waitresses once summed up such phenomena. "Come visit us," she said, "You'll see for yourself."

CHAPTER 16

The Playful Phantom at Rising Sun Tavern

It surely would be helpful if historians could agree on dates and facts. When they don't, things can get confusing. Take the Rising Sun Tavern in old town Fredericksburg, for instance. There is general agreement that this rustic edifice was built around 1760 by or for (take your choice) Charles Washington, the youngest brother of George Washington.

A discrepancy arises when one tries to discern when the tavern ceased to be a tavern. On the one hand, long-time townspeople, including past managers of the facility, contend that it lost its license to serve spirits in 1827, and was a private residence from that time until 1907 when it was purchased by the Association for the Preservation of Virginia Antiquities (APVA). Yet a respected state source claims that the Rising Sun remained a tavern up until "just before the Civil War." Incidentally, it was struck several times by Union artillery shells in the battle of Fredericksburg in 1862.

A second point of argument centers around just when the Rising Sun became a public house for drink, food and lodging. Much has been written that it was a hotbed of political discussion in the years leading up to and through the Revolutionary War (which began in 1775). Yet there also is a reference in the Virginia Landmarks Register which says, "In 1792, Frazer converted the house into a tavern known as the Golden Eagle." And is it John Frazer, or John Frazier? There are published accounts of the spelling both ways.

In "The Handbook of Historic Fredericksburg, Virginia," which is distributed at the Visitors' Center and throughout the town, it says that Charles Washington lived in the building for 20 years after its construction in 1760, "until he moved westward to establish the town now known as Charleston, West Virginia." The handbook goes on to say that the house was leased to John

Frazier in 1792, who announced the opening of the "Golden Eagle Tavern."

Okay! In the book "This is Fredericksburg," published in 1957, author Virginia Carmichael writes that the tavern was kept by George Weedon, "one of Fredericksburg's most prominent citizens, and there probably was not in the town a man more fearless than he in denunciation of England's policies toward the colonies. For that reason the tavern became a rallying place for radicals, and was called a 'hotbed of rebellion'."

Another book on the town, John Goolrick's "Historic Fredericksburg," published in 1922, says that Virginia reached its "golden age" in the years between 1760 and 1776, and that it was "during these times that George Weedon, host of the Rising Sun, made himself famous for his constant advocacy of American liberty." One traveler who put up at the Rising Sun then wrote that he stayed "at the tavern of one Weedon, who was ever active and zealous in blowing the flames of sedition."

It is also written that George Washington "knew the tavern well," and that the establishment and the tavern post office were frequented by Light Horse Harry Lee, Charles Lee, young James Monroe, Charles Carter and other notables. One published account states that "it is a matter of undoubted record that these, and half a hundred other young men, whose names were to become synonymous with freedom, discussed at the Rising Sun Tavern the topics of the day, chief among which was the rights of the colonist."

And, according to author Carmichael, all the leading men of Virginia have passed in and out of the tavern's doorway. "The Rising Sun," she wrote, "has known the hand of Washington, Jefferson, Madison, Mason, Mercer, John Paul Jones, and the famous Lees."

The Fredericksburg handbook notes that the tavern was known as the Golden Eagle until 1821, when it then was renamed the Rising Sun. However, authors have quoted George Washington diaries with numerous references to Weedon, and in one G. W. letter, he wrote to a friend: "Evening at the Rising Sun. Lost money (in cards) as usual. The boys in Fredericksburg are too smart for me."

Perhaps the answer lies in a notation made by the Virginia Landmarks Register. In its 1987 edition, it says, "Recent research indicates that the original Rising Sun Tavern was probably elsewhere in the city."

Well, suffice it to say that by whatever the tavern was known as, wherever it was located and whenever it actually became a tavern — a lot of famous Virginians graced its premises. It has been beautifully restored and today is open to the public. One can no longer stop off for a heady brew, but at least a glass of spiced tea can be served.

Downstairs there is a "great room" for the "landed gentry;" a "common man's" tap room; a ladies' "retiring room" and a tavern keeper's office. Upstairs are three sleeping rooms, an "L" storage room and one "common man's" room, with no fireplace. For no more than a farthing, this room could be rented by the poor in yesteryear to get out of the weather. Gracious hostesses, costumed in colonial style dress, show tourists around.

There is one aspect of the old building that is not shrouded in confusing facts and statistics. It is the general consensus that the Rising Sun is haunted! One tourist brochure states that the tavern is "still a lively historic attraction, and its ghostly inhabitant maintains the spirit of cheer and mischief that once thrived at the tavern."

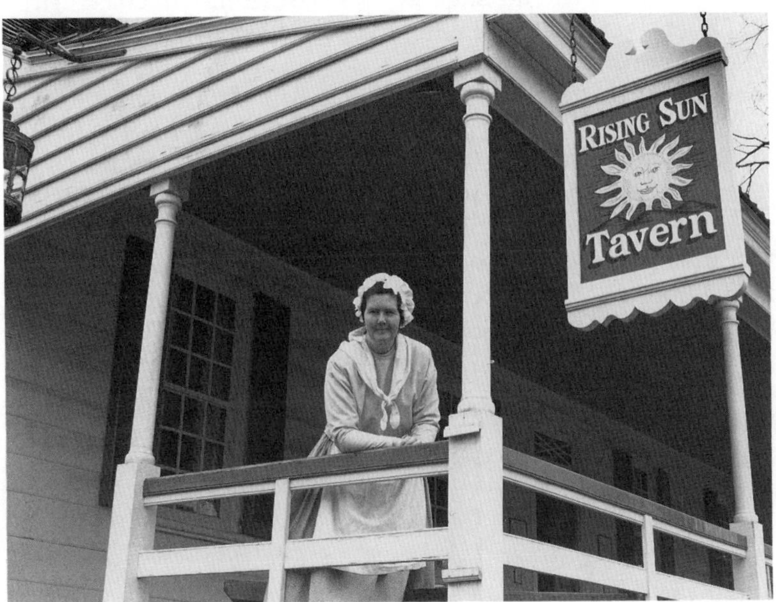

Linda Mix at the Rising Sun Tavern

And there is further agreement as to who the haunter is. Most people believe it is John Frazier, the last tavern keeper. "It's mostly harmless and fun things," says Linda Mix, current manager at the Rising Sun, of the psychic manifestations which occasionally occur. "There's definitely nothing malicious about what happens."

Well, maybe at least one guide at the tavern might take issue with that statement. Or at least perhaps "he" got a little too playful for her liking. A few years ago someone, or something, kept unplugging the lights in an upstairs room. The hostess, tired of reaching down to put the plug back in its socket, decided to mildly scold the ghost. "Come on now, stop it!" she demanded. Then as she turned to leave the room, the "force" or presence yanked the rug out from under her, sending her sprawling to the floor.

And then there was the time another hostess felt something tugging at the hem of her dress as she was descending the stairs early one morning. She looked to see if her colonial skirt had gotten snagged on something, but it hadn't. Yet, something was holding her. Knowing of all the tales associated with the tavern and its mischievous former proprietor, she said, "All right, John, let go!" At that instant she felt herself suddenly freed.

Others have had their mob caps pulled from their heads when no one within sight was around. Candles have inexplicably "moved" from their storage places, and once a candelabra on a wagon wheel crashed down in the front hall one day. What made this particular incident scary was that, as Linda Mix tells it, "Someone would have had to lift it over the bannister for it to fall that way."

Linda says a lot of little unexplained "things" happen at the Rising Sun. The front door has opened and closed on its own at times. "The opening we can understand," she says, but how do you account for the closing right after its been opened? We couldn't. Sometimes you just have a feeling that someone else is in the tavern when you are in it by yourself. This is especially true in the winter when tourists are few and far between. You just feel a presence.

"You know," Linda continues, "like the expression goes, I'm from Missouri and you have to show me. I think some of the things can be explained. If a mob cap flies off, it could be that the elastic was too tight. But I have to admit, there have been a couple of specific incidents that are really mystifying." One took place when a team of professional photographers came in to shoot some tourist promotional pictures. "They were setting up their equipment in one room while shooting in another," she says. "A camera began smoking on its own. Also, they had started one roll of film by photographing another site. When the film was developed, the shots of the other site turned out fine, but the ones taken in the tavern were blank."

Linda describes the other incident: "One of the hostesses was by herself one evening. She had the assignment to close up, and then to come back the first thing in the morning to open the tavern. She says that when she was locking up, she distinctly noticed that there were three hats lined up on pegs on the wall. When she opened up the next morning — and there had been no signs of a break-in or anything like that — the three hats were stacked neatly on a chair in the hallway!"

Despite the continuing series of manifestations over the years, those who work in the tavern are unafraid. "I believe John was a jolly old barkeep in his day," Linda says. "You had to be affable to survive as a tavern owner." Maybe he still feels the urge to carry on his pranks, because it apparently is good for business. "We have people coming in here all the time asking about the ghost," she notes. "They want to hear all the anecdotes we know."

John Frazier probably beams everytime that happens.

CHAPTER 17

A Sampling of Spectral Vignettes

(Author's note: Sometimes, the business (and fun) of tracking down area ghost stories can be frustrating. This is especially true when one hears of a particularly intriguing prospect only to find that the site and/or the source cannot be pinned down, or that the information is too sketchy and questionable to be included. Witnesses of psychic phenomena die, houses get torn down, or the spirits "move out" for reasons of their own. In other instances, there may be just enough tantalizing data and just enough interest for a fragment of a chapter. Following is a selection of such spectral snippets. Enjoy!)

* * * * *

Lamb's Creek Church

A little ways off route 3 about 13 miles east of Fredericksburg in the Graves Corner vicinity stands Lamb's Creek Church. Its elegant proportions, precise brickwork and restrained classical gauged-brick doorways show a sophistication achieved with "minimal ornamentation," according to the Virginia Landmarks Register. It was built in the period 1769-1777 to serve Brunswick Parish, and was used by Union troops as a stable during the Civil War. It was restored to use in 1908 but is today inactive, save for an annual memorial service.

For generations, Lamb's Creek Church has been said to be haunted. During the War Between the States, just prior to the building's desecration, two Confederate officers reportedly entered the church one night seeking shelter in the midst of a fierce thunder storm. They rested at the door facing the chancel. A great flash of lightning lit up the interior and the two soldiers were stunned to see a woman in white kneeling at the chancel rail, obviously in prayer. She remained in sight through two more successive bolts of lightning, which was enough for the two men. Preferring to take their chances with the storm and with mortal enemies, they dashed from the church.

"There have been no additions or embellishments to the story of the ghost since I have been associated with the church," says current pastor Norman Siefferman. "We have services there about once a year, and a wedding on occasion. It's a nice setting for a wedding." Siefferman adds that there are stories about the rectory where he lives in King George County being haunted, too, but he hasn't experienced anything out of the ordinary. "I'd change brands of Scotch if I did hear or see anything," he laughs.

* * * * *

Lamb's Creek Church

A Ghostly Appearance

The following article was published in the *Virginia Herald* September 26, 1870, under the headline, "Appearance of a Ghost." "The people on the western part of town, near Kenmore (in Fredericksburg) are very much exercised about the appearance of what is supposed to be a ghost in that quarter last Sunday morning between 11 and 12 o'clock. It is said that about that time of the day, during the shower of rain, Mr. Mills saw a man crawling on his hands along by the fence dragging his feet after him, as though his legs were paralyzed. He spoke to two ladies standing in the door and asked 'What does that mean?'

"Of course, they could not tell, and Mr. Mills said that he would see, and stepped out to the fence, which was but some ten or 15 feet, by which time the supposed man had passed him some few feet. Mr. Mills got over the fence, and started after the man and asked where he was going. The man straightened up on his feet to full height — which was higher than that of a medium sized man — and said in a distinct tone: 'I am going down,' and vanished out of sight. The figure was dressed in full uniform of a Federal soldier, which was clean and apparently new, with the blue overcoat coming down to near the feet. Mr. Willis did not see the face of the man, but the two ladies did, and say the face was bronze with hard features.

"The persons who say they saw this are of undoubted veracity, and although they do not believe in ghosts, they are unable to account for this sudden appearance and mysterious disappearance in broad daylight. It has created quite an excitement in that part of town."

* * * * *

Ellwood Manor

In Wilderness Run on the Orange-Spotsylvania County line is a Georgian frame house called Ellwood Manor, built in 1781 by William Jones. A number of strange psychic manifestations have been witnessed here down through the years, and a number of famous people have been associated with the house. It is said, for example, that

Lafayette and his forces fled across the old plantation's 4,000 acres during the Revolutionary War with Lord Cornwallis in hot pursuit. Later, in 1824, Lafayette returned to rest at the manor as he traveled from Orange to Fredericksburg.

Robert E. Lee's father, Light Horse Harry Lee, rested and wrote his memoirs in an upstairs bedroom after he was rescued from debtors' prison at Spotsylvania by Colonel Jones of Ellwood. In the downstairs parlor Union generals Ulysses S. Grant and George Meade mapped their plans on the eve of the Battle of the Wilderness, and Stonewall Jackson's amputated left arm reportedly is buried within sight of the old house.

Could any of these esteemed figures be behind the strange occurrences? Possibly. Guests have reported mysterious lights flashing in an upstairs bedroom — in the days before electricity — which disappeared when their source was investigated. Servants told of music emanating from the house when no one was around and the radio was found unplugged. Residents also have heard the voices of a ghostly choir on occasion.

And then there is the door to the small sitting room on the second floor. At times, it has swung back and forth of its own accord. According to local legend, a young man shot himself in that room long ago over a broken romance. The bloodstains remained on the floor for nearly 50 years, surviving endless attempts to scrub them out. They were finally painted over. Supposedly, it is the spirit of the young lover who lurks behind the door, checking to see if his long lost girl friend may yet return.

* * * * *

The Ghost Dogs of Northern Neck

Colorful folklorian tales, which once thrived in the Northern Neck section of Virginia, east of Fredericksburg, have been all but lost in the unblinking glare and clutter of modern day television. One story that has survived, however, involves the periodic sightings — generally in creek pond "bottoms" from which mists often arose above the marshes — of a headless dog. The accounts of its appearances, although always sketchy, nevertheless held children enraptured when recounted around the breakfast or dinner tables. And they were always sworn to with a solemnness that defied challenge.

The headless dog seemed to roam mostly in the lower section of the Neck, where he, or she, was occasionally joined by — take your choice — a white mule. . . a headless man. . . and another dog, this one with a head featuring "glaring red eyes." Scores of witnesses, young and old reported seeing this dog and their descriptions all were remarkably similar. The animal was as large as a calf, brown in color with patches of gray around his mouth. A large chain encircled its neck and dragged on the ground and rattled as the dog moved. And it moved only at night and only between Cockrell's Neck and Heathsville. Lastly, according to the long-held legend, it only was sighted just before or after the death of a local resident!

* * * * *

The Smiling Page of Sabine Hall

Each of the three sons of Robert "King" Carter of Corotoman — perhaps the wealthiest and most charismatic colonist of his time — built an early Georgian mansion on the plantations given to them by their fathers. Today, only the home of Landon Carter, near Warsaw east of Tappahannock in the middle of the Northern Neck, survives. Built around 1735, it is a magnificent mansion still considered to be one of Virginia's finest.

Great Greek porticos stand in front of a spacious hall panelled to the ceiling in heart pine. The carved walnut stair, ascending in a lateral passage, is one of the finest of the period, and, says the Virginia Landmarks Register, the terraced garden, with the top level retaining its original geometric pattern of beds and walks, is a rare surviving example of colonial landscape design.

The spirit of Sabine Hall — as it has been repeated down through the generations of Carter family owners — is a pleasant one. It is said that whenever a newly-wedded couple returns to the mansion, crosses the portico, enters through the wide door, and ascends the handsome stairway — that on the landing, by the window, a sprightly apparition appears. Almost always this figure, in the form of a little page dressed in holiday attire, is seen only by the bride. He greets her with a welcoming smile, and then he vanishes.

* * * * *

The Haunting Appearance of General Minor

General John Minor III was born at Topping Castle in Caroline County in 1761. His second wife was Lucy Landon Carter, of Cleve, an ancestral home of the Carter family in King George County. This stately Georgian mansion, one of Virginia's great plantation homes, was destroyed by fire in 1917. The general and his wife are buried in the old Masonic cemetery next to the James Monroe law office and museum in Fredericksburg. A red marble mausoleum marks the site.

John Minor III joined the Revolutionary Army as a "mere boy" and was at the siege and surrender of Yorktown. He later studied law under George Wythe and settled in Fredericksburg, where he gained considerable stature and reputation for his knowledge of law and for his eloquence. He was made a general during the War of 1812.

A few years later, as a member of the Electoral College for the Commonwealth of Virginia, Minor was in Richmond attending a public dinner at the Swan Tavern. That very same evening a number of his wife's relatives had gathered around the parlor fire at Cleve in King George. William McFarland, a brother-in-law, left the group at 11 p.m. and went upstairs to retire. But a moment later he rushed back downstairs in an alarmed state and proclaimed that he had just seen General Minor, wearing his riding clothes, enter the house through the front door, ascend the stairs to the second floor and pass him without so much as a word. He told the gathering at Cleve that he believed it to be the general's ghost. Everyone laughed at him, and when they followed him up the stairs no one was there.

Early the next morning — as documented in family records — they learned from a messenger that the previous evening, as General Minor had risen at the Swan Tavern to deliver a scheduled speech, he was stricken with apoplexy. He was carried into another room and died a few minutes later — precisely at 11 p.m!

* * * * *

A Strange Occurrence at Foulke

In the 1660s in Stafford County, Colonel Gerald Foulke built a house said to be typical of wilderness abodes of that day in that it was made of stout timber, with heavy chimneys and a high pitched roof that sloped over the porch. When he died in 1669, he was buried under the shade of an old mulberry tree, and his wife, Ann, marked the spot with a large recumbent stone, likely brought by ship from overseas. Here, the good Colonel rested in peace for more than two and a quarter centuries.

However, sometime just after the turn of the 20th century, the brick in the old chimney fireplace of the house gave way. The occupant replaced it with Foulke's tombstone as a fireback. That very evening, as the legend goes, the Colonel's apparition appeared before the person who had taken the stone, causing great fear. The next morning the man unwedged the slab from the chimney and apparently dumped it into the nearby river, as no trace of the inscribed tombstone has ever been found.

* * * * *

Milling Soldiers at Mannsfield

Mannsfield was built in 1749 by Mann Page, a member of the House of Burgesses, in Spotsylvania County a short distance from town at the site that is now part of the Fredericksburg Country Club. It was a large two-story stone mansion which overlooked the Rappahannock River, and was known for its avenue and grove of "magnificent chestnut trees."

During the Civil War, the house was occupied by both Union and Confederate troops — at different times — and also served as a hospital and headquarters for both sides. According to most sources, Mannsfield was burned to the ground by Union forces at the close of the war, although one account states that some Confederate soldiers from Louisiana, in trying to light a campfire on the marbleized wood floor, accidently gutted the structure in 1863.

In the years after the Civil War, stories of sightings of ghostly figures in military uniforms milling around the grove of trees near the ruins of the house became so prevalent that many people refused to go near the place after dark. Mannsfield's century-old reputation as being haunted is largely attributable to a woman who moved near the burned out mansion probably sometime in the early 1890s. She was described as being "clear seeing," which today is interpreted as being a clairvoyant.

According to old timers in the area, she saw mostly Confederate soldiers walking about, sitting or lying in the shade of the trees. At times she viewed doctors ministering to the wounded, and orderlies holding horses. Reportedly, she often became quite frustrated when others couldn't see what she saw, although in later years some residents did tell of witnessing the movements of the apparitional troops among the estate's large trees. Mannsfield was such a pleasant setting that perhaps the soldier spirits wished to linger there in restful repose long after the heat of the battle had abated.

* * * * *

Old Ghost Tales at Ingleside

"You come here and sleep in the house for one night and I guarantee you, you will hear all kinds of noises." Carl Flemer, Jr., chairman of the board of Ingleside Plantation, Inc., and the head of the highly respected Ingleside winery, near Oak Grove in the Northern Neck, is talking about the house that was built in 1833-34, initially as the "Washington Academy of Westmoreland." It operated as a school for less than 10 years, and was renamed Ingleside by 1849. It is today a registered national historic place.

According to Flemer, the mansion is located at the highest elevation of the Northern Neck — about 190 feet above sea level — at a point where the Rappahannock and Potomac Rivers come closest together in their 100 mile course from the fall line to the Chesapeake Bay. "Because of its height, overlooking both rivers, Ingleside is said to have been used as a signal point during the Civil War," he says, adding that rainfall drainage from the front yard goes to the Rappahannock and that from the back yard goes to the Potomac.

Continuing, Flemer says that Ingleside is constructed of brick, most probably fired from clay on the premises. The exterior and interior walls are solid brick as well as the six massive 20 foot columns. There are five full floor levels, including an attic and a basement. Colonel Henry Garnett, one of the original trustees of Washington Academy, purchased the property after the school closed, but the Civil War interrupted his plans for developing the plantation, and after the war Ingleside was used for a while as a Union military court. It later was neglected and became "dilapidated." Flemer's great grandfather bought the estate in 1890, along with the adjoining Walnut Hill. The two properties contained over 1,000 acres.

Flemer at first was a little reluctant to talk directly about ghosts at Ingleside. "It's a steam heated house and the pipes rattle," he says. "There is an old furnace, so a lot of the weird and scary noises can be explained." He did admit, however, that he had heard stories about hauntings since he was a child in the area. Flemer summed up the colorful tales in a presentation he gave to the James Monroe Chapter of the Sons of the American Revolution in September 1989.

Here is what he said: "All houses of this vintage have ghost stories — Ingleside is no exception. It, in fact, has two ghosts — an outside ghost and an inside ghost. The outside ghost is that of Col. Jett of adjoining Walnut Hill. Jett was probably disappointed in the failure of the Washington Academy as a school after so much time, money and effort were expended, so he decided to haunt the place.

"On calm, misty nights you can faintly but unmistakably hear his dappled grey stallion's hooves go clippity clop, clippity clop around the circular driveway. If it is one of those nights when you are in tune with specters of the past, you can actually see him carrying his severed head in his hands and hear the rattling chains. For years, our own riding horses, on certain misty nights, have galloped in a circle in the adjacent pasture, apparently following the horse and ghost of Col. Jett.

"We have also to contend with Col. Henry Garnett's ghost inside the house. I have lived at Ingleside all of my life. The family sleeping quarters are the bedrooms on the third floor. Guests are usually put up in second floor bedrooms. The reason for this is the third floor is haunted and guests would not understand. The room I use today is the same one my brother and I slept in as boys. It is the room with the 150-year-old bloodstains still in the flooring. It is the room where you can more clearly hear the creaks and groans, the midnight sobbing and wailing, the tap - tap - tapping. It is the room where on many a full moon night you can hear and feel a rustle of clothing, a movement of air, and there in the dim light by the antique bed post stands something! A hideous apparition! Apparently, it is the ghost of Col. Henry T. Garnett! It does not move. It is not threatening. It simply stares at you! In a few moments, when you become fully awake, the apparition recedes back into the dusty, secret passages of the old house!

"To live in an ancient house like this and fully enjoy all it has to offer, one needs to have a lively imagination. You will not be disappointed, believe me."

* * * * *

Spirits of Stately Salubria

By following route 3 west out of Fredericksburg past Chancellorsville and Wilderness, then turning northwest, one soon arrives at the small town of Stevensburg east of Culpeper. Near there stands stately Salubria, which has been described as: "a large commodious dwelling of brick and one of the finest pretentious houses on what was the western frontier of Virginia;" and as "among the few representatives of mid-Georgian architecture in Virginia's Piedmont." It dates to the 1760s. The Virginia Landmarks Register says it has outstanding interior panelling, and its "otherwise plain facades are given an elegant rhythm by the use of segmental brick arches above all the openings."

Lady Spotswood, widow of Sir Alexander Spotswood, is said to be buried on the grounds, but her resting place cannot be found today. There is a legend about her son, Robert, who was killed in the French and Indian War. Although his body was never discovered, Lady Spotswood was sent one of his moccasins which was preserved as a family relic. Supposedly, as long as the moccasin was in the house, "fate dealt kindly" with it. After its mysterious loss, however, none of the family held the old mansion any length of time. It also is said that at times occupants of the house have distinctly heard the tread of the moccasin over the floor of the upper hall and in Lady Spotswood's room.

Early in this century Mrs. Grayson, who then lived at Salubria, was in Lady Spotswood's room one night when she happened to glance into a mirror. "A white mist seemed to have enveloped my form," she reported. "I could not move nor utter a sound. As I looked intently, the mist slowly took the form of a face peering over my shoulder and reflected in the glass before me. I felt oppressed and unable to move." At this point, Mrs. Grayson screamed and fainted. An investigation revealed no cause.

On one other occasion two Grayson boys saw "very faintly, a figure dressed in white with black hair falling over her shoulders, her arm outstretched, as she floated noiselessly down the hall!"

A servant told them they had "seen the spirit." A debate still exists. Was it the apparition of Lady Spotswood, still searching for the lost moccasin? Or was it the return of a "Mrs. Hansborough," who allegedly hanged herself in an upstairs bedroom many years ago?

CHAPTER 18

The Lost Legends of Loretto

The headline published in the *Fauquier* (County) *Democrat* on August 20, 1953, was intriguing to say the least. It read: "200-Year-Old Loretto Has Ghosts, Buried Treasure." And, indeed, the legends do abound at this picturesque manor home located about four miles from Warrenton on the old Bethel Road. But interestingly, while the tales of spooks and hidden silver have been told and retold with uncommonly few variations, the actual details of the house itself and when it was built are much more sketchy.

One reference, for example, states that the original three-story brick building was constructed in 1741 by Richard H. Foote. It was then known as "Edmonium." A second book, this one on the history of the county, says the house was built in 1741 by Elias Edmonds. A Virginia Historic Landmarks Commission Report, however, says, "there are few traces at Loretto of the two story brick mansion supposed to have been built after the Revolution by Capt. Elias Edmonds to replace one destroyed by fire in 1789." The report goes on to say that Edmonium was built on land purchased in 1759 by Capt. Edmonds from Richard Henry Lee. An 1878 newspaper article says Elias Edmonds (for whom Edmonium was named) "came hither" to the area about 1741, and that he was "a colonial magistrate and also a Captain in Braddock's War, or more strictly speaking that war between the mother country and France."

Edmond's wife, Frances, improved and enlarged the house after the Captain's death, "using money obtained from the sale of his land bounty warrants in Kentucky." The house passed to the Foote family in 1820, and they sold it to Col. John Scott after the Civil War. Scott's wife changed the name to Loretto, "presumably for a small central Italian town in which there is a celebrated shrine to the Virgin known as 'Our Lady of Loreto'."

Reportedly, the brick in the house was brought from England on a sailing vessel, and, said one author, "it is highly probable slave labor was used in its erection, as the Edmonds were both large land and slave owners."

In her book, "An Old Timer in Warrenton and Fauquier County Virginia," M. Louise Evans wrote: "The whole house has 'atmosphere'. . . Many are the stories told of Edmonium or Loretto noises and unaccountable acts."

It is speculated by some that the house is haunted because it sits atop an old burying ground. Allegedly, during excavations for the cellar, a large number of Indian weapons, bones and other relics were found. In support of this theory, one former resident told of hearing sounds of digging beneath the mansion. According to an article published in the Fauquier Democrat more than 30 years ago, others heard all sorts of strange noises, including the sounds of heavy barrels rolling down the stairway and terrific crashes against the doors. But no evidence of anything damaged or anything amiss ever was discovered.

The paper also quoted a Miss Marshall Jeffries who once lived at Loretto. She said: "One night I was waiting for dinner to be placed on the table when an old clock that had not run in years struck twice. The servant said, 'there will be two deaths in your family in less than a year.' There were two deaths — my mother's and that of a child. The clock never made another sound as far as I ever heard."

Other manifestations that have occurred in the house over the years — as recorded in a variety of sources — include:

* The strains of a violin and the sound of a large party in progress — all heard at different times by family members, servants and guests — with no rational explanation offered.

* The sighting of a "lady in grey" who walks the three flights of broad stairs at midnight, holding a candle.

* A heavy piece of mahogany furniture, either a wardrobe or a bureau, that was "pulled" across the attic floor to block entrance through a door. Whenever this happened, it is said to have taken the efforts of "several men" to push the piece back enabling entrance.

And then there is the tale of the treasure in which Richard Foote is supposed to have buried his silver in the yard with help from one servant. Foote then became paralyzed and the servant died, and although there have been many efforts to locate the horde, nothing has ever been found.

"I can't add a whole lot to what has been written and told

about the spirits here," says present owner William Wilbur. "I have never seen or experienced anything myself. My late wife, who died in 1981, once said she thought she had what she called 'a viewing.' And another time one of my daughters said she felt like someone or something was holding her down on her bed one night. She was really alarmed."

And the treasure? "Oh, yes, I've heard the stories repeated many times," says Wilbur. "We were just talking about it the other day. I keep wanting to get a non-ferrous metal detector and take a look around the house. Maybe one of these day I'll do just that."

CHAPTER 19

A Folio of Fauquier Phantasms

Ghosts seem to abound in Fauquier County, northwest of Fredericksburg. More than 30 years ago, John Daniel McCarty, writing in the *Fauquier Democrat*, said, "In nearly every section of the county an apparition or a strange noise makes some old house its dwelling place. The ghost population seems to be particularly concentrated around Warrenton and in the upper portion of the county." The list of sites in which spirits allegedly have frequented is both long and impressive: Loretto, Longwood, Kinloch, Grace Church, Avenal, Roland, Nordley, Leeton Forest, Morven, Leeds Church, Snow Hill, Edgehill and Greenview, to name a few.

Herewith, then, is a sampler of some of the more colorful Fauquierian haunts:

The Old Gaol

One of the landmark tourist attractions in Warrenton's courthouse square is the old county jail, or the old gaol as it was known generations ago. The Virginia Landmarks Register calls it "one of the more complex representatives of the state's early county penal architecture." It includes the 1808 brick jail, later converted to the jailer's residence, and the parallel 1822 stone jail with its high-walled jailyard. The two-part building served the county until 1964 when it was given over to the local Historical Society and became a history museum. The Register says this edifice "provides a telling picture of conditions endured by inmates of such county facilities over the past century and a half."

One of the most eccentric inmates, according to yellowed local newspaper accounts and other sources, was an "old gentleman" who once owned and lived on a farm in upper Fauquier. For some reason, since lost in time, perhaps senility, he believed that some of his relatives were out to get him and seize his

The Old Gaol

property. He took rather extreme measures to prevent such an occurrence. He decided to set his house on fire while he was still in it!

But, alas, his plot failed. He was rescued, and then unceremoniously brought to court on charges of attempted suicide and arson. His advanced age caught up with him in the old gaol. He contracted pneumonia and died.

Several months later, a woman who had been placed in the same cell the old man had occupied was brought to trial. Curiously, the presiding judge asked her if she had any visitors during her incarceration. She replied, "No sir, not anyone I am acquainted with. . . but a little old man with a long white beard comes to my cell every night. He won't speak to me, and every time he's been there, he's tried to take away the bed clothes!"

When the judge then asked her to characterize the mystery visitor, she gave a perfect description of the old gentleman who had died of pneumonia!

In more recent years there have been reports of additional psychic phenomena in the old place. "A number of people have reported hearing footsteps there when no one was supposed to be in the building," says Mrs. Mead Palmer, who has done some research on the jail for the local historical society. One who has heard the sounds is Shiela Heath. "You hear floorboards creak, like someone is walking across them," she says. "I have definitely heard someone moving around."

"My husband, Gary, was painting in the building one day when no one else was there. He left the room for a minute or two and when he came back there was a child's smudged footprint in the paint on the door sill," Shiela adds. "It can be a very scary place."

* * * * *

The Haunted Woods at Avenal

Some county residents refer to her as "The White Lady." Others call her "The Gray Lady." Whatever, tales of her wispy appearances in the woods near the house known as Avenal, north of Warrenton, have circulated through this rustic countryside for more than 100 years without so much as a single clue as to who she is, or was, or what her purpose was.

Avenal, near Little Georgetown, at the foot of the Bull Run Mountains, was built sometime around 1825 by William Beverley of Blandfield in Essex County for a summer home. As Sir Walter Scott's writings were tremendously popular in the South before the Civil War, many homes were named after his works — "Ivanhoe," "Waverly," and "Rokeby," in Fauquier County alone. Avenal was taken from Scott's "The Monastery." In that novel the "White Lady of Avenal" was a ghostly figure who appeared on occasion.

The "real" White Lady of Avenal was believed to have been sighted by Brad Beverley, son of William, sometime around 1885. A Beverley descendent, Robert Beverley Herbert, wrote about it in a newspaper account more than a quarter century ago. He said Brad and a companion, while riding on horseback starting up a hill entering the woods at the lower gate, saw what looked like "a column of smoke gliding along the edge of the road just ahead of them." Soon after that, two others approaching Avenal saw a figure which they thought at first was a white oak bush with dead leaves in the moonlight. But the figure seemed to move. They discovered there was no bush, and later described it "to be a column of mist or someone dressed in white."

Sometime later, Herbert's grandfather, who had at first scoffed at such stories, admitted that once when he was returned to Avenal late at night, "I saw that thing in the woods." Brad Beverley told of seeing "her" twice, and said a number of house guests and servants had also witnessed the apparition. Once Brad said he saw a "lady" come through the gate and walk towards him, causing his horse to tremble and sink down on its knees.

Brad Beverley further said that on at least three separate occasions people tried to touch or grab the nebulous figure. His uncle "caught at her" as she passed near him and disappeared. "He held nothing in his hand nor did he touch any solid substance," Brad noted. Another time, a boy put his arms around the white lady, "but she melted away in his embrace." The third time a farm tenant put out his hand to her, but she vanished.

Robert Beverley Herbert says he never saw the apparition, but he did report a "strange coincidence" which happened to him in 1911. At the time the house was closed and no one was living there. "I had recently gotten a Kodak and had taken pictures of most of the Virginia places that were connected with the Beverley family, and, of course, wanted one of Avenal, so I walked over there to get a picture," he said.

"I was sorry I had no one with me to put in the foreground to give a better perspective of the size of the trees and the proportions of the house." Or at least he thought no one was with him. When his picture was developed, it had a "representation of a lady dressed in white leaning against one of the big chestnut trees. She appeared," Herbert said, "to be knitting."

* * * * *

Edgehill

About six miles north out of Warrenton off route 17 on the way to Marshall and The Plains, lies a venerable old house known as Edgehill which is said to have been built by James Eustace Jeffries "about 1840, or earlier." Josephine Jeffries, who married Colonel William H. Chapman, was born in the house, which originally had five rooms and a small leanto kitchen with a dirt floor. Colonel Chapman, it should be noted, was second in command to Colonel John S. Mosby — of the famous Mosby's Rangers — and served with distinction through the Civil War. He died in Greensboro, North Carolina, in 1929.

There is a log-bodied section and a stone section of the house. In 1946, the owners raised the roof to a full two stories plus basement, changed the entrance to the basement, changed the porch, and added a kitchen wing. In 1956, Edgehill was opened for the Garden Club of Virginia's annual spring tours, and it was said at the time that a visit "will certainly amply reward the visitor who wishes to look over the handsomely furnished house, attractive garden and planting, and see a typical Virginia country home. . . ."

What wasn't said was that the visitors might also experience some form of psychic phenomena, or perhaps catch a glimpse of the ghost of Colonel Chapman himself, for he allegedly has appeared at Edgehill from time to time. One person who saw him was Anne Rumbough, who lived in the house in the late 1960s with her two young daughters while her husband, Hunt, was serving with the U.S. armed forces in Vietnam.

"All sorts of strange things happened in the house while we were there," Anne says. "Double bolted doors somehow opened by themselves on occasion. When the door which led outside to the kitchen kept opening, my father put a sliding bolt on it. I would latch it before going to bed, but when I would come down the next morning, the door would be open. And it wasn't just ajar, it was wide open, as if someone or something had done it intentionally. And you had to really lean against that door and put a lot of force behind it to get the bolt to slide home. I can't explain how it opened. I know I didn't do it, and my children, who were five and ten at the time didn't do it."

Once photos, taken at a Christmas party at Edgehill, showed a mysterious, ethereal-like form in the background. "I never could explain that either," says Anne. Other "things" included late-night noises and a water tap in the pantry which seemed to turn itself on at times.

The most striking manifestation occurred one day when

Anne was taking a bath upstairs and her standard poodle was making all kinds of noise at the door downstairs. She put on a robe and went down to investigate. "As I went by the library something told me to look into the room and there was a man sitting in the wing chair. He had on a double-breasted Civil War type uniform with a stand up collar," Ann says. "I had this eerie feeling that he wasn't one of us. Yet I wasn't frightened, because somehow I knew he wasn't a living, breathing human being. When I let the dog in, he snarled and curled his lip at the entrance to the library. I had never seen him do that before."

Later, when the door to the library partially opened by itself, Anne told her daughter, Mimi, to go open the door fully. "I said out loud, 'Colonel Chapman, won't you come inside and join us?' I guess Mimi must have thought I was crazy. But you know, that door never opened by itself after that. As soon as we acknowledged 'his' presence the door stayed shut. It was as if all 'he' wanted was recognition — for us to be aware that he was there."

* * * * *

Leeton Forest

About two miles out of Warrenton, near what was once known as Sunset Hill Road is a site where it is said Lord Fairfax once had a hunting lodge. Close by was the home of the Honorable Charles Lee, Attorney General of the United States under Presidents Washington and Adams. This house was known as Leeton Forest. Unfortunately, it burned to the ground sometime early this century, leaving nothing but a high stone foundation and four stone chimneys.

Scattered amid the ashes of the old wide clap-boarding was a host of psychic manifestations which apparently plagued the original house, along with a myth-like story of a fortune in a money box hidden behind a stone in a wall of the foundation. So prevalent were the ghostly stories at Leeton Forest, that it has been often told that servants 100 years or more ago would not come near the house after sundown, and some even refused to work there during the day.

Much of the phenomena seemed to center around the door to one of the bedrooms on the second floor, strangely similar to the door to the library at Edgehill. This door would be closed every evening, only to be found open the following morning. Tenants tried new locks and latches on the door to no avail. One resident had the door padlocked and a chain fastened to the woodwork with heavy staples, but still the door would be discovered open and the padlock unfastened. No explanation was ever forthcoming.

Other occurrences included "someone rocking in a heavy chair." This is ordinarily a very common form of spiritual occupancy, but the odd thing about this rocking was that it did not occur late at night; it was always heard at about seven in the morning. And it was followed by footsteps across a bare floor, the sound of water being poured into a basin, and then a splashing, as if someone were freshening themselves up for the day's activities. There also were "conversations" held in the pantry and kitchen in the back of the house by unseen conversationalists. Investigations by residents turned up no rational cause for any of these incidents.

Sometime around 1913 the property was sold to a John Fielding, who may have been the mysterious "Mr. F." referred to by Margaret DuPont in her book, "Virginia Ghosts," published in 1930. She reported that after the fire had destroyed the house, Mr. F. and a carpenter, in walking around the ruins, "noticed a stone on the inside wall of the foundation near a chimney, which appeared to have no mortar to hold it in place. Mr. F. succeeded in removing this stone, and behind it was a recess which contained a good sized metal box."

The carpenter said Mr. F. took the box into the barn, locked himself inside, and remained there most of the day. Not long afterwards he began making arrangements to build a new home of larger proportions on the old foundations. It was speculated that the box must have contained a large sum of money because it was said Mr. F. had no insurance on the house that burned.

It was further speculated, by one of the former tenants of Leeton Forest, that Mr. F. had been led to his discovery by whatever spirit that had resided in the house; that the ghost's mission had been to guard the treasure as long as the house was standing, but to "communicate its whereabouts" once the house had burned to the ground.

* * * * *

The Haunted Chamber of Longwood

"I've always heard about the ghost stories at Longwood, ever since I was a kid," says Charles Gray. "It's a neat old farmhouse up on Cedar Run that sits on one of the highest hills in the area." The area is near Catlett, north of Fredericksburg and east of Warrenton. An original house at the site was burned during the Civil War. A Virginia Landmarks Commission report says that while there is nothing "spectacular" about the house, it is nevertheless an interesting and comfortable farmhouse, with a former slave residence nearby.

For a long time, the house and property belonged to members of the Hooe family, and in the late 19th and early 20th centuries so many apparitions were reported to have been seen by clan members, that one bedroom upstairs came to be known as the "haunted chamber." In it, the vision of a Confederate soldier, reputedly the sweetheart of one of the young Hooe women, was sighted so often no one wanted to sleep in the room.

One legend, as passed down by the family, was that one night when a severe thunderstorm broke, several dinner guests had to spend the night in the house. They allegedly drew straws to see who would have to sleep in the dreaded room and Rhys Hooe, a cousin of the owner, was selected. Afraid that his friends might try to play a trick on him in the dead of night, he locked the bedroom door and placed the key under his pillow.

Sometime between two and three in the morning he was awakened by the sound of the door being opened. A man dressed in a Confederate uniform and wearing cavalry boots entered, walked across the room, sat in a chair by the window and began pulling off his boots. Rhys, suspecting a practical joke being played on him, got out of bed, went over to the figure and tried to grab his coat collar. Instead, he felt nothing. His hand grasped only air! Shaken, he managed to get the key and unlock the door before he collapsed on the hall floor. Some psychic experts contend that when a mortal touches, feels or walks into an apparitional spirit, it can cause them to faint.

He was revived with the aid of a glass of whiskey, but refused to reenter the haunted chamber.

CHAPTER 20

Bed, Breakfast and Ghosts at Linden

A few miles north of Tappahannock on Route 17, on the way to Fredericksburg, off on the right side of the road, is a weather beaten old house wedged in between two huge trees. The paint is peeling, the shutters look askew, and the house itself is as brooding and foreboding as the old Bates family home, which struck fear in the hearts of millions in the movie "Psycho." It appears to be abandoned, and if ever a place had the appearance of a haunted house, it would rate a "ten" on any list.

Conversely, nearby, on the other side of the highway, set back a few yards off the road, is a large four story brick mansion that — while it is old — it nevertheless is bright, clean, and has the warm look of welcome all over it. This is known as Linden House, and today it is a bed and breakfast Inn. How appearances can deceive! The unnamed old frame dwelling on the one side of Route 17 which looks so sinister has no ghosts, or at least none to speak of. Pastoral Linden, on the other hand, seems rife with psychic phenomena.

"I guess it's not easy to explain," says genial Sandra Pounsberry, who with her husband, Kenneth, runs Linden. "It's true. We've seen and heard things here we really can't explain, but there doesn't seem to be anything evil about the place." Still, to be on the safe side, the Pounsberrys have had a priest out to give the house his blessing.

They bought the venerable 240-year old house in 1990, and have spent considerable effort and care in renovating it. "It was moldy and mildewy all over," Sandra says. "It took 185 gallons of paint to redo it. We used light colors because it was so dark. The project was delayed once when a massive bolt of lightning struck the large linden tree on the front lawn, bore six feet into the ground, and spewed dirt all over the new paint job. The surge went through the house, damaging a wall and the downstairs floor and knocking out the phone system, but the Pounsberrys persevered.

During the renovation process, the foundations of what is believed to have been a smokehouse, a kitchen and a stable were uncovered and several pieces of original hardware were found. The couple hopes eventually to restore the outbuildings and turn the estate into a working farm complete with livestock. Linden, indeed, is set scenically on rolling grounds and seems an ideal place for wedding receptions, business retreats, picnics and family reunions, which the Pounsberrys cater to.

And if one stays overnight to partake in the next morning's full plantation breakfast, he or she, or both, may well meet, hear or see some "unseen guests." "A lot of strange things have happened since we have been here," Sandra says. "For one thing, we have smells. At times you can distinctly determine a sweet tobacco smell on the third floor. It's almost like the aroma you get in a tobacco store. And there are noises occasionally. We have heard footsteps on the third and fourth floors when no one else was in the house.

"We had some friends over once, and when they were on the third floor, they heard the front door slam shut. Now it is barred like it was in colonial times, and there is no way it could open or shut on its own. When they learned this, they excused themselves and left in a kind of hurry."

The most unusual phenomena took place when the house was still being worked on, and the locks had not been placed on the bedroom doors. "There were times when it looked like someone, or something was trying to peek through the openings," Sandra says. "One night when I was in bed, light yellow rays came through the keyhole. As I sat up, they seemed to shrink back. Then they turned to an orange color. It was a little scary. I don't know what it was, but I don't think I have lost my mind, either. I definitely saw it. I didn't imagine it."

It makes for interesting conversation at the breakfast table.

* * * * *

(Author's note: As a postscript to Linden, I contacted Edward Wright Haile of Chesituxent, whose grandmother, Esther W. Saunders, had written about an experience she had in the house in the mid to late 1880s or the early 1890s. She drafted a manuscript, titled "A Ghost Story," for a composition course she took in the 1920s at Harrisonburg Teacher's College — now James Madison University. Edward was good enough to share this fascinating account with me, and so here are some excerpts from Esther Saunders' encounter of more than 100 years ago.)

"Not so many years ago during the nicest kind of summer weather, a girl friend came to visit me. My plans to entertain her included a trip to Vawters Church in the upper part of the county. . . . To break the drive and also for further entertainment, one Saturday afternoon, after a refreshing rain, I proposed that we spend the night with a lady who lived not many miles from the church. This lady, Miss Lucy Lee, lived with her maiden aunt, Miss Jane Gray, in a large brick house (Linden) in a grove of trees, some distance from the highway.

"The loveliest furniture was in this house, real antiques; a rosewood piano, a tall hall clock, tables of every description with claw feet, gilt mirrors, wide mahogany beds, brass candelabra, and things too numerous to mention.

"Miss Jane Gray had been deaf since she was 13 years old. She was very beautiful and I have heard that when this incurable deafness came upon her suddenly, her mother was so distressed she allowed her to do anything she chose, and she chose to sleep

all day and sit up and read all night. Servants waited on Miss Jane Gray, brought her meals to her, and obeyed her every behest. When her mother died, other members of the family continued to humor her till at last there were none left but her and her niece (sic), Miss Lucy Lee. This niece followed the example of the others and humored her aunt in every possible way. My mother told me that this niece (Lucy Lee) when young was engaged to be married to a young doctor and that this young man was taken sick and died.

"Outwardly it did not sadden her life. She seemed to live entirely for others, and found joy in service. . . . All loved to go to her home, and she delighted to entertain. Many were the dinings, teas, parties had in her home, and many people were the recipients of her hospitality. On this particular afternoon, Miss Lucy Lee received my friend and me with the greatest cordiality.

"We did not go to bed until late. There were two double beds in this large room and Miss Lucy said that tho' it was her custom to sleep downstairs, that night she would sleep in the room with us. My friend and I slept together, and just before blowing out the light (lamps were then in use) Miss Lucy put a box of matches by the lamp and said, 'Now if either of you needs to light the lamp during the night, here are the matches.'

"I was awakened by my friend saying, 'Esther, are you asleep? Stay awake a little while. Please don't go to sleep. I hear a noise in the hall.' We had left the door open. I said, 'Oh, it isn't anything!' Just at that time I heard a noise in the hall as if someone was walking to our door. I said, 'What is that?' My friend said 'That is what I have been hearing and I wanted you to hear it. Miss Lucy has gone down the stairs and hasn't come back.' Just as she said that, I heard the swish of skirts, as of someone coming up that long flight of steps and walking with soft foot steps the whole length of the hall till our door was reached. There, every sound ceased. There was no sound of anyone turning and walking back.

"This was repeated again and again. The swish of skirts, someone walking up the steps, and stopping at our door; no steps going back. I felt cold chills running up my back. I suppose my friend felt just as I did. I was never so frightened in all my life! I felt myself getting so scared I could hardly move.

I whispered to my friend, 'This will never do! We must find out what that is! She said, 'Yes, but what can we do?' I felt she was just as scared as she could be. I whispered, 'I am going to jump to the dresser and light the lamp.' I felt I was too scared to walk there, but that I must summon all my strength, and make one spring for the dresser and light the lamp. I sprang and landed near the dresser, but when I reached for the matches, they were gone. I hardly know how I got back to the bed, I was so terror stricken. Miss Lucy never came back, and the hours passed. It seemed ages. I don't know how we lived through the night.

"Finally morning came. . . We were thoroughly unnerved and exhausted. We both said, 'What are we to do? If we could only be satisfied about what we heard last night! Oh, if we could only know what that was!' But how could we find out? It would never do to let Miss Lucy know we had heard a ghost in her house. . . But to my amazement, when I said, 'Miss Lucy, you left us last night,' she looked awfully confused and blushed violently, but all she said was, 'I remembered I had left one of the windows up and went down to let it down.'

". . . . To this day the mystery of that night has never been solved. . . . Since that night I have heard it said that the house is haunted. When I saw my friend not long ago, she referred to that night, and we both still think we were never so frightened in all our lives."

As a postscript to the postscript on Linden, Edward Haile writes, "This was the premier ghost story of my childhood told with faithful accuracy to me by my mother, Margaret Saunders Haile, daughter of the writer."

Haile adds that he was told Jane Gray "took to wearing a cloth or shroud wrapped around her face. She slept the day and paced the house through the night. People were sure she was odd. In death she is reported to have appeared in the yard as a spirit in black silks."

Ethereal Events in Essex County

(Author's note: Essex County, bordering the Rappahannock River in and around the town of Tappahannock, an hour's drive southeast of Fredericksburg, has more than its share of stately old mansions and ghosts to go along with them. The multiple spirits of Elmwood, for example, were included in my earlier book, "The Ghosts of Tidewater." At Kinloch, the spectral manifestation of a love-sick student who cut his throat during a fit of depression, was said to periodically reappear in a timeless search for his sweetheart.

For years, rumors of a haunting "blue lady" have been passed along by those attending St. Margaret's Girl School. Brooke's Bank is a charming small colonial plantation house completed in 1751 under the personal supervision of a woman — Sarah Taliaferro Brooke, a most uncommon occurrence in the 18th century. Her husband, John, was killed in a naval battle between the French and the English, and there is a legend that once, witnesses saw what has been described as a "phantom ship" sail up the river, whereupon a man disembarked, walked to the house and entered the front door. Those who claimed they saw him swore it was John Brooke.

At the McCall House, the daughter of a Scotsman, Archibald McCall, was seen descending the stairway in "shimmering robes and white satin slippers" for generations after her death. And at Mount Clement the story is told of a young girl, who, while dressing for a gala party, saw the apparition of a man in chains in her long mirror. Horrified, she bolted from the room, ran screaming down the corridor, tripped, and fell headlong down the spiral staircase. She died the next day, but not before giving a vivid description of the frightening image she had seen. For years afterward residents and guests alike swore they could hear the swish of a silken petticoat rushing toward the stairs.

Thus this sampling of the spectral phenomena that have

pervaded Essex County serves as a prelude to the following account of ghostly manifestations at the magnificent ancestral home of the Beverley family at Blandfield.)

Members of this family, one of the landed families of Virginia, must have been psychically ahead of their time, because it seems as if spectral manifestations have followed them around the state. There was, for example, a mysterious "white lady" at the Beverley summer home at Avenal (see the chapter "A Folio of Fauquier Phantasms.") So, too, it appears that Blandfield, the family seat for about eight consecutive generations, is haunted.

Robert Beverley, Virginia's first native born historian, originally acquired land in Essex County in 1680. His grandson began planning Blandfield on the Rappahannock in the late 1760s as the mansion house for the family plantation. It probably was ready for occupancy by 1774, although the grandson continued to order materials for it for 20 years. Fashioned of exceptionally fine brickwork, Blandfield has been described as "an outstanding illustration of the influence of English Palladianism on Virginia architecture, and represents Colonial American house building at its grandest and most formal."

During the Civil War, with Sheridan's gun boats in the middle of the river, the house was occupied by Northern troops, who, according to a history of Essex County, carried off "14 wagon loads of furniture, portraits, silver, and supplies. . . but Blandfield itself fortunately was spared."

One of the first sightings of an apparitional woman in the mansion was reported in the 1880s by Captain J. Bradshaw Beverley. He rode down from Avenal one chilly autumn evening and the caretaker, a Mrs. Hutchinson, asked him if he wanted to sleep in the lone heated bedroom upstairs. He asked her why she would ask such a silly question, and she told him that was the room in which several people had seen a phantom woman go into. The Captain told her he was not afraid of such stuff, and he slept in the room for several nights without incident.

A short time later, he had occasion to revisit Blandfield and this time, as he was walking up the stairs to bed at about 11 p.m., a "woman with a candle in hand, solid and substantial," passed him on the stairs. The incident happened so fast, he didn't get a good chance to see the woman, although he remembered that Mrs. Hutchinson had on a dark wool dress that evening, and the figure which passed him in flight was wearing light-colored clothing. As he looked up "she" went into the bedroom and slammed the door on him.

Shaken, he called out, "Mrs. Hutchinson," and the caretaker answered him — from the first floor below. He instantly realized what he had witnessed was not human, and he shouted down to Mrs. Hutchinson, "I have just seen your ghost." Then he went into his room and searched every inch of it, but found no trace of the lady.

Others in the house have reported thunderous noises emanating from the roof at times and strange bright lights filling up the house on moonless nights — phenomena that have never been satisfactorily explained. In more recent years, Mrs. William Nash Beverley told a newspaper reporter of guests sighting a woman in a long flowing gown fleeing through the house.

Mrs. Beverley herself said she and her two dogs were in the downstairs library one afternoon, and the only other person in the house at the time was an ill relative asleep in an upstairs bedroom. Suddenly, heavy footsteps thudded against the floor in the room directly over the library, startling her. "First, I thought I would take a shotgun and go up," she said. "I was uneasy to say the least. I put a leash on each dog and we rushed up the steps. The dogs became more excited. Their hair stood straight up."

Mrs. Beverley checked on the relative who was lying in bed asleep. The dogs then strained at their leashes pulling her towards the room where the noise had come from. She opened the door to that room and the dogs bounded in, snarling. But it was empty. She looked around, but there was no one there. Still, it was several minutes later before the dogs quieted down.

Some years afterwards, the last Mrs. Beverley in the ancestral line to live at Blandfield told of an unusual experience which happened to her and some of her friends one evening. They had been playing bridge and the session was running later than normal. Precisely at midnight, the lights flicked off for a few seconds and then came back on. The women resumed play. Then the lights flicked off again. This happened three or four times in succession. Finally, Mrs. Beverley got up and announced, "Ladies, I think it's time to go home!" It is said that the women didn't argue with her at all. They left promptly.

In the 1980s, Blandfield passed out of the Beverley family, and it is currently owned by James Wheat of Wheat Securities and his wife. They have carefully restored it to its formal splendor. Mrs. Wheat says that she has a friend who said she saw an apparition in the house. "But we have been here since 1986, and I really haven't seen or heard anything out of the ordinary." Mrs. Wheat muses that maybe the spirits are at rest now.... or perhaps they followed the Beverley family to newer haunts.

CHAPTER 22

Lost Apparitions at Mt. Airy

There are, according to legend, two separate ghosts at Mount Airy, an imposing manor near Warsaw, a few miles east of Tappahannock, sited in an "impressively commanding position on a ridge above the broad bottomlands and marshes of the Rappahannock River." Or, at least, there were two spirits. They were last seen more than half a century ago, and according to Mrs. Polly Tayloe, present mistress at Mount Airy, "We don't have ghosts here. I would love to have them. I've read about references to them in books and such, but, I swannee, I don't know anything about them. I haven't even heard one, let alone seen one."

But even if the specters of yesteryear have found contentment and moved on, it perhaps is worth the retelling in that both this splendid house, a national historic landmark that has been called "the most architecturally sophisticated of all of Virginia's colonial seats," and at least one of the former ghosts are colorful enough to merit inclusion here.

The house was built of native brown stone and white sandstone quarried on Aquia Creek during the years 1748-1758 by John Tayloe II, a wealthy planter. It replaced an earlier family house that burned. A second fire, in 1844, destroyed the "exceptionally rich" interior fashioned in the 1760s by distinguished designer and joiner William Buckland. The interior was immediately rebuilt in a plain Greek revival style.

In 1774, a tutor known as "Fithian" said of Mount Airy: "The house.... is built with stone, & finished curiously, & ornamented with various paintings & rich Pictures...In the dining room, besides many other fine Pieces, are 24 of the most celebrated among the English Race-Horses, Drawn masterly, & set in elegant gilt Frames. He (Colonel John Tayloe) has near the great House, two fine two Story stone Houses, the one is used as a Kitchen, & the other, for a nursery, & Lodging Rooms — He has also a large well-formed, beautiful Garden, as fine in every Respect as any I have ever seen in Virginia. In it stand four large beautiful Marble Statues." Fithian added that the main entrance was guarded by a pair of bronze dogs.

It is in one of the two story stone houses, referred to above, that the apparition of an old woman was reported seen for a period of at least 70 to 80 years. The first recorded sighting occurred in 1850 when a Miss Mary Leiper was engaged to teach the Tayloe children at Mount Airy. The family had gone off for a long weekend, leaving her alone in a ground floor room. According to her account, passed down from generation to generation, she awoke Friday night — her first night at the site — and envisioned an old lady with white hair, standing in the room. The teacher described her as being dressed in an "old-fashioned costume," and she came towards the bed, with her hands extended "as though to push the curtains apart," although they were already open. Aghast, Miss Leiper watched the figure for a few minutes only to see it gradually drift into a corner of the room and disappear. This was followed, for some time, by the sound of sobbing and moaning.

The same manifestation reoccurred on both Saturday and Sunday nights. When the Tayloes returned on Monday, Miss Leiper told them at the dinner table of her experiences. The only surprise they registered, was that the teacher had slept in the downstairs bedroom. They told her it was haunted.

But while there was no explanation given as to the identity of the old woman with white hair, or why she might frequent that particular bedroom, there is a possible identification to the other ghost who was seen from time to time at Mount Airy. Some have speculated that it is Sir Jenings Beckwith.

In her fine book, "Virginia Ghosts," published in 1930, Margaret DuPont Lee said Sir Jenings was an "ever-welcome visitor — gay, debonair, a devotee of pleasure, an ardent huntsman." This, of course, was in the heyday of fox hunting. Apparently, this gentleman spent a considerable amount of time at the manor, and, as Miss Lee wrote, "was one day brought to bay in the great Race of Life, finally unhorsed, and his burial service read at the open door of the little vault beside the Rappahannock." But, in elegant prose, Miss Lee added that Sir Jenings had not, however, "gone to that bourne from whence no traveller returns. . . and more than 100 years later, to rest in a little graveyard upon a bluff quite near the mansion he loved so well and to which his spirit returns throughout the years, his body was brought from the vault on the crumbling bank of the ceaselessly encroaching stream."

It is, thus, the apparitional return of Sir Jenings Beckwith, that the Tayloes in residence at the time talked of seeing in the 1870s. A recent bride then told her husband of sighting a man in "the costume of the Revolutionary period" walking in the hall. Her husband told her that the man had been seen by many people through the years, but always downstairs. He added that if she felt nervous about it, they could move into a suite upstairs.

Was this, in fact, Sir Jenings returning? If so, why? Present Mount Airy owner Polly Tayloe may have provided a clue when she said to the author that Sir Jenings indeed was in love with one of the Tayloe daughters more than two centuries ago, but his proposal of marriage was turned down.

CHAPTER 23

Veiled Visions at Verville

(AUTHOR'S NOTE: It is perhaps stretching it a bit to include a house in Lancaster County in a book on "Fredericksburg area" ghosts. However, the story of historic old Verville, nine miles north of the Kilmarnock in the Southern tip of the Northern Neck, seemed so intriguing it was hard to pass up. Initial research uncovered the fact of a strange story concerning an old well at Verville, and ghosts somehow related to it. But these spirits seemingly disappeared more than 80 years ago. Yet after further conversations, including some with the gracious current owners, Ammon and Kathy Dunton, it was learned that other forms of psychic phenomena — quite a few others, in fact — have surfaced and continue to manifest at this venerable house. With some geographic liberties, then, here is the story.)

It was not clear exactly when Verville was built. Some references date it to the late 17th century, although the Duntons think it is more likely to have been constructed sometime during the first half of the 18th century, possibly around 1740. "We know from the diaries of James Gordon, who lived here in the 1750s, that the house had been in existence for some time," says Kathy Dunton. Some authorities say the builder was Thomas Carter, who purchased the property in 1674, while others think it was Gordon himself.

The walls are of Flemish bond, topped by a hipped roof covering large, high ceilinged rooms replete with handsome wainscoting, beaded cornices, and carved mantels. Gracefully tall twin chimneys flank dormer windows. The Duntons have carefully restored the main house and added on three bedrooms, a breakfast room and a porch. There are "about 18" rooms according to Kathy, not to mention deep cellars used long ago to store food and wine.

Interestingly, though, the most noted ghosts associated with Verville "spring not from the house, but from an old deep well once located in a garden nearby." The legend of this particular phenomenon has been told and retold down through the generations and was chronicled by Margaret DuPont Lee in her 1930 book, "Virginia Ghosts." Miss Lee quoted Mrs. Louisa Currie Hall who had once lived in the mansion.

She reported that after the well had run dry, perhaps sometime early this century, all attempts at filling it up proved frustratingly unsuccessful. Apparently, for years afterward the soil around the well would mysteriously sink several inches. The depressions would be filled in, but the soil would sink again.

As the tale went, the spirits of a "lady and a little child" would rise from the depths of the well, enter the house, and make their way up the stairs to the "Blue Room" on the second floor. This bizarre, oft-repeated journey would always occur late at night, and as soon as these apparitional figures entered the room, they would turn on a light — a light which was claimed to have been seen by servants, and by guests, some of whom were even awakened in the room by it. Yet whenever anyone mustered the courage to investigate the source, they would find the room empty, silent and dark!

No one knew who the lady or the child were or what their nocturnal mission might be, but as time went on word got around that for some reason they would discontinue their quest once the ground around the old well stopped sinking. And, sure enough, this seemed to happen in 1907 following a torrential flood in the area which washed away crops, destroyed bridges, and covered fields with standing water. In the aftermath of the flood it was discovered that the old well had sunk about six feet, and, in the words of Miss Lee: "The sides were as smooth as if it had been freshly dug, and there six feet down lay the sod that had been a part of the field the day before." This time, however, once the well was filled in again, the sinkings stopped and the lady and child — and the light in the Blue Room — were never seen again.

The Duntons know well of this story, but have never run across any explanation for it. Nor do they know of the origins for the multiple psychic manifestations which periodically still occur. Ammon Dunton is reluctant to talk about the subject, saying that he doesn't believe in ghosts, but he admits that his wife and a number of house guests claim to have experienced psychic activity. He does find it interesting that some of the guests have reported such activity even though they were never told of the legends surrounding Verville.

Kathy talks more openly about it. "A lot of funny things have happened here, and I can't explain them," she says. "We have had guests who reported seeing lights at night and hearing weird sounds, including those of children speaking. There have been all sorts of things. One of our children was off in a wing of the house one night when there was a loud banging on the door — which was really loud — but there was no one there. Another child was in a room at two in the morning once when the door suddenly flew open and a harsh cold draft hit her neck.

"At other times our children brought home friends from college and they told of hearing odd noises. I, too, have heard the sounds. They used to frighten me, but nothing bad ever happens, so I don't worry about it anymore. I just think maybe we have some friendly poltergeists. But there definitely is something strange here. Sometimes you can almost feel it."

There is a story, too, of a "Mr. Alves" who was a relative of Verville's owners some years ago, and occasionally spent the night at the house when he was in the area on business. It has been passed down that on one occasion, he retired early in the evening and went to sleep in an upstairs bedroom. Later that night, he awoke with a start, and felt the tight grip of "hands on his throat." He leaped out of bed and ran downstairs to tell what had happened, but the owners seemed unconcerned. "Oh, that's just our resident ghost," they said.

The most haunting manifestation of all is the apparition of an old woman, hunched over and wearing a shawl, who has appeared before several members of the Dunton family and to a number of friends as well. "My children, my mother and my sister all have seen her on separate occasions," Kathy says, "although I have not. She is always seen coming up the back stairs and entering the back bedroom. This is a room that was rediscovered during the renovations. It had been bricked over for 100 years, and we really don't know why, because it is a charming room with windows and a fireplace. The woman always comes into the room, looks around, and then just disappears. The peculiar thing is that everyone who has seen her has described her exactly as others have without knowing that others have seen her, too."

Could this be the reappearance of the "well lady?" It is a puzzling question that remains unanswered. "We'd love to find out who she is and what she is doing," Kathy says. "Maybe someday she'll let us know."

C H A P T E R 2 4

Blithe Spirits at Bell House

In a book on the history of Colonial Beach, a 35 minute drive due east of Fredericksburg, the town is called "a rare period piece, an example of the small waterside resort. In its oldest sections the density and variety of its blocks of Edwardian cottages creates a sunwashed impression unique in Westmoreland, if not all of tidewater Virginia north of the James."

Colonial Beach "prospered" on tourist trade, steamboat excursions, summer housing and its attractive business and residential establishments. Writing in the monthly journal "American Genius," in 1882, Frederick Tilp captured the interesting spirit of growth in the area. He paints a vivid, if somewhat prejudicial picture of a bygone era, as follows:

"There has been a steady increase for the past few years in summer trips to the salt waters of the Potomac. As the capital (Washington) grows, so will the desire to find healthful recreations, and summer residences on this most interesting part of the river.

"Two classes of people go down in the hottest months of the year, and each chooses for itself, for they have not tastes in common. The more numerous is composed of people who go as often as their purses and time will allow. They go merely for the sake of going, they are excursionists, and care but little where they land, if the bathing, fishing, eating, and dancing are provided. The boats are crowded with them. For this class such a place as Lower Cedar Point is well adapted. Professor Pistorio's Brass and String Band of 15 pieces has been engaged for this entire season. The elegant steamer 'George Leary' leaves D.C. every morning at 8:30 a.m., returning at 9:30 p.m. Positively no improper characters will be allowed aboard.

"The second class represents those who prefer to send their families to some romantic place on the river, where wives and children can rusticate in harmless indifference and where the husbands and fathers can join them every Saturday night. It is a plain choice of quiet country life, and this means, with them, that no excursion shall be allowed to touch the beach on which they stay. They go for rest. They need it. There are in Washington scores of families who will agree to select a 50 x 150 lot on a quiet and romantic beach, in a healthy locality, on the salt-water stretch of the Potomac, to erect thereon, cottages of their own, beautify the grounds with flowers and fruit, and to contribute as far as they are able to make the surroundings beautiful and harmonious; but, it must be a condition that excursions shall not land on this bower or repose to spoil.

"Two summers ago, the writer saw an excursion land at Blakistone's Island, and within a half hour, every fruit tree, grape vine and flowering shrub was plundered. This is the penalty paid for giving over a good beach to excursionists. Piney Point and Blakistone's Island are much the same in outward appearance now as they were a dozen years ago because no one could be interested in beautifying the grounds after such vandal hordes had made frequent visits."

The excursion boats, of course, have long passed from the scene, and many other east coast stretches of shoreline are favored by today's summer tourists, although Colonial Beach still draws a loyal clientele. To the homeowners along the waterfront, as Mr. Tilp described, it is perhaps just as well that the vast hordes of people no longer annually descend.

Many of the old houses still stand along this strand of the Potomac, visual reminders of an arguably grander era. One of the most famous, along historic Irving Avenue, is known as the Bell House — named either for Alexander Graham Bell, inventor of the telephone, among many other things, or his father, Alexander Melville Bell, renowned himself as the creator of "Visible Speech." Or perhaps it was named for both Bells.

This beautiful Victorian edifice originally was named "Burnside Cottage," after its builder, Colonel Burnside, paymaster in the Union army and the son of General Ambrose Burnside of Civil War note, who also is said to have coined the word "sideburns." The Colonel built the house for his bride to be, but ran into financial problems with the government, and the house was sold at auction, as a summer home, to Melville Bell in 1886.

Complete with roofed balconies, tower, wraparound ve-

randa and such "period delights" as heavily corbelled chimney caps, polychromed glass overlights and decorative cross saw work, the Bell house has been declared a Virginia Landmark. A noted elocutionist and an astute businessman, the elder Bell's Visible Speech became an internationally-accepted system by which those who had lost their hearing from disease, could speak and understand the words of others. That he enjoyed his later years at this pleasant mansion at Colonial Beach was well expressed by one of his close friends, who once wrote: "To see him ensconced in his chair on the well shaded vine-clad veranda of his riverside home, at times reading and smoking, or watching the brooding, ever chattering sparrows he had encouraged to build their nests along the inner eaves, was to see incarnated content upon his countenance."

A frequent visitor in the early 1900s was Bell's famous son who inherited the house when his father died in 1905. Oddly, no mention of the summer resort was made in Alexander Graham Bell biographies. It has been noted, however, that Melville Bell conducted many experiments while living here, including the sailing of paper kites and "other paper contraptions" from the second floor balcony. Some of this effort led to the discovery of the tetrahedron, a three-sided pyramid design, described as the ideal space flight frame.

The house eventually passed from the Bells through several owners, and at times sat idle. Such neglect may in part explain why it slowly developed a local reputation as being haunted.

Current owners are Judy and Bob Warsing, a professional couple who work in Fredericksburg, commuting to and from Colonial Beach daily. "We had heard stories about the house being haunted even before we bought it," Judy says. "Kids in the area told of seeing faces in the front windows, although the house was vacant for two years before we moved in." And once the Warsings moved in, it didn't take them long to personally experience psychic manifestations, some conventional, some otherwise.

"There are plenty of strange noises in the house," Judy says, "but we pretty much have gotten used to them. Most of them you could probably explain anyway. It's an old house." Nevertheless, incidents kept occurring that were much more difficult to understand. Bob, for example, had two scary encounters. "Once he was going up the stairs from the first to the second floor, when he said he felt something 'swoosh' past him," Judy continues. "He said the air moved as if someone was passing him on the stairs. He was white as a sheet."

The other time, Bob got up in the middle of the night to go to the bathroom. He flipped on a light switch to avoid stepping on the family cat. As he was ready to get back into bed, he flipped the switch off, and in the flash before the room darkened, he glimpsed a wispy figure leaning out of the bathroom. But when he went to investigate it, there was nothing there.

Judy, too, has had "brushes" with the inexplicable. "There have been times when I have been in the kitchen, and it is difficult to hear anyone upstairs. I have heard someone or something calling my name, 'Judy.' But each time I went to the foot of the stairs and asked Bob what he wanted, he said he hadn't called me. He heard my name also."

One of the strangest and most uncommon forms of the phenomena concerns hairpins. "We have found them all over the house," Judy says. "I have vacuumed the floors thoroughly, only to find hair pins afterward. And these are not tiny pins. They are about two inches long. Old fashioned wire hairpins.

Once, we sanded, varnished, waxed and vacuumed the floor with a heavy duty vacuum to suck up wood shavings. Even then, I found hairpins afterward. Another time, I walked through the house passing over the light colored carpet in the front. When I came back through the hallway, there was a hairpin on the carpet. I can swear to you it was not there the first time I walked over the carpet!

"I can tell you, it was a little unnerving. We believe the pins are left behind by Bertha." Bertha Bryon was the previous house owner and lived in the house for about 50 years, the last 20 or so by herself, after her husband died. "She loved the house," Judy says. "Her father had been friends with the Bells, and she often visited the house as a little girl. She was a piano teacher, and served tea to guests. She was very refined. Bob and I think she is pleased with what we have done with the house. We've taken good care of it without really changing anything dramatically." Judy doesn't know why Bertha leaves hairpins around. Perhaps it is some sort of signal to let the Warsings know she approves of them living there.

"I have never felt afraid or threatened here," Judy says. Still, she once had a priest come out and bless the house. She also paid a visit to the well-known Fredericksburg psychic, Beverly Newton. She took a picture of the house with her and asked if there were any spirits there. "She looked at the picture and told me she smelled grapes. She said good wine had been made in the house," Judy says. "I found that fascinating, because there is a grape arbor in the back of the house and beautiful concord grapes grow there. We learned, too, that Bertha did make wine in the house. Beverly told us she felt spirits in the house, and she told us to cleanse it with pine chips. If there are still spirits here, I think we have convinced them we can peacefully coexist. There hasn't been much activity in the past year or two."

Of all the phenomena associated with the Bell house, however, possibly the strangest manifested before the Warsings moved in. "The house was completely empty then," Judy notes. "There was no furniture, no curtains, nothing. I bought a couple of plants and put them on the front porch. A friend of ours took a photograph of the house, and we didn't notice anything out of the ordinary then. But about a year later, we were showing some photos in an album to some friends, when we took a closer look at that picture again. In the front window, you could see clearly the image of a man standing at the window peering out. It was white and wispy, but you could distinguish features. The man had white hair and a white beard." Judy says the man was identical in appearance to that of a man taken in a photograph decades ago and published in an area newspaper.

That man was Melville Bell!

CHAPTER 25

Some Ghosts that "Should Have Been"

There may be more ghosts in Fredericksburg and its nearby environs than in any comparable area in America. The concentration in the old houses and on the old grounds — as evidenced by the dozens of stories in this book — is legendary. And yet it somehow seems odd that there are no reports of the spirits of some of the greatest names associated with Fredericksburg and the surrounding counties; luminaries larger than life. Washington, Jackson, and Lee, for instance, are missing from the long spectral list. So, too, are John Paul Jones, Hugh Mercer and many other local dignitaries. The same is true for a plethora of historic houses. Why is one mansion haunted, while another stands silent? Consider the following examples:

Why is there no ghost of George Washington? Born at Pope's Creek Plantation in neighboring Westmoreland County and raised at Ferry Farm on the outskirts of town, the Father of the Country seemed to be in and out of Fredericksburg for most of the rest of his life. The specter of his brother-in-law, Fielding Lewis, has been sighted at Kenmore, and there are claims that his mother's presence has been felt at the Mary Ball Washington House — but there are no accounts of the area's most famous resident ever "returning."

"There aren't any ghosts here that I know of, I haven't heard of any stories from others, and I don't know of any ghosts in George Washington's past," says Dwight Storke, superintendent of Pope's Creek Plantation run by the National Park Service. Storke, who lives on land originally granted to his ancestors in 1667, also is a descendent of the first President. "A lot of the Storke women married Washington men," he explains. "I have read a lot about Washington over the years, but I just can't think of any reference to anything psychic-related."

One might think a sighting would be made at Ferry Farm —

site of the cherry tree and silver dollar legends. He spent his youthful formative years here, although out of necessity, he was asked to shoulder some man-sized responsibilities at a relatively early age, following his father's death and his older brother's illness.

"I would love to have a ghost here," says Bob Siegrist, executive director of Ferry Farm today. "There is one thing about this place, though, and there may be an explanation for it, but I don't know what that would be. And many people have made the identical comments and observations, and I have to agree with them, because I have felt the same sensation. There is an atmosphere of peace and quiet here that seems to permeate. I've had workmen say, it's so peaceful and quiet here. Many visitors have said the same thing. Once an eight-year-old schoolboy came up to me and said, 'Mr. Siegrist, it's really peaceful here.' It affects me the same way. There are days when I walk around the farm, that I don't want to go back inside. It's just a feeling you get. I don't know if that has anything to do with George Washington or with psychic phenomena, but someday I would like to have a psychic expert walk around the place and see what he or she sensed."

Curiously, there are no Washington legends at Kenmore, Chatham, the Mary Washington House, or the Rising Sun Tavern — all places the great man visited during his lifetime. And, surprisingly, there are none, either, at Mount Vernon, according to historian John Riley. In fact, the only even faintly related psychic experience associated with Washington concerned a "vision" he once may or may not have had, and which Riley says that "in good conscience," he discounts.

There have been several accounts of this alleged vision, and most seem to stem from an article published in the *National Tribune* — the forerunner to the *Stars and Stripes* military service newspaper — which first appeared in December 1880. The publisher of that paper told of an interview he had in 1859 with one of the last surviving veterans of the Revolutionary War, a man then said to be 99 years old. His name was Anthony Sherman.

He said he had overheard a conversation Washington had at Valley Forge during the harsh winter of 1777. The Commander in Chief is said to have said he saw a "singularly beautiful being" in his tent after he had given orders not to be disturbed. Sherman quoted Washington as saying, "Gradually the surrounding atmosphere seemed to fill with sensations, and grew luminous. Everything about me seemed to rarify, the mysterious visitor also becoming more airy and yet more distinct to my eyes than before. I began to feel as one dying, or rather to experience the sensations which I have sometimes imagined accompany death."

Sherman said Washington then witnessed dark manifestations inside the tent, including black clouds, lightning bolts, the light "of a thousand suns.... the thundering of the cannon, clashing of swords, and the shouts and cries of millions in mortal combat." Some have said the interpretation of the vision was the sensing of the continuation of the Revolutionary War and the premonition of the Civil War and either World War II or World War III. Washington reportedly acknowledged that the "vision" said "Three great perils will come upon the Republic. The most fearful for her is the third. But the whole world united shall not prevail against her." The vision then vanished, and Sherman said Washington concluded: "I started from my seat and felt that I had seen a vision wherein had been shown me the birth, the progress, and destiny of the United States."

Whether or not such an event actually happened is thus based on the thinnest conjecture; on the testimony of a very old man whose name could not even be found in the Revolutionary War records. There are tens of thousands of Washington letters and documents on file, not to mention his voluminous diaries. In carefully researching the supposed vision, former archivist John Rhodehamel concluded that "Nowhere in any of this material is to be found a reference to a vision or any other mystical experience." Could it have occurred and the great General was reluctant to record it because of its ethereal nature? Possibly, but not probably. It is an interesting tale nonetheless.

* * * * *

The Montross Inn is just down the road a few miles south of Stratford Hall, birthplace of Robert E. Lee, in Westmoreland County on route 3. In 1932, in her little-known second book on ghosts, Margaret DuPont Lee wrote of the spirit of an old slave named "Peleg" being heard from here on occasion, and the apparition of a "figure in white." But this must have been at another site, separate from the present Montross Inn, because the reported phenomena supposedly occurred in the late 1920s, at a time when the present Montross Inn was not known as the Montross Inn.

Confused? Well, the present owners, Michael and Eileen Longman, who run a splendid hotel and dining room at the Inn today, say that their establishment was a hotel or apartment building during the 1920s, but they had found reference to another place then being called the Montross Inn. The Longman's Inn has been known by many names since it was built in 1790 over the foundation and wine cellar of another structure dating to 1683. It has been called John Minor's Ordinary, Spence's Tavern, Sandy's Steamboat Hotel, the Harris Hotel, and now, since 1975, the Montross Inn.

"And we don't have any ghosts here, nor have we ever heard of any," says Michael. "Oh, once we had a guest, an elderly lady who had quite a bit to drink, and she told us someone was rocking in a rocking chair in her room that night. But we didn't take her too seriously, because there was no rocking chair in the room."

Just where the other Montross Inn and old Peleg are, or were, remains a mystery. But again, the Longmans are hospitable hosts and they set a fine table, ghosts or no ghosts.

* * * * *

One might suspect a spirit or two hiding out in historic Montpelier, President James Madison's magnificent home in Orange County almost due west of Fredericksburg. After all, there would be plenty of room for them to be comfortable — a rambling 55-room mansion and dozens of support buildings all scenically set amidst a vast 2,700-acre estate. But, alas, director Christopher Scott says there are no prominent ghosts here. "Oh, you hear snitches of a story every once in a while, but they are just faint rumors, nothing really to substantiate."

* * * * *

Why are there not more ghost stories about Civil War soldiers in the Fredericksburg area? After all, 17,000 men died here and another 80,000 were wounded in four great battles. Many of them lie in rest in the various cemeteries scattered throughout the city that knew "every cruelty, horror and depredation of war." Yet the tales of Yankee and Confederate spirits returning to the places where they met traumatic and tragic deaths and mutilations are precious few.

Why is there no ghost of Lucy Ann Cox, who lies buried in the Confederate Cemetery on Washington Avenue at Amelia Street? She was made an honorary Confederate veteran after accompanying her soldier husband through four years of the war. Her tombstone is inscribed: "A sharer of the toils, dangers and privations of the 30th Va. Infy. C.S.A. from 1861-1865." Is it because she is at peace interred beside her husband?

Why has there been no return of Stonewall Jackson, the great Confederate general who was shot by his own men during the battle of Chancellorsville on the night of May 2, 1863, and died a few days later near Guinea, Virginia? One might ponder why he has not been "seen" searching for his amputated left arm, which was buried separately.

Why aren't moans and cries heard late at night in Fredericksburg, Chancellorsville, Spotsylvania Court House and the woods of the Wilderness — where so many heroic young men fell and suffered? But, strangely, all is quiet.

C H A P T E R 2 6

Haunting Apparitions of Stratford Hall

American history is full of curious coincidences, some of which surely provide fascinating studies for psychics among others. Consider, for example, the fact that two of the nation's greatest patriots, statesmen, intellects and U.S. Presidents — John Adams of Massachusetts and Thomas Jefferson of Virginia — died within hours of each other on the same day in 1826; and that day was (can you guess?). . . . July 4th!

Perhaps less dramatic than that, but nevertheless an interesting anecdotal footnote, is that two successive Presidents, William Henry Harrison (the 9th), and John Tyler (the 10th), were born practically within a stone's throw — actually, just a few miles — of each others ancestral home in Charles City County, about halfway between Williamsburg and Richmond.

Consider also that two of the indisputably greatest names in American history were born only a few minutes drive apart in Westmoreland County in the Northern Neck of Virginia; George Washington at Pope's Creek, and just down the road a piece, Robert E. Lee at Stratford Hall. While G.W.'s house burned to the ground in the 18th century, the baronial home of the Lees stands as proud today as it did in the late 1730s when it was built under the direction of Thomas Lee, a highly respected colonial leader.

Perhaps this fact is less of a coincidence, because as one historian phrased it, "The county of Westmoreland, with its diversity of hill and dale, its mild climate, fertile soil, and attractive scenery, at an early period won the attention of the Washingtons, the Fairfaxes, Lees, and other distinguished families."

Stratford Hall has been described as one of the great houses of American history. A brochure points out: "Its magnificent setting on a high bluff above the Potomac River and its bold architectural style set it apart from any other colonial house." As one Lee biographer wrote: "No picture of the mansion gives any adequate idea of its chateau-like massiveness." Fashioned of brick made on the site and timber cut from virgin forests, its fortress-like walls are two and two and a half feet thick, arranged in an "H" configuration. The brochure says, "The great hall in the center of the house, 29 feet square with an inverted tray ceiling 17 feet high, is elaborately paneled. It is one of the most architecturally significant rooms to survive from colonial America."

And yet, as imposing as the mansion and its surrounding 1,600 acre estate are, an even more impressive distinction arises from the prominence of the family which resided there for so many years. Indeed, the Lees of Virginia certainly were one of the — if not the most renowned families in the country. Richard Henry Lee, for instance, made the motion for independence in the Continental Congress. "Light Horse Harry" Lee was a hero of the Revolution and a favorite of George Washington. He also was the father of Stratford's most famous resident, Robert E. Lee, who was born in the house on January 19th, 1807.

Young Robert moved from the plantation when he was but three and a half years old after his father more or less "lost" the estate through a series of bad investments which eventually landed him in debtors' prison. It is interesting to note that the home on Oronoco Street in Old Town Alexandria to which the Lees moved is allegedly haunted with the spirits of two young girls and the ghost of a dog. There are many written accounts of this, including one that says the apparition of a young boy, believed by some to be Robert E. himself, has been sighted running with the dog in the backyard of the house.

At Stratford today, however, tour hostesses are mostly reluctant to mention the presence of any form of psychic phenomena. They prefer to dwell on the rich history and superb architecture and setting of the house and grounds, and well they should. The plantation's grandeur is more than enough in itself to warrant visits and revisits. It has been faithfully restored to its original elegance and contains many fine pieces of period furniture, family portraits, and other pieces of Lee memorabilia.

As with so many worthy old estates, there is ample justification for ghostly encounters at Stratford Hall, for along with its integrity and eloquence, the great house and some of the family members have had their share of tragic events. Late in his life,

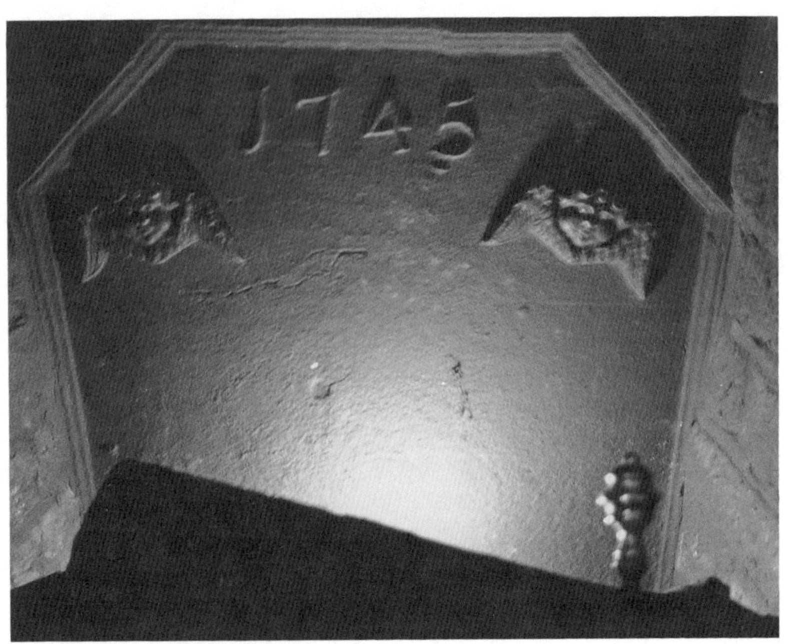

"Angels" at Stratford Hall

Light Horse Harry Lee and some of his friends were brutally beaten by an angry mob in Baltimore. They were "stuck with penknives and had hot wax poured into their eyes." Lee had part of his nose cut off and was permanently disfigured. Would not one speculate that "he" might return to his ancestral home, scene of much happier days? As we shall see, maybe he did.

There is the case of Henry Lee, Robert's older half brother, who got his wife's sister "in the family way." That unfortunate incident, plus the tragic death of their young daughter, undoubtedly contributed to the fact that Henry's wife, Ann, eventually became addicted to a powerful drug, and Henry earned the dubious sobriquet of "Black Horse Harry."

Or what about young Robert himself? A poignant story often is told about the day when the Lees moved out of the mansion. Robert was missing. A search found him in his room saying goodbye to his "angels" — two cherubs forged on an iron fireback in his bedroom. Mrs. Walker Allard, who has worked at Stratford Hall for more than 40 years as an historical interpreter and as custodian of historic buildings, says there is no basis of truth to the tale. Yet today hostesses continue to relate it.

Area oldtimers still talk about a black worker who lived on the grounds all his life. He was known affectionately as "Uncle Wes," and it is said he was related to slaves who once toiled in the plantation's fields. He supposedly was full of ghost stories, but he apparently "took them with him" when he died years ago.

Mrs. Allard says the only fragmentary account she ever came across concerning psychic energy was the reported sighting of a ghostly figure at a desk in the great house. "Yes," she says, "that happened some time ago. There was a young maid who said she did see a man's figure at the desk." The woman opened a door to the library and was to go in the room to clean it. She went in and came right out again. Her supervisor asked her what happened and she told her she "didn't want to disturb the gentleman in there." When they reentered the library, no one was there. Could it have been Light Horse Harry? The maid said the figure seemed to be checking over some papers, possibly inventories. "She became very frightened and ran from the house," Mrs. Allard says. "But like I say, she was very young, and probably very impressionable. I think just about every old house has a ghost if someone wants to see a ghost."

Stratford Hall, it appears, after conversations with a number of both current and retired employees, is no exception to this theory. There have been, in fact, numerous accounts of psychic activity. Margie McGrath, a former hostess, says she was taking a couple through the house one day, and as she stopped to answer questions near the end of the tour, she felt "a sharp tug" at her hoop under her full, period-costume skirt. "I kept talking, but I brushed my hand to the area where I felt the pull, and my skirt wasn't hiked or out of place or anything, and no one else was in the room." she recalls. "Then I felt the tug again. Something or someone had pulled on my skirt!"

Mrs. McGrath says that on another occasion a few years ago she escorted a psychic on a tour. "She apparently was well known and had been asked to visit a house in Fredericksburg," Mrs. McGrath remembers. "When we passed through the great hall on the second floor, she stopped and said, 'Oh, I have so many good impressions,' and she said she could see the room full of Lees, and that there was dancing and music and entertainment. At the end of the tour she came to me and said that the Lees were pleased with how the house was being taken care of.

And then she told me she had seen more of the family playing croquet on the lawn as she had approached the main house. I was fascinated. I don't laugh at any of this."

Jo Ann Boyer, a former chief hostess at the mansion, now retired, also has heard some strange stories and had a chilling confrontation of her own. "I have heard that the gentleman who the maid said she saw in the library that day has also appeared in one of the outbuildings," she says. "He has been seen with a ledger in his hands. Those who saw him say he was dressed in black with a ruffled shirt and white stockings, much like the clothing worn in the 18th century."

Mrs. Boyer says her personal encounter occurred on a "dismal, dark winter afternoon. It was late in the day when I took a group through the house," she recalls. "Toward the end of the tour, we were in the far upper west end, and I had my back to the door and the people were facing me. Suddenly, I saw a woman and a child in the room in colonial period costume. The woman had on a gray cape and the child a red cape, and their hoods were up. I just thought to myself, who was that child with Mrs. McGrath, who was another hostess on duty with me that day. She had remained downstairs when I went on the tour. She had grandchildren who occasionally come to the house, and I just assumed it was Mrs. McGrath and one of her grandchildren. But I couldn't figure out why she was upstairs, and why did they have hoods on?

"So when the tour was over, I went downstairs and asked Mrs. McGrath, and she looked at me like I was crazy or something. She said she hadn't left the room downstairs, and no one was with her. At first, I thought she was joking, but when she realized that I was serious, she lifted her hand and covered her mouth, and said that I had finally seen them. I had seen Ann Lee, the distraught and broken hearted wife of Black Horse Harry Lee, and their little daughter, Margaret, who had died in the house at age two after falling down the stairs. People have heard the woman calling the little girl, and the sound of the child running and then both of them laughing, as if they were playing together. We had talked about it, but it never dawned on me when I saw them that day, that it was Ann and Margaret Lee," Mrs. Boyer says. Little Margaret Lee died in 1820.

At least two of the Stratford Hall security officers have experienced various forms of psychic manifestations in recent years.

They voluntarily recounted the events, but asked to remain anonymous. "A lot of things happen, sometime in the great house, and often in the Southwest dependency building," one of them says. "We have heard all kinds of noises at night, but never found any physical reason for it. What kind of noises? I mean racket. Loud racket at times." Both of the officers have reported the sounds of heavy furniture being moved about, but investigations revealed nothing out of place. Both have heard distinct footsteps on the second floor of the house when it is closed to the public and no one is in it. And both say they have heard the sound of "stiff clothing" — possibly rustling petticoats and skirts, rubbing against chairs and tables. "It's like a cloak, or a coat, or a stiff skirt, or something like that," one says. "But how can you hear something and you don't see anything? That's what I can't explain. How can you hear furniture being moved around, yet you don't see it. I have no idea."

One officer reports he has heard fiddle music on occasion and once heard a harp being played. "I've heard doors slamming at two or three in the morning, but I could never find any cause for it," he says. "Now, I know in an old house there are going to be a lot of sounds anyway. Floors creak. The house settles. But I'm talking about noises that aren't like settling sounds. I was in the dependency one night when I heard something that sounded like a cinder block hitting the cabinet right behind me.

"And I'll tell you something else," the officer continues. "I was sitting in a chair one night when something got hold of my sleeve and lifted it up. Lifted my arm straight up. How do you explain that? Another time I was reading a book one night when I put it down to make my rounds. When I came back the book was gone. No one else was on the grounds. I was alone. Did this scare me? At first, maybe it did. But I got used to it. Whatever it is, or was, it didn't cause me any harm. It didn't bother me. But it did frighten some others. We had one man who started to work one night — his first night on the job — and he quit after just one hour. He wouldn't even talk about what happened to him." Another time, one of the officers said he met a psychic from Hanover County who had just been through the house. "He seemed shook up, so I asked him what was the problem, and he told me, 'you won't believe it, but there are ghosts in that house.' I asked him how many, and he said 'five'!"

Perhaps of all the phenomena the two officers have been exposed to, the most interesting was the sighting of a young boy, about four years old. Both have seen the apparition, on separate occasions. "I saw him late one afternoon," one says. "He was standing by the fence on the road some distance from the gate. He was wearing dark purple britches and a light colored purple shirt, kind of like they did in colonial days. As I drove past him in my truck, he came out into the middle of the road, and then he motioned toward the cows in the pasture, as if he wanted them to come to him.

"Well, I thought he might be lost, so I stopped the truck down the road apiece and got out to ask him where his parents were. Now I could see in all directions for at least a quarter of a mile or so, but that boy had disappeared. He just vanished. I looked all around, but I never found him. I believe he was a spirit. If he wasn't, where did he go?"

The other officer saw the same young boy at least twice. Once he sighted him in the old slave quarters. The second time, he saw him in the dependency building. He walked across the room as if he had lost something and was looking for it. "He appeared to be white all over," the officer says. "He was a little boy as near as I could tell. I believed he was either a ghost or an angel. I called (the other officer) and asked him what I should do, and he said not to worry, that whatever it was I was seeing wouldn't hurt me. And then he disappeared."

Who was this mystery child? Here, historically, there is at

least a clue. Phillip Ludwell Lee was the son of Thomas Lee, the founder of Stratford Hall. And he had a son also named Phillip. According to family tradition, this boy fell down the stairs in the great house one day in 1779 and died. He was to have been the heir to the estate.

He was four years old!

* * * * *

(Author's note: Just as this book was about to go to the printer, I received a call one evening from one of the security officers at Stratford Hall. He told me that I should call a man named J. R. "Butch" Myers, who lived in Richmond. He said Myers was a craftsperson who had been at the mansion over a weekend in June 1989 demonstrating his skills with leather. He travels around the country recreating how 18th century shoes are made. The officer said Myers had a frightening experience which drove him from the dependency building just south of the main house. Intrigued, I called Myers, and, as a footnote, the following is his account of what happened.)

"We had completed the show Saturday evening, and a few of my fellow crafts people had gathered in the dependency where I was to spend the night alone just to talk over the day's activity and compare notes. The session broke up around 12:30 or 1:00 a.m. I had lit six candles in stands, as there was no electricity in the building. As I was getting ready to turn in, I had sort of an uncanny feeling. I can't quite describe it. But then I saw a couple of sawhorses and a heavy sheet of plywood in the corner of the room, and it struck me that this would make a good bed for the night, so I unrolled my bedroll on top of it.

"As I kicked my shoes off, I heard the approaching footsteps outside of the security guard making his rounds. I grabbed a cigarette and started toward the door to chat with him for a few minutes. It was a particularly hot evening, with the temperatures high in the 90s during the day, and it hadn't cooled off much that evening.

"I took about two steps toward the door when a sudden down draft of freezing cold air hit me, taking my breath away. I mean it was icy cold. It was like walking into a cold storage locker. I got goose bumps all over. And just as this happened, there was a thunderous noise in the chimney. It sounded like the whole building was going to collapse. I didn't find this out until later, but the chimney was sealed top and bottom. There was no way anything alive could be in it.

"If this wasn't scary enough — and believe me, it was — I turned around just in time to see the candles go out. And they just didn't go out at once, as if blown out by a down shaft of air. They went out one at a time, in sequence, as if someone was snuffing them out. So I said to myself, 'okay, who's playing funny?' Now, I have some relatives in the area, some cousins, and they had told me about how Stratford Hall was haunted, and all that. So I figured maybe one of them was playing a little joke on me. But I was sober as a judge, and I didn't see anybody in the room except myself. How could anyone have done that with the candles?

"I got to the door and told the security guard what had happened. He didn't seem particularly surprised. He just said, 'oh, you've just met our friend.' He asked me if I had seen anyone, and I had to say no. In a little while, he walked on off to complete his rounds, and I went back inside the room and relit the candles.

"Now you can believe this or not, I don't care. But the icy coldness in the room hit me again, and the racket kicked up in the chimney, which really scared me now, because the guard had told me about it being sealed. There was no breeze, or wind at all in the room, but someone, or something, very methodically extinguished each candle again, in reverse order this time. And I knew now, for a fact, that no one else was in the room. At least no one living. I was by myself.

"But there definitely was something there, a presence or whatever you want to call it. And that was enough for me. I said, 'listen, you can have the room. Just let me get my pillow and blanket, and I'll get out of here.' And I did. I got out of there as quick as I could, and I went over to the dependency on the other side of the mansion, where the guard was, and I told him I was spending the night with him!

"The next morning, I went back to the room and everything was just as I had left it. It was cool inside, but the air wasn't freezing as it had been the night before. I gathered up my stuff and left.

"I went back to Stratford in the summer of 1991, for another craft show, but I didn't stay in the dependency. No sir. I walked around to it one evening, and in front of the big house there was a nice gentle breeze blowing. But when I got to the front of the dependency, everything was deathly still. Nothing was stirring. It was an eerie feeling. I put my hand on the doorknob and it was like clutching an icicle. That's as far as I got. I wouldn't go back into that room. There was something in there that didn't want me inside. The guards told me it wouldn't hurt me, but that's easy for them to say. They didn't feel what I felt in that room. I'm not saying definitely that it was something evil, but I didn't want to stick around to find out for sure.

"It had made its point with me. I'm not psychic or anything, but I definitely believe there is something to ghosts and spirits, and there's a lot we don't understand about all that yet. But I can say for sure that I am certain there is something strange at Stratford Hall. There was something in that room. And one experience with whatever it was, or is, was enough for me!"

CHAPTER 27

The Survival (?) of John Wilkes Booth

It has been written that when he was a school boy, he once had his palm read by a Gypsy who told him he had a "bad hand, full of sorrow and trouble." The fortune teller said that he would "break hearts, but they'll be nothing to you. You'll die young, and leave many to mourn you. You'll make a bad end... Young sir, I've never seen a worse hand, and I wish I hadn't seen it, but if I were a girl, I'd follow you through the world for your handsome face."

The Gypsy was talking about the palm of John Wilkes Booth, the ill-fated assassin of Abraham Lincoln.

With the possible exception of the assassination and the ensuing storm of controversy which engulfed the death of John F. Kennedy, there is, arguably, no chain of historic events so shrouded in mystique and myth greater than that associated with Booth following his shooting of Lincoln at Ford's Theater in Washington.

While it has been only a generation since Kennedy's death, the confusion and contention which cloaked Booth's death — or alleged death — in a farmer's barn four miles from Port Royal, Virginia, just south of Fredericksburg, has lasted for more than 125 years and still rages today! The questions still are asked.

Was Booth shot by a Yankee soldier, or did he kill himself? Was it Booth who was trapped in the burning barn, or was it someone portraying the handsome actor? Did he somehow escape the cordon of soldiers tracking him through the Virginia countryside to live out his life, as many believe, first in San Francisco and later in London? Why did the U.S. Government rush his body out of Caroline County and secretly bury it? Was this all part of a massive coverup to hide a much broader conspiracy against Lincoln and members of his cabinet?

Why was Booth's diary impounded by Secretary of War Stanton for two years after Booth's death? And why, after it finally was released, were 18 pages missing? Why were Booth's co-conspirators so cruelly treated before their trial, each shackled to a 75-pound iron ball, with his head encased in heavy canvas padded an inch thick with cotton, with one small hole for eating through, no opening for eyes or ears, and laced so tightly around the neck that speech was impossible?

Such questions were fanned for decades after his supposed death by countless reports of sightings of Booth all over this country and in Europe. As one writer put it early in this century, "Booth's ghost, a will-o'-the-wisp, has stalked the Republic, no witness sufficiently impartial and free from suspicion having been found to swear that he looked upon the disputed corpse and knew it either to be or not to be J. Wilkes Booth."

Millions of words have been written about Booth's life and death. Many authors, including immediate members of his family, have sworn that it was not Booth who was killed in Richard Garrett's barn in the early morning hours of April 26, 1865. But if not Booth, who was it, and what happened to the one-time matinee idol?

Adding to the deep mystery are scores of strange facts and happenings:

* Booth's alcoholic father claimed to have had "ghostly experiences."

* The ghost of Mary Surratt, said to have been one of Booth's co-conspirators in the assassination plot, and the first woman ever executed for murder in the United States, haunts the Surratt House and Tavern near Washington.

* The Sergeant who claimed to have shot and killed Booth was described as being a crazy man "who talked directly to God."

* Many of the main characters involved in the Booth story reportedly died strange and mysterious deaths.

* And, 20-odd years ago, a simple midwestern farm boy, under professional hypnosis, claimed to have been John Wilkes Booth in a past life. What made this story of reincarnation unusual was that this young man recited obscure details of Booth's life that he had no way of knowing anything about. He also said that, in fact, he had not died on the porch steps of the Garrett farmhouse!

Many of the circumstances of Booth's escape are well known and are fairly unchallenged. After shooting Lincoln in his box at Ford's Theater, Booth, a fairly athletic young man of 27, leaped upon the stage. However, a spur in his boot snagged a draped flag and he fell awkwardly, breaking a bone in his lower left leg. He nevertheless managed to escape by horseback with another young man, named Davy Herold. They stopped at Mary Surratt's tavern around midnight, bolted down some whiskey, and rode on. At dawn the next morning Dr. Samuel Mudd treated Booth's leg, patching it in pasteboard splints. They slept in Mudd's house until near evening. Booth shaved off his trademark mustache, and he and Herold rode off.

For the next 12 days they eluded trackers on a winding route that took them through part of southern Maryland and into Virginia. Eventually, they shot their horses, and on April 24, 1865, crossed the Rappahannock River on a ferry with three Confederate soldiers returning from the war. A short time later Booth and Herold arrived at the Garrett farm, pretending to be soldiers on their way home.

Suspicious of the visitors from the start, Garrett's sons mistakenly believed Booth and Herold were horse thieves, and they locked them in their tobacco barn. Tipped off to their whereabouts, a troop of 26 Union soldiers rode hard from Bowling Green, 13 miles away, and surrounded the Garrett farm at about two in the morning. They encircled the barn and demanded that the fugitives come out and surrender. Herold did, but Booth, playing the actor to the hilt, shouted tragedian speeches, and threatened to fight the troops with his crutch if he had to. In an effort to smoke him out, the soldiers set fire to the barn.

The objective was to take Booth alive, but as the flames began consuming the barn, an inexplicable thing happened. A single shot rang out, striking Booth in the back of the skull, oddly at virtually the same spot Booth's bullet had entered Lincoln's head. At first, soldiers who dragged Booth out, had thought he had shot himself, but then a sergeant named Boston Corbett, a former hat cleaner known as the "Mad Hatter," admitted that he had pulled the trigger of his pistol, felling Booth. When he was asked why, Corbett said, "God Almighty directed me."

Barely alive, Booth was taken to the porch of the Garrett farmhouse where his bleeding head rested on a pillow in the lap of Lucinda Holloway, a spinster relative of the Garretts. He died shortly afterwards, and she cut off a lock of his dark, curly hair, which according to a 1977 newspaper article, can still be seen at the Caroline County Historical Museum. Old time area residents said that for years afterward whenever it rained the bloodstains could still be seen on the porch. In fact, souvenir hunters so haunted the farm that the Garretts finally had to remove the boards and refloor the porch.

One of the many who claimed to have seen Booth, if indeed the man laying in Lucinda Holloway's lap was Booth, was William B. Lightfoot, a native of Port Royal who had just returned from Appomattox a few days earlier. Years later, in an interview, he told of seeing something he could never explain. "There was always one queer thing about the barn," he said. "The center post, against which Booth was leaning just before they shot him, didn't burn. Next day everything was burned up but it. It stood up there, sir, all blackened but still sound, mightily strangely, in all the ashes."

Equally extraordinary, was the highly secretive manner in which Booth's body was literally whisked from the Garrett porch, rushed back to the Washington area, and buried. The corpse was rolled into a blanket and loaded onto a cart commandeered from a black neighbor named Ned Freeman. He was ordered to drive it northward at break-neck speed. The king bolt on a wheel snapped en route causing the front end to fall, sending the dead man's body lurching forward in the red-soaked blanket. As Freeman worked on the broken bolt, blood dripped on his hands, sending him tumbling backwards screeching, "It's the blood of a murderer — it will never wash off!" Another wagon was appropriated and Freeman left his cart by the side of the road, never to use it again.

At the Potomac River, Herold and the body were transferred to the ironclad Montauk. Ironically, because of all the mystery arising from this curious action, rumors began circulating all over Washington that the body aboard ship in the middle of the river was not Booth. As dense crowds gathered on the bank, Booth's body next was lowered into a skiff and placed into a makeshift coffin — a gun-box. As the skiff drifted downstream, the crowds of spectators on the shore followed, "splashing through the shallows" to keep pace. Under the disguise of darkness, the boat turned into the great swamp behind Geeseborough Point, and the spectators could follow no further, because this area was a swampy morass into which worn out horses and mules were thrown.

At midnight the weird sojourn continued. Oarsmen rowed

stealthily upstream to the old penitentiary building, where a hole had been chopped in the masonry to allow them to enter. Here, on the grounds where Mary Surratt and three other Lincoln conspirators later were hanged, Booth's body, now reposed in a white-pine casket, was buried under a warehouse floor. Everyone involved in this bizarre ritual was sworn by sacred oath never to disclose what they had seen or done, and the entrance door was bolted.

Is it any wonder, under such fantastically abnormal circumstances, that the enormous wellspring of myth and lore about Booth's death was born? It began immediately. Many believed his body had been weighted and tossed into the swamp. Grotesquely, fishermen said the body had been dissected and its parts, heavily shotted, were dropped overboard from the skiff. One newspaper reported: "Out of the darkness Booth's body will never return. In the darkness like his great crime, may it remain forever; impassable, invisible, nondescript, condemned to that worse than damnation — annihilation. The river-bottom may ooze about it, laden with great shot and drowning manacles. The fishes may swim around it or the daisies grown white above it; but we shall never know."

Soon, the myth swept across the nation that all the secrecy surrounding the burial had been maintained to hide the fact that the wrong man had been shot; that Booth had escaped. From the great groundswell of rumor came scores of reports of "Booth sightings." While the government, in the worst traditions of Watergate, stonewalled, and refused to comment, suspicion throbbed to hysteria proportions. Booth was allegedly seen in the South, in Illinois, in Canada, and on ships bound for Mexico and South America. By mid-year 1865, the staid *Richmond Examiner* reported in its columns, "we know Booth escaped."

One of Booth's nieces once told a news service that there were "stories" in the family of her uncle's survival after the assassination, one of which told of Booth meeting his mother in San Francisco in 1866 in which he told her how he escaped. His mother told several members of the family she had "visited" with her son.

Booth's granddaughter, Izola Forrester, wrote a book about her famous ancestor, "This One Mad Act." In it, she proclaimed that older residents in a certain area of the Telegraph Hill section of San Francisco shunned a "badly dilapidating" house they

John Wilkes Booth

considered to be haunted by the spirit of Booth. She added that newspaper accounts published a year after the end of the Civil War mentioned a "mysterious stranger" who roamed about only after dark at this house and was described as being aloof, handsome and cloaked.

Adding to the fury, which continued to burn for years afterward, was a sequence of inexplicable occurrences quickly caressed by the superstitious. Mary Todd Lincoln, it was pointed out, died pitifully after years of insanity. Little Tad Lincoln died before reaching manhood. Major Rathbone and Miss Harris, guests in the Lincoln box at Ford's Theater on the fateful night, were caught in "the evil spell," when the Major later killed himself and Miss Harris after they were married. There were reports that all nine Union officers on the commission that had tried and condemned Mary Surratt and three others in the conspiracy, had died violent deaths, "most of them driven to suicide by remorse for having hanged an innocent woman." While at least this story proved to be fiction, Captain Willie Jett, a Confederate officer who had helped Booth on his flight, was said to have perished miserably.

Louis Weichmann, a chief government witness in the trial against Mrs. Surratt and the others, reportedly lived in fear of being avenged by either an escaped John Wilkes Booth or his ghost. Whether this is true or not is uncertain, but historians have said that when he died in 1902, "he was old and broken far beyond his 60 years."

In the years from the end of the Civil War even into the early 20th century, dozens of men stepped forward and claimed to have been Lincoln's slayer. Most were dismissed as lunatics, but the myth was kept alive, at times bordering on the ludicrous. One man in Texas who claimed to be Booth killed himself, whereupon his body was mummified and exhibited across the South and Southwest for ten to 25 cents a look.

And then there is the legend of Mary Surratt, who claimed to her death she was innocent. She was hanged on July 7, 1865 at the old Washington Arsenal Prison, which has since been converted to Fort Leslie J. McNair. It was there, in an officer's quarters, that an Army lieutenant, in 1977, reported seeing "the apparition of a stout, middle-aged woman, dressed in black, seemingly floating through the hallways." Strange sounds, unexplained voices and the sensation of being touched by an unseen hand, also have occurred here. A major's wife said she, too, had seen a "woman in a long, dark dress floating around." She told psychic investigators it was Mary Surratt.

In a book titled "Myths after Lincoln" by Lloyd Lewis, published in 1929, the author said Mary Surratt's "wraith" was seen haunting the lodging house she had run on H Street in Washington. Hearing of this, crowds gathered outside the house daily. Mrs. Surratt's daughter sold the house for a "bargain" $4,600, but the purchaser was driven away within six weeks because "his nervous system was reputedly shattered by what he had seen and heard." *The Boston Post* noted how other tenants came and went in "swift succession, swearing that in the dead of night Mrs. Surratt walked the hallways clad in her robe of death."

Lastly, there is the incredible story of Dr. Dell Leonardi a hypnotist of Kansas City, who wrote a book in 1975 titled "The Reincarnation of John Wilkes Booth," based on 73 hours of taped conversations with a young man named "Wesley." Under hypnosis — or in regression as the psychics say — he said he had been Booth in a past life. Dr. Leonardi, after painstakingly checking Wesley's comments about his former life against historical fact, came to believe that the young man indeed had lived before as the notorious assassin.

Wesley's story, as reported in book excerpts and reviews published in the mid-1970s, was that, as Booth, he had evaded his pursuers and had not been shot at Garrett's farm in 1865. He had, instead, fled to San Francisco and later lived in England where he continued his acting career, dying years later of a natural death in Calais, France.

"I have talked with the infamous John Wilkes Booth," Dr. Leonardi said. "I believe that to be a fact."

In her book, Dr. Leonardi asked was it reincarnation or was it "an entity" (Booth's ghost?) who claimed Wesley's body during hypnotic trance? She believed it to be reincarnation. Nevertheless, the question arose.

And so, it seems, the haunting mystery continues. The questions remain. In Caroline County there is an historic marker in the median strip of Route 301. It reads: "This is the Garrett place where John Wilkes Booth, assassin of Lincoln, was cornered by Union soldiers and killed April 26, 1865."

But was he?

CHAPTER 28

Multiple Manifestations at Old Mansion

Do you want to spend the night in a real live old haunted house!

How about a fine old manor home that literally creaks with age, dating back to the late 17th century? One that features a wide variety of inexplicable psychic phenomena including a headless horseman who dashes around an old race track in front of the house. . . the returning apparition of a former owner which signals an imminent death in the family in residence. . . the reappearance of a woman who was frightened to death there. . . plus an assortment of mysterious footsteps, lights, noises and countless other manifestations?

You get all this, and — if you survive the night — a hearty home-cooked breakfast, too, at a place called Old Mansion on the outskirts of Bowling Green, about 25 minutes south of Fredericksburg. Your host will be a pleasant and gracious gentleman named Peter Larson, and even if you don't see or experience a spirit, he will enliven your evening by recounting the many rich tales which have been handed down, generation to generation, for centuries. Peter today operates a bed and breakfast at the house, which is 11 miles east of interstate 95 (exit 41) on route 207. The food, he says, is "more than you can eat. It's things I make myself, but basically good stuff." The room accommodations are large and comfortable, but, as you will see, they can be scary, too.

Old Mansion is, without question, the oldest house in Caroline County. Just how old it is is not precisely known, although historians seem to be certain that it was built "not later than 1675." According to the Virginia Landmarks Register, the property on which "this venerable pre-Georgian manor house" is located originally was called Bowling Green after the long green sward before the entrance. The name was changed to Old Mansion when its owner, a charismatic and colorful fellow named

Colonel John Waller Hoomes, donated property for the courthouse and permitted the newly formed county seat to take the name of his estate.

The house itself, built of bricks brought from England, is of the one-and-a-half story type so prevalent in those days to avoid the prohibitively higher taxes on two and three story dwellings. That is, it actually is a two-story structure, but appears to be less than that because of its high-pitched jerkinhead roof, tall chimneys and hipped dormer windows. A gambrel-roofed rear wing, added later, increases the architectural interest.

The Register calls Old Mansion "an excellently preserved example of Virginia's distinctive colonial idiom."

As the Hoomes were sportsmen and imported thoroughbreds, at one time a race track circled the front lawn, flanked by cherry trees. Giant cedars and "avenues of elms and aspens" surrounded the house. Box-bordered plots in the front and a succession of terraces in the rear, added to the natural beauty of the site.

Of the many legends which abound at Old Mansion, at least one has some historical backing. It concerns General George Washington and his troops during the Revolutionary War, or right after the war's end, depending upon which report you take stock in. One account says the general and his weary soldiers rested on the spacious lawn here on their way to the final battle at Yorktown in 1781.

More likely, thinks Peter Larson and many others, Washington and his men stopped by on their way home after the final siege at Yorktown. Marshall Wingfield, in his fine book, "A History of Caroline County Virginia," published in 1924, says, "of more authentic historicity is the story that Washington, returning from Yorktown after the surrender of Cornwallis, made a great banquet on the lawn in honor of LaFayette, which was spread on three great tables extending almost across the lawn, at one of which was seated the guests of honor, Washington and the officers of his army and at the other two the private soldiers."

"My guess is that the victorious troops did stop here and had some sort of celebration," Peter says. "But whether or not Washington himself was here, I'm not sure. My understanding is that his step-son, the son of Martha Washington, was quite ill at the time with camp fever, and was laid up in bed at another house some distance away. According to Washington's diary — and he kept a rather accurate one — he had gone to visit the boy on the same day the troops were supposed to be holding their party here. Maybe he did stop off here and saw that his men were being taken good care of and then he rode off on this other mission. I don't know for sure."

Either way it is somewhat interesting to note that the Father of the Country is not among the ghostly lore associated with this grand old house. But there certainly are plenty of other references to spirits. In fact, Old Mansion has such a reputation for being haunted that it has scared off people for more than two and a half centuries! One tradition is that Sophia, the only daughter of Colonel Hoomes, never would visit the house during the day after her father had built her a home nearby called Oak Ridge. This is curious in that her coachman said she did make long visits at night only, and for generations afterward neighbors claimed to see her ghost journeying to Old Mansion in her coach. Peter adds that even though today his 10-year-old son won't go upstairs in the house after dark. "He's very frightened of it," Peter says.

And no wonder. A newspaper reporter doing a Halloween feature once wrote, "from a basement that looks like a tomb — to narrow, winding back stairs ripe for midnight terror — this place has got atmosphere all right." To this, Peter adds, "I definitely think this house has a spirit."

As best as can be determined, the plethora of psychic phenomena which seem to swirl around Old Mansion began early in the 18th century during the "reign" of Colonel John Waller Hoomes. Again, there are two and possibly three separate accounts, any one of which brought on a premonition of the impending death of a male member of the family.

In his Caroline County history, Wingfield says that after Colonel Hoomes died, his ghost always appeared to each member of the family before their death, "walking in full view, dressed as when in the flesh and not in grave clothes." Such an appearance is said to have signalled an "unfailing warning" of the approach of death to some member of the family. This gets a little confusing, because Wingfield also states that, "another hair-raising ghost story connected with this old place is that a headless horseman, riding furiously around the old race track, always heralded the approaching death of an eldest son."

Now which is it? The third vision has been ascribed to other long-time county residents and has been recorded by several writers, including Margaret DuPont Lee in her book, "Virginia Ghosts." According to Lee and others, the tradition began one night when Colonel Hoomes (apparently then still quite alive) and several guests were seated around the dining hall table, which the host, whimsically or otherwise, always had set for 13 people. During the dinner everyone present heard "distinctly" the sound of horses' hooves galloping rapidly around the track in front of the house.

Since all of the Colonel's horses should by then have been safely locked in their stables, Hoomes and his guests got up from the table and went to the front door. Peering into the twilight, they could see no one around the track (not even the alleged headless rider), but, mysteriously, at the far end of the track near the road gate, they all reported seeing a group of children playing on the grass. No one thought to ask who they were. where they had come from, or why they were there.

"On the morrow," the eldest Hoomes son was suddenly taken ill and died!

Was it coincidence or was it supernatural phenomena that created the exact same circumstances a year later at Old Mansion? Again the horse's hooves were heard, and again the children were seen playing on the grass. And the following day the next son in line of descendency died! This time all the neighbors were called upon and asked if their children had been out at the hour of the apparitional appearance. None had.

The next year the house was filled with fear and apprehension. Yet there appeared to be no escape from the ghostly rider who heralded the approach of death. Sure enough, one night the dreaded hooves were heard once more racing up the gravel track, then dying in the distance, and the same bank of spectral children were seen at the far end of the yard. The next day the third son was stricken and died!

Then, for some unexplained reason, there was a welcomed break in the terrifying sequence. Nevertheless, several years later the phenomena was repeated and another son died. It has been said and written that this eerie experience was repeated until all of Colonel Hoomes' sons — it has never been specified how many there were — had passed on and were buried beyond the box hedge on the left side of the house. Lee penned: "Never

Peter Larson at Old Mansion

was that rider seen; nor were those appearing gaily dancing on the lawn, children of earth." Once the last son died, so did the phenomena.

Other spirits arose, however. Another of the lively legends at Old Mansion concerned a couple only known as "the Woodfords," who lived in the house some time after it had passed out of Hoomes' ownership. Mrs. Woodford was an invalid, stricken with "serious heart trouble," and was cared for, in part, by a widowed buxom housekeeper who lived in the frame addition to the house. At some point in the long, lingering illness of his wife, Woodford became amorously involved with the housekeeper, and more and more distressed and angered with his wife, who was said to be "demanding" at the least.

Soon, he hatched a fiendish plot. One night while his wife slept, he placed a sheet over himself and donned "a hideous mask" with a jack-o-lantern for an "elevated head." He then sneaked outside, "emerged from the Hoomes' burying ground," and pressed his mask against the window in the bedroom where Mrs. Woodford rested. When she awoke and looked out the window, it is said that she gave "one terrified scream and expired."

With his frightening act, and his performance of consummate

grief at the subsequent funeral, a case could be made for Woodford's talent as an actor. He even borrowed a sheet to wipe away his tears, and sat on his horse backwards, claiming to be so distraught as to not know the animal's head from its tail. When word leaked out about his Halloweenish escapade, he soon departed the county, never to be heard from again, and was followed shortly thereafter by the buxom housekeeper.

His invalid wife, however, remained in the house for some years afterward, in spirit form, scaring the wits out of a series of occupants while seeking retribution upon her sadistic husband. Those who slept in Mrs. Woodford's bed chamber were frequently awakened at night by unnerving groans and the ringing of servants' bells by unseen hands. One family even left most of its furniture and ancestral silver behind, "so great was their haste in departing."

The manifestations have continued unabated down through the years and still occur. In the 1970s, when Patty Farmer lived at Old Mansion, she told newspaper reporter Rob Hedelt about an encounter her husband had. He was at home alone one night when, Patty said, "Suddenly, he heard a woman's blood-curdling scream coming from downstairs. He ran down the steps to where the sound came from. There was no one there — only the dog, and it was cowering in the corner, shaking all over."

Reporter Hedelt said the house had also yielded unexplained footsteps, wailing and singing, slamming windows and lights flicking on and off. Peter Larson says he can't add too much to the tales, other than what people have told him.

"Oh, when I first moved here, I guess I had been somewhat influenced by all that I had been told. I kept thinking I heard 'things'. Like I would be in the back of the house and I would imagine the sounds of a carriage arriving around front. I would look, but there was never anything there. I think part of it is psychological. If you tell people about such things it sticks in their mind. They are keyed up. Maybe it's the power of suggestion."

Still, Peter admits, some of those who have stayed overnight at the bed and breakfast claim to have seen things he can't explain. "One lady who said she was a psychic consultant swore she had seen a carriage with horses in the front of the house, but her husband was with her at the time and he just shook his head. He hadn't seen anything. Another time a couple was spending the night in an upstairs bedroom, and the wife said she woke up and saw a strange bright light appearing on the back of the bedroom door. She woke her husband up and he said he saw it, too."

Peter doesn't pretend to have answers to all that has happened in the house, even since he has been there. For example, one day several years ago a Bowling Green couple new to the area arrived at the front door and told him they had heard so much about Old Mansion that they would love to have a tour. Peter willingly obliged.

The couple, Michael and Diane Buckley, seemed enchanted until they got to the upstairs bedroom with two double beds. Peter showed them two low sitting chairs in the room and said that was where gentlemen of olden days sat while they slipped off their boots. "I can't explain it, but I had a most uncomfortable feeling the whole time I was in that room," Diane says. "There was just something about it that made me feel uneasy. I'm very sensitive to surroundings."

Sometime after that, Peter's former wife had an Episcopal priest come out to bless the house. Diane says she is not sure if it worked, but she has been in the upstairs bedroom since then and has not had the same feeling. But exorcism or not, neither Diane, her husband, nor Peter can offer a rational explanation for what happened the day the Buckleys came to look at some old period furniture in the basement of the house during a time when Old Mansion was being renovated.

"I will never forget it as long as I live," Diane says. "It was some years ago, and we were down in the basement (the one the reporter said looked like "a tomb") examining some Windsor chairs and other pieces." Peter and Michael had wandered off somewhere, and Diane was in an old room used for food storage. "I thought they had gone upstairs," she says, "because I heard the sound of footsteps coming from above and no one else was in the house. But these weren't ordinary footsteps. They were very heavy. The heels hit the floor hard. In my mind, I pictured someone in boots.

"I called out to my husband, and as I did, the weirdest thing happened. There was an old upright cupboard in the room, and it started creaking. Then it started falling towards me. I screamed. Peter and Michael came running into the room — they hadn't been upstairs — Peter held up the cupboard, but it came apart right down the middle! I know there was no way I could have caused the cupboard to move. It was on a dirt floor, and I hadn't even moved. I had been standing still in the middle of the room. Peter later told me he had heard me say, 'Ooh, I don't like it in here.' He was right!"

Still want to spend the night in a haunted house?

CHAPTER 29

The Sad Return of Sarah Henry

"Gentlemen may cry, peace, peace — but there is no peace. The war is actually begun! The next gale that sweeps from the north will bring to our ears the clash of resounding arms! Our brethren are already in the field! Why stand we here idle? What is it that gentlemen wish? What would they have? Is life so dear, or peace so sweet, as to be purchased at the price of chains and slavery? Forbid it, Almighty God! I know not what course others may take; but as for me.... give me liberty or give me death!"

Those, of course, were the words of the great patriot and orator Patrick Henry. They rank high among the most famous words ever spoken. They helped launch a war that won America's freedom. When he finished speaking on March 23, 1775, at St. John's Church in Richmond the audience sat in silence, stunned. Edmund Randolph later said Henry's words vibrated so loudly, if not in the ears, at least in the memory of this audience, that no other member was venturous enough to interfere with that voice which had so recently subdued and captivated.

Today, practically every school child in America can recite lines from that remarkable speech. Yet very few people — then or now — were aware that the feisty Henry was heartsick the day he spoke from a still-burning deep personal tragedy. Only recently had his first wife and the mother of the first six of his 17 children, Sarah Shelton Henry, died following a long, terrible illness which emotionally drained the entire family, and which haunted them, both literally and figuratively, long afterwards.

This all occurred during the seven years Henry lived at Scotchtown, a great sprawling estate in upper Hanover County a few miles west of Ashland off route 54. Scotchtown was the creation of Charles Chiswell who came to Virginia from Scotland late in the 17th century. He held nearly 10,000 acres of land in the area in 1717, and, according to local historians, he originally wanted to build a Scottish castle on the site. But after several of his native craftsmen became ill and died of fever, he settled, instead, for the more modest "barnlike" house which stands today. It is believed that Scotchtown was built in 1719. The Virginia Landmarks Register calls it "probably the largest one-story colonial house in Virginia, with eight rooms and a center passage on the same floor." It is over 80 feet long and nearly 40 feet deep. It is only one story high, but that is deceiving, because there are eight additional rooms in the full height basement, and there is an enormous attic in which parties and balls were held. One author said of the attic: "It could have housed a swarm of merry and none too finicky guests, congregated for a dance or house party."

In "An Historical Sketch of Scotchtown," compiled by Robert Bolling Lancaster of Ashland, it notes: "The manor house was originally placed to form one side of a courtyard. The yard was artistically planted with oaks and other trees, boxwood and variegated shrubbery. Around the house were grouped smaller houses which were used to quarter the young men of the household, and for the schoolhouse, office, kitchen, warehouse, ash-house and blacksmith shop. There were 30 cabins and a mill below the hill on the Newfound River." This was, Bolling said, "quite an establishment considering the early date and its location in such a remote area."

If Scotchtown has an aura of tragedy about it, it likely began with Colonel John Chiswell, who inherited the house from his father in 1737. Following a series of unfortunate investments, including a lead mining company known as "Chiswell's Mine," he was forced to sell the plantation in 1760. John Chiswell, who was described as "a testy and choleric man," became involved in a drunken brawl at Ben Mosby's Tavern at Cumberland Court House in 1766, during which he ran a sword through his friend, Robert Routledge, killing him. He subsequently was charged with murder.

Before his trial came up, however, he died, on October 17, 1766, and there seems to be some confusion as to how he died. His physician said he expired from "nervous fits" owing to constant uneasiness of mind. Others speculate he committed suicide. In either case, when his body was brought back to Scotchtown for burial, a bizarre incident occurred. Routledge's

Patrick Henry

friends followed the coffin and demanded that it be opened to verify that the corpse was that of Chiswell. When it was determined that indeed it was, he was buried in the small cemetery located about a mile back of the house.

Debts also plagued John Robinson, who had bought the house from Chiswell and it was sold at auction. John and Mary Payne became owners during this period and for a short while they lived at Scotchtown with their daughter who later married James Madison, the fourth President of the United States. She was the famous Dolley Madison.

Patrick Henry then bought the house and property in 1771 for about $18,000. Why did he buy it? The plantation was productive and considered a good investment. There were open fields, woods and the river providing a vast playground for Patrick and Sarah's six children. It was within reasonable (27 miles north) commuting distance of Richmond, and a day's ride from Williamsburg. And, it seemed, the time had come for Henry to "establish" himself as a country squire with an imposing home.

One biographer noted: "Here, Henry might have enjoyed the amenities of life on a large plantation with a number of slaves while continuing his legal and political activities. But again fate intervened. Did the tragic death of Colonel Chiswell cast a shadow over Scotchtown?" The author was referring to the distressing and traumatic illness of Sarah Henry that was to darken the great orator's days at the mansion.

Much has been written about Sarah's illness, and still there is much mystery surrounding it. In fact, in family accounts there is a singular absence of information about her Scotchtown years. There are scores of references from biographers, authors, historians and others. One wrote: "Family illness of a most distressing sort and the outbreak of the Revolution soon blasted Henry's hopes for happiness on the plantation." There are reports that her sickness began about the time of the birth of her sixth child, Edward, in 1771. A biographer speculated: "Perhaps she had an innate tendency to break under strain; the wife of a statesman often has to pay an even more onerous price for greatness than does her husband."

In another account, it is stated that Sarah suffered from a "protracted mental illness. Certain details are lacking, but the convincing family tradition is that several years before her death Sarah developed 'a strange antipathy' to her husband and children." Another insight as to the extreme seriousness of her condition was offered in a publication, years later, by the son of Patrick Henry's personal physician who attended to Sarah. He wrote: "Here (at Scotchtown) his family resided whilst Henry had to encounter many mental and personal afflictions known only to his family physician. Whilst his towering and master-spirit was arousing a nation to arms, his soul was bowed down and bleeding under the heaviest sorrows and personal distresses. His beloved companion had lost her reason, and could only be restrained from self-destruction by a strait-dress (a forerunner to today's straight jacket)."

Sarah was confined — for how long is uncertain — to two dungeon-like rooms in the cold basement of the house and watched after by a servant. Most evidence points to the fact that Henry was heartbroken over his wife's deteriorating condition. Henry once spoke of himself, while only about 40 years old, as "a distraught old man." When he was home from his frequent travels, he would visit Sarah by descending a secret staircase off the backhall of the building. However, one of Sarah's cousins asserted that Henry was hard on his wife, saying he was interested in outside projects and not in Sarah.

In those ill-informed days, people with mental illness were often considered to be demon possessed. And as time wore on with Sarah strapped in confinement and rarely seen by anyone other than immediate family members, fear spread through the plantation. Many workers, especially servants, were afraid to go in or near the house. Even when the tormented woman died, she was buried in an unmarked grave, which, again, was the custom in the 18th century for the burial of "crazy" people. It is not known exactly where her body is located today.

Although he was "crushed with grief," Henry was somehow able to put the finishing touches on his famous speech at St. Johns Church which he delivered only a short time after Sarah's death. For the next two or three years he was away much of the time, and in 1777 he sold Scotchtown to move to the newly-renovated Governor's Mansion in Williamsburg.

The great house in Hanover County went through several owners over the next 180 years and eventually became abandoned, with "infrequent and neglectful tenants." It was for a time even occupied by squatters who "quartered goats in the basement and raised chickens in one of the first-floor rooms. The plaster was falling, the roof was leaking and many of the windows on the main floor were gone."

In June 1958 the Association for the Preservation of Virginia Antiquities bought Scotchtown, then "in a sad state of repair," and began to plan for the mansion's restoration. This has been accomplished with dignity and integrity, and today the house is open to the public. It is now much like it must have been in 1782 when Baron Ludwig von Closen wrote in his journal after a visit: "The house is spacious and handsome, extremely well furnished and delightfully well ordered. In a word, it is one of the most pleasing establishments in America."

It also is haunted!

There are, conceivably, multiple spirits here, but certainly the predominant one — as attested to by many who have claimed to have seen and heard her — is Sarah Henry. "If this house wasn't haunted, it definitely should be," declares Ron Steele, Scotchtown's director today. "It is a very spooky place, especially at night when the wind is blowing. It can get very scary inside. You hear all kinds of noises. When the wind is blowing real hard, you can hear it whistling through the old house. It sounds kind of like a moaning."

Steele and his wife Alice keep check on the house during the off season — it is open from April through October — and he says there have been occasions when both he and the local police were reluctant to go into the house at night. "We have motion alarm systems inside, and someone or something has to be at least four feet tall to set them off," Steele says. "In the past two or three years the alarms have been set off a number of times, and when the police come out, they ask me to go in the place first. We only have lights in the hall, so it's pretty dark, and it can get kind of oppressive in the house." He adds that one of the most frightening phenomenons has to do with the portrait of Joseph Shelton which hangs in the dining room. "You go in that room at night and his eyes follow you all across the room, no matter where you go. It is very scary."

Alice Steele had a terrifying experience of her own. "We had a bad storm one night, and the lights in the main house went out," she remembers. "I went out with a flashlight to turn them on. You have to open the door to the secret stairway to the cellar. I turned the key but the door wouldn't open. It was almost as if someone were on the other side holding it. It took all of my strength to get it open, and, finally as I opened the door the flashlight went dead, even though I had put fresh batteries in it. Well, have you ever had a feeling that someone was standing right behind you? I got that feeling. I could feel the hair on the back of my neck standing up. I just knew Sarah was there. There definitely was a presence. Even when I got the lights back on, I wouldn't dare turn around." Ron adds that when Alice got back to their house, she was white as a sheet.

The Steeles also report that pieces of furniture seem to get moved around inexplicably at times. Once during the winter when the house was closed, they discovered a tea caddy had been moved from the center of a table and placed on a chair seat and the top of a teapot had been taken off. "It appeared like someone was having a little tea party," says Alice. Several times a cradle in a downstairs bedroom which belonged to the Henry family has been out of place. "It's happened to both Alice and me," Ron says. "Sometimes we go into that room in the dark and we bang our shins on the cradle, because somehow it has been moved from its place beside the bed to the middle of the room. This has happened periodically, yet we are the only ones who have keys to the house. How does the cradle get moved? Maybe we have it in the wrong place and 'Sarah' puts it back where it was 200 years ago."

But the Steeles are not the only ones who have experienced psychic manifestations. "Patrick Henry's great, great, great granddaughter was reluctant to talk about it, but she was convinced the house was haunted," Ron says. "She would never come here at night." Right after Halloween 1990, a police officer told Steele that a neighbor had told him she noticed what looked like a candle in one of the windows of the house. She had taken

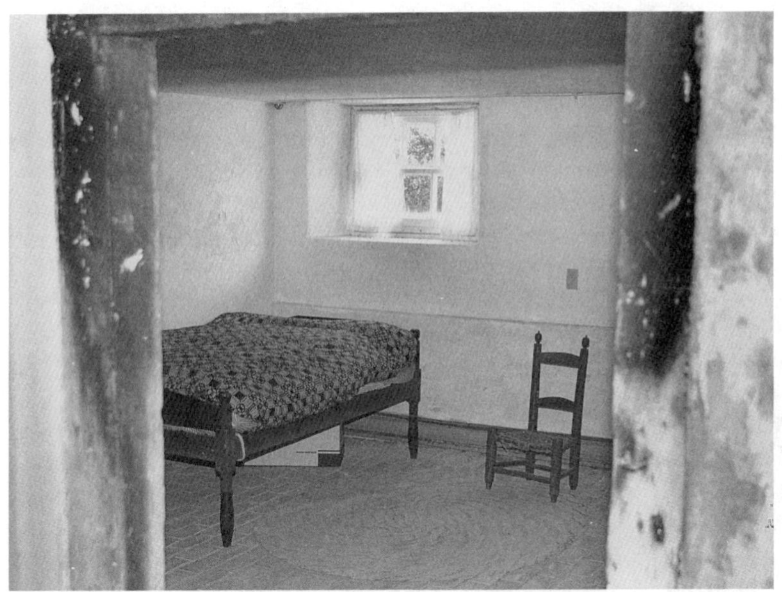

Sarah Henry's room at Scotchtown

her kids out trick or treating when she saw the light. She pulled up into the yard and said the light suddenly disappeared, as if the candle had been blown out. She added that at that instant she saw a "fleeting image" which looked like someone holding a candle. Ron says the whole episode was strange because he and his wife were out of town at the time and there was no one in the house.

There are other questions which remain unanswered. Why can't the inner walls of the basement rooms in which Sarah Henry was confined be painted? The paint will not adhere. If there is a rational reason, the Steeles haven't found it yet. Why, on a breezy day in early April did a swarm of flies and wasps cluster against an attic window? What is the explanation for the sound of chains being dragged across the floor of the attic when no one is up there? Such sounds have been heard by more than one person.

"We know of at least one sound here that wasn't caused by ghosts," says Stuart Womeldorph, director of the Hanover County branch of the Association for the Preservation of Virginia Antiquities. "Once the residents reported hearing the old piano being played downstairs when no one was downstairs. They went down to see what was causing it, and darned if a rat wasn't running up and down the keyboard!"

Alan Ward is another who has had supernatural feelings at Scotchtown. He now lives in Ruckersville, but several years ago he had what he calls "an incredible experience" during his first visit to the house. He had no prior knowledge of any ghostly legends.

"I was walking around in the basement area, by myself, and when I got into one particular room, I could feel something there. I didn't see anything," Ward recalls. "I just had this feeling that there was something there. There was a real sensation of presence there. Afterwards, I told Ron and Alice about my experience, and their eyes got wider and wider. When I described where I had been, they told me that was the room where Sarah Henry had been kept and where she had died. As they told me this a really incredible feeling came over me. I'm not the kind of person who believes in ghosts or anything, but I really believe there was something there."

John Taylor of Ashland told a *New York Times* reporter 20 years ago that when he and his brother were boys, they remembered seeing the "ghost of a lady at dusk passing from the basement of Scotchtown to the slave quarters." He said they tried to catch 'her' but she vanished before their eyes.

Several years ago, a tour guide was taking some tourists from Michigan through the house when they stopped to talk in the dining room, which is located directly above the room in which Sarah occupied in the basement. When the guide started to tell the story of Sarah, suddenly the group heard shrill screams emanating from the basement. "They all ran from the house as fast as they could," Ron says.

Mary Adams, who lives in the small town of Montpelier nearby (not to be confused with James Madison's home in Orange County) lived at Scotchtown from 1933 to 1940, before its deterioration, and says she experienced all sorts of psychic phenomena. "We were scared at first," she recalls, "but we got used to it. There were a lot of unnatural sounds. We would hear chains dragging across the floor and other real weird noises. But I really enjoyed living there. There was a lot of room to play, and you could whoop and holler and do whatever you wanted."

Mary says that once she was in the house playing with a group of kids. "I guess there were about eight or 10 of us, and the grownups were in the back part of the house, away from us. All of a sudden, we saw this figure. It looked like a person, like a woman with a long flowing gown. She was all in white. We all just stared at it. We were transfixed. Somehow, we knew it wasn't a real live person. The only thing that we could imagine was that it was a ghost. It was right scary. I can tell you that. We must have watched it for a half minute or more, and then it just disappeared. We bolted out of there and ran to our folks, but, of course, by the time they investigated, the room was empty. But even after I moved from there I would always get the feeling whenever I went back to visit that the ghost lady was there. I still think she is today.

"Was it Sarah Henry? I really don't know. It could have been."

CHAPTER 30

Footsteps at the Fork Church Rectory

When Patrick Henry lived at Scotchtown he worshipped at nearby Fork Church in St. Martin's Parish in the Episcopal Diocese of Virginia, as did such other notables as Dolley Madison and Thomas Nelson Page. It was built around 1735 or 1736, and is one of the Commonwealth's few colonial churches not to have been vandalized during the Civil War. Named for its location near where the North and South Anna Rivers join, it is a registered Virginia Historic Commission Landmark, and is listed in the National Register of Historic Places.

In the adjacent cemetery lies the wife of General Thomas Nelson, Washington's aide in the Revolutionary War and a signer of the Declaration of Independence. Also buried there, beneath a small, obscure obelisk, is a woman named Mary Love Alrich, and it is about her that the following account centers.

She was the wife of William Augustus Alrich, rector of the parish from 1869 to 1872. They lived in the small, L-shaped rectory, a short distance through the woods from the church, which was built in 1842. Mary died in childbirth, while bearing twins, in 1872. According to those who have lived in the rectory since, she comes back periodically to "visit," but only when there is an infant in the house. Such visitations have gone on for more than 100 years.

"When we first came to Fork Church in 1969, the previous tenants told us about Mary," says Faye Joy, whose husband, Charles, served the parish from 1969 to 1980. Phillip Mason was rector at Fork Church for 39 years before the Joys took over. "When they (the Masons) told us about the ghost, we didn't believe them at first, but later, we changed our minds," Faye says. "They told us she only appeared when there was a baby living in the rectory. We didn't hear or sense anything unusual until our son, Austin, was born in 1970."

For the next two years, Faye and Charles attest, Mary made her presence in the house known often, mostly in the form of strange sounds in the night. "We would hear her walking across the wooden floors," Faye continues. "Now, I know, in an old house the boards can creak because of the wind and temperature changes. But these footsteps were distinct. There was no mistaking them."

Almost always, the footsteps would be heard, either ascending the stairs, or near the second floor nursery where young Austin slept. "She was very quiet on the stairs," Charles says, "as if she didn't really want to disturb us. A wing of the house was added in 1906, but you never heard her there. There was never any sense of anything evil with these manifestations, and we never saw her, but she was there."

"A whole lot of quirky things happened," Faye picks up. "Once, a lamp was moved across the room. Charles thought I did it, and I thought he did it. We never could explain that. And one night the footsteps were particularly pronounced. We both heard her. Charles woke up and as we sat in bed, we heard her walk across our bedroom to a window. We guessed she wanted to look out. Then she walked back." When Faye was asked if she felt anything during that encounter, she laughed, and said

Fork Church

"Fear. You knew something was there. Those floorboards wouldn't have creaked like that otherwise."

Faye says that they told a couple, friends of theirs, about the nocturnal visits once. "They didn't believe us, but we invited them to stay in the house overnight, and they heard the sounds," Faye says. "They told us they would never sleep in the rectory again."

Faye and Charles think Mary came back to see that any infants in the house were properly cared for. "After Austin was about two and a half, we didn't hear her anymore. It could have been that once a child reached a certain age, she was satisfied. She had a two-year-old child when she died."

There is, too, an inexplicable and fascinating footnote. In 1972, Charles Joy was in Alexandria at the Library of Theological Seminary doing some research. "I was in the stacks," he recalls vividly, "when for some reason my eye fell on a small book on the top shelf. I don't know why, but I seemed to be drawn to that book. It didn't have a title in the spine of the book. I reached up and pulled it down. It was a 19th century children's book. I opened it, and in the fly leaf there was a handwritten signature. It said, 'Mary Love, 1868'!"

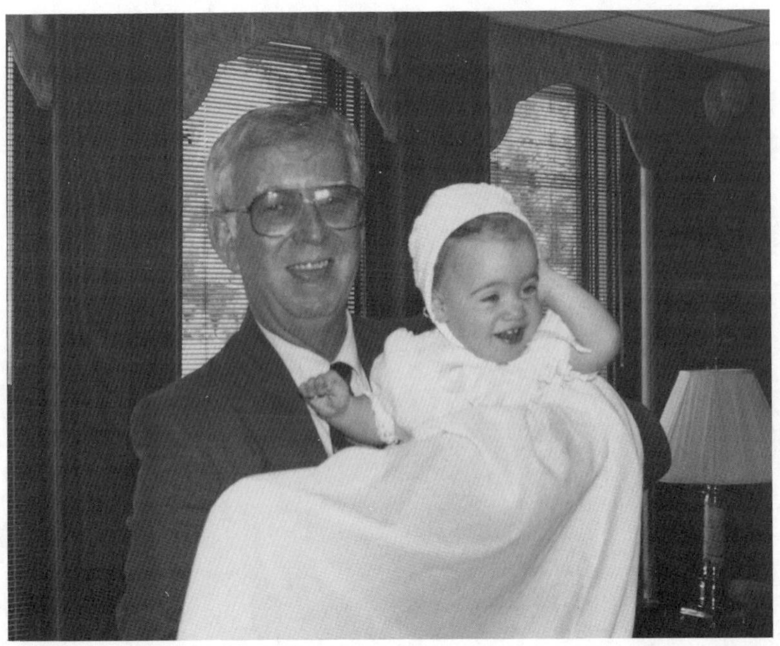

L. B. Taylor, Jr., with granddaughter, Emily

About the Author

L. B. Taylor, Jr. — a Scorpio — is a native Virginian. He was born in Lynchburg and has a BS degree in Journalism from Florida State University. He wrote about America's space programs for 16 years, for NASA and aerospace contractors, before moving to Williamsburg, Virginia, in 1974, as public affairs director for BASF Corporation. He retired in 1993. Taylor is the author of more than 300 national magazine articles and 30 non-fiction books. His research for the book "Haunted Houses," published by Simon and Schuster in 1983, stimulated his interest in area psychic phenomena and led to the publication of five regional Virginia ghost books preceding "The Ghosts of Virginia."

(Personally autographed copies of: "The Ghosts of Williamsburg" — 84 pages, illustrated, $6; "The Ghosts of Richmond" — 172 pages, illustrated, $10; "The Ghosts of Tidewater" — 232 pages, illustrated, $11; "The Ghosts of Fredericksburg" — 177 pages, illustrated, $10; "The Ghosts of Charlottesville and Lynchburg" — 188 pages, illustrated, $10; and "The Ghosts of Virginia" — 401 pages, illustrated, $14 ($55 for all 6 books, $42 for the 5 regional books) are available from: L. B. Taylor, Jr., 248 Archer's Mead, Williamsburg, VA, 23185 (804) 253-2636). Please add $2 shipping and handling charges for single book order, $3 for more than one book. Also please specify to whom you wish the book (s) signed.

"...mortals lie down, and do not rise again..."
Job 14:12

"The third day [Jesus] rose again from the dead."
The Apostles' Creed

"When they heard of the resurrection of the dead, some scoffed; but others said: 'We will hear you again about this.'"
Acts 17:32

Charles Foster is a barrister and writer. He has written, edited or contributed to nineteen books and has written hundreds of articles for publications ranging from *Esquire* magazine to *The Times*, from the *Countryman* to the *Journal of Philosophy, Science and Law*, and from the *Journal of Zoo and Wildlife Medicine* to the *Contemporary Review*.

He read veterinary medicine and law at Cambridge University, researched the immobilization of gazelles and the comparative anatomy of the Himalayan Hispid hare, and was a Research Fellow at the Hebrew University, Jerusalem. He was called to the English Bar by the Inner Temple and to the Bar of the Republic of Ireland by Kings' Inns, Dublin. He practises at the London Bar in the area of medical law. He has been involved in many of the most significant and controversial cases of recent years. He teaches medical law and ethics at the University of Oxford, and is a Recorder (part time judge) of the Crown Court.

A good deal of his life is spent on expeditions. Recent expeditions have included ventures to the Danakil Depression in Ethiopia, the Quirimbas Archipelago in Mozambique, and the White Desert in Egypt. In 2002 he was a member of a successful British ski expedition to the North Pole.

He appears regularly on radio and television.

He is married to Mary, a doctor. They live in London and are members of Holy Trinity Brompton.

THE JESUS INQUEST

CHARLES FOSTER

MONARCH
BOOKS

Oxford, UK & Grand Rapids, Michigan, USA

First published in the UK in 2006 by Monarch Books (a publishing imprint of Lion Hudson plc),
Mayfield House, 256 Banbury Road, Oxford, OX2 7DH.
Tel: +44 (0) 1865 302750 Fax: +44 (0) 1865 302757
Email: monarch@lionhudson.com
www.lionhudson.com

ISBN-13: 978-1-85424-752-0 (UK)
ISBN-10: 1-85424-752-2 (UK)
ISBN-13: 978-0-8254-6105-7 (USA)
ISBN-10: 0-8254-6105-7 (USA)

Distributed by:
UK: Marston Book Services Ltd, PO Box 269,
Abingdon, Oxon OX14 4YN.
USA: Kregel Publications, PO Box 2607,
Grand Rapids, Michigan 49501.

The text paper used in this book has been made from wood independently certified as having come from sustainable forests.

British Library Cataloguing Data
A catalogue record for this book is available from the British Library.

Printed and bound in Malta by Gutenberg Press.

CONTENTS

Map of Palestine at the time of Jesus Christ

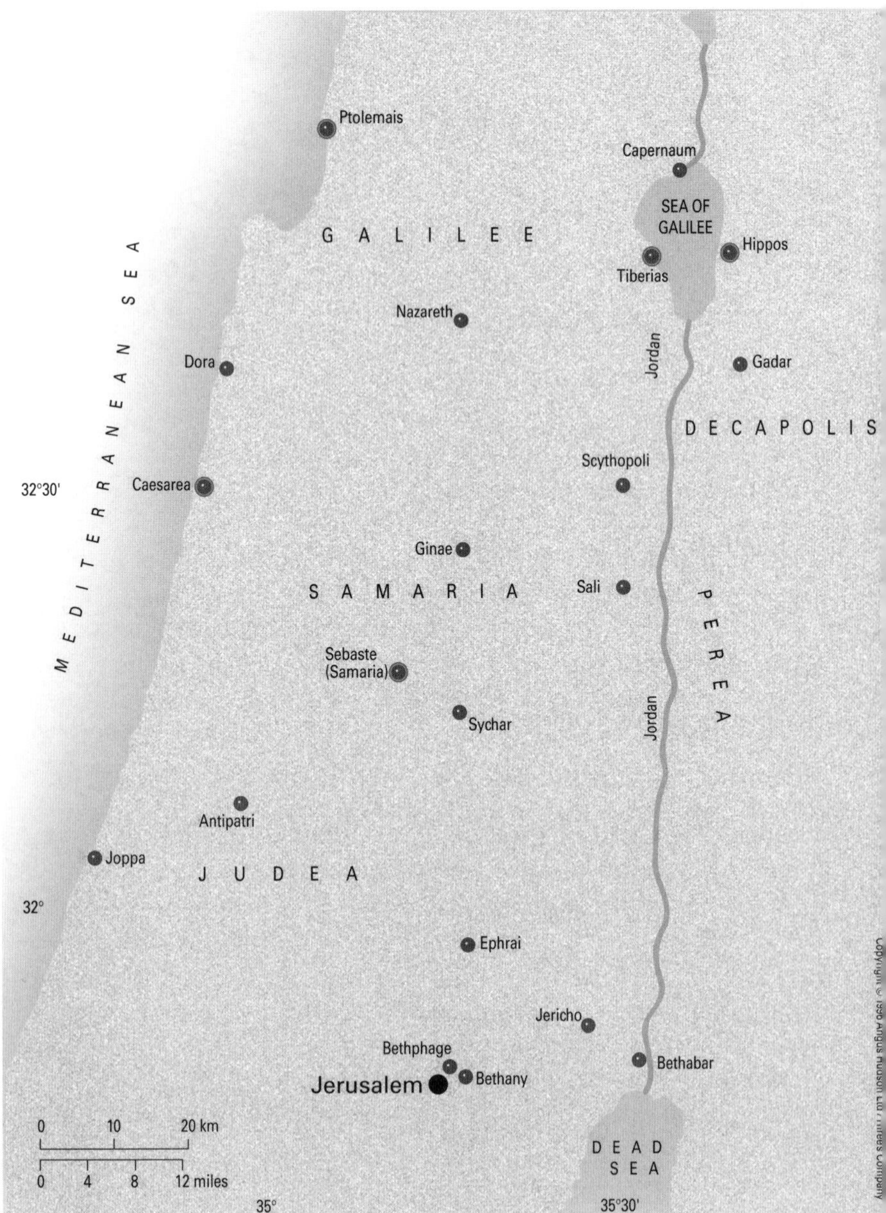

FOREWORD

This is a novel work dealing with the circumstances on which the Christian faith is based: that Jesus died on the cross, rose from the dead and ascended from this world.

Charles Foster, a barrister, is used to inviting tribunals to reach conclusions where the facts are disputed. He applies such techniques, used daily in the courts, to the evidence for the Christian faith and the historical truth upon which it is based. He uses an adversarial method to sift through the large mass of material that needs to be marshalled and considered, first describing the evidence that appears to contradict the Christian position and then presenting evidence in support. The reader is then well placed to reach his or her own conclusions.

How comprehensive is his material? How fairly has he presented the opposing arguments? The case is fully set out: though many of the arguments have been explored by previous authors, many more are his own. In my view he shows an encyclopaedic knowledge of the relevant literature and has provided the reader with a full bibliography for further reading.

As any experienced advocate will know, the success of a presentation often depends on the order in which it is given. In this instance, the case against the Christian position is presented first. Consequently, the Christian view has the benefit of the last word. However, the various arguments against the historicity of the Resurrection do anticipate and deal with the arguments in favour, in such a way that this benefit has been removed in so far as it is possible. In contrast with the situation in a Court of law, the advocate for is also the advocate against; when presenting the material he is fully aware of the mind of his adversary.

This is a work that repays detailed study. I know of no more balanced analysis of the material relating to these crucial questions that go to the heart of the Christian faith. Ultimately, the reader's assessment of the author's approach will affect the judgement he or she reaches. The arguments are set out so clearly, however, that the individual can make those adjustments to them that the differences in their approach may require.

The foundational matters of the Christian faith merit careful rational discussion. This work is a valuable contribution.

Lord Mackay of Clashfern, former Lord Chancellor and Law Lord
House of Lords,
London, SW1

ACKNOWLEDGEMENTS

A lot of people have given up a lot of time listening patiently to my drivellings as I was trying to work out what was going on in first-century Palestine. It is invidious to name names, but I need to mention Joe Zias, formerly of the Israel Antiquities Authority, and doyen of Israeli forensic anthropologists, who spent days wandering with me round tombs in Jerusalem; Professor Yosef Patrich of the Department of Archaeology at the Hebrew University, Jerusalem, who was enormously helpful on the matter of first century Jewish burial practices; Dr Andrew Macintosh of St John's College, Cambridge, a great Hebrew scholar who helped me grope through the murk of Old and inter-testamental beliefs about the afterlife; Dr Graham Tomlin, Principal of St Paul's Theological Centre, who scraped off some of the scales that have always covered my eyes whenever I have looked at St Paul, and Rev. Nicky Gumbel, of Holy Trinity Brompton, whose gift of never losing sight of the wood in the dense theological forests of modern Christianity remains an inspiration. Rob Frost taught me that to voice a doubt is to empty it of half its force. James Wade sat and listened to me saying stupid things about Greek grammar, and then put me graciously right. David Monteath pulled me back from some dangerous exegetical extravagances. Matthew Grayshon read the whole manuscript and made many important and penetrating comments.

The final positions adopted by Y, and all the misconceptions along the way, are my own.

No one could ask for more congenial publishers than Tony

Collins, Simon Cox and the team at Monarch; I am so grateful to them for their courageous belief in this project.

Helen Birkbeck was the model copy editor: fast, erudite and hawk-eyed. She let me get away with nothing.

My wife, Mary, bore with astonishing grace the brunt of my absence, obsession and moodiness. My mother and my sister gave some sterling help sorting out the bibliography.

This book is dedicated to my father, who, while this book was being written, very nearly tested empirically whether or not Christianity is true. He was pulled out of the test only by a heroic cardiac surgeon. He does not agree with me about these things. Our unresolved debates about the resurrection have wrecked many a dinner. He taught me, though, that some things are true and some things are not, and that everyone has a duty to try to find out which is which. I hope he will think that this book is at least an honest, ham-fisted attempt to do that.

PREFACE

I wouldn't want anyone to be misled: I am a Christian. I wrote this book because I was worried that I should not be. There are many legitimate objections to the Christian case. When I woke in the early hours, turning those objections round in my head, I went to the Christian books for answers. I did not find what I needed.

I saw reams of mere assertion, and noted that assertion is neither argument or evidence. I saw that the Christian assertions were immensely robust, and generally unqualified by doubt or caveat. I presumed that all this was because there was neither compelling evidence nor sustainable argument. I saw no reference to the things that really worried me, and concluded that no Christian apart from me had considered them before (arrogant nonsense, of course, but unpleasant), or that Christians had considered them, found there to be no satisfactory answer, and decided that a conspiracy of silence was the best strategy.

I saw that a common method of Christian argument was to say: "Professor Smith thinks that the Christians are correct, and he has an enormous brain and lots of degrees." I wasn't impressed by that. Lots of militant atheists have enormous brains, and both rabid Christian fundamentalists and hysterical atheists have psychological agendas which compel them to believe things regardless of what the evidence says. You don't decide the truth of propositions by comparing the brain weights of the people who believe them with the brain weights of the people who don't. I didn't like the Christian tendency to patronise, and I didn't like the Christian tendency to set up straw men and then knock them down, crowing about the triumph of Christian reason and revelation.

I felt that the Christians had been unfair to their opponents. The Christians hadn't, anywhere that I could find, represented the non-Christian arguments fully. And so I couldn't be sure that there *were* satisfactory Christian answers. To argue both sides was a big, fascinating and worthwhile brief.

I am a barrister: I am in the business of trying to prove things and to convince people. I am an intellectual prostitute, used to standing on metaphorical street corners with my gown hitched up, plying my mind and my mouth on behalf of whomever is prepared to pay. I am used to arguing points that I find personally offensive. I find that I am more diligent in preparing and arguing those points than I am when I am arguing points with which I instinctively agree. That is a common experience amongst advocates: we are so worried that our own prejudices will get in the way that we over compensate. I found that with this book. The submissions of X are far longer, have far more footnotes, and took far longer to write than those of Y. Anyway, I wondered what would happen if I picked up the non-Christian brief and argued it as thoroughly as a brief I was being paid to argue. I wondered what the end result would look like, and what it would do to me.

Most of the arguments coming from X are objections to the Christian position that I think are arguable. A few others I have included because some people feel very strongly that they are arguable and would think that the book was worthless if they had not been aired.

This book, then, is a debate with myself. I was honestly not sure what the outcome would be. I filled suitcases with the books written by Christianity's main opponents, went off to a farmhouse in the mountains of Cyprus, and started to read. And as I read I became more and more alarmed and surprised.

But here's the thing: the main surprise came not from the books of those opponents, but from the canonical gospels themselves. I wasn't prepared for the immense strangeness of the Christian story. This was a story I thought I knew, but it took the coherent and articulate criticisms of Christianity's opponents to make me read it properly. (It wasn't until fairly late in the research that I discovered Tom Wright's magisterial book *The Resurrection of the Son of God*, which articulates the mysterious truths behind the historical resurrection better, I'd imagine, than anyone else ever will).

So where did I end up? Since it's the evidence that matters, not what I've made of it, I'm reluctant to say. But I'm still a Christian, and a far more convinced one than before. But a rather more awed one than before – less ready with the slick, dogmatic sound bite. Scripture is bigger and deeper and stranger than I thought it was.

Can you prove the resurrection? I don't like the question – really because it begs so many others. I doubt whether anyone has ever become a Christian (or declined to become a Christian) simply on the basis of the evidence for the resurrection – whatever they say. But, if I'm made to answer, then, being as dispassionate as I can, I think that the merely historical evidence for the resurrection is very good. It doesn't, I'd say, amount to evidence beyond reasonable doubt, but I think the case is made out on the balance of probabilities. The historical resurrection is easily the most probable explanation for all the data that we have. You do have to believe some remarkable things if you don't believe the resurrection. And I don't have the faith to believe those things.

This has been a stern test of my objectivity, and of course I have failed it. The non-Christians will say that I have not put their case as fully and aggressively as it can be put, and no doubt they are right. But there is some comfort in the thought that they will be more than matched in numbers and volume by the Christians who think that I have been pathetically equivocal in putting the Christian case, and that it is demonic of me to have put the other side at all.

The Christian arguments come after the non-Christian arguments. It will be said that to do it that way round gives the Christians an unfair advantage. But it seemed to me to be structurally inevitable. Everyone knows what the basic Christian position is: it is that Jesus rose. But there are many potential and actual objections to that position, many of which are not obvious. I thought I had to state those and then try to answer them. I have tried to minimise the advantage of the final word by making the non-Christian sections bristle with pre-emptive strikes.

I have not dealt with the common comment: "Only a barbaric God would do that to Jesus". The answer is a theological one, and this is not a theology book. Better to decide first whether the resurrection happened or not. If it didn't, then the issue doesn't arise: there's no reason to implicate God in the death at all. If the resurrection did happen, then and only then do you need to start grappling with the problem of what Jesus' death says about the character of God.

The book ends abruptly. It ends where I think the relevant evidence ends. There is no attempt to sum things up. Everyone has to do that for him or herself.

Charles Foster
London
February 2006

INTRODUCTION

This book is a debate between two characters, X and Y.

X presents the non-Christian view. Where there are many non-Christian positions, he presents all those he thinks are arguable, plus some others that are too popular to be ignored. Because he has to argue many different positions, he cannot always be internally consistent, but he tries.

Y follows, presenting the Christian view. Normally he uses exactly the same headings that X has used. But sometimes that doesn't work. Sometimes he adds headings of his own.

X and Y don't disagree on everything. Sometimes they agree on a lot. Much of the first chapter (on the basic sources) consists of a statement of their agreed position. In other chapters there is sometimes an introduction which indicates what, if any, common ground there is.

The running head at the top of each page indicates whether you are in X or Y's section.

CHAPTER 1

Does all this matter?

> The jar was not unusual. Like the cistern itself, it was of a kind common to the period, used for storing olives or grain, with a wide neck and a tapered stem. It was too large to have been used to draw water from the cistern… Mordecai held the lamp, while Ya'acov and Asher separated the two halves of the broken jar, lifting one off the other like the lid from a box. Dagan crouched to examine the skeleton. "How curious," he said. He took a magnifying glass from his pocket and looked more closely. Ya'acov, Mordecai and Asher watched in silence. Then the professor glanced up, his face pale. "We must touch nothing", he said. "Leave everything exactly as it is. We must have a witness to this, another archaeologist – someone, above all, who is not a Jew."
>
> *On the Third Day*, Piers Paul Read

> If Christ has not been raised, your faith is futile…
>
> St Paul, *First Letter to the Corinthians*, chapter 15:17

The fact that you've opened this book suggests that you think that the resurrection business might matter. X and Y certainly think that it does. If tomorrow's paper says that the bones of Jesus have been found, Y will be in despair.

X thinks that the resurrection is the most monstrous hoax ever perpetrated, or the most ridiculous fairy tale ever to have been believed. Also that the consequences of belief in that hoax or that fairy story have been catastrophic. He points (rather predictably, thinks Y), to the long history of anti-Semitism; to the Crusades; to the Inquisition; to the hideous theocracy of Calvin's Geneva; to the agony of the Catholics under Elizabeth and the agony of the

Protestants under Mary; to the sectarian hatred of Belfast; to the "God Hates Fags" website; to the sheer, life-denying joylessness of much of Christian culture. "Thou hast conquered, O pale Galilean," wrote Swinburne. "The world has grown grey with thy breath." Or red, X would add. And X regrets that, with that addition, Swinburne was, for much of the Western world up to now, absolutely right. And he is still right about some of it – notably a big part of the US, whose belief in the resurrection of a Jewish medicine-man, nailed to a piece of wood in the first century, seems apparently and bizarrely to suggest to them that there is a moral mandate to bomb the living daylights out of a distant part of Mesopotamia. X regrets too that the Pale Galilean seems to have engendered in the world such a taste for repression, bigotry and faction that when his stranglehold is released, others, even more sinister than him, move in unopposed to take over from him.

Y agrees with much of this. He can offer no defence for the obscenities committed in the name of the itinerant Jew he worships. He agrees that if the Jew didn't rise, then Christianity is a disgusting lie. St Paul, after all, said that if the Easter story isn't true then Christians are to be pitied more than anyone else. Not only pitied, Y might add, but denounced for their gullibility and their distinct genocidal tendencies. But Y also says (and X agrees) that if the Jew *did* rise, then the world changed dramatically on that first Easter Sunday.

Both X and Y agree, then, that this is a worthwhile debate. Whether Jesus rose or not isn't affected by the brutality or chauvinism or downright tediousness of his followers through the ages. It's a matter of mere history: the fact or fallacy of the resurrection is in the same class of alleged facts as the contention that the Battle of Agincourt was fought in 1415, or that I caught the 08.56 train this morning. And so it is subject to the same sort of historical enquiry.

There is one caveat, though. We know that battles are sometimes fought, and that people sometimes do catch trains. We don't know that men who are dead and buried sometimes rise. In fact it is the Christian contention that they don't. The Christians say that it happened only once. If it happened more than once – if it was merely extremely rare instead of wholly unique – Christianity would have been shown to be simply wrong. We should then turn the cathedrals into bingo halls and the mission stations into brothels.

All this must have an effect on the way we approach the evidence.

It must mean that we should prefer natural explanations over supernatural ones. Put another way, the burden of proving this wholly extraordinary event must be on the shoulders of the Christians. But it also means that X won't be so stupid as to say: "This didn't happen because these sort of things don't happen." If that's the starting point, it is also the ending point. Discussion is doomed. This might sound obvious, but it has often dogged academic discourse. Here is Gerd Ludemann dismissing the ascension:

> As a rule in such a case we did not ask the historical question. In this particular case let me hasten to add that any historical element behind this scene and/or behind Acts 1:9–11 must be ruled out because there is no such heaven to which Jesus may have been carried...[1]

You can't begin to debate with an opponent like that.

There is a lot of ground to cover. We need to go deep into the characters of the people at the centre of the drama; we need to know quite a lot about first-century Jewish burial practices, and about the controversies that dogged the early church. We need to know a bit of Greek and some archaeology. We need to know whether that difficult, turbulent man Paul was a poet, a theologian, a soap box orator or a psychotic. But first we need to know something about the basic documents.

CHAPTER 2

The sources

> To be still searching what we know not by what we know, still closing up truth to truth as we find it (for all her body is homogeneal and proportional), this is the golden rule in theology as well as in arithmetic
>
> Milton, *Areopagitica*

This chapter contains three sections. It starts off by setting out what X and Y are agreed upon. Then X outlines his position, and Y follows.

X and Y: An agreed statement

We disagree on quite enough. There is no point in squabbling where we don't have to. We will get on faster and more coherently if we state our agreement about the sources we will be using. What follows is a statement of the broad consensus of biblical scholarship. Not everyone will agree with all of it. Some will disagree with most of it.

The canonical gospels and Acts

The canonical gospels (Matthew, Mark, Luke and John) were probably written in the first century AD. The general trend over the last half century has been to push the dates of composition backwards. It would have been a hallmark of dangerous fundamentalism for a scholar in the first half of the twentieth century to assert that John was first-century. Now it would be rather eccentric not to assert it. Most people would opt for a date for John some time in the 80s or 90s.

The order of writing

Most agree, too, that Mark is the first in time. The date is much disputed. Conservatives put it in the 50s or earlier; others (most) in the 60s. Matthew and Luke follow: the order in which they follow is contentious. There is general agreement that they both preceded John.

The relationship between the gospels

Some people spend their lives talking about the relationship between the gospels, and we cannot begin to do justice to the complexity of the arguments. But the story probably went something like this: Mark was first: he may or may not have had some pre-Markan passion narrative in front of him. Matthew and Luke had Mark in front of them. They also had a bundle of sayings (rather than doings) of Jesus. That bundle is known cryptically as "Q". But, in addition, Matthew had something that Luke did not have, and Luke had something that Matthew did not have. What that something was is again the subject of bitter and learned argument. It might have been documents; it might have been personal memory; it might have been tradition.

Then there is John. He seems to have taken his own line across country. Some would say that he'd had a look at some of the earlier gospels, but if he had he doesn't seem to have had them on his desk when he wrote. Perhaps he had seen them long before, or had them summarised to him by a secretary. His chronology is different from that of the synoptic writers and he is much more Jerusalem-o-centric.

Look at any table comparing the contents of the synoptic gospels with those of John: at first blush they look (at least until you get to the very end) like biographies of different men. On second blush they are clearly not, but the question remains: why do they look so different? We don't know. Theories abound. Perhaps John knew what the others had written and was simply plugging the gaps.

He makes no bones about his purpose in writing the gospel: it is written "so that you might come to believe that Jesus is the Messiah, the Son of God, and that through believing you may have life in his name".[1] This is disarming frankness. X will suggest later that it is artfully disarming. But it might indicate why John differs so much from the others. His theological agenda is in some ways different. Perhaps he is merely picking out from the mass of material available to him (he acknowledges that he cannot include it all – there's far too much[2]) the best vehicles for his theological points.

Who wrote the gospels?

We have used "Matthew", "Mark", "Luke" and "John" as if those are the names of the authors. There is no agreement about this. The identity of the authors does not matter for now. Three things are important: first, the quality of the information upon which the accounts were based; second, the extent to which the author's own theological or other agenda intrudes into the story telling, and, third, what later editors have done with the basic account. These three issues mark out the battleground for many of the later spats between X and Y.

Although we cannot agree about authorship, we can summarise the various mainstream positions that are held. From the end of the first century, the tradition was that Mark (whoever he was) was the companion and scribe of the apostle Peter. There is no convincing reason to doubt this – or at least to doubt that Peter was the source of many of the traditions recorded in the gospel. X would say that there is no very convincing reason, apart from the tradition, to believe it either. Y would say that the gospel is full of the sort of details that come from eyewitnesses and no one else, but concedes that this says nothing about the identity of the eyewitness.

The early Christians thought that the author of Matthew's gospel was the apostle Matthew, the tax collector. This is unlikely. If he had been an eyewitness himself he would presumably not have relied as heavily on Mark as he does.

Why is Matthew credited with the gospel? Perhaps because he was the source of some of the other material in the gospel that doesn't come from Mark. Matthew may be "Q". The issue doesn't matter much for our enquiry, since we are interested in events, not sayings. "Q" doesn't intrude into the death and resurrection accounts.

Luke was a non-Jew who knew Paul, and he makes several appearances in Paul's letters. He was not one of the apostles. Acts is just Luke Part Two. The gospel and the book of Acts are dedicated to someone called Theophilus[3] – presumably some sort of patron of Luke[4]. We know nothing at all about Theophilus.

Luke boasts about the diligence of his research and the excellence of his sources:

> Since many have undertaken to set down an orderly account of the events that have been fulfilled among us, just as they were handed on to us by those who from the beginning were eyewitnesses and servants of

> the word, I too decided, after investigating everything carefully from the very first, to write an orderly account for you, most excellent Theophilus, so that you may know the truth concerning the things about which you have been instructed.[5]

Whether the boast was justified is contentious.[6]

And then there is John. To mention his name is to disturb a nest of the most virulently poisonous theological hornets. Their numbers and the sound of their buzzing makes it difficult to keep perspective. They have settled quite a bit over the last quarter of a century, though.

The second-century church thought that the gospel was written by the apostle John, somewhere in Asia, when he was a very old man. The gospel itself does not say who wrote it. But it does talk about "a disciple whom Jesus loved", and says that this disciple was involved in some way in writing the gospel. Here is what it says. Talking about the flow of blood and water from Jesus' side, the gospel notes, in its own brackets: "(He who saw this has testified so that you also may believe. His testimony is true, and he knows that he tells the truth)."[7] And right at the end: "[The beloved disciple] is the disciple who is testifying to these things and has written them, and we know that his testimony is true."[8] This last sentence is a teaser: the disciple has "written" these things in some sense, it says, but "we" (presumably the physical writer?) know that he's telling the truth. Whoever the disciple was, he is clearly saying that he was an eye witness. Perhaps, sitting old, arthritic and blind in Ephesus, he was dictating his reminiscences to a scribe.

John, too, is a book that has clearly been added to. Chapter 21 (which puts the risen Jesus in Galilee, doing some very interesting things) was very obviously added later. Chapter 20 ends: "Now Jesus did many other signs in the presence of his disciples, which are not written in this book. But these are written so that you may come to believe that Jesus is the Messiah, the Son of God, and that through believing you may have life in his name."[9] Curtain down, you'd have thought. But no, it goes up again straight away for the final scene, only to end 25 verses later with another grand and rather similar peroration.

X, of course, will contend that this is suspicious. The activities of Jesus in chapter 21 are too blatantly symbolic to be real, he will say. The author is making theological and political points. We can't conclude from chapter 21 that the risen Jesus was ever seen in Galilee at all. Y, of course, disagrees. But that's beside the point for the moment. The consensus of scholarship is that there is no reason to suppose that the author of chapter 21 is not also the author of the rest of the gospel. The style's the same, chapter 21 contains no obvious anachronisms, and the clumsy tacking-on of chapter 21 is incompatible with a sinister intent to mislead.

The Gospel of Peter

The discovery of this strange document is itself a great story. It is mentioned by some of the early church fathers[10], but was thought to be completely lost. Then, in 1886/7, a monk's grave in Upper Egypt was dug up. In it was part of the gospel. And then, in 1972, it was realised that two bits of the Oxyrhynchus Papyri came from the same book. It was then possible to put together what we have today. A translation of the relevant parts is at Appendix 3. It is generally thought to have been written in the second century AD; just when in the second century is discussed greatly and inconclusively.

The overwhelming majority of biblical scholars reckon that Peter is a late, legendary encrustation on the canonical gospel stories[11]. But a few (and notably John Dominic Crossan) think that they can identify a very early strand in Peter (which Crossan calls the Cross gospel), upon which the canonical gospel writers relied. Since Crossan is very much out on a limb, his (very technical) arguments from the Gospel of Peter do not feature further in this book. The Gospel itself is mentioned further, by both X and Y, to make various rhetorical points.

New Testament letters

Paul's letters are important to this debate. Three of them are particularly important. First Thessalonians, generally thought to be the first of Paul's surviving letters, is usually dated to around AD 50–51. 1 Corinthians 15 contains the earliest written assertions about the *historicity* of the resurrection that we have. A lot of the argument in this book will centre on it. Most authorities date it at around AD 54 – significantly before the date that most people would give to all the gospels. And then there is Romans – probably from about AD 56–57.

Other non-canonical sources

Apart from the canonical books and the Gospel of Peter, many sources from around the time of Jesus are mentioned in this book. Most of them deal with peripheral matters such as what Jewish burial practices were at the time. Many other sources often appear in Christian apologetic books – often whipped out triumphantly like trump cards. But if you accept, as the overwhelming majority of scholars do, that Jesus of Nazareth actually lived, and was executed in the early 30s AD by the Romans, most of them are pretty unhelpful. They are mentioned here in order to clear the decks for later argument.

Tacitus

Tacitus: (c. AD 55–117), was a Roman historian with no love for Christians. He noted scornfully that Jesus, "was put to death by Pontius Pilate, procurator of Judea in the reign of Tiberius: but the pernicious superstition, repressed for a time, broke out again, not only through Judea, where the mischief originated, but through the city of Rome also".[12] It has been suggested that this "pernicious superstition" might refer to the resurrection itself[13], but the passage hardly reads like that. It seems more likely that the "superstition" was the whole corpus of Christian belief. And if the reference really is to "resurrection", that hardly takes us further. We don't need Tacitus to tell us that at least by the time Paul wrote 1 Thessalonians in the early 50s, Christians were talking about and believing in "the resurrection".[14] The important question so far as this first generation of believers is concerned is not whether they believed in the resurrection: they plainly did. We need to know what it was they meant by that belief. And we need to know that only because it may suggest something about the nature, and perhaps quality, of the old apostolic evidence for the historicity of the resurrection.

Suetonius

Similar comments apply to Suetonius (AD 69– after 122 AD), who wrote enthusiastically about the punishments meted out by Nero in Rome in AD 64 to the Christians, "a class of men given to a new and mischievous superstition".[15]

Mara Bar-Seraphion

More helpful (at least to X) is a letter from Mara Bar-Seraphion, a Syrian philosopher writing from prison to his son, some time after AD 70.

> What advantage did the Jews gain from executing their wise King? [Evidently Jesus]... But Socrates did not die for good; he lived on in the teaching of Plato. Pythagoras did not die for good; he lived on in the statue of Hera. Nor did the wise King die for good; He lived on in the teaching which He had given.

It will be a matter for later debate whether that is an accurate summary of early Christian belief, or merely an expression of Bar-Seraphion's own philosophic conclusion. It seems, in any event, to confirm the execution of Jesus.

The Gemara

So, for that matter, does the Babylonian Talmud (the Gemara), composed between the third and fifth centuries AD. "It has been taught", says the Gemara, "on the eve of Passover they hanged Yeshu [Jesus]. And an announcer went out in front of him, for forty days [saying]: 'He is going to be stoned, because he practiced sorcery and enticed and led Israel astray. Anyone who knows anything in his favour, let him come and plead in his behalf.' But, not having found anything in his favour, they hanged him on the eve of Passover."[16]

Everyone agrees that "hanged", here, is a euphemism for crucifixion.[17]

The darkness during Jesus' crucifixion: Thallus, Phlegon and Julius Africanus

All the synoptic gospels mention the darkness that fell during Jesus' crucifixion. It sounds like theological metaphor (and indeed X says that it is). But there might be some secular corroboration. Thallus, a Roman writing around AD 52, apparently mentioned it. "Apparently" because all his work has gone missing, and we have to glean what we can from other writers who cite him. Julius Africanus, writing in about AD 221, notes: "Thallus, in his third book of histories, explains away this darkness as an eclipse of the sun – unreasonably, as it seems to me (unreasonably, of course, because a solar eclipse could not take place at the time of the full moon, and it was at the season of the Paschal full moon that Christ died)."[18]

Another contemporary writer, Phlegon, is said to have mentioned the darkness too, again attributing it to a solar eclipse. His work met the same fate as Thallus' and he, again, is known only through Julius Africanus. We have to be slightly cautious about Julius Africanus: he was a Christian. But it seems unlikely that he would lie about what these authors said. That, after all, could have been very easily checked at the time. Note, too, that there was evidently nothing controversial about either the fact of the darkness or the timing of it: Julius simply disagreed with Thallus and Phlegon about the cause.

Josephus

Then there is Flavius Josephus (AD 37/38 – sometime after AD 100). He was a Jew who knew that the best route to longevity in first-century Palestine was to side with Rome. And that is what he did. His *Jewish Antiquities* contains a famous passage known as the Testimonium. It reads:

> About this time there lived Jesus, a wise man, [if indeed one ought to call him a man.] For he was one who performed surprising deeds and was a teacher of such people as accept the truth gladly. He won over many Jews and many of the Greeks. [He was the Messiah.] And when, upon the accusation of the principal men among us, Pilate had condemned him to a cross, those who had first come to love him did not cease. [He appeared to them spending a third day restored to life, for the prophets of God had foretold these things and a thousand other marvels about him.] And the tribe of the Christians, so called after him, has still to this day not disappeared.[19]

Some say that all this is bogus – a clear piece of Christian propaganda. Some say that it is all authentic, and make it a major plank of Christian apologetic. The majority view is probably that the bracketed sections were indeed inserted by over zealous Christian scribes, but that the remainder is genuine Josephus. If that is right, Josephus, Suetonius and Tacitus all tell us more or less the same: a troublesome Jew called Jesus caused a bit of bother for Rome when he was alive, and was executed. He then caused a good deal more trouble after he was dead.

The Gnostics, Nag Hammadi, the Dead Sea Scrolls and The Da Vinci Code

It is unfortunately necessary, since everyone in the world seems to have read *The Da Vinci Code*[20] and taken it seriously, to say something about the Gnostics, the Nag Hammadi documents, and the Dead Sea Scrolls. The Dead Sea Scrolls first. This is simple: there is not a single word in any of them about Jesus.

Now the business of the Gnostics and the Gnostic documents at Nag Hammadi. The Gnostics flourished throughout the eastern Mediterranean world in the first century. Dan Brown says, as if there was some sort of sinister cabalistic secret about it, that the mainstream church sought to suppress Gnosticism. There's nothing secret about it at all: a good deal of the history of the early church is the history of its fight against Gnosticism.

Did the church try to suppress Gnostic documents, like those dug up at Nag Hammadi? Absolutely. But there is no evidence at all that any of the documents that form part of the New Testament canon originally had Gnostic elements that were excised in the name of orthodoxy.[21] And none of the Gnostic documents was ever a candidate for inclusion in the canon.[22]

Who were the Gnostics? "Christian" Gnosticism[23] was a broad, theologically slippery church. It had three basic beliefs: first, it was dualistic: it thought that the supreme good was the supreme spirit, God. Material things were created by God's opponent – an anti-spirit. Matter, therefore, was despised. Second, there was a corpus of secret, esoteric knowledge which, when possessed by the initiates, gave some sort of access to divine mysteries. This knowledge was for the elect – those who, inside the unfortunate material that composed their much-resented bodies, sheltered a divine spark of pure spirit. It was not for the riff raff. And third, Jesus was an ambassador of the divine – a conduit of the sacred knowledge. It followed, of course, that he was not really human: he only *seemed* human.

This was where the orthodox church and the Gnostics really parted company. Jesus was fully God *and* fully man, said the Christians. "Fully man?" said the Gnostics, "What a disgusting, blasphemous idea." So Dan Brown has things completely the wrong way round. It was the Christians, not the Gnostics, who were keen to assert the historical, earthy Jesus – the one who ate, drank and was sometimes merry and sometimes tearful. And if Jesus really had married, there is no reason to suppose that the early church would have had a problem with it. The Gnostics would have had a problem: sex was dirty and unspiritual. If anyone was going to suppress knowledge of Jesus' marriage to Mary Magdalene it would have been the ascetic, women-hating priests of Gnosticism.

It will be suggested by X that the early church's battle against Gnosticism is the explanation for many of the things in the canonical documents upon which the Christians rely in asserting the physical resurrection of Jesus. Those suggestions will be dealt with when they arise. For the moment it is enough to notice that those powerful arguments against Christianity can be mounted only because Gnosticism believed precisely the opposite of what Dan Brown thinks it said. To any half competent historian Dan Brown's thesis poses no threat at all to orthodox Christianity.

The canon

Mention of the Gnostics means that we have to mention one further thing about the canon. What criteria were used by the early church in deciding which of the many Christian writings it should endorse? The answer is that several were. But there was one crucial qualifying criterion, without which a document came nowhere near the canon. This was apostolicity. The document had to come from the age of the apostles, and to be connected in some ways with them.[24]

X, while acknowledging that this criterion was used, thinks that the original apostles got the wrong end of the stick; subsequent accounts aren't made reliable by their writers being somehow in contact with the people who had made the mistake in the first place.

Y, of course, notes that the fact that the apostolicity criterion was used denotes a basic integrity. The church was concerned to get it right – by which they meant keeping it original. The church wasn't merely concerned with being popular or filling its coffers or filling its buildings. This might suggest a certain reassuring reluctance to wield the editorial blue pencil – a reluctance, says Y, amply demonstrated in the documents we have. Further, Y says, getting it right clearly meant getting it *historically* right. It wasn't concerned merely with philosophically pure doctrine, or rather it saw philosophically pure doctrine as indistinguishable from accurate history.

When the number of the apostles fell from twelve to eleven due to Judas's unfortunate defection, what criterion was used to decide who should replace him? The ability to be an accurate eyewitness of the central historical events: "…One of the men who have accompanied us during all the time that the Lord Jesus went in and out among us, beginning from the baptism of John until the day when he was taken up from us – one of these must become a witness with us to his resurrection", said Peter.[25]

X and Y, then, agree on a good deal. But this, sadly, is where the agreement ends. The many points of disagreement will emerge in the general statements from X and Y below, and in the chapters that follow.

X: general position on the canonical documents

> Whatever religious or non-religious convictions we have, we find ourselves entering the field, as we see it, as the champions and zealots for a straightforward and accurate understanding of the Bible as an ancient text, and of the resurrection accounts as natural accoutrements of such literature. In our opinion, it is the fundamentalist, the apologist for Christian supernaturalism, who is propagating false and misleading views of the Bible among the general populace. We are not content to know better and to shake our heads at the foolishness of the untutored masses. We want the Bible to be appreciated for what it is, not for what it is not. And it is not a supernatural oracle book filled with infallible dogmas and wild tales that must be believed at the risk of eternal peril.
>
> Robert M. Price, *The Empty Tomb: The Second Life of Jesus*[26]

I will make my points in the contexts in which they arise, but several themes will keep emerging:

(a) The biblical accounts are hopelessly self-contradictory.
(b) They were written a long time after the events they purport to describe. Memories fade.[27]
(c) In no case can we be sure that we are dealing with genuine eyewitness testimony.
(d) Probably, at best, we are dealing with multiple hearsay. Anyone who has played Chinese whispers knows how dangerous that is.
(e) The writers in each case are prosecuting an obvious agenda. They appear to have been convinced themselves, and bolster their accounts to try to convince others. That wouldn't have seemed to them to be dishonest. They no doubt thought that disbelief would have nasty eternal consequences and that anything that helped to snatch the infidel from the flames was justified. Paul comes close to saying precisely that.[28]

There were other agendas too, apart from the simple one of trying to make others believe in the resurrection (whatever "the resurrection" meant). One of the main ones, already mentioned, was to do down the Gnostics. The main way of doing that was to overstate the case for the physicality of Jesus' resurrection body.

Thomas, for instance, is a theatrical creation designed to combat Gnosticism: if he reaches out his hand and really touches Jesus' wounds, Gnosticism is exploded. The other, spiritual world is material after all. Similarly Jesus' ostentatious eating at almost every post-mortem opportunity: at the tavern in Emmaus; on the beach at Galilee; and so on. If you were a Gnostic, eating was regrettable at the best of times. But eating after you had risen from the dead was as offensive an affirmation of material stuff as you could have.

There was yet another agenda: keeping in with Rome. Christianity's spread in the early years was mainly in the Roman Empire. Christianity used the Pax Romana and the unprecedentedly good Roman infrastructure to go to the ends of the civilised (for which read Roman) world. Christian missionaries marched along Rome's matchless roads, were protected from pirates by Rome's terrible laws and splendid ships, and Paul, ever the pragmatist, invoked his Roman citizenship to get him out of scrapes. But Rome was fickle, as the Christians found when Nero lit his gardens with them. It needed to be kept sweet. Its empire was too big, and it didn't want to spend time and money on putting down little rebellions in remote places. The Christians needed to convince Rome that they would be no trouble.

Paul was a master of this art. Whole theologies have been built on his comments (intended for Roman imperial ears) that slaves should submit to their masters and subjects to their rulers.[29] "We'll not bother you," Paul was saying to the Romans. "Let us go about our business." And the gospel writers, or their editors, were saying exactly the same thing. It was embarrassing for them that Jesus had been executed at the hands of the Romans. But the damage could be minimised by making the Romans kill Jesus very reluctantly, and putting the real blame on the Jews (who had the capacity to create far fewer problems for the emerging church than the Romans had, and who in any event were routed after the destruction of Jerusalem in AD 70). Hence the implausible passion accounts in the canonical gospels: Pilate acts honourably, with impeccable judicial objectivity, but finally has his hand forced by baying crowds of hysterically homicidal Jews. "We know you are fair," the gospels say, sycophantically, to Rome. "We have every confidence in you." It's a classic case of backing the known winner.

(f) Even if the original gospel accounts were genuine attempts to tell the unvarnished truth, they have been extensively edited by people who had these agendas very much in mind. The editorial massaging makes it impossible to reconstruct the original shape

Y: General position on the canonical documents

Histories make men wise
Francis Bacon, *Of Studies*

What was the point of the gospels in the early church?
It is not surprising that we focus on the canonical gospels. They are our main source of information about the death and alleged resurrection of Jesus. But in evaluating the documents we have to be careful not to be misled into thinking that the early church used the documents in the same way that we do.

Why weren't the gospels written down earlier?
X is at pains to point out that the gospels weren't written down until a long time after Jesus' death. He's almost certainly right. But why was that? It was because no one, for a while, thought that it was necessary. The early Christians had the original witnesses among them. It wasn't a very bookish culture. History, as is still the case in many parts of the Near East, was mainly held in heads rather than in libraries. And heads were no doubt better at holding it than most Western heads are today. Oral tradition, in cultures with no TV, is remarkably consistent.

Why were the gospels ever written down?
But all this begs the question: why bother to write it down at all? There are probably two reasons. The first one – so obvious that its significance is easily missed – is that that the early Christians

thought that it was particularly important to be working from the original sources. They didn't view the cornerstones of their faith as they would have regarded the poems of a bard or the prayers of a righteous man. Historical accuracy mattered. And this could only be because they thought the faith stood on the basis of something that happened in history. If Christianity were just a set of ethical principles or a bundle of uplifting parables, the gist would do. But it wasn't like that. There was a problem, though: the original eye witnesses weren't immortal. They started to get senile and die. It was important to take statements from them while they were still there.

The second reason has already been mentioned. The doctrine of the early church was being polluted by Gnosticism. The Gnostics, to repeat, thought that Jesus wasn't really human; he just seemed human. That lie needed to be laid to rest. And it would be impossible to do it without the testimony of the men who had shuffled round Palestine with Jesus, eaten the fish cooked by him after his resurrection, and seen those crucifixion wounds. X thinks that he can see in the gospels things written just to confound the Gnostics. And again he is right. We will see some of them as we look at the texts. They are to do with how obviously dead Jesus was, and how obviously physically alive he later became. But it does not begin to follow, as X says it does, that these anti-Gnostic details are fabrications. The position of the early Christians wasn't generated as a response to Gnosticism: it preceded it. The Christians were defending the position on Jesus's physical resurrection that they had always held. Yes, the Gnostics made them more vocal and more explicit in that defence; the Gnostics didn't force them into that position in the first place.

Was anyone in the early church ever converted by "the gospels"?

This brings us to another crucial point. We tend to think of the gospels as evangelistic tracts. They are handed out by smiling people at church doors. They are cited in football stadiums by shiny suited Texan preachers. But that's not how the first Christians saw them. Because they didn't see them at all; the gospels just didn't exist at first. Absolutely no one was converted to Christianity by a compelling expository sermon on one of the gospels for at least the first 20 years after the death of Jesus, and probably a great deal longer. And yet the church existed, thrived and multiplied.

What were its sermons about? We know from the book of Acts and from the New Testament letters. We will look at some of them later. At the heart of every sermon was a belief in the physical resurrection of Jesus. This belief wasn't preached by expounding Mark, Matthew, Luke or John. They still had to be written, or at least disseminated. The belief was preached on the basis of a tradition coming straight from the testimony of the eye witnesses. All that Mark, Matthew, Mark and John did was to put down on papyrus what the church had been teaching from the beginning.

All four gospel writers were no doubt enthusiastic members of their local churches. They went along there every Sunday; sometimes they preached themselves; sometimes they listened to the sermon and nodded when the tradition was repeated accurately. And eventually they were prevailed on to write down their own or their sources' recollections of the facts that had generated the tradition. This is why it is silly for X to say: "Mark wasn't written until the 50s at the earliest. That's a good 20 years after Jesus died. Mark couldn't be expected to remember things clearly after all that time." Mark didn't hibernate between the death of Jesus and the time he wrote his gospel, then take out his pen, scratch his head and say: "It was a long time ago, and I'm trying to remember this for the first time, but so far as I remember it went something like this."[30]

Harmonising the gospels

I think that there are real discrepancies between the gospel accounts. If that makes me a heretic, then I'm a heretic. I'd rather be faithful to what scripture actually says that to some synthetic doctrine of verbal inerrancy.

Efforts at harmonisation seem to me to fail, and to bring Christianity into embarrassing disrepute when they do. The classic example relates to the number of times the cock crowed after Peter denied Jesus. Some harmonisers, thinking that they are being obedient to the principle that "all scripture is God-breathed"[31], elaborately calculate that the passages relating to Peter's denial of Jesus and the famous cock crows can be read together if you say that Peter actually denied Jesus six times: three times before the cock crowed once, and three times before it crowed the second time.[32] This is clever stuff. But nowhere in real scripture (rather than the imagined scripture inside the harmonisers' heads), does it say the cock crowed six times. I prefer real scripture. It couldn't matter less to me and to my eternal destiny whether the cock crowed once or twice.

I know that if I were a barrister trying to establish the credibility of the various witnesses to the cock-crowing, I would love to have the witnesses disagree honestly, as real people from various standpoints, with varying hearing, in different crowds speaking with different volumes, would tend to do. If every witness to a road traffic accident says the same thing you know that you're dealing with an attempt to defraud the insurance company. I know that one of the most powerful arguments for the integrity of the early church is that they did not iron out the discrepancies. A perfect account, with no wrinkles, would be highly suspect.

In the canonical gospels we've got a splendid sheaf of flawed, baffled, baffling, and therefore ultimately utterly compelling witness statements. Those early compilers of the canon had immense confidence that the truth was contained in, and would emerge from, the whole bundle of scripture read together. That confidence has resulted in a complex, variegated and highly credible collection of documents. They make the forensic apologist's job a lot easier.

The discrepancies wholly take the wind out of the sails of those who, like X, say that there has been significant later scribal addition to the basic texts. You hear this all the time. "This was added later to see off the Gnostics," they say. Or: "Someone put this in in the second century so that the gospel would be concordant with Isaiah." Rarely is there any textual evidence to support these contentions. Usually the agenda behind the contention is annoyance that the account is so compelling – so complete. If there had been significant later scribal emendation, the scribes, who could spot a barn-door problem, would have made a better job of it: they wouldn't simply have tinkered with minor details in the accounts in the way that some say that they did. They'd have got rid of the really big textual problems. I sometimes wonder whether the modern church would have the restraint to leave the accounts saying what they do say. Or would there be a tendency to say: "Scripture as a whole tells us that Jesus, after his death, was in both Jerusalem and Galilee. Luke mentions only Jerusalem. As faithful expositors it's our duty to tell the whole story. So let's import the Galilean sections of John into Luke"? I hope not.

Jersusalem at the time of Jesus Christ

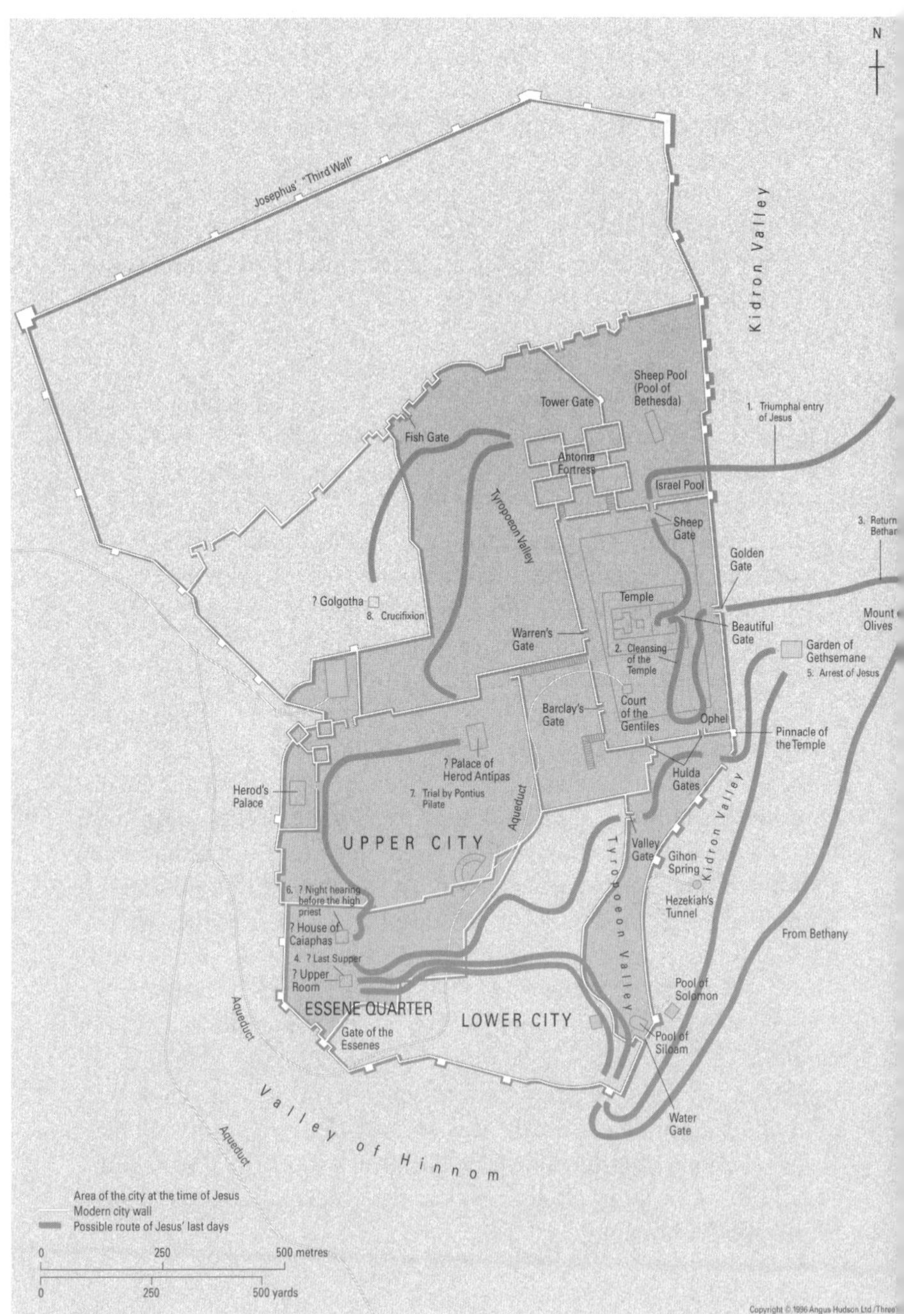

N
Josephus' "Third Wall"
Kidron Valley
Sheep Pool (Pool of Bethesda)
Tower Gate
Fish Gate
Antonia Fortress
Israel Pool
Tyropoeon Valley
Sheep Gate
1. Triumphal entry of Jesus
3. Return
Golden Gate
? Golgotha
8. Crucifixion
Temple
Warren's Gate
2. Cleansing of the Temple
Beautiful Gate
Mount Olives
Garden of Gethsemane
5. Arrest of Jesus
Barclay's Gate
Court of the Gentiles
Ophel
Pinnacle of the Temple
? Palace of Herod Antipas
7. Trial by Pontius Pilate
Herod's Palace
Hulda Gates
Aqueduct
UPPER CITY
Valley Gate
Gihon Spring
Kidron Valley
Tyropoeon Valley
6. ? Night hearing before the high priest
? House of Caiaphas
Hezekiah's Tunnel
From Bethany
4. ? Last Supper
? Upper Room
Pool of Solomon
ESSENE QUARTER
LOWER CITY
Gate of the Essenes
Pool of Siloam
Aqueduct
Water Gate
Valley of Hinnom
Aqueduct
Area of the city at the time of Jesus
Modern city wall
Possible route of Jesus' last days
0
250
500 metres
0
250
500 yards

CHAPTER 3

The death

The sources

Mark 15

16Then the soldiers led him into the courtyard of the palace (that is, the
governor's headquarters); and they called together the whole cohort.
[17]And they clothed him in a purple cloak; and after twisting some thorns
into a crown, they put it on him. [18]And they began saluting him, "Hail,
King of the Jews!" [19]They struck his head with a reed, spat upon him, and
knelt down in homage to him. [20]After mocking him, they stripped him of
the purple cloak and put his own clothes on him. Then they led him out
to crucify him.

21They compelled a passer-by, who was coming in from the country,
to carry his cross; it was Simon of Cyrene, the father of Alexander and
Rufus. [22]Then they brought Jesus to the place called Golgotha (which
means the place of a skull). [23]And they offered him wine mixed with
myrrh; but he did not take it. [24]And they crucified him, and divided his
clothes among them, casting lots to decide what each should take.

25It was nine o'clock in the morning when they crucified him. [26]The
inscription of the charge against him read, 'The King of the Jews.' [27]And
with him they crucified two bandits, one on his right and one on his left.
[29]Those who passed by derided him, shaking their heads and saying,
"Aha! You who would destroy the temple and build it in three days, [30]save
yourself, and come down from the cross!" [31]In the same way the chief
priests, along with the scribes, were also mocking him among themselves
and saying, "He saved others; he cannot save himself. [32]Let the Messiah,
the King of Israel, come down from the cross now, so that we may see
and believe." Those who were crucified with him also taunted him.

33When it was noon, darkness came over the whole land until three in
the afternoon. 34At three o'clock Jesus cried out with a loud voice, "Eloi,
Eloi, lama sabachthani?" which means, "My God, my God, why have
you forsaken me?" 35When some of the bystanders heard it, they said,
"Listen, he is calling for Elijah." 36And someone ran, filled a sponge with
sour wine, put it on a stick, and gave it to him to drink, saying, "Wait, let
us see whether Elijah will come to take him down." 37Then Jesus gave a
loud cry and breathed his last. 38And the curtain of the temple was torn
in two, from top to bottom. 39Now when the centurion, who stood facing
him, saw that in this way he breathed his last, he said, "Truly this man
was God's Son!"

40There were also women looking on from a distance; among them
were Mary Magdalene, and Mary the mother of James the younger and
of Joses, and Salome. 41These used to follow him and provided for him
when he was in Galilee; and there were many other women who had
come up with him to Jerusalem.

Matthew 27

27Then the soldiers of the governor took Jesus into the governor's headquarters, and they gathered the whole cohort around him. 28They
stripped him and put a scarlet robe on him, 29and after twisting some
thorns into a crown, they put it on his head. They put a reed in his right
hand and knelt before him and mocked him, saying, "Hail, King of the
Jews!" 30They spat on him, and took the reed and struck him on the head.
31After mocking him, they stripped him of the robe and put his own
clothes on him. Then they led him away to crucify him.

32As they went out, they came upon a man from Cyrene named
Simon; they compelled this man to carry his cross. 33And when they came
to a place called Golgotha (which means Place of a Skull), 34they offered
him wine to drink, mixed with gall; but when he tasted it, he would not
drink it. 35And when they had crucified him, they divided his clothes
among themselves by casting lots; 36then they sat down there and kept
watch over him. 37Over his head they put the charge against him, which
read, "This is Jesus, the King of the Jews."

38Then two bandits were crucified with him, one on his right and one
on his left. 39Those who passed by derided him, shaking their heads 40and
saying, "You who would destroy the temple and build it in three days,
save yourself! If you are the Son of God, come down from the cross." 41In
the same way the chief priests also, along with the scribes and elders,
were mocking him, saying, 42"He saved others; he cannot save himself. He
is the King of Israel; let him come down from the cross now, and we will
believe in him. 43He trusts in God; let God deliver him now, if he wants

to; for he said, 'I am God's Son.'" [44]The bandits who were crucified with him also taunted him in the same way.

45From noon on, darkness came over the whole land until three in the afternoon. [46]And about three o'clock Jesus cried with a loud voice, "Eli, Eli, lama sabachthani?" that is, "My God, my God, why have you forsaken me?" [47]When some of the bystanders heard it, they said, "This man is calling for Elijah." [48]At once one of them ran and got a sponge, filled it with sour wine, put it on a stick, and gave it to him to drink. [49]But the others said, "Wait, let us see whether Elijah will come to save him." [50]Then Jesus cried again with a loud voice and breathed his last.[51]At that moment the curtain of the temple was torn in two, from top to bottom. The earth shook, and the rocks were split. [52]The tombs also were opened, and many bodies of the saints who had fallen asleep were raised. [53]After his resurrection they came out of the tombs and entered the holy city and appeared to many. [54]Now when the centurion and those with him, who were keeping watch over Jesus, saw the earthquake and what took place, they were terrified and said, "Truly this man was God's Son!"

55Many women were also there, looking on from a distance; they had followed Jesus from Galilee and had provided for him. [56]Among them were Mary Magdalene, and Mary the mother of James and Joseph, and the mother of the sons of Zebedee.

Luke 23

26As they led him away, they seized a man, Simon of Cyrene, who was coming from the country, and they laid the cross on him, and made him carry it behind Jesus. [27]A great number of the people followed him, and among them were women who were beating their breasts and wailing for him. [28]But Jesus turned to them and said, "Daughters of Jerusalem, do not weep for me, but weep for yourselves and for your children. [29]For the days are surely coming when they will say, 'Blessed are the barren, and the wombs that never bore, and the breasts that never nursed.' [30]Then they will begin to say to the mountains, 'Fall on us'; and to the hills, 'Cover us.' [31]For if they do this when the wood is green, what will happen when it is dry?"

32Two others also, who were criminals, were led away to be put to death with him. [33]When they came to the place that is called The Skull, they crucified Jesus there with the criminals, one on his right and one on his left. [34]Then Jesus said, "Father, forgive them; for they do not know what they are doing." And they cast lots to divide his clothing. [35]And the people stood by, watching; but the leaders scoffed at him, saying, "He saved others; let him save himself if he is the Messiah of God, his chosen one!" [36]The soldiers also mocked him, coming up and offering him sour

wine, 37and saying, “If you are the King of the Jews, save yourself!”
38There was also an inscription over him, “This is the King of the Jews.”

39One of the criminals who were hanged there kept deriding him and
saying, “Are you not the Messiah? Save yourself and us!” 40But the other
rebuked him, saying, “Do you not fear God, since you are under the
same sentence of condemnation? 41And we indeed have been condemned
justly, for we are getting what we deserve for our deeds, but this man has
done nothing wrong.” 42Then he said, “Jesus, remember me when you
come into your kingdom.” 43He replied, “Truly I tell you, today you will
be with me in Paradise.”

44It was now about noon, and darkness came over the whole land
until three in the afternoon, 45while the sun’s light failed; and the curtain
of the temple was torn in two. 46Then Jesus, crying with a loud voice, said,
“Father, into your hands I commend my spirit.” Having said this, he
breathed his last. 47When the centurion saw what had taken place, he
praised God and said, “Certainly this man was innocent.” 48And when all
the crowds who had gathered there for this spectacle saw what had taken
place, they returned home, beating their breasts. 49But all his acquain-
tances, including the women who had followed him from Galilee, stood
at a distance, watching these things.

John 19

So they took Jesus; 17and carrying the cross by himself, he went out to
what is called The Place of the Skull, which in Hebrew is called
Golgotha. 18There they crucified him, and with him two others, one on
either side, with Jesus between them. 19Pilate also had an inscription written and put on the cross. It read, “Jesus of Nazareth, the King of the
Jews.” 20Many of the Jews read this inscription, because the place where
Jesus was crucified was near the city; and it was written in Hebrew, in
Latin, and in Greek. 21Then the chief priests of the Jews said to Pilate,
“Do not write, ‘The King of the Jews’, but, ‘This man said, I am King of
the Jews.’” 22Pilate answered, “What I have written I have written.”
23When the soldiers had crucified Jesus, they took his clothes and divided
them into four parts, one for each soldier. They also took his tunic; now
the tunic was seamless, woven in one piece from the top. 24So they said to
one another, “Let us not tear it, but cast lots for it to see who will get it.”
This was to fulfil what the scripture says,

“They divided my clothes among themselves,
and for my clothing they cast lots.”

25And that is what the soldiers did.

Meanwhile, standing near the cross of Jesus were his mother, and his
mother’s sister, Mary the wife of Clopas, and Mary Magdalene. 26When

Jesus saw his mother and the disciple whom he loved standing beside her,
he said to his mother, “Woman, here is your son.” 27Then he said to the
disciple, “Here is your mother.” And from that hour the disciple took her
into his own home.
28After this, when Jesus knew that all was now finished, he said (in
order to fulfil the scripture), “I am thirsty.” 29A jar full of sour wine was
standing there. So they put a sponge full of the wine on a branch of hys-
sop and held it to his mouth. 30When Jesus had received the wine, he said,
“It is finished.” Then he bowed his head and gave up his spirit.
31Since it was the day of Preparation, the Jews did not want the bodies left on the cross during the sabbath, especially because that sabbath
was a day of great solemnity. So they asked Pilate to have the legs of the
crucified men broken and the bodies removed. 32Then the soldiers came
and broke the legs of the first and of the other who had been crucified
with him. 33But when they came to Jesus and saw that he was already
dead, they did not break his legs. 34Instead, one of the soldiers pierced his
side with a spear, and at once blood and water came out. 35(He who saw
this has testified so that you also may believe. His testimony is true, and
he knows that he tells the truth.) 36These things occurred so that the
scripture might be fulfilled, “None of his bones shall be broken.” 37And
again another passage of scripture says, “They will look on the one
whom they have pierced.”

Introduction: The medical cause of Jesus’ death

There is a vast amount of learned literature that speculates on what finally caused Jesus’ death (if indeed he did die on the cross). That literature is not directly relevant to this enquiry. This is a book looking at whether Jesus was raised bodily from the dead. The important issue at this stage is simply whether or not he did die on the cross. If he did, it doesn’t matter much what medical label a pathologist would use to describe how it happened. It is sometimes said that the medical route to death is relevant because it may corroborate or contradict some of the recorded behaviour of Jesus. If death was by asphyxiation, for instance, is it probable that he would have said as much from the cross as Luke records him as saying? Both X and Y think that this is trying to make bricks with no evidential straw at all. But so that people can make up their own minds about this, the evidence about the various possible causes of death is summarised in Appendix 1.

Part 1: X

> There were two next-door neighbours. One had a rabbit, one had a dog. One day the dog owner was horrified to see the dog run into his house with the rabbit, stone dead, in his jaws. He took the rabbit from the dog, washed the blood off it, dried it with the hairdryer and then, the next night, crept out and put the rabbit back in its hutch.
>
> The following week the neighbours were talking over the fence. "What sort of week have you had?" asked the dog owner. "Rather strange," said the former rabbit owner; "The rabbit died. We gave it a funeral for the sake of the children; prayers and all, and then some really sick person dug it up and put it back in its hutch."
>
> Story told by Charlie Mackesy

There are three possibilities here: that Jesus wasn't crucified at all; that he was crucified but didn't die; or that he was crucified and did die. I don't spend time on the third of these possibilities, other than to say that of course it is a possibility.

There are trends in biblical scholarship just as there are trends in shoes: I have to acknowledge that although it used to be fashionable to contend that Jesus survived the cross, there are now no mainstream biblical scholars who contend for this. But there are plenty of popular writers who do. The station bookstalls are full of paperback speculation about it. Those theses therefore need an airing.

But before we move on to try to evaluate the evidence, we need to ask whether the quality of the evidence put forward allows us to say anything at all about the circumstances of Jesus' death. If the evidence isn't up to the job the only intellectually reputable conclusion is an open verdict – a conclusion that says: "He might have been crucified. Or he might not have been. We don't know."

The unreliability of the basic sources

The way that the narratives are told[1]

Look at the way that the crucifixion narratives are told. Everyone agrees that Mark changes style when he gets to the Passion. Until then he is in staccato mode, telling one cracking yarn after another, not bothered about smoothing over the space between them. For decades this has been euphemised as the "string of pearls". But the string vanishes when we get to the arrest of Jesus. After that the abrupt Mark becomes smooth and felicitous. Why? Because Mark the reporter had become Mark the fiction writer, Mark the myth-maker. There were no pearls to string together. Mark could, and did, make it all up. It is smooth because he didn't have to accommodate any lumpy facts. He had a good template, though. For ages a traditional form of Jewish tale had been circulating, the story of the Suffering and Vindication of the Innocent Righteous One. If Mark thought sincerely (as he no doubt did) that Jesus was innocent and righteous and that his apparently failed Messiahship bid fitted in some way the role of the suffering servant, how better to honour his memory and make his audience reflect on Jesus' life than to make his death fit that pattern?

Mark wasn't alone in changing his style when he came to the passion. John has been dramatically different from the other gospel writers up to then. He has been more reflective, more philosophical, more cryptic. But in the passion story he is very like Mark – who is clearly his literary inferior. He doesn't abandon his literary creativity, though. Note how cunningly he splits Peter's denial into two parts with the interrogation sandwiched between. It is a splendid, if rather obvious, literary device.

Lack of agreement on the date

One would expect the gospels, if they are telling the truth, at least to be able to agree about the day when Jesus died. They appear to think that the death of Jesus was the most important day in the history of the universe. Wouldn't the date be tattooed indelibly on the subconscious of everyone who cared? The authorities even helped to make it memorable by executing Jesus (according to all the gospels) on a day very close to a major Jewish holiday. But John disagrees with the others about the day. He puts it on Passover Eve and Sabbath Eve. The others say that it was on Sabbath Eve too, but claim that it was already the first day of Passover. John is plainly making a theological point: he wants everyone to know that Jesus is the Passover lamb. You can't trust a man who is prepared to play so fast and so loose with the truth.

Where John is alone

Several of the incidental details, so beloved of apologists and sermonisers, appear only in the account of the discredited John. The three most important are the spear thrust, the famous flow of blood and water, and the business of leg-breaking (Jesus, alone of the victims that day, didn't have his legs broken). It is not a point to be developed here, but cast doubt on these three details, as we have to, and you have diminished significantly the medical evidence relied on by those like Y who say that Jesus was plainly dead when he was taken down from the cross.

How many independent witnesses are there?

The main elements of Matthew and Luke are plainly lifted straight from Mark. There's nothing wrong with using secondary sources, but Y really mustn't pretend that he has four independent witnesses. Y has tried to dodge the damaging observation that the gospels were written well into the second half of the first century by asserting that the gospel writers were drawing on an old, consistent and living tradition. Well, Matthew's and Luke's dependence on Mark suggests that they had no independent tradition of the Passion in their own communities.

Mark, Matthew and Luke don't speak with one voice about everything, though. Far from it. While using Mark as the basic template, Matthew and Luke feel free to exercise their own theological hobby horses. That freedom disqualifies them as serious witnesses. An example: Mark's Jesus says nothing to the men crucified with him, and they too are silent. Matthew's Jesus is taunted by them. In Luke the thieves are positively chatty, and Jesus tells the polite and repentant one (and of course Luke's audience) that remembering Jesus is a key to heaven. It's a sermon, and it is obviously Luke's sermon, not Jesus'.

Theology, not history

Speaking of sermons, there is a plainly unhistorical tendency in all the gospel writers to make theological points. The stories get more elaborate as we move from Mark to the more recent accounts, but even Mark can't resist a tantalising metaphor. When Jesus died, he says, the veil of the temple was torn in two from the top to the bottom. There's not a word about this in any Jewish or secular chronicle of the time, and it is plainly not history.

Mark's theological point is obvious. The curtain separated the Holy of Holies (the special dwelling place of Jahveh, entered only once a year, and then only by the high priest) from the rest of the Temple. Tear it down and anyone can approach the Almighty directly. Mark is saying that you don't need priests to get to God.

You have direct access because of what Jesus has done. And note where the initiative comes from: the rip is from the top down. God takes the initiative. It is a ready-made sermon and has been dutifully recycled every Sunday for the last couple of thousand years. Matthew and Luke obediently copy it down. But note this: Mark does not flag it up as theology; he tells it in the same voice as he talks about the vinegar on the sponge. We are meant to think of it as history. And that, for anyone scratching through these stories trying to sift the historical wheat from the theological chaff, is very worrying.

John's crucifixion account is straight from and for the pulpit. He makes a point of mentioning that Jesus' legs were not broken[2] and his side was pierced.[3] This is not merely an incidental detail – something he has just remembered that he thinks people might be mildly interested in. John is unusually terse when it comes to the passion. No: he wants his readers to think back to the Old Testament and conclude that Jesus is the Passover Lamb. To be fair to John, he is quite blatant about it: these things happened, he said, so that scripture might be fulfilled.[4]

Matthew does it too, but he goes rather too far and plays straight into the hands of any anti-Christian advocate. He gives us an earthquake.[5] It seems to be quite a significant earthquake. So significant, in fact, that rocks are split, tombs are opened, and something quite dramatic happens, which we'll come to in a moment. But none of the other gospel writers apparently noted it, or, if they did, they apparently didn't think it was worth mentioning.

What happens then? Well, "the tombs were opened" (what, all the tombs in Jerusalem? And if not which ones?) and many bodies of "the saints who had fallen asleep", were raised.[6] They don't do anything for a while, it seems. Having been "raised" they just lie there until the resurrection, at which point they come out of their tombs, wander round Jerusalem, and appear to many.[7] There's not a word outside Matthew, needless to say, about this massive invasion of the dead. We're not told what happens to them. Presumably after this rather selfish but symbolically important disturbance of their sleep they just go obediently back and tuck themselves up in their graves to wait for the real resurrection at the end of time. It is too easy to mock, but the mockery makes a serious point. Here we are plainly in the realm of fable, not fact.

There is so much theologising in all the gospels that we are far safer to think of them as theology historicised than as history theologised.

No corroboration

Apart from the secular sources (Tacitus, Josephus, etc.) mentioned in Chapter 2 (who could well simply be reporting what the Christians believed happened, not what actually happened), there's no corroboration of the gospel accounts. Calvary isn't mentioned once in the canonical books outside the gospels. For a church that is said to have been founded on the death of Jesus, that's odd. The gospel accounts are so seriously dubious that we simply can't know what, if anything, happened on that hill sometime around Passover in AD 30. Certainty clearly isn't possible: nor is any sort of finding. The best we can do is shrug doubtfully.

The possibility that Jesus wasn't crucified

This possibility has some powerful proponents. The Koran, talking about the Jews, says:

> They denied the truth and uttered a monstrous falsehood against Mary. They declared: "We have put to death the Messiah, Jesus the son of Mary, the apostle of God." They did not kill him, nor did they crucify him, but they thought they did: [He was made to resemble another for them]. Those that disagreed about him were in doubt concerning him; they knew nothing about him that was not sheer conjecture; they did not slay him for certain. God lifted him up to Him; God is mighty and wise. There is none among the People of the Book but will believe in him before his death; and on the Day of Resurrection he will bear witness against them...[8]

Many Muslims, too, believe the account given in the Gospel of Barnabas.[9] This says that Judas looked very like Jesus and was crucified instead of him.[10]

Related theses have been promulgated widely, notably in *The Holy Blood and the Holy Grail*[11], a book on which Dan Brown drew when writing *The Da Vinci Code*. The suggestion there is that the crucifixion was a private affair. John notes that "...in the place where [Jesus] was crucified there was a garden, and in the garden a new sepulchre in which no one had yet been buried."[12] All the gospels agree that the crucifixion was rather rushed. To avoid offending

Jewish law the bodies had to be down and buried or otherwise dealt with before dusk. The sepulchre in which John says that Jesus was buried belonged of course to Joseph of Arimathea. If the tomb was his, the argument goes, he at least had some control over the garden and what happened in it. In short, he could play tricks with the crucifixion. Here is what *The Holy Blood* said happened:

> ...[Jesus] would seem to have had friends in high places; and these friends, working in collusion with a corrupt, easily bribed Roman Procurator, appear to have engineered a mock crucifixion – on private grounds, inaccessible to all but a select few. With the general populace kept at a convenient distance, an execution was then staged – in which a substitute took [Jesus'] place on the cross, or in which [Jesus] himself did not actually die. Towards dusk – which would have further impeded visibility – a "body" was removed to an opportunely adjacent tomb, from which, a day or two later, it "miraculously" disappeared...[13]

It is acknowledged that there are a number of difficulties with this theory. Scholars have not smiled on it. But every look at this issue is a look through a 2000-year-old prism. That prism is bound to have been scratched and distorted by the years.

If Jesus was not crucified, what happened to him? That issue is dealt with in the next section.

The possibility that Jesus was crucified but did not die

A plausible conspiracy theory

It is distinctly possible that Jesus didn't die. There are some suspect features in the stories. We are told that Pilate, the man in overall charge, didn't want Jesus dead.[14] And nor did Pilate's wife. She made quite a scene about it.[15] The power of a forceful wife should never be underestimated.

There was a real bond between Pilate and Jesus at the trial. Any reader can feel the electricity between them. Pilate was convinced of his innocence, and made an ostentatious display of renouncing responsibility for his death, calling for a bowl and washing his hands. That has all the hallmarks of a man who protests a bit too much. If you say, as loudly as he did: "This man's death isn't my fault", it implies strongly that you know that it really is. Pilate knew that he had the power to release Jesus. He said so explicitly.[16]

Perhaps he used that power. There was a way to placate Jewish demands and his own conscience: let Jesus be crucified and apparently killed. But actually spare him death.

Or perhaps Joseph of Arimathea was the orchestrator of the plot, with or without Pilate knowing what the whole plan was?[17] Certainly, whoever the ringleader was, Joseph (assuming he existed) was fairly close to the centre of the conspiracy. It would have been easy enough for him, without reference to Pilate, to fix the apparent death of Jesus and his hurried removal. A few shekels to the soldiers responsible for the crucifixion might have worked wonders. We will deal with Joseph's motives in the next chapter.

Several small points in the stories hint strongly that we are dealing here with a fairly sophisticated plot. First: the "sour wine" (or "vinegar") on the sponge. Second: the speed with which Jesus died. Third: the fact that Jesus' legs were not broken. And fourth (although it is a point that belongs to the "Burial" chapter), the fact that Pilate was happy to hand over Jesus' body to Joseph of Arimathea. All but point four are looked at below.

Did anyone survive crucifixion?

First, though, something needs to be said about the intrinsic possibility of surviving crucifixion. People sometimes did survive. Here is Josephus:

> ...when I was sent by Titus Caesar...to a certain village called Thecoa...as I came back I saw many captives crucified, and remembered three of them as my former acquaintance. I was very sorry at this in my mind, and went with tears in my eyes to Titus, and told him of them; so he immediately commanded them to be taken down, and to have the greatest care taken of them, in order to achieve their recovery; yet two of them died under the physician's hands, while the third recovered.[18]

The mechanics of crucifixion

Christian apologists are fond of referring, whenever the possibility of survival is mentioned, to the dreadful wounds associated with crucifixion. Although the hands and feet were indeed commonly nailed, this was not always so.

In 1968 some building contractors were working in Giv'at ha-Mivtar, one of Jerusalem's northern suburbs. They found a Jewish tomb from the first century AD. There was nothing unusual about this: tombs like that are two a penny in Jerusalem. But there was something unique inside. In a stone ossuary (a bone box) were the remains of a man in his twenties. We know his name from the inscription on the ossuary: “Jehonanan the son of HGQWL.” He had been crucified. His right calcaneum (heel bone) was pierced by an iron nail 11.5 cm long. See Fig 5. The nail had evidently hit a knot in the wood of the cross and bent over, making it impossible to withdraw the nail from the heel when Jehonanan was taken down from the cross.

The find was originally reported by Haas, who said that both legs were fixed with one nail, and that both forearms had also been nailed.[19] These conclusions have been widely reported and continue to appear in some modern books. A later examination by Zias and Sekeles, however, showed that both these findings were wrong.[20] There were two nails fixing the feet. The legs were astride the vertical beam and the ankles had been nailed individually to the side. The forearms had not been nailed at all. Presumably Jehonanan’s arms had been tied in place. Tying is known to have been common.[21] A speculative reconstruction is shown at Fig 6.

There is no reason to suppose that crucifixion practices were uniform across the Roman Empire. They may well have varied according to the resources available, the number of victims who had to be crucified, and the sadistic imaginations of the soldiers responsible. But Jehonanan indicates that it does not follow that Jesus, even if he was crucified, was necessarily nailed to the cross, at least by his hands. The gospels, in those passages dealing with the crucifixion, don’t tell us: they simply say that he was crucified. The only mention of wounds in the hands and the feet comes from stories of the risen Jesus. And by then we’re in plainly mythological territory.

If we are to wander in mythological territory, as we must do later, it is as well to point out that the only two writers who mention the post-resurrection wounds are Luke[22] and John.[23] Both of them talk about wounds in the hands (Greek *keiras*). We happen to know that, despite its popularity with Christian artists down the centuries, nailing through the hands couldn’t have happened. Experimental studies using corpses indicate that if you nail a body through the palms the weight of the body pulls the nail through.[24] Luke and John are caught out by modern research.

Before we leave the post-resurrection observations of Luke and John it is worth noting that, although both mention hand wounds, only Luke mentions foot wounds. John, in addition to hand wounds, is interested only in the wound in Jesus' side. If a wound in the side was present, Luke doesn't consider it worth even a word.

Putting this together, we know nothing at all about the mechanics of Jesus' crucifixion. We do not know, for instance, if his cross had a *sedile* – a small seat sometimes used by the Romans. This prolonged death by allowing the victim to get some respite from the respiratory compromise caused by the hanging position. We do not know if his cross was a low T-shaped Tau cross (although this was in vogue in Palestine at the material time), or a taller Latin cross (as appears in most later depictions). We do not know if there was any standard procedure for spearing the side of a crucifixion victim. All these uncertainties are problems for anyone trying to contend that there is real evidence for the Christian version of events.

Was the "vinegar" all it seemed?

First the suspicion: look at the following passages side by side:

> Mark: "…At three o'clock Jesus cried out with a loud voice, 'Eloi, Eloi, lama sabachthani?', which means 'My God, my God, why have you forsaken me?' When some of the bystanders heard it they said, 'Listen, he is calling for Elijah.' And someone ran, filled a sponge with sour wine, put it on a stick, and gave it to him to drink, saying: 'Wait, let us see whether Elijah will come to take him down.' Then Jesus gave a loud cry and breathed his last." [25]

> Matthew: "From noon on, darkness came over the whole land until three in the afternoon. And about three o'clock Jesus cried with a loud voice, 'Eli, Eli, lama sabacthani?', that is, 'My God, my God, why have you forsaken me?' When some of the bystanders heard it, they said, 'This man is calling for Elijah'. At once one of them ran and got a sponge, filled it with sour wine, put it on a stick, and gave it to him to drink. But the others said, 'Wait, let us see whether Elijah will come to save him'. Then Jesus cried again with a loud voice and breathed his last."[26]

> John: "…when Jesus knew that all was now finished, he said (in order to fulfil the scripture: 'I am thirsty'. A jar full of sour wine was standing there. So they put a sponge full of the wine on a branch of hyssop and held it to his mouth. When Jesus had received the wine, he said, 'It is finished'. Then he bowed his head and gave up his spirit."[27]

(Luke does not deal with the "vinegar".)

The most obvious point is that Jesus appears to die immediately after he is given the "sour wine". Despite the rigours of crucifixion he is, until immediately before his death, capable, according to Mark and Matthew, of crying out with a loud voice – hardly compatible with a man at the end of his physiological tether and about to be catapulted into eternity by asphyxiation, haemorrhage, shock or any of the other mooted causes of death. Perhaps he wasn't treated quite as badly as all that? Perhaps someone wanted him to survive? It is interesting, too, that Jesus appears to dictate the time of being given the wine, and therefore of his death. He is a man in control. And finally: what is that mysterious "jar full of sour wine" doing there, along with the means for giving it to a man lifted several feet off the ground?

A suspicious mind begins to think that there is a connection between the apparent death and the substance administered immediately before it. And the obvious pharmacological candidate is opium.[28]

Opium has been known since antiquity in the eastern Mediterranean.[29] Though Jewish communities were more coy about its use than Hellenistic ones, there is no doubt that it was used in the Holy Land at the time of Jesus.[30] The opium poppy was depicted on King Herod's coinage in honour of the cults of Demeter and Kore at Samaria[31], and gas chromatography has demonstrated opium in Late-Bronze-age juglets from Palestine.[32]

It would be perfect for a job like this. It can be given orally, as opiates still are in modern medicine. It is a potent, fast-acting hypnotic and analgesic. It slows the respiratory rate, which is just what you would want if you needed to feign death. It has a short half-life, which means that it would wear off quickly: the patient, after the necessary medical attention, could soon be walking again. Perhaps some of the hurry to get Jesus to the tomb was a pharmacokinetically intelligent worry about him waking up, rather than a pious Jewish fear of violating the sabbath.

There is a non-chemical possibility too, suggested in some of the "Jesus in Asia" literature, discussed below. Jesus was, by any standards, a mystical, charismatic, remarkable man. He may, it is thought by some, have been a practitioner of deep Samadhi, or Nirodha. This is an advanced type of meditation which results in a general slowing of the metabolic rate. The heart can slow almost to a stop, breathing is imperceptible, and the body temperature falls to well below normal. The subject can look dead. Indeed, Buddhist writings cite several examples of villagers finding yogis in states of Nirodha, assuming they were dead, and actually getting to the stage of lighting their funeral pyres before the yogi woke up.[33]

The speed with which Jesus died

It was common for men to spend days on the cross before dying. Yet the speed of Jesus' death takes everyone by surprise. Pilate is specifically recorded as being surprised – so much so that he asks the centurion if it was really true that Jesus was already dead.[34] In the light of what we have seen we might begin to wonder whether he was really so surprised. In any event, he shows an odd intensity of interest in this obscure Galilean preacher. Pilate was responsible for thousands of deaths. Why bother even to ask the question about this man?

In assessing how premature Jesus' death was, we have two controls: the men who were crucified at the same time as Jesus. Jesus died before either of them; they had to have their legs broken. Yet they were presumably subjected to the same pre-crucifixion abuses as Jesus. Flogging was routine.

Jesus appears to have been in reasonable physical condition before his crucifixion. He was a great walker. Only days before he had made the long journey on foot from Galilee – a good week's walk to the north. To die so quickly was right out of physiological character.

Why were Jesus' legs not broken?

Breaking the legs of crucified victims to speed their death was a well documented practice. It even had its own technical Latin term: *crucifragium*. It probably hastened death either by releasing fat emboli into the circulation, or by reducing the ability of the victim to push up from the feet – so resulting in more rapid asphyxiation. It was the fate of the two controls.

Christian apologists are fond of saying that the soldiers responsible for the crucifixion would themselves have lost their lives if they had made a mistake and taken down a still-live Jesus. Of course, if Pilate was in on the plot to any degree, they were perfectly safe. And even if he wasn't, money talks. If they were genuinely concerned only with ensuring Jesus' death, why not go through with the *crucifragium*? It was the standard technique, and didn't require much more effort than poking Jesus with a spear.

If you wanted Jesus alive, of course, it was particularly important to avoid broken legs. He needed to be mobile quickly – to be spirited away to whatever convalescence was planned.

Piercing the side

This could have happened, and, as discussed in Appendix 1 on the cause of death, the apparent issue of blood and water might indeed have indicated death. Certainly, if the pericardium was pierced, death would result. And even if the pericardium was not pierced, but the chest wall was, a dangerous pneumothorax would be likely to result. If the abdominal rather than the thoracic cavity was pierced, again, this did not bode well for long-term survival.

But it is by no means clear that the body was pierced. It is mentioned only by John. He may have meant something cryptically theological by the flow of blood and water. Suggestions that the side was routinely pierced by Roman soldiers find little support in the literature. The evidence about this has been well summarised:

> The postmortem nature of the side wound also exactly parallels the biblical account, and again there is no historical mention of a practice of this or any method of coup de grace during crucifixion, other than the crucifragium in Palestine. Bulst (1957:121) interprets an ambiguous phrase in Quintilian (1st century) as suggesting that piercing the corpse may have preceded its release for burial. However, an exhaustive search by Vignon (1939) and Wuenschel (1953) turned up only one slightly dubious reference to such a practice: the martyrs Marcellus and Marcellinus were dispatched with a spear during their crucifixion ca. 290 because their constant praising of God annoyed the sentries. In this instance, as in that of Christ, the spearing appears as a spontaneous act by the guards. One might conclude that similar transfixions may have occurred occasionally, were it not for the universal attitude in the early church toward the issuance of blood and water from Christ's side. Christian apologists of the 2nd and 3rd centuries – a period of frequent crucifixions – believed the flow to be a miracle. Origen, who had witnessed crucifixion, could write: "I know well that neither blood nor water flows from a corpse, but in the case of Jesus it was miraculous." Certainly such a belief could not have prevailed if piercing the corpse sub alas had been other than a very rare happening indeed.[35]

If Jesus survived, what happened to him?

We have to be careful not to fall into the same trap that the Christians blunder into whenever they deign to enter a historical debate – wild, unevidenced speculation. But a few things can be said.

First: whoever was responsible for helping him survive would want him off the scene as soon as possible. Jerusalem, and indeed Palestine, was no place for him. His career as an aspirant Palestinian Messiah was over.

Second: there are some ancient traditions that suggest that Jesus might have been seen after the crucifixion, far from the Holy Land.

The post-crucifixion Jesus in Islam

The Koran says: "We made the son of Mary and his mother a sign to mankind, and gave them shelter on a peaceful hill-side watered by a fresh spring."[36]

This sounds like a permanent arrangement. It sounds like a retirement refuge.

Did Jesus go to India?[37]

There are many traditions of Jesus in Syria, Turkey, Iran and Afghanistan.[38] Mir Muhammed bin Khawand Shah Ibn-i-Mohammed, for example, wrote in 1417 that Jesus, his mother, Mary, and a man called Thomas went from Jerusalem to Nisibis (Nasibain), near Urfa in southeast Turkey.[39]

The Jesus figure in these stories is commonly known as Yuz Asaf. And strangely persistent in the tales is the idea that he arrived and settled in Kashmir. Some of these traditions are old.[40] Mullah Nadri, writing in 1420, summarised them.[41] The most interesting and evidentially significant part of his summary is his mention of the inscriptions on the so-called Throne of Solomon in Srinagar. These are dealt with below.

The traditions about Jesus' trek across Asia were collected in the nineteenth century by Hazrat Mirza Ghulam Ahmad, who founded the Ahmadiyya. He wrote them down in his book *Jesus in India*.[42] The Ahmadiyya are regarded by orthodox Muslims as a heretical sect of Islam. It is accepted that the claims of the Ahmadiyya and those of others who think that Yuz Asaf was the historical Jesus have not had a polite reception from Western scholars. But there are some pieces of hard evidence that suggest that the legend should be taken seriously.[43]

Some believe that Yuz Asaf is buried in the old Khaniyar quarter of Srinagar, Kashmir. The tomb is known as the Rozabal – the "sacred tomb."[44] Fig 11. It attracts hundreds of pilgrims annually from the Muslim, Hindu, Buddhist and Christian faiths. The date of the tomb is unknown. Some say that the tomb was at one stage painted the quintessentially Jewish colours of blue and white, and that the casket of Yuz Asaf inside is oriented in the way that Jewish bodies are oriented. But there is something even more strange. For many years the wax from devotional candles covered the floor next to Yuz Asaf's tomb. When it was scraped off it was seen that there were two footprints carved into the stone. see Fig 12. There were marks on each foot consistent with their being crucifixion marks.

Dating the advent of Yuz Asaf in India by reference to the documents is difficult. But there are two pieces of evidence that might help. Near the Dal Lake in Srinagar is a temple called The Takhat Sulaiman (Throne of Solomon). Inscriptions on this monument (now illegible) apparently used to read:

> (a) " The mason of this pillar is Bhisti Zargar year 54" and (b) " Khawaja Rukun son of Mirjan erected this pillar. During this period Yusu Asaph declared his ministry. He was Yusu, the Prophet of the Children of Israel."

Year 54 according to which calendar? We don't know; Mullah Nadri, writing in 1420, might be able to help. He puts the repairs to the temple as in the reign of Rajah Gopadatta. Gopadatta's dates are thought to be AD 79–109, from which some have maintained that this makes Year 54 AD 78 .[45] Others say AD 107.[46]

Some believe, too, that Jesus makes an appearance in the ancient Hindu writings, the Bhavishya Maha Purana – thought to have been written about AD 115. If the Bhavishya does indeed refer to Jesus, and is original, then Jesus has arrived in India at a historically credible time. "Jesus" has a conversation with King Shalivahan, who is thought to have reigned from AD 39–50. The Bhavishya says this:

> ...One day, Shalivahan, the chief of the Sakyas, went into the Himalayas. There, in the Land of the Hun (Ladakh, a part of the Kushan empire), the powerful king saw a man sitting on a mountain, who seemed to promise auspiciousness. His skin was fair and he wore white garments.
>
> The king asked the holy man who he was. The other replied: "I am

> called a son of God, born of a virgin, minister of the non-believers, relentless in search of the truth." The king then asked him: "What is your religion?" The other replied, "O great king, I come from a foreign country, where there is no longer truth and where evil knows no bounds. In the land of the non-believers, I appeared as the Messiah. But the demon Ihamasi of the barbarians (dasyu) manifested herself in a terrible form; I was delivered unto her in the manner of the non-believers and ended in Ihamasi's realm."[47]

In the following passage the Jesus-figure outlines his religious beliefs, and calls himself "Isa-Masih", which some have seen as "Jesus, Messiah". "Isa" is Arabic for Jesus.

All this is woolly, true. But it raises a suspicion that cannot simply be dismissed.

Did Jesus become Apollonius of Tyana?

Apollonius was a charismatic teacher and miracle worker who wandered widely throughout the eastern Mediterranean and to India in the first century. He was said to have been born at around the start of the common era, and to have died in AD 97. His biography was written hagiographically by the Athenian Sophist Philostratus.[48]

It has commonly been suggested that Apollonius was really Jesus. Philostratus describes a man with many of Jesus' characteristics: he brought back to life, for instance, a girl who had recently died – one of Jesus' most notorious miracles.[49] A Greek pseudonym would be helpful in travelling unscathed around the Roman world after his escape from crucifixion, and, as so often, the Christians generate suspicion by being over protective about Jesus. Eusebius, the Christian Bishop of Caesarea, rather hysterically denounced Apollonius, or rather people who were comparing Apollonius and Jesus.[50] Why should he have needed to be so vocal in his denunciation if the comparison was not a dangerously good one?

The curious business of Irenaeus

Irenaeus (c. AD 130–200) was a scourge of the Gnostics and a bulwark of Christian orthodoxy. His main work, forbiddingly called *Against Heresies*, is a rollicking defence of the traditional Christian position. And yet right in the middle of it is a characteristically strident denunciation of those who believe that Jesus was just 30 years old when he died. He was at least 50, screams Irenaeus, and it is nigh on blasphemous to say otherwise. Now that is strange, but here is the really interesting thing: "On completing His thirtieth year", says Irenaeus, "He suffered, being in fact still a young man, and who had by no means attained to advanced age."[51] Now what is the natural meaning of that? The obvious answer is that he was crucified at the age of 30 (as the rest of the evidence about crucifixion suggests that he was), but somehow survived until the age of 50.

Was Jesus at Masada?

In AD 73 the hilltop fortress of Masada, in the Judean desert by the Dead Sea, the last stand of the Jewish zealots, fell to the besieging Roman army. Most of its defenders committed suicide rather than fall into Roman hands. But was Jesus there, perhaps playing a part as a nationalist Messiah? The Australian journalist Donovan Joyce thinks that there is evidence that he was.[52]

That evidence, he says, is or was written in Aramaic on a 3 to 4 metre long parchment scroll, shown to Joyce in the gents' toilet at Tel Aviv airport by a "Professor Max Grosset". The "professor" was acting under a false name, and offered Joyce $5,000 to smuggle it out of Israel. Joyce refused. The "professor" had already translated the scroll, and told Joyce what it said. The scroll had supposedly been written the night before the fall of Masada by an 80-year-old writer calling himself "Jesus of Kinneret, son of Jakob". "Jesus" said that he was the last surviving heir of the Hasmonean throne of Israel.

Joyce contends that Jesus was indeed descended from the Maccabees and married to Mary Magdalene. Having survived the crucifixion, he went to live in the Essene community at Qumran, where he stayed until the community went off to Masada to stand in the line along with the last remnant of Jewish resistance.

The thesis has had little recent attention, and never any scholarly approval. *The Holy Blood and the Holy Grail* thinks it "intriguing and persuasive".[53] And it is not wholly incredible. Jesus and the Essenes were natural allies, and remote, ascetic Qumran would have been a good place for a wounded refugee to hole up. The gospels clearly indicate that Jesus thought of himself as some sort of Messiah figure: it is not hard to read his statements about himself in the canonical gospels as assertions that he had come to usher in the new Maccabean kingdom.

Conclusion

There are lots of perfectly arguable alternatives to the notion that Jesus died on the cross. Some of those alternatives have the imprimatur of great antiquity and multiple, apparently independent testimony. And let's not forget that the best witnesses against the resurrection are the gospel writers themselves. If they are right when they talk about the post-mortem appearances of Jesus, overwhelmingly the most likely explanation is that he was alive because he had never been dead.

Part 2: Y

> Marley was dead: to begin with. There is no doubt whatever about that. The register of his burial was signed by the clergyman, the clerk, the undertaker, and the chief mourner... There is no doubt that Marley was dead. This must be distinctly understood, or nothing wonderful can come of the story I am going to relate. If we were not perfectly convinced that Hamlet's Father died before the play began, there would be nothing more remarkable in his taking a stroll at night, in an easterly wind, upon his own ramparts, than there would be in any other middle-aged gentleman rashly turning out after dark in a breezy spot – say Saint Paul's Churchyard for instance – literally to astonish his son's weak mind.
>
> Charles Dickens, *A Christmas Carol*

It is worth noting just how isolated X is. All the high priests of agnosticism have abandoned him.

X contends that the Christian account of the post-resurrection appearances should be rejected. One of the main reasons for saying this is that it is hugely more probable that a man didn't rise from the dead than that he did. This is a good argument. Its force has already been acknowledged, and it will be acknowledged again later. But this type of argument cuts both ways. And it cuts the ground from under X's feet in this chapter. The Christians, in this chapter, are the stern rationalists. X will quite properly try to mock Christianity out of court later, but what is sauce for the materialist goose is sauce for the Christological gander. Accordingly: if you believe X's contentions in this chapter, you'll believe anything.

The unreliability of the basic sources

The notion that there simply isn't enough evidence to conclude whether or not Jesus died on the cross is an old forensic ruse. And a transparent one. "There's a Golden Thread running through British justice", Rumpole was fond of saying (when he really had to scrape the bottom of the evidential barrel). "And that is that the prosecution have to make you sure of guilt. If you are not sure, then you must acquit, even if you are highly suspicious of guilt." That's fine if you are being asked to decide between guilt (which can happen in only one way), and non-guilt (which can typically happen in an infinite number of ways). But that's not what we've got here. We have only two stark possibilities: death and non-death. If you are not sure that Jesus died, then you must countenance the possibility that he lived. And if you think that he might have lived, then you are catapulted immediately into realms of fantasy far, far more exotic than anything the Christians have ever believed.

The way that the narratives are told

True, the gospel writers appear to change their tone when they get to the passion. Mark's narrative indeed gets smoother; John gets less overtly theological. But there's no great mystery about this. Mark has felt able to jump quickly between often very geographically disparate scenes because of the relative unimportance of those scenes. Relative, that is, in comparison to what he is now dealing with. He has finally got to the climax. This is what the whole story is about, and he's not going to skimp now. The story itself provides the form and the pace. He needn't think about blending tales together (which he never bothered to do), because the events do it for him. When you are dealing with events like the passion you don't have to worry about sounding literary. The shabbiest tabloid reportage of these events would sound like Dante. And it all happens fairly fast, and in a small area.

Yes, John tends to leave his beloved messianic metaphors behind. But that is a reason to trust his historicity all the more, not to doubt it more. Nowhere does John's evidence stink more obviously of eyewitness testimony than when he embarks on the passion and resurrection accounts. He gets a new earnestness, assuring his readers: I was there; I saw.

Lack of agreement on the date

Yes, there's a discrepancy, which raises three important general points. Two have been raised already in Chapter 2. The first is that anyone hoping for a systematic harmonisation of the gospels will be disappointed. It is impossible. The second is that harmonisation is forensically undesirable: the discrepancies are impressive testimony to the integrity of the early church. They didn't massage their sources. We can be sure that we've got more or less kosher documents.

The third point, of course, is that the lack of agreement sends bubbling to the bottom the idea that John depended on the synoptics. Whatever you say about his memory for dates, you have to acknowledge his independence.

The dates don't agree. And indeed John might have been making a theological point. But it is surely more likely that by the time this account was committed to papyrus so much water had flowed under the bridge that the exact date was the least of John's concerns. Around this time the disciples' world had been turned upside down, and the disciples had subsequently turned the world of many others upside down. One can excuse the elderly John for saying: "I can't be sure whether it was on Passover Eve or the first day of Passover. But I *am* sure what happened, and I am sure that it was the start of a new world."

Where John is alone

The objection here is to John's account of the spear thrust, the blood and water, and the leg-breaking.[54]

Christian preachers have indeed been interested in the spear thrust and the leg non-breaking because they appear to show that the death of Jesus accorded with some Old Testament prophecies. But it is bizarre and deeply unhistorical to say that because a particular detail corresponds to a bit of a Psalm or a bit of Zechariah it could not have really happened. If that were so it would mean that whenever the whole of Christianity was demonstrably internally consistent it was by definition fraudulent. X is being unfair. He is trying to have his expository cake and eat it. He says that Jesus' side was not pierced precisely because John says that it was. But if the gospels did not say that the side was pierced, X would be on his feet in a moment, saying: "This shows that Jesus could not have been the expected Messiah, because the expected Messiah was pierced."

Here we see John at his most earnest: ("He who saw [the blood and water] has testified so that you also may believe. His testimony is true, and he knows that he tells the truth").[55] In relation to the blood and the water, it is hard to see what theological deeper meaning might be implied. If John was being subtle, he was being so subtle that most subsequent readers (apart from those with dazzlingly creative theological intellects) have wholly failed to get his point.

To say that John was trying to establish death is nonsensical. He was no pathologist. He had no idea of the significance of what he was describing. If he was anxious to make it clear that Jesus had died there would be far easier ways of doing it. The obvious way would be to let the soldiers administer the *crucifragium*. If there had been a real concern about this, fulfilment of the prophecy about no broken bones would have been a good trade for assurance of death. Or he could have had an examination by a doctor. Or a more emphatically fatal heart wound.

And let's not lose sight of the bigger picture. If you think that John was making all this up, you have to ask yourself: why? What did he think really happened? We'll return to this later.

How many independent witnesses were there?

The comments about the dependence of Matthew and Luke on Mark are fair enough *until* you get to the passion accounts. And when you get to the resurrection accounts you could be forgiven for thinking that all four of the gospel writers were going out of their way to write accounts as different from each other as possible.

In relation to the account of the death, X appears to acknowledge that all the writers diverge radically from Mark. Yes, there's a template, but it's a template given by the story itself. How many basic ways are there of saying that Lorry A smashed into Lorry B? Not many. If it helps you to call the statement "Lorry A smashed into Lorry B" a template, then fine. But most normal people would simply call it the story. It is the same with the crucifixion accounts. All four gospel writers tell more or less the same story. They differ, precisely as you'd expect, on details. X has suggested that there are deep theological reasons for diverging on the details. He gives the example of the different accounts of what Jesus said from the cross. But while he has said that there are clearly implicit sermons in the different accounts, he has not suggested what the sermons might be.

He really is crediting the notoriously spare, terse, and downright ordinary gospel writers with some remarkable metaphorical powers.

Those bluff Galilean fishermen wouldn't know whether to be more surprised, flattered or outraged to have sophisticated post-modernist creativity attributed to them. As far as the death scene is concerned, we've got four more or less independent accounts. Again, note what X is doing: where the accounts agree, he shouts collusion. Where they do not, he bellows fabrication. And in either case he signally fails to suggest any motive.

Theology: not history?

Yes, there is some theology in the death stories. But two points need to be made. First, as has already been pointed out, the fact that something might be theologically significant does not mean that it could not have happened. And, second, it is generally perfectly obvious when a theological point is being made.

Turning to the examples X gives:

The torn veil

We certainly don't know that this didn't happen. It is strange that X suggests that we don't know. Here we have several ancient documents, known to be reliable in many other contexts, which say that it did. True, there is no corroboration outside the Christian accounts, but to think that this in itself casts significant doubt on the story is to misunderstand the sources. There really isn't much literature from this period. Secular historians rely significantly on the uniquely detailed and well-observed Christian documents for their knowledge. If the Temple veil *had* been ripped, and the rip was associated in time and in gossip with the death of Jesus, Jewish accounts may well have suppressed the account to avoid boosting the Christian camp. And the Romans probably couldn't have cared less.

John: the unbroken legs, the pierced side and the blood and water

These have already been discussed: see above.

Earthquakes and opening tombs in Matthew

All this is, frankly, a bit of an embarrassment. I wish that Matthew hadn't written these things. But he did, and something has to be said about it. It raises all sorts of difficulties. It is difficult to know what Matthew himself intended us to make of it all. It is plain, for example, that he doesn't believe that the final, general resurrection has happened, although at the beginning of his wakening-dead story it looks as if he is about to say that it has. There's no obvious room in any theology, ancient or modern, for Matthew's half-cock not-quite-general resurrection. Is the earthquake supposed to be connected to the tomb-opening? Is the earth literally shaking the dead awake with its outrage at the death of God? We don't know.

Tom Wright, taking the Matthean bull bravely by the horns, and not, like most writers, being gored horribly by it in the process, has identified four broad possibilities:[56]

(a) Matthew might have invented the story with the intention that it would illustrate dramatically and metaphorically what had happened to Israel's God on the cross.
(b) Matthew might have invented a story which fitted in and "fulfilled" texts such as Ezekiel 37, Isaiah 26, Zechariah 14 and Daniel 12.
(c) Matthew might be echoing the tradition in the Gospel of Peter, in which the moment of the resurrection itself is seen.
(d) Matthew might know of a tradition that speaks of these phenomena, and is trying to retell that tradition "in such a way as to give a biblically alert reader a sense of their meaning: this is the real return from exile, the dawn of the new age, and perhaps even the harrowing of hell."[57]

Tom Wright says (and for what it is worth I agree with his analysis) that (a) and (b) are unlikely. Anticipating the arguments in later chapters, there was nothing in pre-Christian Judaism that would associate even a small foretaste of the general resurrection with the death of a supposed Messiah. Even if such ideas crept into later Christian thinking, they crept in along with the resurrection of the Messiah, not his execution. For the dead to awake on Easter Day might, although highly theologically eccentric, be just comprehensible. For them to awake on Good Friday as the Messiah gave up the ghost would be plain exegetical gibberish.

As to (c), almost everyone agrees that Peter is very late, and that none of the canonical gospel writers knew either his book or his tradition.

Which leaves us with (d). And as to the historicity of the events, Tom Wright cannot be improved on. While acknowledging that things mentioned by one source only may be suspect,

> ...it remains the case that the events Matthew describes in 27:51–3, as well as being without parallel in other early Christian sources, are without precedent in second-Temple expectation, and we may doubt whether stories such as this would have been invented simply to "fulfill" prophecies that nobody had understood this way before. This is hardly a satisfactory conclusion, but it is better to remain puzzled than to settle for either a difficult argument for probable historicity or a cheap and cheerful rationalistic dismissal of the possibility. Some stories are so odd that they may just have happened. This may be one of them, but in historical terms there is no way of finding out.[58]

No corroboration

The objection here is that the events of Calvary aren't mentioned once outside the gospel accounts. It is a fatuous objection. The rest of the New Testament runs red with references to Jesus' death and what it has achieved. The mechanics of the death didn't matter. It is interesting that, as interest in the physical details of Jesus' death rises, understanding of what that death achieved diminishes. It wasn't until the Middle Ages that Christianity became cultically fixated with the wounds of Christ.

The possibility that Jesus wasn't crucified

The Koran says that Jesus was never crucified. It is important to remember why the idea of Jesus' crucifixion is so abhorrent to Muslims. It is because Jesus, for them, was a great prophet, beloved of Allah. To say that Allah would allow one of his favoured ones to be done to death in this way is to question Allah's power and benevolence. The Koran's statement is therefore a theological one about the nature of God. It is not directly addressing the historical question of what happened on Calvary. It was, in any event, written in the seventh century AD. While the Koran's comment is important in understanding many later views about the historicity of Jesus, it does not help this historical inquiry.

The Gospel of Barnabas, cited by many Muslims as authority for the proposition that Judas was crucified instead of Jesus, is thought by the huge majority of mainstream scholars to be a mediaeval forgery.[59] Some, however, think that it may preserve some remnants of an earlier apocryphal text[60] which has been edited into conformity with Islam. The two earliest-known manuscripts have been dated to the late sixteenth century. They are written in Italian and

Spanish. The earliest Spanish version still surviving is an eighteenth-century copy. Its deployment by Islamic apologists is very recent: it has only sprung into prominence in the last 50 years. There is a crushing consensus on the value of the Gospel of Barnabas as a source on the life and death of Jesus: the Gospel is worthless.

The reconstruction by Baigent *et al.* in *The Holy Blood and the Holy Grail* sells books but buys no serious converts. Think of what would have been involved in a conspiracy like this.

Was it a last-minute plan? Surely it would have had to be, since the arrest of Jesus in Gethsemane and the subsequent murderous course could not have been anticipated. That gave the conspirators a very short time to concoct the plan. Who were they? Jesus wasn't noted for his friends in high places. Anyway, whoever they were, they would have had to arrange for a private crucifixion (contrary to everything we know about Roman crucifixions, which were by definition obscenely public). If Baigent is right, the conspirators apparently arranged too for two thieves to be crucified in the same private place, so that it did not look too suspicious. They presumably kept the crowds (angry at being deprived of their Friday afternoon outing) out of the garden at spearpoint. It was a shame that the conspirators could not stop people looking in, but no doubt those people had terrible eyesight and could not notice a body-switch. Although they could, apparently, see blood and water oozing out, and hear Jesus talking. Or was that made up (and by whom and why?).

There was a lot of bribing to be done, of course: Pilate, very importantly; then the soldiers; then the others who slipped through the cordon at the entrance to the garden. Very tricky, too, you'd have thought, to grease the palms of the watching Jewish officials, who seemed genuinely keen to have the real Jesus dead. It was just as well that there was someone who just happened to look like Jesus who was prepared to be crucified on his behalf that day, or had to be crucified in any event. When was the switch made? It was presumably in the garden: Jesus had to go through the trials and the flogging. The crowd knew perfectly well who he was, and would have spotted a substitute. So Jesus would presumably have had to be exchanged for his substitute just before the substitute was nailed up. Presumably he took refuge immediately in the nearby tomb. At this stage, of course, it was still broad daylight. All the stuff about Joseph, then, is pure fantasy. And Jesus, as well as churlishly accepting the offer of the substitute to die on his behalf, would have had to abandon all his followers immediately and make off as soon as the coast was clear. That somehow doesn't seem like him.

If there was a pre-made plan, Jesus would presumably have been in on it. He would have had to agree to be arrested, tried, flogged and then subjected to the fake crucifixion before creeping out into obscurity. And why on earth would he do that? If his main objective was to save his own skin, and he knew what was in store for him in Jerusalem (as he would have had to in order for the plan to be made in the first place), why not spare himself all the bother and simply not come to Jerusalem? And if the anonymous "friends in high places" knew about a plot on his life, why not just tell him to steer clear of the danger?

You have to ask, also, why every single one of the gospels says what it does about the crucifixion. Were they all concocted as part of a conspiracy to mislead, too?

But credit where credit is due: Baigent is a good read, like many other nursery stories.

The possibility that Jesus was crucified but did not die

A plausible conspiracy theory?

X alleges that Jesus might not have died. Pilate was part of a conspiracy to save him. Pilate, it is suggested, might have been so intoxicated by Jesus, or so browbeaten by his own wife, that he decided to save him. Joseph, in any event, was at the centre of any plot.

Before we dive into the detail, let's just pause and look at the broad picture. All the basic information relied on by X comes from the canonical gospels themselves. They tell us, for example, that Pilate's wife did not want Jesus to die; that Pilate tried to save him; that Jesus was offered and took "vinegar" just before he died; that Jesus' legs were not broken. All these facts can be used by any anti-Christian apologist in precisely the way that they have been used by X.

The gospel writers weren't stupid. Indeed, X credits them, for some of his purposes, with immense literary cunning. They knew very well how some of the things they were writing might have been taken. If they had known about a conspiracy to save Jesus, and wanted to cover it up: (a) Why would they have written the gospels in the first place – documents which present a view of Jesus wholly incompatible with a man who has fraudulently cheated the executioners and crept off to ignominious obscurity? And (b): Why, if for some reason they did decide to write the gospels, would they include clues that might suggest the very conspiracy that they were trying to conceal? It makes no sense at all. So we are bound to conclude that whoever wrote the gospels knew nothing of any conspiracy. If the conspirators are trying to pull the wool over our eyes, they were also trying to pull the wool over the gospel writers' eyes too: and they succeeded. The gospel writers, whatever you say about them, believed that Jesus died and rose, and were telling the story of that death and resurrection.

Pilate doesn't seem the sort of man likely to have been moved by a brief meeting with a Galilean peasant. Elsewhere X is quite happy to outline the historical evidence about Pilate's grotesque insensitivity and self-interest. I am happy to adopt it. Pilate, from everything we know about him, was cruel and self-obsessed. X says, though, that Jesus affected him so deeply that after a few minutes of chat Pilate was prepared to act in a career-endangering way by entering into an elaborate conspiracy. If this had been discovered by the Jews there would have been big trouble. And, again, to repeat what I said in answering Baigent's contentions, it was a conspiracy concocted with astonishing speed.

But there's a more obvious objection to the Pilate-as-chief-conspirator theory. Let's suppose that he did have some sort of deep religious experience as he gazed into the dark eyes of the Gailean. Let's suppose that he had been hen pecked by a superstitious wife into acting compassionately. Why not just refuse to kill Jesus? Yes, the crowds and the priests would have kicked up a fuss for a bit, but there were plenty of other options. Jesus could have been slung into jail for a while until tempers cooled and the crowd's wrath moved to the next aspirant Messiah. And then, if Pilate still chose to be merciful, Jesus could have been quietly released or banished.

What about Joseph of Arimathea? We will have more to say about him in the next chapter, but for the moment a few points need to be made. First: if he engineered Jesus' survival he was more than just a casual friend. Remember that he was a member of the Sanhedrin. He was risking their lethal wrath. To help a condemned blasphemer was potentially to be a condemned blasphemer.

Second: the notion that he could simply have bought the Roman soldiers off with a few shekels is laughable. X himself has cited the

Roman novel *Satyricon* in Chapter 4. The Roman soldier there, who, having been deputed to guard the corpses of crucified men, lets one go missing, is so terrified of punishment that he contemplates suicide. How much greater would the punishment have been for a soldier who allowed a crucifixion victim to survive and be carried off? Riches beyond the dreams of avarice would have been needed to pay the bribes of all the people who would have had to be paid off.

Third: all the points made in the context of the *Holy Blood, Holy Grail* thesis about time for the plan to be hatched apply equally here: if Joseph knew that Jesus was going to be crucified, it would have been hugely easier and more sensible to avoid it. And if he didn't know in advance, then there simply wouldn't have been time to devise and exercise a plot of such diabolically fraudulent complexity.

Fourth, and finally: Everything that X says about Joseph in this chapter is wholly at odds with almost everything he says about him in Chapter 4. Here he wants him as a fanatical Christian, prepared to risk all for his secret Master. There he pours scorn on that idea, dismissing it as a late, legendary development, and says instead that Joseph was a pious, religious Jew whose real motive was simply to ensure that Jewish burial laws were not violated. In Chapter 4, according to X, Joseph cares so little about Jesus that, come the Saturday night, when all the funerary decencies have been carried out, he is happy simply to move the body to the municipal graveyard of the condemned without even telling Jesus' family and friends where it has gone. We will find a lot of this dramatic internal inconsistency in X's position.

Did anyone survive crucifixion?

Indeed they did. But it was a great rarity. It was precisely because it was such a rarity that Josephus mentions it.

The mechanics of crucifixion

Most of what X says is agreed. Not all crucifixion victims were nailed, at least through the hands. The gospel writers, from their descriptions of the post-mortem appearances, clearly thought that Jesus had been nailed somewhere in the hands or wrists. And that would be very common. Jehonanan was lucky to avoid it.

There's nothing for X in Luke and John's use of the word "*keiras*" to describe the site of the forearm wound. The word is used to describe the hand *or* the wrist. And in any event the work on experimental crucifixion that suggested that a body could not be suspended from nails through the palms is seriously flawed. Details are given in Appendix 1.

Was there a standard procedure for spearing the side of a crucifixion victim? We don't know. There is an ambiguous reference in Quintilian (referred to by X under the heading "Piercing the side") which has been held by some to imply that the body of a crucified man who had been speared with a lance could be released for burial. If this is right it might imply a standard procedure.

Luke and John's different statements about the position of the wounds are interesting, but they are damaging only if we assume that they wrote absolutely everything about every scene that they are describing on every occasion that they described it. And we know that that is not the case. Luke's gospel contains some classic examples: if you just read the gospel, you would think that Jesus appeared to his disciples only on the day of his resurrection, and ascended that day. Read on in Acts, though, and it is plain that that is not the case. For whatever reason, Luke chooses not to put in his gospel a great deal of the information he has about Jesus' postmortem activities.

The physical wounds of Jesus weren't the most important thing about him at the time that these observations were made. The most important thing was that he was alive – the first dead man to rise again. The witnesses can perhaps be forgiven for not performing, or at least not recording, a full clinical examination. We know that the side wound, for whatever reason, had stuck in John's mind. He, alone of all the gospel writers, mentions it in his crucifixion scene. It is unsurprising that he looks for it and notices it in the resurrected Jesus.

Was the "vinegar" all it seemed?

We're now well into the conspiracy theory, of course. And anything that X says from now on that sounds plausible has to be read in the knowledge that it presupposes belief in an utterly implausible thesis.

I'll make the point again: the suspicion comes directly from the gospel accounts. Here, X says that the fact that Jesus "died" immediately after getting the "vinegar" implies something sinister. Well, plainly the gospel writers didn't think so, or they wouldn't have believed in Jesus in the first place, or (if they were involved in the conspiracy) have written down the very account from which people might be able to guess that they were guilty.

Jesus "cried out with a loud voice": inconceivable, says X, in a man near death. But it's a last, agonal scream. He's not making speeches to the assembled multitudes. To describe a request for a drink by a dying, dehydrated man as an indication that he was "in control" is odd. If he was play-acting, surely he'd have brought the charade to an end long before. He was hanging there for hours. Was he really saying: "Just another couple of hours and they won't think it's suspicious when I appear to die"?

What X says about the availability of opium and its pharmacological action is correct. But it was a very high-risk strategy indeed. It is a profound respiratory depressant, as anyone who has heard of heroin addicts dying on the point of a needle will know. What X appears to envisage is Jesus going into a complete opiate coma. Only that would suppress breathing sufficiently for his body to look like a corpse. Only that would produce sufficient analgesia to prevent him wincing as his body was taken down from the cross. But unfortunately his chances of surviving a coma of such depth would be remote.

The speed with which Jesus died

Yes, it was quick. It sometimes could be. One of the more credible recent theories of the cause of death (reviewed in Appendix 1), is that Jesus died from pulmonary embolism. That would produce a quick, sudden death. And remember that the death is suspiciously quick only if you have already signed up to one of the conspiracy theories.

Why were Jesus' legs not broken?

Because he was dead. That has seemed to the vast majority of commentators, both Christian and non-Christian, hugely more likely than the Byzantine alternative mooted by X. See too the comments above, under the heading "When John is alone".

Piercing the side

This issue has already been dealt with. See the comments above, under the heading: "When John is alone".

If Jesus survived, what happened to him?

First, some perspective. In case anything that X says sounds arguable, remember that you get to this stage only if you conclude that Jesus survived the cross. Let's be generous to X and say (contrary to the views of almost everyone who has looked at the issue seriously) that there is a 1% chance that Jesus walked (or more likely limped badly or was stretchered) away from Calvary. And let's say that you conclude (again in the teeth of all informed views) that if Jesus survived, there is a 10% chance that the story of the Kashmiri Jesus is true. That means that the actual chance of the Kashmiri Jesus story being true is 1/100 x 10/100, which is 1 in 1,000.

The post-crucifixion Jesus in Islam

The Koran's description of the shelter given to Jesus and his mother could relate to any time in their lives, could be wholly metaphorical, and in any event could be anywhere in the Near East. There are plenty of "peaceful hill sides watered by a fresh spring" west of Srinagar.

Did Jesus go to India?

The background to the "Jesus-in-India" stories is the Islamic notion that Jesus did not die on the cross, but that he only appeared to have done so. If you believe that, then you have to do something with Jesus after the time of his supposed crucifixion. And there has been no shortage of legend-weavers prepared to help out.

If you take the folk tales seriously, there are few areas between Suez and China that Jesus (with or without his mother, and with or without a coterie of selected disciples) has not settled in. His mother, Mary, has umpteen graves throughout the Near East.

It is true, of course, that Christian missionaries spread the Jesus stories far and wide very early. Within the first century the apostle Thomas is said to have taken the message to India. By the fourth century at the latest, Christianity was well established there. So the presence in Kashmir and along the Silk Road of tales about Jesus is not remotely surprising. If those feet at the tomb in Srinagar really do show crucifixion wounds, the tomb might indeed have been a Christian shrine. But they are unlikely to have been the feet of Jesus, if for no other reason than that the marks on Jesus' feet would, had he survived, have been marks not of glory but of shame. If he survived the cross as part of a guard-bribing conspiracy, or worse, he abandoned all those who loved and trusted him, leaving them to their own fate, and crept away out of Palestine with his tail between his legs. His feet were nothing to boast about. And to boast would be actively dangerous. He was a craven refugee from Judaeo-Roman justice. If the wounded feet were iconically important they were much more likely to have been carved into the stone because of a missionary tale about the saving wounds of Jesus. Perhaps Thomas himself, who famously believed in Jesus because he saw the crucifixion wounds, told the Kashmiris the story that inspired the imprints. But we have no idea how old the carvings are. For all we know they could be nineteenth-century Ahmadiyya carvings.

There are only two pieces of real evidence about Jesus in India. Both have been laughed out of court by serious scholars. They have both been cited by X. The first is the inscription on the pillar at the Takhat Sulaiman. How old is the inscription? It is unclear, although the mention in Mullah Nadri's Tarikh-I-Kashmir suggests that it was there before 1420. Let's assume that it was indeed written in the mason's "year 54". The earliest date that this could be is AD 78. The latest is AD 107. What does the inscription amount to? That someone calling himself "Yusu Asaph" declared his ministry then. And what was his ministry? He was "the prophet of the Children of Israel". If this was Jesus, we have to ask ourselves what he had been doing up to then. Most give his birth date as about 4 BC. That would make him 84 in AD 78 and 111 in AD 107. Either is a ripe old age to "declare your ministry" – which sounds very much like the start of a campaign. Was "Prophet of the Children of Israel" the sort of language that a defeated Jesus would have used of himself? Well, possibly, I suppose, if he really had given up all his messianic ideas. But there's frankly not much point in proclaiming yourself Prophet of the Children of Israel when you're in India. It is a very bad campaign strategy. Far better, if you think that you have something spiritual to offer, to proclaim yourself Prophet of the Children of Srinagar.

If the Yuz Asaf of the Takhat Sulaiman pillar had anything whatever to do with the Jesus movement, he is hugely more likely to have been an early missionary, bellowing the words of salvation into the hills of Kashmir and being, it seems, comprehensively misunderstood.

The alleged meeting of King Shalivahan and "Jesus" in Ladakh is more interesting. Let's begin by completing the quotation from the

Bhavishya. After saying that he was delivered into the hands of the demon Ihamasia, and "ended in Ihamasi's realm", the Jesus-figure continues:

> "O king, lend your ear to the religion that I brought unto the non-believers: after the purification of the essence and the impure body and after seeking refuge in the prayers of the Naigama, man will pray to the Eternal. Through justice, truth, meditation and unity of spirit, man will find his way to Isa in the centre of light. God, as firm as the sun, will finally unite the spirit of all wandering beings in himself. Thus, O king, Ihamasi will be destroyed; and the blissful image of Isa, the giver of happiness, will remain forever in the heart; and I was called Isa-Masih." After the king heard these words, he took the teacher of the non-believers and sent him to their pitiless land.[61]

This does not look much like the religion that Jesus taught in Palestine. It does look very much, though, like the sort of syncretism that anyone trying to assimilate Christianity into Hinduism might produce. And that is probably what this bizarre exercise is about. The Bhavishya was probably written about AD 115. By this time Christian missionaries may well have been making significant progress in western India. What better way to inoculate Hindus against Christianity than to tell Hindus, in an authoritative text like the Bhavishya, that Jesus was for all practical purposes a Hindu and had nothing material to add to Hinduism?

The dates for the meeting that X suggests are almost certainly much too early. He says that Shalivahan reigned from AD 39–50. Those dates are lifted from the Tomb of Jesus website, whose mission is to convince the world that the Rozabal tomb is the Tomb of Yuz Asaf, and that Yuz Asaf is Jesus. While there is some uncertainty about the dates of these ancient Hindu dynasties, the scholarly consensus is that Shalivahan established his Shalivahan Shak dynasty in AD 78[62]. Jesus would then have been 82 years old. The meeting, if it is historical, must therefore have happened after that.

But all this is to take the citation as history. It doesn't look like it. It is told in the typical mythopoieic style of the Hindu epics; it is one of an endless series of meetings between kings and enlightened *sadhus*; it talks of journeys to demonic realms; it serves an obvious political and religious purpose.

Did Jesus become Apollonius of Tyana?

This is one of the stories that periodically do the rounds, surviving only because of highly selective citation of the sources.

The answer is that Jesus was certainly not Apollonius. We know, from Philostratus, a great deal about Apollonius. He was born in the small town of Tyana, in what is now Turkey, to an extremely rich man. He lacked nothing material in his childhood, we are told, and was fascinated with human greatness. On arrival in any new place he would go first to visit the local monarch. When he was fourteen he was sent by his father to Tarsus to finish his education. Appalled by the loose morals there, he apparently took a lifelong vow of celibacy. He then studied at Aegae under the great Epicurean teacher, Euxenes, and was inducted into the esoteric mysteries of Pythagorean practice. He underwent a self-imposed four year vow of silence, and then started his astonishing travels. They took him throughout the Near East, to Babylon, Egypt and Spain, and, most importantly, to Gangetic India. In India, like so many Western travellers, ancient and modern, he had some sort of spiritual epiphany. He returned to Greece determined to disseminate the Eastern wisdom he had learned – and probably to show its continuity with the Eleusinian Mysteries into which he had been initiated. He seems to have died in his eighties, probably in Ephesus. There are various legends about the manner of his death: his body was never found, and there is no tomb. It may well have been this mystery that led to people associating him with Jesus.

But, apart from some miracle-working, there is no real similarity at all. Jesus was a rather parochial religious Jew, who probably never went beyond Palestine. He had no friends in high places. He kept the company of prostitutes and drunkards, not philosophers and kings. He was no priest of Eleusis. Apollonius – one of the most fascinating and well-documented figures of the first-century Mediterranean – was the classic aristocratic, cosmopolitan Greek sophisticate with mystic leanings. He and Jesus might have some interesting conversations (and might have liked each other very much indeed), but shared no common cultural language.

X reads far too much into Eusebius' denunciation of those who thought that Apollonius was Jesus. Eusebius might have been rather counterproductively loud, but he was protesting because the idea that they were the same was absurd, and because Apollonius and Jesus believed very different things about the world.

The curious business of Irenaeus

Yes, curious indeed. And there is no real explanation for Irenaeus' profound eccentricity on the question of Jesus' chronology. Irenaeus was entirely on his own in reconstructing things in the way that he did. But, although interesting, this is a non-point for X. Irenaeus repeatedly and expressly affirms his entirely orthodox belief in the (eventual) death and bodily resurrection of Jesus.

Was Jesus at Masada?

X has been reading some strange things. Donovan Joyce's book is now difficult to find. It was never on university reading lists.

It is a wholly incredible and very good story, which is centred on toilets. It has really brightened up for me the gents' toilets at Ben Gurion Airport. Donovan Joyce's nose was put seriously out of joint because Yigael Yadin, director of the Masada excavation, refused him access to the investigation. Israeli secret-service agents, according to Joyce, made his life miserable by blocking his toilet. The book may be Joyce's revenge. Then we cut to the other toilet, at the airport, where the pseudonymous professor unfurls the scroll (itself a remarkable achievement in that small space). It was 3 or 4 metres long, says Joyce. There were no whole scrolls found at Masada, only fragments. But perhaps the professor was lucky. If he was lucky, he was pushing that luck by unfurling the scroll: scrolls that ancient can't be unrolled without breaking. And why unfurl it anyway? Why did Joyce need to see it? And why did Joyce need to be provided with the translation that the professor had already managed to do? The scroll, unsurprisingly, has gone missing.

But, even if all this cynicism is misplaced, and the scroll was genuine and the translation is accurate, so what? Jesus was a very common name. The Jesus of the scroll was said to be the son of Jakob and to have been 80 years old. Masada was the last stand of the Jewish people: it would be wholly unsurprising if there had been there someone holding themselves out as the last of the Hasmoneans. If this Jesus existed he was not the one the gospels are talking about.

Conclusion

Jesus certainly died on the cross. The alternatives require massive and prolonged suspension of common sense, and dramatic ignorance of the sources.

CHAPTER 4

The burial

The sources

Mark 15

42When evening had come, and since it was the day of Preparation, that is, the day before the sabbath, [43]Joseph of Arimathea, a respected member of the council, who was also himself waiting expectantly for the kingdom of God, went boldly to Pilate and asked for the body of Jesus. [44]Then Pilate wondered if he were already dead; and summoning the centurion, he asked him whether he had been dead for some time. [45]When he learned from the centurion that he was dead, he granted the body to Joseph. [46]Then Joseph bought a linen cloth, and taking down the body, wrapped it in the linen cloth, and laid it in a tomb that had been hewn out of the rock. He then rolled a stone against the door of the tomb. [47]Mary Magdalene and Mary the mother of Joses saw where the body was laid.

Matthew 27

57When it was evening, there came a rich man from Arimathea, named Joseph, who was also a disciple of Jesus. [58]He went to Pilate and asked for the body of Jesus; then Pilate ordered it to be given to him. [59]So Joseph took the body and wrapped it in a clean linen cloth [60]and laid it in his own new tomb, which he had hewn in the rock. He then rolled a great stone to the door of the tomb and went away. [61]Mary Magdalene and the other Mary were there, sitting opposite the tomb.

62The next day, that is, after the day of Preparation, the chief priests

and the Pharisees gathered before Pilate [63]and said, "Sir, we remember
what that impostor said while he was still alive, 'After three days I will
rise again.' [64]Therefore command that the tomb be made secure until the
third day; otherwise his disciples may go and steal him away, and tell the
people, 'He has been raised from the dead', and the last deception would
be worse than the first." [65]Pilate said to them, "You have a guard of soldiers; go, make it as secure as you can." [66]So they went with the guard
and made the tomb secure by sealing the stone.

Luke 23

50Now there was a good and righteous man named Joseph, who, though
a member of the council, [51]had not agreed to their plan and action. He
came from the Jewish town of Arimathea, and he was waiting expectantly for the kingdom of God. [52]This man went to Pilate and asked for
the body of Jesus. [53]Then he took it down, wrapped it in a linen cloth, and
laid it in a rock-hewn tomb where no one had ever been laid. [54]It was the
day of Preparation, and the Sabbath was beginning. [55]The women who
had come with him from Galilee followed, and they saw the tomb and
how his body was laid. [56]Then they returned, and prepared spices and
ointments. On the Sabbath they rested according to the commandment.

John 19

38After these things, Joseph of Arimathea, who was a disciple of Jesus,
though a secret one because of his fear of the Jews, asked Pilate to let him
take away the body of Jesus. Pilate gave him permission; so he came and
removed his body. [39]Nicodemus, who had at first come to Jesus by night,
also came, bringing a mixture of myrrh and aloes, weighing about a hundred pounds. [40]They took the body of Jesus and wrapped it with the
spices in linen cloths, according to the burial custom of the Jews. [41]Now
there was a garden in the place where he was crucified, and in the garden
there was a new tomb in which no one had ever been laid. [42]And so,
because it was the Jewish day of Preparation, and the tomb was nearby,
they laid Jesus there.

Part 1: X

Whereso'er I turn my view,
All is strange, yet nothing new
Samuel Johnson

Introduction

If Jesus did indeed die on the cross, what was done with his body? The canonical gospels, of course, say that Jesus was buried by Joseph of Arimathea in a rock sepulchre, closed by a stone. The later gospels elaborate that basic story greatly.

This chapter considers four broad possibilities. First: Jesus might not have been buried in a tomb at all. Second: if he was buried in a tomb it might not have been the tomb of Joseph of Arimathea, as the canonical gospels suggest. Third: if he was interred at all in the tomb of Joseph of Arimathea, it may have been only a temporary burial; he may have been moved later. Fourth: the canonical gospels might tell a basically true story about the burial. To assess this fourth possibility we have not only to assess the first three possibilities (all of which would have to be discounted if the gospels are correct) but also to look generally at whether the accounts given in the canonical gospels are remotely credible.

The evidence for the first three of these possibilities is so convincing that it disposes of the fourth.

The bodies of the crucified in Roman times

In the eyes of the ancient world the agony of crucifixion did not end with the death of the victim. To the victim's physical suffering was added the psychological and spiritual suffering of knowing that he was unlikely to get a proper burial.

Burial meant much more to them than to us. It meant being grafted again into the community. Throughout the Old Testament the phrase "he was gathered to his fathers" recurs again and again. We often assume it is a polite euphemism for death, but it was meant quite literally. After the flesh had rotted, the bones of the deceased would be gathered up and put on the mound of his ancestors' bones. The father's bones would be mingled with the son's. To know that this was going to happen was a real comfort. To think that it might not was an unspeakable horror. Not only did it mean that one was alone; not only did it mean that one was stigmatised, it also meant that the community of the dead had been let down.

The Romans knew all about this. Crucifixion was not just a punishment: it was a deterrent. Proper deterrence meant maximum horror, and that meant denial of burial. When Augustus arrested the plotters responsible for the death of Julius Caesar, one of them pleaded for a decent burial. The response was: "The carrion birds will soon take care of that."[1] When Tiberius moved to crush Sejanus and his supporters in AD 31, some chose suicide instead of execution:

> ...these modes of dying were rendered popular by fear of the executioner and by the fact that a man legally condemned forfeited his estate and was debarred from burial; while he who passed sentence upon himself had his celerity so far rewarded that his body was interred and his will respected...[2]

One more example – this time from a gruesome Roman novel, *Satyricon*, written around AD 61 by Petronius, who had been an acolyte of Nero. One scene is in Ephesus. A widow is at her late husband's grave, mourning him. The governor of the province orders that some robbers should be crucified near the tomb. A soldier is posted by the crosses "to stop anyone from taking down a body for burial". He notices the widow. She is easily distracted from her grief, and allows him to seduce her for three consecutive nights. His absence is noted:

> ...the parents of one of the crucified men, noting how careless was the guard, took the body down one night and performed the last rites over it. In his absence from duty the soldier was thus circumvented; and next day, finding one of the crosses without its corpse, he was scared at the prospect of punishment... [He contemplates suicide, but the widow talks him out of it, saying...] "I'd rather see a dead man crucified than a living man dead." She thereupon bade him remove her husband's corpse from its coffin and fix it up on the empty cross...and the people wondered next day by what means a dead man had ascended the cross...[3]

The point is obvious: crucified men usually hung there until the birds or the dogs dealt with them. We come now to the rather special case of crucified Jews. But, nonetheless, it is as well to bear in mind that non-burial was part of the crucifixion package.

What about crucified Jews?

Jews, at least in Palestine (where there was a potentially inflammable Jewish majority) were rather different. Jewish law was clear about what should happen to crucified men:

Here is Deuteronomy 21:22–23:

> When someone is convicted of a crime punishable by death and is executed and you hang him on a tree, his corpse must not remain all night upon the tree; you shall bury him that same day, for anyone hung on a tree is under God's curse. You must not defile the land that the Lord your God is giving you for possession.

It seems that initially this referred to exposure of bodies after the victim had been killed by other means.[4] But it is clear that by the time we get to the first century it was understood to apply to people killed by crucifixion too: it had become assimilated into the general Jewish understanding that burial should be on the day of death. According to the Mishnah tractate *Sanhedrin*, when the crime was blasphemy the corpse was hung up to be displayed on a pole, resembling a crucifixion.[5] In the case of Jesus the Romans had done their bit to fulfil the demands of the Jewish law. In any event, says the same tractate, the body has to come down by sunset, barring special circumstances.[6] Hence the hurry with Jesus' body. It might be possible to postpone official burial for a while (a subject to which we will return), but down the body had to come.

Religious theory is one thing; religious practice is quite another. Did this really happen in practice? Indeed it did. It was taken very seriously in first-century Jerusalem. Here is the Jewish historian Josephus describing the Jewish "constitution" which had come from Moses:

> Let him who blasphemes God be stoned to death and hung during the day, and let him be buried dishonourably and out of sight…[and]…when he has continued there for one whole day, that all the people may see him, let him be buried in the night. And thus it is that we bury all whom the laws condemn to die, upon any account whatsoever. Let our enemies that fall in battle be also buried; nor let any one dead body lie above the ground…[7]

Josephus had nothing but scorn for the Zealots, who, in the exigencies of war, neglected these ancient imperatives. They were nothing but animals:

> They proceeded to that degree of impiety as to cast away their dead bodies without burial, although the Jews used to take so much care of the burial of men that they took down those who were condemned and crucified, and buried them before the sun went down.[8]

Decent Jews keep the law, says Josephus. Keeping the law means taking the crucified down, and giving them some sort of burial.[9] But on the eve of a particularly important sabbath? Did that make any difference?

Burial on the eve of the sabbath

Burial on the sabbath itself was simply forbidden.[10] Burial on the first day of a festival was also forbidden[11], and, depending on which gospel you believe, Jesus may have died on the first day of Passover. If they were remotely pious Jews, once the sabbath started, Joseph and any helpers he might have had would have had to down tools. If Jesus died on the first day of Passover, they should never have picked up their tools in the first place. Even if they did start legitimately on Friday before sundown, they are most unlikely, given the rush that the gospels are unanimous about, to have been able to finish. Accordingly, however you look at it, Jesus could not have been fully buried (i.e. everything done – all the obsequies and whatever interment was contemplated) on the Friday night. At best, by the time Joseph went home for his Shabbat meal, Jesus' body was work in progress – to be resumed on Saturday night.

What sort of burial would Jesus have had?

Would Joseph have overridden Jewish tradition in Jesus' case?

Put at its highest, Joseph was "a secret disciple". If that is right, would his devotion to Jesus have caused him to disobey the ancient Jewish imperatives, and simply do what he thought was best to honour his guru?

This has to be answered partly by a critical look at how the gospels say that Joseph behaved. As appears below, there is nothing obviously unorthodox in anything that Joseph did.

But there is perhaps another clue. Luke tells us that the women, having prepared spices and ointments for anointing the body, rested on the sabbath according to the commandment.[12] The women were particularly devoted to Jesus. They had followed him from Galilee, and presumably everywhere else during his itinerant ministry. They (or some of their number, depending on which gospel you read) were the first ones at the tomb at the crack of dawn on the Sunday morning, zealous to anoint his body. If even they felt inhibited by Jewish law from going to the tomb on the sabbath, surely a man like

Joseph (much less close to Jesus, and presumably, because of his status as a member of the Sanhedrin, a religious man) would have felt similarly or more constrained.

Did Jesus' body get the traditional Jewish funerary treatment?

If the gospels are to be believed, Jesus' body did get some respect. The usual ritual involved closing the eyes, washing the corpse with ointments and perfumes and plugging the orifices. As to grave-clothes, the position is much less clear. It seems that, sometimes the body, after washing, would simply be dressed.[13] Sometimes, strips of cloth would be wound tightly around the body – just as described in the case of the raising of Lazarus.[14] The jaw would be closed and bound shut and the feet would be tied together.[15]

Sometimes, though, there were exceptions. It was thought important to keep as much as possible of the blood with the body, and so when death had been bloody the body might not be washed, and a single sheet – a *sovev* – would be put over it.[16] Matthew, Luke and John all use a verb meaning "wrap up"[17] to describe what was done to the body. Mark opts for "tie up".[18] Either of these descriptions would be consistent either with a *sovev* or with Lazarus-like bandaging. All three synoptic gospels talk about Jesus being wrapped in a "*sindon*".[19] This can indicate either a bolt of linen, or something like a tunic, drape or veil made of linen.[20] John, however, talks about binding the body with cloths; the implication is that there was more than one. This may imply a more elaborate burial than merely being covered with a simple linen shroud, as the synoptics allow us to believe.[21] John also, later, talks about a separate head piece. The gospels talk about Jesus' own clothing having been gambled away by the soldiers. It seems unlikely, therefore, that there would have been any clothes for him to have been buried in. The body would often be anointed with spices – partly as a sign of respect, and partly to inhibit the stench of decomposition. In the case of Jesus the account of the anointing raises other and significant difficulties.

None of the accounts in the gospels about the way that Jesus' body was treated (apart from the massive amount of spices used) is at odds with what we know about first-century funerary practices. Nor are they in any way inconsistent with him being "dishonourably buried". Dishonourable burial covers a multitude of possibilities. But one of those possibilities is almost certainly what happened to Jesus.

The idea of dishonourable burial

Back to Josephus: "Let him who blasphemes God be…hung during the day and let him be buried dishonourably and out of sight."

Was Jesus guilty of blaspheming God? On that at least the Christian evidence is clear: the Jews certainly thought he was, and that was why they wanted him dead.[22]

The Romans had done the dirty work of killing and "hanging" Jesus. The usual course would then be to bury him "dishonourably" and "out of sight".

Dishonourable burial meant two things. First, it meant being buried away from the family tomb. Second, it meant being buried without the usual rites of mourning.[23] When Josephus talks about being buried "out of sight" he probably meant both of these things. The idea was that the deceased was cut off from his people both physically and culturally.

Did Jesus go to one of the graveyards of the condemned?

If Jesus followed the usual pattern, then, where would he have been buried? The Mishnah *Sanhedrin* talks about graveyards of the condemned, and that is certainly a possibility.[24] But the important thing for the Jewish religious authorities was not where the deceased was buried, but where he was *not* buried. One guilty of contaminating the Jewish people by his blasphemy while he was alive must not be allowed to contaminate the Jewish people by his presence when dead.

Food for the jackals?

It is therefore entirely possible that Jesus was not buried properly at all. He could have suffered the eventual fate of thousands of victims of Roman crucifixion, and been slung onto a rubbish tip or into a shallow grave, to be food for the jackals.

There is an intriguing suggestion that this might have been the case. One of the manuscripts dug up at Nag Hammadi was a Coptic book dating back to perhaps the first half of the second century AD. It is known as the Secret Book of James. It describes Jesus as having been buried "in the sand". This may indicate an early tradition that there was no tomb burial, but rather a makeshift shallow grave.

Temporary non-burial

But there is another alternative – one which allows some credence to the story in the gospels. This is temporary burial. Suppose that Joseph of Arimathea really was, as his stated membership of the Sanhedrin would suggest, a pious man. He would have been keen to see that the Jewish law was kept. That meant that the crucified Jesus had to be down from the cross by sunset, and eventually put in the graveyard of the stoned and crucified. This is more probable than complete non-burial. Non-burial was a horrible deterrent. There seems no particular need for it in Judea at the time, or in the specific case of Jesus. And some Jews might have been offended by the non-burial of such a man – perhaps particularly on the eve of sabbath, which was also the eve of a particularly holy festival.

Being buried in the graveyard of the condemned didn't necessarily mean that there would be no funerary decencies at all. A man in Joseph's position might genuinely have had some sympathy for Jesus, and been anxious to give him as respectful a burial as was consistent with Jewish law. The point for now is simply that there was nothing unlawful about observing these basic last courtesies.

Everything we know about Jesus' burial suggests that he was not honourably buried.[25] There are of course Christian commentators who contend otherwise.[26] It is difficult to understand why they are bothered, and the contentions are in the face of all the evidence. The canonical gospels themselves plainly describe a dishonourable burial: no family tomb; no proper mourning, with mourners "sitting shiv'ah" for seven days after the death.[27] The canonical gospel writers are clearly embarrassed by the fact of dishonourable burial: they do their best to highlight the unusual features of Jesus' funeral arrangements. But it is not until we get to the elaborate and late Gospel of Peter that all the giveaway signs of dishonourable burial have been excised and covered over with the trappings of royal death.

On the day of Jesus' death things were plainly rushed. Any pious Jew, looking at Jesus on the cross and looking at the sun, would have been worried that there was about to be an infringement of those solemn injunctions in Deuteronomy 22. The land might be about to be cursed. It was particularly important not to violate this sabbath: it was an especially holy one – the one before the Passover.

So what was the priority? It was to get Jesus down. The rest could wait. The remainder of the Jewish law (about the necessity for dishonourable burial) wasn't so pressing. If any basic decencies were to be allowed, they could be performed after the sabbath ended at sundown on the Saturday.

In the meantime, though, the corpse had to be stored somewhere. If Joseph of Arimathea really was in favour of giving Jesus some final funerary respect, and if John is right that Joseph had a tomb near Golgotha, Joseph's tomb was the obvious solution to the pressing legal problem. Perhaps, then, the gospels are right: perhaps the body *was* put into Joseph's tomb. But it wasn't buried there: it was just parked there. The intention was to move it (to the graveyard of the condemned or to a shallow grave) as soon as it was lawful to do so. That meant Saturday night.

Who saw where the body was put? If you believe Mark and Matthew, it was Mary Magdalene and Mary the mother of Joses.[28] If you believe Luke, it was some unnamed women who had come with Jesus from Galilee.[29] John is silent on the point. But, whoever they were, they were right out of Joseph of Arimathea's social league. He wouldn't chat with the likes of them. There is no reason at all to suppose that Joseph told them that the tomb was just a temporary chapel of rest. Perhaps they did see the body laid in there on the Friday night and the stone put across the door to stop the animals getting in. If so, it was natural to conclude that Jesus had just been buried. Which is, of course, precisely what they, and millions since, have indeed concluded.

But all this has taken the gospel accounts at face value. It is time to stop being so uncritical. The first thing to do is to look carefully at that very curious but wholly central character, Joseph of Arimathea.

Did Joseph exist, and, if so, who was he?

One of the classic ways of demonstrating the legendary development of the Bible is to look at how the New Testament gradually elaborates its account of Joseph of Arimathea.

In Mark, Joseph is "a respected member of the council, who was also himself waiting expectantly for the kingdom of God..."[30] Matthew, building on Mark, tells us that Joseph, a "rich man from Arimathea...was also a disciple of Jesus."[31] Luke is even more forthcoming: Joseph was "a good and righteous man...who, though a member of the council, had not agreed to their plan and action. He came from the Jewish town of Arimathea, and he was waiting expectantly for the kingdom of God."[32] By the time we get to John, Joseph is "a disciple of Jesus, though a secret one because of his fear of the Jews..."[33]

This development, along with the fact that Joseph fulfils an obvious Christian need in the passion story (the need to have someone with sufficient clout with Pilate to get the body, but also sufficient sympathy with Jesus to help give Jesus a decent burial), has caused some to think that Joseph is a literary creation.[34] Joseph, they say, is just too convenient to be true. And he behaves in a most improbable way. To give his tomb to Jesus for burial proper, the argument goes, he would have to be more than just a casual admirer. He would be offending against the clear rules of the Jewish law –itself a potentially career- and status-destroying thing for a man in his position to do. And he would be defiling his own, apparently brand new, tomb.[35] It would not have been a suitable place for him or any of his family to be interred afterwards. The gesture was a financially ruinous one. Only fictional characters behave like that.

It is interesting, too, that in the gospel stories Joseph buries only Jesus. What about the two thieves, who were doubtless Jewish? If Joseph's concern was to ensure that Jewish law wasn't violated, surely he would have looked after all three of them. His particular concern for Jesus' burial and Jesus' burial alone merely underlines the peculiar, inexplicable devotion that he must have felt for Jesus. Again, this is the devotion of fiction.

There are other doubts about Joseph that should niggle with anyone interested in the truth. Why, having been such a key player in the central act of this great drama, does he bow out so completely once Jesus is interred? We never hear of him again. Not only does he not come on to take a bow, and make the expected averment that Jesus really was in his tomb and was properly buried there, but he's never even mentioned again in passing. That's a bit ungrateful, at best. You might expect a little footnote in some apologetic sermon. There's not a trace. But perhaps that's because there's no mention of the empty tomb outside the gospels either – of which more later.

We also have no real idea where Arimathea was. Luke says that it was a "city of Judea", which should make it easy enough to identify. But we can't. Perhaps it can't be identified because it didn't exist. Perhaps Joseph, who was so pivotal to the story, was given a definite but unidentifiable origin in order to put him beyond denial. He had to have the appearance of reality, and so had to have an origin.

But to say he was from a non-existent place was the safest strategy. No one could say: "I live there, and there's no one there who answers to that description." The non-identification of Arimathea is a little point, it's true, and perhaps would be a non-point on its own. But it is not on its own. Look hard at Joseph and you see nothing but mystery, contradiction and question.

You have to feel for the gospel writers: they are faced with a tricky bit of literary footwork. The difficulties of Mark's simple, bet-hedging solution – downplaying the attachment that Joseph felt but making him a vague kingdom-seeker – are clearly understood by the subsequent writers. The solutions get more and more sophisticated, and it is that, ultimately, that gives them away. They are imaginative word-artists: they are not telling the truth. Joseph is their creation.

Was it likely that Pilate would release the body to Joseph?

History, courtesy of the New Testament, has been too kind to Pilate. He was not the weak but basically principled philosopher of the gospels, asking, puzzled but genuine: "What is truth?" He was cruel, corrupt and notoriously insensitive to Jewish feelings. A letter from King Agrippa 1 to Caligula, written about AD 41, says that Pilate used "briberies, insults, robberies, outrages, wanton injuries, constantly repeated executions without trial, ceaseless and supremely grievous cruelty".[36] Knowing perfectly well that Jewish law prohibited the making of images, he brought effigies of Caesar into Jerusalem.[37] The result was entirely predictable: the Jews were outraged. They begged Pilate to take them away. He refused. For five days and nights the petitioners lay prostrate round his house. Pilate's immediate thought was murderous coercion. He invited the demonstrators to come to the stadium to present their complaints. His soldiers were hidden there, waiting. Submit or die, the demonstrators were told. They called Pilate's bluff, saying that they would rather be martyred than back down. Pilate, knowing the effect such a mass murder would have, petulantly let them go.[38]

When Pilate again outraged Jewish sensibilities by selling sacred Jewish treasure to build an aqueduct, the streets filled with protesters. Pilate's response was to infiltrate his soldiers into the crowds, dressed as Jews. With their clubs the troops beat indiscriminately both rioters and onlookers.[39]

This, then, was the man who is said to have been so alert to the importance of not offending Jewish religious sensibilities that he kept crucified corpses off the usual municipal tip, and so compassionate that he released the body so that it could have the few respects permitted by the law.

Is it really likely that the body was released at all? There was nothing in it for Pilate, and that, along with sadistic pleasure, seems to have been Pilate's main criterion in all his decision-making. If there had been a whiff of expectation about the resurrection (and Jesus, remember, had said that he would return), any governor wanting an easy life would have been slow to release the body to the very friends who would be likely to be involved in a resurrection scam. Of all the men crucified that day, Jesus was plainly the most likely to cause trouble after his death. The veneration of tombs of prophets and martyrs was an increasingly popular religious craze at the time.[40] Pilate would have been particularly reluctant to create a shrine. Take the body down by sunset, perhaps: it was no particular trouble to appease the Jews in that way. But far better to keep the body under reliable Roman guard. The Jews capable of making a fuss about Jewish legal violations were the Jewish establishment. They wouldn't get too upset if the blasphemer was put out for the dogs.

Who is Nicodemus?

He appears only in the latest of the gospels, John, and so is immediately and rightly suspect. He has appeared there before, of course. He is a device used regularly by John to make rhetorical points. Nicodemus, according to John, was a Pharisee who had come secretly to Jesus by night, to ask him, apparently respectfully, some deep theological questions.[41] Presumably impressed with his answers, Nicodemus becomes at least a sympathiser. He doesn't always skulk fearfully in the shadows. Equipped by Jesus' teaching he becomes a proper man – so much so that he demands a fair trial for Jesus from his fellow Sanhedrinists.[42] By the time of Jesus' burial he is consorting with Joseph, who, John tells us, is "a disciple". So Nicodemus is plainly by now in the camp of the good. And his reward for his developing boldness is to play a central part in the cosmic drama of the death of God. It's all a parable, designed to give hope and backbone to John's beleaguered Christian audience. Perhaps John also realised that as a matter of mere mechanics the older stories about Joseph dealing with the body alone lacked credibility. What was Joseph supposed to have done at the cross? Slung Jesus over his shoulder and walked off to the tomb with him? More hands make lighter and more credible work. And, certainly, if you are going to have a hundred pounds of spices, you need some help.

The spices

Nicodemus, John tells us, "brought a mixture of myrrh and aloes, weighing about a hundred pounds."[43] He and Joseph "took the body of Jesus and wrapped it with the spices in linen cloths, according to the burial customs of the Jews."[44]

John, as so often, is overplaying his hand, and this time he has been caught out. "…[A]bout a hundred pounds" is an absurd amount. The Roman *litra* or pound was about 12 ounces. John is therefore talking about 75 (modern) imperial pounds.

There is a huge, bitter, technical and inconclusive debate about whether the myrrh and aloes were powdered or in liquid form.[45] For present purposes it doesn't matter. However you look at it, it is far too much. If the spices were dry, they couldn't possibly have wrapped the body up with them in the linen cloths: they would have had to bury the body under a great mound. If the spices were in the form of oil, they would have drenched the body: Joseph and Nicodemus would have had to wade out through the puddles they had made.

John is theologising again. Great kings have sackloads and bucketfuls of spices at their funerals.[46] Jesus is a king in his death, John is saying. Pilate had recognised it: "King of the Jews", he had said, mockingly or otherwise.[47] Pilate was right, says John: And you, the hearers of my gospel, should acknowledge it too. It's a good sermon, perhaps. It's not history.

Who buried Jesus?

This might seem a stupid question. The canonical gospels, after all, are clear that it was Joseph (Mark, Matthew and Luke) or Joseph and Nicodemus (John) who put Jesus in the tomb.[48] But all is not necessarily what it seems. The doubt starts in Acts: here is Paul preaching in Antioch of Pisidia: "Even though [the inhabitants of Jerusalem and their leaders – i.e. the Jews] found no cause for a sentence of death, they asked Pilate to have him killed. When *they* had carried out everything that was written about him, *they* took him down from the tree and laid him in a tomb…"[49] (added emphasis). Now that's odd. Here is Paul saying that the Jews who were responsible for Jesus' death were also responsible for taking him down from the cross and burying him. It seems that Paul didn't know about, or didn't believe, the Joseph of Arimathea tradition. If Christianity's principal apologist doesn't or won't accept Joseph, why on earth should we?

Archaeological improbabilities

To understand this we have to jump forward to the accounts of the empty tomb. It is there that the New Testament gives most information about the tomb in which it says Jesus was laid.

The New Testament information about the tomb

Golgotha, where Jesus was crucified, was outside the city walls[50], but near to the city.[51] At or near Golgotha was a garden, and in that garden was a new tomb, in which no one had ever been laid.[52] This tomb belonged to Joseph of Arimathea, and was hewn out of rock.[53] Joseph rolled a stone to or against the door of the tomb.[54] The stone was very large.[55] It was necessary to stoop to look into the tomb.[56] Peter and John were able to go into the tomb.[57] Mary is said to have seen two angels sitting where the body of Jesus had been laid. One was at the head end; one was at the foot end.[58] Three women were able to go into the tomb[59], and when they did so saw a young man sitting on the right side[60], or two men.[61]

Accordingly there seems to have been room there for at least five people: two of these could sit. Sitting was possible on the right hand side, where Jesus had lain.

There are two features in this description that make it improbable. First, its simplicity. And second, the rolling stone. Taking these in order:

The curious simplicity of the tomb described

Most of the first-century tombs in the Jerusalem area are more complex than this. They tend to consist of a low door opening onto a central chamber where mourners could gather. Off the central area, cut at right angles into the rock, are small tunnels or niches, called *kokhim*. Bodies would be laid in those *kokhim*. There are often several interconnected chambers, each with many *kokhim*. In first-century Palestine the practice of secondary burial was common. This meant that the body would be left to rot for a year. The bones would then be gathered up and put in a stone bone box – an ossuary – sometimes with an inscription indicating the identity of the occupant. The ossuaries would be left in the tomb. Typical tombs with their *kokhim* and ossuaries are shown in Figs 13-17. If the Holy Sepulchre Church in Jerusalem really does contain the remnants of the tomb of Jesus, Jesus' tomb may well have been part of the tomb complex of which the surviving tomb, which is now a Syrian chapel, was a part. That surviving tomb is illustrated at Fig 29. It is a textbook first-century rock tomb with the expected *kokhim*.

But this is not what the gospels appear to describe. Although this was the tomb, we're told, of a rich man, it was very simple indeed. Instead of the *kokhim*, there seems to have been a burial bench, at least on the right-hand side. One would have thought that Joseph would have wanted better for himself and his family.

The rolling stone

And then there is the famous rolling stone. The Christians want it to be huge. What do we know about it? Mark says that Joseph "...rolled a stone against the door of the tomb..."[62], and notes that the three women, coming on Sunday morning, thought that they would need help rolling it away.[63] The stone was "very large".[64] Matthew says that Joseph "rolled a *great* stone to the door of the tomb..."[65], and notes that it was big enough for an angel to sit, presumably comfortably, on it.[66] Luke notes that the stone was "rolled away"[67]; John merely says that when Mary Magdalene came to the tomb "...the stone had been removed from the tomb..."[68]

The comments on the size of the stone reek of late apologetic, designed to help scotch rumours of grave robbery or a grave-break by a revived Jesus. But, if they are to be taken seriously, they are wholly at odds with the account of a simple tomb.

Some first-century Jerusalem tombs were closed with rolling stones.[69] But they are few and far between. Of the hundreds of known Jewish tombs in the Jerusalem area of the right date, only four were known to have been closed by a geometrically perfect circular stone rolling in a prepared groove.[70] All of these were the glamorous tombs of the very rich. The best two examples are at the entrance to the Tomb of Queen Helena of Adiabene, at the "Tombs of the Kings" (Figs 18, 19 & 20) , and at the entrance to Herod's family tomb (Fig 22 & 23).

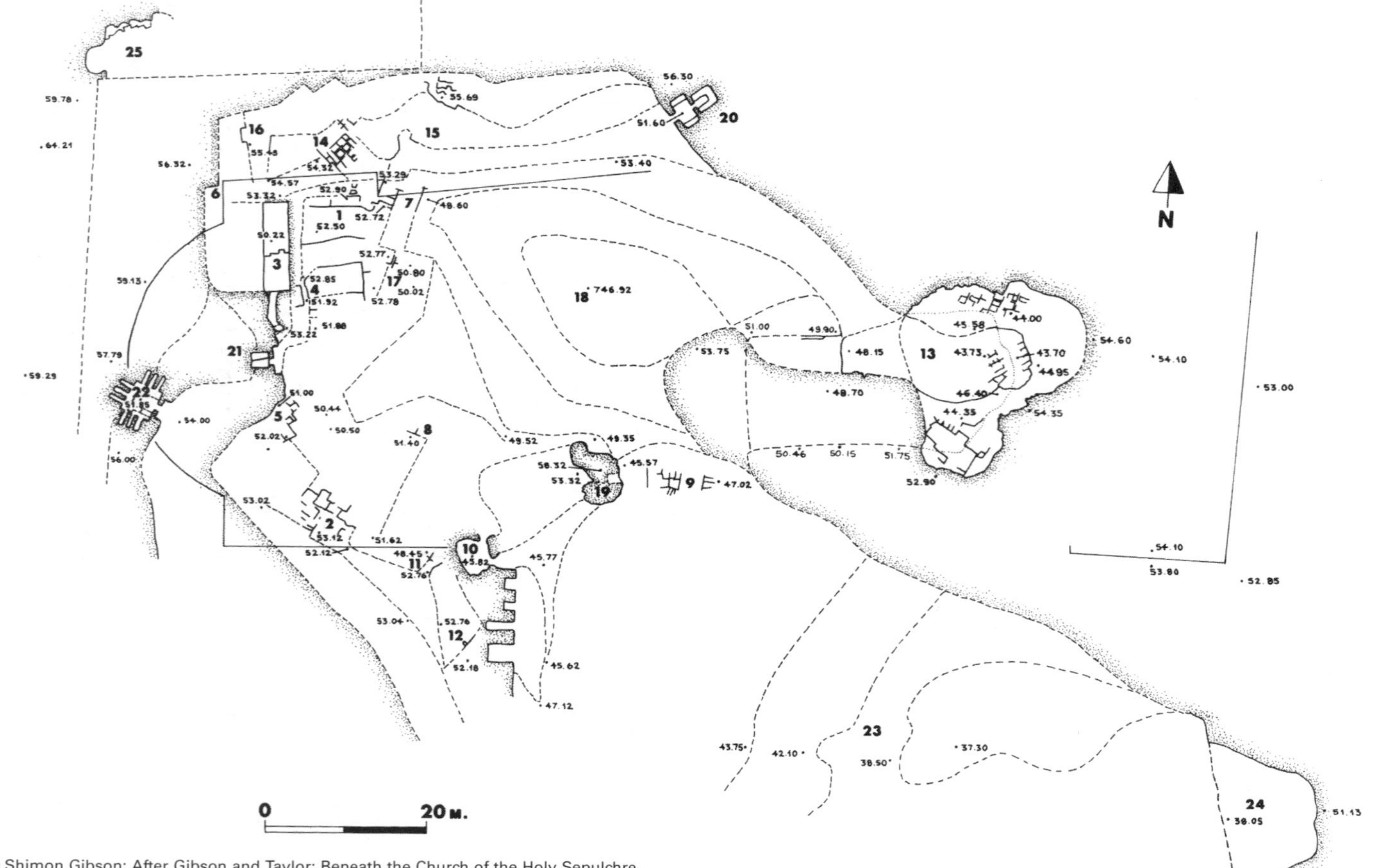

© Shimon Gibson: After Gibson and Taylor: Beneath the Church of the Holy Sepulchre, Jerusalem. London, Palestine Exploration Fund, p.52

Plan of ancient quarrying, caves and rock-hewn tombs in the environs of the Church of the Holy Sepulchre, Jerusalem. The western end of the church is shown in outline.

Key:

1. Quarrying below the northern transept
2. Quarrying with separation channels and disengaged blocks, below the southern transept.
3. Rock cuttings in the floor of an underground chamber.
4. Quarrying near a pilaster of the Rotunda.
5. Quarrying for squared blocks between the Edicule and a column of the Rotunda.
6. Quarried corner north of the Rotunda.
7. Quarrying for squared blocks of stone north east of the Rotunda.
8. Quarrying south east of the Rotunda.
9. Quarrying for squared blocks of stone east of the Rock of Calvary.
10. Rock-cut cave below the façade of the church.
11. Quarrying below the east side of the church façade.
12. Rock-cuttings below the southern courtyard.
13. Quarrying in the Chapel of St. Vartan and the Cave of the Invention of the Cross.
14. Quarrying with partly-detached blocks.
15. Quarrying.
16. Quarrying.
17. Quarrying for squared blocks of stone.
18. Bedrock surface at elevation 746.92.
19. Rock of Calvary
20. Rock-cut Iron Age tomb below the Coptic monastery.
21. The Tomb of Jesus
22. Reconstructed kokhim tomb south-west of the Edicule.
23. Quarrying below the vaulted cistern in the Monastery of St. Abraham.
24. Large cave below the Russian property south-east of the church.
25. Quarrying behind the Patriarchion.

Archaeology's verdict

What does this come to? The rolling stone was a late, legendary development. It served two apologetic purposes. First, it helped to give the impression that Jesus' burial was not as humiliatingly dishonourable as it clearly was, and to shore up the notion that, as the prophets had foretold, Jesus would be "with a rich man in his death". Unfortunately for the Christians, the airbrushing of the dishonourable parts wasn't complete. The writers left behind traces of a much more probable story: that Jesus' body was left overnight in a tomb to which Joseph of Arimathea, as a member of the Sanhedrin, had access, but which wasn't Joseph's own. And, second, the rolling stone was designed to lay to rest persistent alternative explanations for the absent body: grave robbery and revival. The Christians are always caught out by real history.

Part 2: Y

> Numquam ponenda est pluritas sine necessitate: (which loosely translates as): The simplest answer is usually the correct answer.
>
> William of Ockham

Introduction

There is a good deal of common ground here. Much of the basic history is agreed, but X's spin on the history is not. X's arguments are complex – far too complex to be probable.

The bodies of the crucified in Roman times

The general position is as X says that it is. One of the intended horrors of crucifixion was non-burial. But much of the information that we have about crucifixion comes from much more stressful times than those of Jesus.[71] The Romans didn't have any particular need to make a sadistic example of Jesus *pour encourager les autres*. Indeed, X has spent a lot of time arguing in Chapter 3 that Pilate was rather taken with Jesus. Pilate would apparently have been happy not to crucify Jesus at all: it is likely, then, that he would have been happy to release the body to friends or family.

This wasn't unknown. Indeed, the only bones of a crucified man that have been dug up in the Holy Land were those of a man – and a Jew – whose body was plainly released to his family. He is Jehohanan of Givat ha'Miv'tar, and he has already been mentioned.

His body did not find its way to the rubbish tip or (probably) to the graveyard of the condemned. If he did start his post-mortem career in the graveyard of the condemned, he didn't stay there. At some point (and the logical point is immediately after his death), he found his way into the family tomb. Once his flesh had decomposed, his bones were gathered up in the conventional first-century Jerusalemite way and placed in an ossuary.

There is textual evidence, too, that the bodies of crucified men were sometimes given to their families. Denouncing the barbarity of Avillius Flaccus, the governor of Egypt, Philo says that proper governors (unlike Flaccus) handle crucifixions at festal times either by postponing them or by allowing burial:

> I have known cases when, on the eve of a holiday of this kind [an imperial birthday] people who have been crucified have been taken down and their bodies delivered to their kinsfolk, because it was thought well to give them burial and allow them the ordinary rites. For it was meet that the dead also should have the advantage of some kind treatment upon the birthday of the emperor and also that the sanctity of the festival should be maintained. But Flaccus gave no orders to take down those who had died on the cross.[72]

What about crucified Jews?

Jehohanan makes the point that a crucified Jew might well have found his way into a decent tomb.

Burial on the eve of the sabbath

X is right about the rush to get Jesus down and interred on the Friday. That urgency appears in all the gospels. But he overestimates how elaborate a proper Jewish funeral needs to be. It can be, and often is and was, done very quickly. Anointing is not mandatory. Washing is customary, but can be cursory. As X acknowledges, in the case of someone who has met a violent death it is likely to be omitted altogether. This is a consequence of the idea that the body must be kept as far as possible intact. Blood on a sponge used for washing a body is blood that will not be buried with its body. A macabre example makes the point: when a bomb explodes in modern Israel, hot on the heels of the blue-light emergency services come teams of religious Jews with bags, whose job it is to comb the area and collect every last body part. Each part is united with its body as far as possible; each is in any event given a decent burial.

If Jesus was going to have any sort of regular interment there was plenty of time to do the basic funerary necessities. But was he going to have a proper burial?

What sort of burial would Jesus have had?

Would Joseph have overridden Jewish tradition in Jesus' case?

There is every reason to suspect that Joseph was, as the gospels indicate, at least a profound admirer of Jesus. He had really put himself on the line. The ruling religious body, of which Joseph was a member, had condemned Jesus to death. To be seen to be allying himself in any way with Jesus was potentially a very dangerous, or at least a career-damaging, thing to do.

X suggests that Joseph might have been acting purely out of respect for Jewish funerary practice, and that once the demands of the law had been met (by Jesus being off the cross and decently stored before the start of the sabbath), Joseph had done everything that his conscience demanded of him. But this ignores three crucial points:

(a) The primary responsibility for ensuring that the land was not contaminated by failure to comply with the Deuteronomic laws and the funerary norms lay with the Jewish powers-that-be. It was none of Joseph's business. And he was making an awful lot of work for himself, wholly unnecessarily. If Joseph had not stepped in, the authorities would have made sure that the Jewish law was kept. This was not an unusual situation. There were systems in place that dealt with it.

(b) The law, as X is keen to point out, was easily satisfied. Jesus just had to be taken down and interred in the graveyard of the condemned or in a shallow grave. Even if Joseph had for Jewish reasons of his own decided to act as a freelance funeral director on behalf of the Jewish authorities, there was absolutely no need to offer Jesus his own tomb or give him any of the other elaborate honours (such as anointing with spices) that the gospels talk about.

(c) In fact there was every reason why he shouldn't offer his own tomb: Jesus was, in Jewish ritual law, beyond the pale; a

> condemned blasphemer who had no place, even in death, with decent, law-abiding Jews. A tomb occupied by such a corpse would be ritually debarred to others. A tomb was often one of the most expensive items of outlay in a first-century Jew's accounts. It wasn't something you would just throw away to an outlaw whose body you were trying to keep from polluting the land of Israel. A tomb that had been used as a temporary mortuary for such a corpse would need to be expensively and tediously decontaminated before it was fit for nice people.

In this, as in so many other areas, the straightforward biblical account is so much simpler, and therefore more credible, than the clever, convoluted alternatives of X. X points out that the women felt constrained by Jewish law not to come on the Saturday. This is an indication, he says, of the power of Jewish law over even people known to be devoted to Jesus. How much more so, he says, would Joseph feel constrained. Well, fair enough. But Joseph, in putting Jesus' body in his tomb as per the New Testament account, has done nothing against the law. We will come to that.

Did Jesus' body get the traditional Jewish funerary treatment?
X summarises the available evidence fairly.

The idea of dishonourable burial
Again, X describes the idea accurately.

We know little about the burial of poor people in first-century Palestine. Some were probably laid in earth graves; some had shaft tombs – 5–7 metre trenches with a niche at the bottom for the body.[73] Had Joseph not taken pity on him, and if his body had escaped the graveyard of the condemned and been released to his family, one of these variants was probably the sort of grave that would have awaited Jesus. Such burial was not as sociable as the clubbable post-mortem experience that rich people had. Usually in such a poor burial there would be no mingling with one's fathers. The distinction between honourable and dishonourable burial presumably consisted in the fact that your family had buried you, although they would generally not be buried with you; and in the fact that your family could ensure that all the mourning rites were observed.

Did Jesus go to one of the graveyards of the condemned?

This would indeed have been a common course for a crucified blasphemer. But here we have positive evidence that it was not the case. The gospels say that Jesus was placed in a tomb belonging to Joseph.

There was nothing offensive to Jewish law about burial in Joseph's tomb, and so the story cannot be ruled out as intrinsically improbable. Indeed, the Joseph story fits the only probable reconstruction of Joseph's motives and behaviour very well: see above.

If Jesus was destined for one of the graveyards of the condemned, why on earth not send him straight there? Why this strange story about Joseph? To say, as X does, that the Christians need the Joseph story as a central element in their resurrection fabrication is nonsense. If you are going to fabricate a story about a missing body, it is actually rather easier to site the story in the graveyard of the condemned. The readers of the gospels would know that the usual fate of a crucified blasphemer would have been the graveyard of the condemned. To have the story elsewhere is to invite raised eyebrows. If you are concerned about fabricating fulfilment of the prophecy "[he was] with a rich man in his death", and have introduced Joseph's grave to do that, then again you are making life difficult for yourself. You are much less likely to be caught out in your lie by saying simply that there was a nameless rich man interred that night in the same graveyard of the condemned.

Food for the jackals?

Jews didn't like this. It offended their sensibilities, even when the deceased was a blasphemer. So, although it was a common fate for non-Jewish victims, it is intrinsically unlikely for a Jew in Jerusalem. Whatever Jesus was, he did have friends and followers in Jerusalem at the time of his death. His body, if slung on a heap, would be likely to have been retrieved and interred anyway.

But if his body was destined for the tip, there's no reason why it couldn't have gone there on the Friday night. You don't give expensive, exotic obsequies to a corpse that will soon join the garbage of Jerusalem. So, if the body did ultimately end up on the midden, it makes the whole Joseph story immensely improbable, which again raises the question: why invent it?

Temporary non-burial

This thesis is a rhetorically cunning halfway house. But it fails for the reasons already identified. You really didn't have to do much to bury a crucified blasphemer legally. What was necessary could have been done immediately. And it wouldn't have been done by a Joseph figure: it would have been done by the authorities. Allow Joseph into the story at all, and you must allow him in to play precisely the part that the gospels say he played. He makes no sense in any other role.

But let's stay with the thesis for a moment longer. Let's assume that Joseph had no real attachment to Jesus. Let's assume that he had no motive other than to ensure rigid compliance with the Jewish law. If so, he would have been wholly scandalised by the suggestion that this blasphemer whose corpse he had given a temporary home to had burst out of his tomb and risen from the dead. He would have been the first to scotch the rumour. "Don't be ridiculous," he'd have said; "I took him down to the graveyard of the condemned on Saturday night."

Or let's say that Joseph was short of being a disciple, but was friendly with Jesus. If so, he would surely have known at least some of the other people in Jesus' coterie. X's point about different social status is overplayed. Joseph didn't have to have them round for dinner to know who they were. It would then have been an act of basic compassion and decency for Joseph to have said to them, when the empty-tomb rumour began: "Sorry; you've got the wrong end of the stick. I moved him before your people got there on the Sunday morning."

This is as good a place as any to deal with the question of whether Jesus had an honourable or a dishonourable burial. Many gallons of academic ink and vitriol have been expended on this subject. Many Christian apologists, for some reason I cannot understand, have been anxious to establish that he was honourably buried. But for once I agree with X: the gospels do tell a story that, to any first-century Jewish readers, would have meant dishonourable burial. He was not buried in a family tomb, and there was no proper mourning. Words like "So what?" spring to mind. This seems to me to have no apologetic consequences whatsoever.

Did Joseph exist, and, if so, who was he?

Many of the relevant points have been made already. But it is worth reiterating that if Joseph was not real, he was a wholly unnecessary and very dangerous literary device.

X blithely says that the gospel writers "need to have someone with sufficient clout with Pilate, but also sufficient sympathy with Jesus to help give Jesus a decent burial". And it sounds attractive. But stand back a bit. Why would the writers need this? *Something* happened to the body once it was taken down from the cross. If, for some reason of their own (and we will come to those reasons in later chapters), the gospel writers decided to fake a missing body, it would have been far easier and safer to do it without making up a story about an unusual departure from usual funerary practices by a high-profile, named, Sanhedrin member whose place of origin (to compound the danger of contradiction), is given too.

While we are on the question of Joseph's home town, it has to be acknowledged that Arimathea has proved tricky to pin down. Wherever it was, it was a small and obscure place. But that adds to the credibility of the Joseph figure. If Arimathea didn't exist at all, the gospel readers would simply have said: "Doesn't exist: this is nonsense." And if it existed but Joseph didn't come from there, people would have said: "I asked Rachel, who's lived there all her life, and she's never heard of him." If you want a fictional figure who won't be unmasked, best not to mention where he comes from at all, or to say that he's a foreigner from some vast, anonymous metropolis.

There are several suggestions for the location of Arimathea. The arguments for and against the authenticity of each are complex and irrelevant for these purposes.[74]

X suggests that it is odd that Joseph doesn't bury the two other men crucified that day. Well, not from the Christian point of view, it isn't. It underlines what the Christians have always said: Joseph thought that Jesus was really special and was prepared to do him particular favours.[75]

X thinks it suspicious that once Jesus is interred, Joseph bows out from the New Testament entirely. It is quite the contrary, in fact. If Joseph had been wheeled on again, it could have been only to say that the body was indeed in the tomb on the Friday and Saturday nights. He put it there on the Friday and didn't move it. That would have been said only if the "temporary non-burial" hypothesis had been raised as a possible explanation for the empty tomb. And if he had said this, X would be incandescent with barristerial indignation, blustering about late textual emendation for transparently apologetic purposes. The temporary non-burial hypothesis, if credible, would have been far more familiar to the first century investigators than to us. The fact that it was not specifically scotched by Joseph suggests that it wasn't thought even remotely arguable by Christianity's opponents in those early days.

Was it likely that Pilate would release the body to Joseph?

I have dealt already with the likelihood, in the Roman world in general, of crucified victims' bodies being released by the authorities.

X says simply that Pilate was too much of a brute to have done the compassionate thing. It is true that Pilate had a record of great insensitivity. But that did not mean he was relentlessly bad all the time. Perhaps, as X was keen to say at one point of his emetically inconsistent argument, there really was some rapport between Pilate and Jesus. Perhaps Pilate's wife really did get to him. Perhaps Pilate was corrupt and needed a backhander from Joseph. There are many possibilities. In any event, releasing Jesus' body was no skin off Pilate's nose. It was not likely to cause civil uproar. The Jews wanted Jesus dead. They had got their wish. They had no particular wish to see him degraded after his death. Pilate had no reason to be worried about a resurrection scam. There is not the slightest evidence that Pilate knew of any predictions that Jesus would rise until he was told about the rumour on the Saturday (as he was according to Matthew). Even if he did know about them he is unlikely to have bothered much. The Jesus movement was a tiny, apparently insignificant one. There was no reason to think that Jesus could cause trouble from beyond the grave. For Pilate to have pre-empted the resurrection story by himself insisting on a guard would be wholly counterproductive: it would give credence to the insane religious rantings of the resurrection-lobby, if there was one. If Pilate gave half a thought to the idea that the Jesus-bother had not been ended by his death, he would probably have thought that Jesus' body was far safer in the custody of a nice, respectable, well-scrubbed, educated, middle-class chap like Joseph than in the hands of whomever else it might otherwise fall into.

Who is Nicodemus?

There's no problem here. The idea that Nicodemus had to be created because a credible Joseph would have needed a hand with the body is ridiculous. Anonymous horny-handed sons of toil would have done the job better, and again their existence couldn't be contradicted. To name fictional characters, or characters who didn't actually play the part you said they played, is dangerous and wholly unnecessary.

The spices

Yes, a hundred Roman *litra* is a lot, whether it was a hundred *litra* of powder or of liquid. But John might not have meant that. The Greek in the text we have reads: "...*litras hekaton*..."[76] If you add one letter (easily lost in scribal copying), you have "*hekaston*", which would transform the meaning to: "myrrh and aloes, about a pound each."[77]

Or *litra* may be a measure of volume rather than weight[78], in which case the total volume has been calculated at something like 3 gallons[79] or 4 gallons.[80] Or it may be Johannine hyperbole. John may indeed be making a point about Jesus' kingship. He may be trying to mitigate the shame associated with a technically dishonourable burial. Whatever the case, there is no reason to doubt the core of the story: the body was treated in some way by some spices of some consistency.

Who buried Jesus?

Acts 13:27–29 is indeed slightly ambiguous. But there is no sinister mystery here. Joseph was a Jew. He was a member of the Sanhedrin. Although Joseph had not been at the meeting of the Sanhedrin that had condemned him, it was indeed the Sanhedrin that had pressed for the execution of Jesus. It is natural enough to roll Joseph up with the rest of the Sanhedrin for the purposes of the sermon, and accordingly say that those who had condemned Jesus had also buried him. Everything we know about the time when the gospels were written suggests that the Joseph story had been in circulation for a long time before Paul preached this sermon, and continued in circulation during and after the preaching of the sermon.

Stand back a bit. Luke wrote Acts. He also wrote Luke's gospel. Luke's gospel is explicit about Joseph's role in the burial.[81] Luke was in no doubt about the Joseph story. Luke travelled with Paul. It is unlikely that Paul didn't know about it. The glitch in the sermon report might well be simply a bit of infelicitous expression. And if Paul didn't know the Joseph story, that is hardly the end of the Christian case. This Christian business is the story of Jesus, not Joseph.

Archaeological improbabilities

The New Testament information about the tomb

X sets this out accurately.

The curious simplicity of the tomb described

Yes, the tomb is simple. But not everyone chose to spend their money on their tombs; Joseph might have had other priorities. We know only about Joseph's status, not the state of his bank account. The family tomb of the high priest, Caiaphas, is extremely plain, although he himself had a splendid ossuary. There are plenty of first-century tombs in Jerusalem like the one described in the gospels.

The rolling stone

As to the size of the stone, how large is "very large" or "great"? All the evidence has been summarised by X. If you get into the tomb by bending double, then a stone that would cover the entrance would be pretty large and pretty heavy, and the women might well wonder how they were going to move it. There's little point in speculating beyond that.

It is perfectly true that there are very few known examples of huge, perfectly round stones that roll in a groove. It is also true that those that there are are associated with very big, very expensive tombs. But the gospel accounts don't imply that Joseph's tomb was like that. That's a Hollywood gloss. The stone is likely to have been trundled rather than rolled, and to be more rectangular than round.[82]

Archaeology's verdict

X puts two and two together and makes some huge and strange number. The most informed view we have on what the tomb was like comes from Professor Martin Biddle's excavations in the Holy Sepulchre Church and his study of what is known from previous excavations and in the literature about the history of the tomb. It is as follows:

(a) The tomb had two components (Fig 30): there was an unroofed or partly covered rock-cut forecourt (3–4 metres wide and 3–4 metres deep), which opened by a low entrance into a fully enclosed square or rectangular tomb-chamber (probably about 2.8 metres square and 2 metres high) cut out of the rock;
(b) The entrance to the tomb chamber from the forecourt was closed by a large stone. There is no evidence that this was round; it is more likely to have been roughly dressed and to have been trundled rather than rolled across the entrance.
(c) On two or three sides of the burial chamber there were probably burial couches cut out of the rock. These were about 2 metres long and 0.8 metres wide. Their surfaces were about 0.5 metres or slightly less above the floor.
(d) The ceiling of the burial chamber was probably flat. Suggestions that the burial couch that survives was within a niche below a neatly rounded *arcosolium* arch are unsupported by the evidence.
(e) Between the burial couches was a deeper excavated area, the "standing pit", which allowed visitors (including burial attendants and bone gatherers) to stand upright inside the tomb. This pit was probably about 1m by 2 metres.[83]

All of this is entirely concordant with the account in the gospels. Having summarised the information given about the tomb in the gospels, Martin Biddle says:

> What is clear is that the kind of tomb suggested by the gospel accounts is consistent with what is now known of contemporary practice in the Jerusalem area… The difficulty perhaps that such a tomb is too simple; burial couches on more than one side [which he eventually concludes the tomb probably did have], long narrow rectangular niches or loculi (*kokhim*) in which a body might be inserted at right angles to the walls of the tomb, and multiple chambers are commonplace. The absence of such features may be due to the sparseness of the gospel accounts: they may not be mentioned because irrelevant, but that does not mean they were not there. In a new tomb, however, they are not perhaps to be expected. It was only with time that additions were needed, and the more complex Jerusalem tombs are clearly the product of successive generations.[84] (Original emphasis.)

CHAPTER 5

The empty tomb

Sources

Mark 16

When the sabbath was over, Mary Magdalene, and Mary the mother of
James, and Salome bought spices, so that they might go and anoint him.
[2]And very early on the first day of the week, when the sun had risen, they
went to the tomb. [3]They had been saying to one another, "Who will roll
away the stone for us from the entrance to the tomb?" [4]When they looked
up, they saw that the stone, which was very large, had already been rolled
back. [5]As they entered the tomb, they saw a young man, dressed in a
white robe, sitting on the right side; and they were alarmed. [6]But he said
to them, "Do not be alarmed; you are looking for Jesus of Nazareth,
who was crucified. He has been raised; he is not here. Look, there is the
place they laid him. [7]But go, tell his disciples and Peter that he is going
ahead of you to Galilee; there you will see him, just as he told you." [8]So
they went out and fled from the tomb, for terror and amazement had
seized them; and they said nothing to anyone, for they were afraid.

Matthew 28

After the sabbath, as the first day of the week was dawning, Mary
Magdalene and the other Mary went to see the tomb. [2]And suddenly
there was a great earthquake; for an angel of the Lord, descending from
heaven, came and rolled back the stone and sat on it. [3]His appearance
was like lightning, and his clothing white as snow. [4]For fear of him the
guards shook and became like dead men. [5]But the angel said to the

women, "Do not be afraid; I know that you are looking for Jesus who was crucified. 6He is not here; for he has been raised, as he said. Come, see the place where he lay. 7Then go quickly and tell his disciples, 'He has been raised from the dead, and indeed he is going ahead of you to Galilee; there you will see him.' This is my message for you." 8So they left the tomb quickly with fear and great joy, and ran to tell his disciples. 9Suddenly Jesus met them and said, "Greetings!" And they came to him, took hold of his feet, and worshipped him. 10Then Jesus said to them, "Do not be afraid; go and tell my brothers to go to Galilee; there they will see me."

11While they were going, some of the guard went into the city and told the chief priests everything that had happened. 12After the priests had assembled with the elders, they devised a plan to give a large sum of money to the soldiers, 13telling them, "You must say, 'His disciples came by night and stole him away while we were asleep.' 14If this comes to the governor's ears, we will satisfy him and keep you out of trouble." 15So they took the money and did as they were directed. And this story is still told among the Jews to this day.

Luke 24

But on the first day of the week, at early dawn, they came to the tomb, taking the spices that they had prepared. 2They found the stone rolled away from the tomb, 3but when they went in, they did not find the body. 4While they were perplexed about this, suddenly two men in dazzling clothes stood beside them. 5The women were terrified and bowed their faces to the ground, but the men said to them, "Why do you look for the living among the dead? He is not here, but has risen. 6Remember how he told you, while he was still in Galilee, 7that the Son of Man must be handed over to sinners, and be crucified, and on the third day rise again." 8Then they remembered his words, 9and returning from the tomb, they told all this to the eleven and to all the rest. 10Now it was Mary Magdalene, Joanna, Mary the mother of James, and the other women with them who told this to the apostles. 11But these words seemed to them an idle tale, and they did not believe them. 12But Peter got up and ran to the tomb; stooping and looking in, he saw the linen cloths by themselves; then he went home, amazed at what had happened.

John 20

Early on the first day of the week, while it was still dark, Mary Magdalene came to the tomb and saw that the stone had been removed from the tomb. [2]So she ran and went to Simon Peter and the other disciple, the one whom Jesus loved, and said to them, "They have taken the Lord out of the tomb, and we do not know where they have laid him." [3]Then Peter and the other disciple set out and went towards the tomb. [4]The two were running together, but the other disciple outran Peter and reached the tomb first. [5]He bent down to look in and saw the linen wrappings lying there, but he did not go in. [6]Then Simon Peter came, following him, and went into the tomb. He saw the linen wrappings lying there, [7]and the cloth that had been on Jesus' head, not lying with the linen wrappings but rolled up in a place by itself. [8]Then the other disciple, who reached the tomb first, also went in, and he saw and believed; [9]for as yet they did not understand the scripture, that he must rise from the dead. [10]Then the disciples returned to their homes.

11But Mary stood weeping outside the tomb. As she wept, she bent over to look into the tomb; [12]and she saw two angels in white, sitting where the body of Jesus had been lying, one at the head and the other at the feet. [13]They said to her, "Woman, why are you weeping?" She said to them, "They have taken away my Lord, and I do not know where they have laid him." [14]When she had said this, she turned round and saw Jesus standing there, but she did not know that it was Jesus. [15]Jesus said to her, "Woman, why are you weeping? For whom are you looking?" Supposing him to be the gardener, she said to him, "Sir, if you have carried him away, tell me where you have laid him, and I will take him away." [16]Jesus said to her, "Mary!" She turned and said to him in Hebrew, "Rabbouni!" (which means Teacher). [17]Jesus said to her, "Do not hold on to me, because I have not yet ascended to the Father. But go to my brothers and say to them, 'I am ascending to my Father and your Father, to my God and your God.'" [18]Mary Magdalene went and announced to the disciples, "I have seen the Lord"; and she told them that he had said these things to her.

Part 1: X

> …in Jerusalem the prudence of reason has little chance against the certitude of piety…
>
> Jerome Murphy-O'Connor, *The Holy Land*

The significance of the empty tomb

This is uncontroversial. If Christianity is true, the tomb has to be empty. But if the tomb is empty, it does not follow that Christianity is true.

The finding of the empty tomb: Discrepancies in the canonical gospel accounts

These are glaring. Put the accounts side by side (as is done below) and the absurdity of the Christian contentions is clear. There is no need for any comment: the differences speak eloquently for themselves.

We agree that Mark is no use to any historical enquiry after verse 8, where the oldest manuscripts end.

Who came to the tomb first?

Mark: Mary Magdalene, Mary the mother of James, and Salome.[1]

Matthew: Mary Magdalene and "the other Mary".

Luke: Unclear: "The women who had come with [Jesus] from Galilee" followed Joseph as he took the body away, and saw "how his body was laid". "They" then prepared spices and ointments, rested on the Sabbath, and then "they" came to the tomb. Later, the whole story is told to the disciples by Mary Magdalene, Joanna and Mary the mother of James and "the other women with them". This might imply that all these people were at the tomb, or the witnesses might have told other women the story before they told it to the disciples.

John: Mary Magdalene.

Why did they come?

Mark: They brought spices so that they could anoint the body.

Matthew: Not stated.

Luke: They brought the spices that they had prepared, presumably to anoint the body.

John: Not stated.

When did they come?

Mark: Very early on the first day of the week, when the sun had risen.

Matthew: After the sabbath, as the first day of the week was dawning.

Luke: On the first day of the week, at early dawn.

John: Early on the first day of the week, while it was still dark.

How did they think that they were going to get into the tomb?

Mark: They didn't know. They had been saying to one another: "Who will roll away the stone for us from the entrance to the tomb?"

Matthew: Not stated.

Luke: Not stated.

John: Not stated.

What was the first thing they saw when they got there?

Mark: They looked up and saw that the stone (which was very large) had already been rolled back.

Matthew: "Suddenly there was a great earthquake; for an angel of the Lord, descending from heaven, came and rolled back the stone and sat on it. His appearance was like lightning, and his clothing white as snow. For fear of him the guards shook and became like dead men."

Luke: They found the stone rolled away from the tomb. They went into the tomb, but did not find the body. They were perplexed.

John: Mary saw that the stone had been removed from the tomb. She then ran and went to Simon Peter and "the other disciple, the one whom Jesus loved". She said to them (although the gospel does not record her noting that the body was gone): "They have taken the Lord out of the tomb, and we [who are "we"?] do not know where they have laid him." Then Peter and "the other disciple" set out and went toward the tomb. The two were running together, but "the other disciple" outran Peter and reached the tomb first. "The other disciple" bent down to look in, and saw the linen wrappings lying there, but he did not go in. Then Simon Peter came, following him. He saw the linen wrappings lying there, and the cloth that had been on Jesus' head, not lying with the linen wrappings, but rolled up in a place by itself. Then "the other disciple" also went in, and he saw [what?] and believed [what?]. Strangely, the gospel says that the other disciple believed "…for as yet they did not understand the scripture, that he must rise from the dead". The disciples then returned to their homes. Mary

Magdalene seems to have returned to the tomb with the disciples. She evidently stayed there.

Whom did they see, and where?

Mark: As they entered the tomb they saw a young man, dressed in a white robe, sitting on the right side.

Matthew: As above.

Luke: While they were in the tomb, perplexed, suddenly two men in dazzling clothes stood beside them.

John: Peter and "the other disciple" did not see anyone on their visit to the tomb, but Mary stayed behind at the tomb after they went home. She was weeping outside the tomb. As she wept she bent over to look into the tomb. She saw two angels in white, sitting where the body of Jesus had been. One was at the head end; one was at the foot end.

What was their immediate response?

Mark: They were alarmed.

Matthew: Not stated.

Luke: They were terrified, and bowed their faces to the ground.

John: Not stated.

What conversations were there?

Mark: The young man said to them: "Do not be alarmed; you are looking for Jesus of Nazareth, who was crucified. He has been raised; he is not here. Look, there is the place they laid him. But go, tell his disciples and Peter that he is going ahead of you to Galilee; there you will see him, just as he told you."

Matthew: The angel said to them: "Do not be afraid: I know that you are looking for Jesus who was crucified. He is not here; for he has been raised, as he said. Come, see the place where he lay. Then go quickly and tell his disciples, 'He has been raised from the dead, and indeed he is going ahead of you to Galilee; there you will see him'. This is my message for you."

Luke: The men said to them: "Why do you look for the living among the dead? He is not here, but has risen.

Remember how he told you, while he was still in Galilee, that the Son of Man must be handed over to sinners, and be crucified, and on the third day rise again."

John: The angels said to her: "Woman, why are you weeping?" She said to them: "They have taken away my Lord, and I do not know where they have laid him."

What did they do then?

Mark: They went out and fled from the tomb, for terror and amazement had seized them.

Matthew: They left the tomb quickly with fear and great joy, and ran to tell the disciples.

Luke: They remembered that Jesus had indeed told them about the resurrection, and returned from the tomb, evidently to the disciples.

John: After complaining to the angels, with remarkable self-possession, about the missing body, Mary (who was still evidently outside the tomb, having just looked in) turned round and saw Jesus standing there.

Did the women meet Jesus? If so, what happened?

Mark: No meeting.

Matthew: Yes they did. Somewhere en route from the tomb to the disciples: "...suddenly Jesus met them and said: "Greetings!". And they came to him, took hold of his feet, and worshipped him. Then Jesus said to them, "Do not be afraid; go and tell my brothers to go to Galilee; there they will see me."

Luke: No meeting.

John: Mary Magdalene did: just outside the tomb, just after turning round from seeing the angels inside the tomb. At first she did not know that it was him. He said to her: "Woman, why are you weeping? Who are you looking for?" She supposed that he was the gardener, and said: "Sir, if you have carried him away, tell me where you have laid him, and I will take him away." Jesus said to her "Mary!". She turned and said to him in Hebrew "Rabbouni!" (teacher). Jesus said to her: "Do not hold on to me, because I have not yet ascended to the Father. But go to my brothers and say to them: " I am ascending to my Father and your Father, to my God and your God."

Did they speak to anyone about what they had seen, and, if so, to whom? What was said? What was the response?

Mark: They said nothing to anyone, for they were afraid. And there the gospel ends.

Matthew: Nothing recorded.

Luke: Yes: Mary Magdalene, Joanna and Mary the mother of James and "the other women with them" told the full story to "the eleven and to all the rest" (whoever that might be). Almost in the same breath[2] the gospel said that they told this to "the apostles".

John: Yes. Mary Magdalene went and announced to the disciples: " I have seen the Lord." She told them what Jesus had said to her.

Did anyone else come to the tomb? If so, who, and what happened?

Mark: The gospel ends before this point.

Matthew: Nothing recorded.

Luke: "The apostles" thought that this was an idle tale, and they did not believe the women. But Peter got up and ran to the tomb; stooping and looking in, he saw the linen cloths by themselves; then he went home, amazed at what had happened. Later, in 24:34, Luke mentions that there was an appearance of Jesus to Simon Peter. It is not at all clear when this was supposed to be.

John: Peter, "the other disciple", and Mary Magdalene were the only visitors.

Elaboration continues: The story in the gospel of Peter

The gospel of Peter is useful. It is at Appendix 3. Unless you agree with John Dominic Crossan that buried in Peter is an ancient, independent – in fact *the* most ancient – account of the passion and resurrection story (and not many people do agree with him), Peter helps to demonstrate the direction of literary elaboration. He demonstrates that Matthew, Luke and probably John are elaborations of the basic story in Mark: they are all edging in the direction of Peter.

Getting rid of Mark

If we can knock Mark out, certainly Matthew and Luke (and probably John), fall too.[3] The old cliché – that the evidence for the empty tomb rests on the testimony of four independent eyewitnesses – is laughable. Matthew and Luke are clearly Mark's creatures. John seems to have known at least of the tradition that underlay Mark's account. So we are probably dealing with, at best, one genuine witness or transcriber of an old tradition (Mark); and one witness (John), whose relationship with the facts may never have been first hand, and who is writing down old recollections from a memory contaminated with acquaintance with other testimonies, and befogged with senility.

Getting rid of Mark is really not hard: he is riddled with improbabilities.

Mark is using an ancient template

Mark is very keen on Elijah. He's particularly keen to put Jesus in Elijah's company whenever he can.[4]

And that is what he does with Jesus' death. Look at 2 Kings 2: Elijah and Elisha cross the Jordan near Jericho. The famous chariot of fire arrives and Elijah goes up to heaven in a whirlwind. The prophets, apparently watching from afar, speculate about what has happened to Elijah's body. They offer Elisha help in searching for the corpse: "…it may be that the spirit of the Lord has caught him up and thrown him down on some mountain or into some valley." Elisha declines the offer, but they insist, and he relents. They send off 50 men, who search in vain for three days. When they tell Elisha that the search has been fruitless, he shrugs: "Did I not say to you, Do not go?"[5]

Here we have the key to Mark's story[6]. Jesus, for Mark, is like Elijah. He has been taken up into heaven. The transfiguration story hinted at exactly that. There's no point in looking for a body, just as there was no point in looking for Elijah's. And it is hardly surprising that Mark ends his gospel where he does: not only is there no body to find, but if Jesus has been taken up to heaven, he is not going to be found wandering round Palestine.

Mark's abrupt ending

There are two other cryptic hints in the story that suggest, intelligently construed, that Mark is offering us his very own spin: that the story is his own literary cocktail of myth, Old Testament legend, messianic hagiography and downright fairy tale. The first has already been mentioned: that creatively abrupt ending, worthy of the most tortured of the post-modernists.[7] "If you listen properly," he's saying, "my silence will speak far more eloquently than all the credulous words of the other writers. In fact nothing happened other than an empty tomb: and that means that Jesus has been plucked into the heavens like Elijah."

The strange young man in white

The second hint is even more curious, but chimes well with the first. Mark has no truck with angels. There's just one "young man" in his story, dressed in a white robe. There's nothing to suggest that he is in any way a supernatural being. And what does he do? He tells the tale of what has happened to Jesus. He takes over the narrative from Mark the gospel writer. Or does he? The women, in Mark, don't tell anyone what has happened. How then could Mark have known? *Because he was the young man.* He was the eyewitness to what there was to be seen – the emptiness of the tomb. There's nothing other than the empty tomb in this earliest of gospels because there was never any more than the empty tomb. Mark thought that this was because Jesus was following in Elijah's heavenly footsteps. It was an appropriate end to a messianic career.[8]

What were the women thinking of?

They were going to anoint the body, according to Mark. But that was a deeply eccentric thing to do. If you believe John (which would be unwise), the body got the mother of all anointings on the Friday night. Why then another anointing? Jewish law knows of no such thing.[9] Either you're anointed or not. And if you are anointed it happens before you are buried, not afterwards. There are brutally practical reasons for that. Even in April in Jerusalem, after a day and a couple of nights one might expect a body to be beginning to turn. If the women really were going to anoint, this implies that there was no proper burial – precisely the main contention in Chapter 4.

Even if there was no anointing on the Friday (which is far and away the most likely position), would the women have known that? And if they did, why not come on the Saturday? Jewish law permits anointing of a body on the sabbath. And another thing: it would be more common for men to prepare the body of a man.

How did they think they were going to get into the tomb? Even they, according to Mark, realised the difficulty and were pondering it on the way. This is cunning of Mark. He needs to have the stone big to exclude all the sordid natural explanations of the empty tomb, but he still needs the women on site to be witnesses – to add to the otherwise isolated testimony of his own observation as the "young man" at the tomb. It makes no sense for them to go if the stone is so huge – so, juggling things as best he can in the interests of credibility, he puts into their own mouths the very doubt that will spring immediately to any reader's mind. And so he takes some of the force of the natural objection away. Every barrister knows the trick. If your own client candidly acknowledges the bad points in his case, they are not as bad.

The other gospels: Craven dependence on Mark and shameless divergence from him

At this point I am going to try to have my cake and eat it. I have said that Matthew and Luke clearly follow Mark, and that John at least knows Mark's tradition. But this chapter opened by pointing out the massive discrepancies between the books. How can those contentions come coherently from the same mouth? Very easily, is the answer. Mark was first. But then, as the church developed, it became important that the gospels said the right things. Mark wasn't good enough for those purposes. His embarrassing silence after verse 8 gave red faces to the preachers of the resurrection. Scepticism about the empty tomb made it necessary to demonstrate the fallacy of non-Christian explanations for its emptiness. Power conflicts in the early church required some supposedly authoritative account of which of the apostles had priority. And, quite simply, it became necessary to impress Christianity's audience. Mark was a bit prosaic: a bit dowdy. Angels would get onto the front page: young men in white shirts wouldn't. And so scripture expanded to fill the role it had to play. The accounts were tailored to the needs of the audience and the preachers.

With these thoughts in mind, some comments about the other gospels.

Matthew: Power, glory, earthquakes and fake guards

Matthew doesn't know where to stop. He's an incurable lily-gilder. He doesn't know that sometimes less is more. But that is ultimately a good thing. Without him the resurrection story would be considerably more credible and the wool might have been pulled over even more eyes. He's mighty keen on earthquakes and supernatural phenomena, transforms young men effortlessly into supernatural beings, isn't content with stones merely being rolled back (he has to see them being pushed back by angels), and having made up the guard, actually sees them being disabled with fear. And then he can't resist having Jesus meet the women in an unspecified place, with a predictable little cameo of feet-hugging worship.

The guard is a blatant apologetic device.[10] It is unclear whether it is supposed to be a Roman guard or a Temple guard. The chief priests and the Pharisees merely ask Pilate if he will "command the tomb to be made secure until the third day" to stop the disciples stealing the body and proclaiming the resurrection. Pilate then replies: "You have a guard; go, make it as secure as you can."[11] Debate rages over whether Pilate is saying: "I am giving you a guard", or "*You* have a guard yourself: use it". Note, too, while we are talking about those conversations, that inverted commas are second only to earthquakes in Matthew's list of literary likes. He loves reporting conversations that he could never possibly have heard. The posting of the guard[12] and the report of the guard[13] contain plenty of examples.[14] That's fine if you set out to write fiction. But this is purporting to be reportage.

If you believe Matthew, you can't believe any of the other gospels. You have to take your pick. If there was a guard there, precisely to prevent access to the body, how did the women expect to gain access? When the women arrive in the other gospels (just Mary Magdalene, in the case of John), the stone is already rolled back. The most ingenious harmonisers have failed to square this with Matthew's story of the stone being rolled back as the women watch.[15] Matthew is a festering thorn in the side of any apologist.[16]

Matthew is a very Jewish writer. He is marinated in the Old Testament. It has been plausibly suggested that his guard story has its origins in the story of Daniel in the lions' den.[17] There are some striking parallels. They were not lost on the early Christians: Daniel's release was a common symbol for resurrection. It was not surprising. The lions' den was closed with a stone. King Darius placed a seal on the stone. He visited the tomb at dawn. Angels play a big role in Daniel, and one (in a different context) is strikingly white and meteorological: he has a face: "like lightning".[18] Matthew's angel's appearance was "like lightning". Daniel's accusers were thrown into the den and died. Matthew's guard, curiously (but now, we can see, significantly), become "like dead men." These parallels cannot be accidental. They suggest deliberate fabrication.

But even if we suppose that the guard is wholly historical (although the other writers forgot about it or didn't think it worth a mention), and that it was composed of the sturdiest, most vigilant and most disciplined Roman soldiers, it doesn't dispose of the possibility that the body might have been taken. The guard was posted some time on the Saturday.[19] If someone wanted to steal the body, they might very well have stolen it on the Friday night. There was, after all, less chance of being disturbed then than on the Saturday night when the Sabbath was over. And that is what might have happened. If Matthew is right, the world's finest soldiers might have spent their Saturday night guarding an empty tomb.

Luke: An introduction to the primacy of Peter

Luke shows much more restraint than Matthew. But there is one obviously dubious passage. By the time that Luke was writing it was getting important for the early church to sort out who was boss. There had been bitter power struggles. Peter was coming out on top, but he still needed all the help he could get. What better claim to apostolic primacy could there be than to be curious when the other apostles dismissed the women's story as "an idle tale", and then go to the tomb to see, before any of the others, some of the crucial evidence of the resurrection?[20] In Acts, Luke reports Peter's leadership very sympathetically. There is no doubt whose side Luke is on. Or perhaps, by the time that Luke wrote, Peter had established his authority. If that was the case, Luke knew which side his bread was buttered on. He would have wanted to keep in with the winning side. Luke gave Peter exactly what Peter, politically, wanted and needed to hear.

John: Strange graveclothes and a race for power

John is an odd one. It has to be acknowledged that commentators who are confidently gung ho in their approach to Matthew are more chastened and respectful when it comes to John. He does seem to take his own line across country, and even if he does know of Mark or the Mark tradition, you would hardly guess it. He does seem to have first-hand knowledge of Jerusalem, and the Christians can be forgiven for saying that his account has the distinctive smell of eye-witness testimony about it.

That said, we may be dealing simply with a convincing author. Or a *more* convincing author. Perhaps John shines particularly brightly only against the background of Matthew and Mark.

In John's empty-tomb story there are two plain fables. The first is the race between Peter and the beloved disciple; the second is the graveclothes.

Peter and "the other disciple" were running together towards the tomb. The beloved disciple outstripped Peter and got to the tomb first. He didn't go into the tomb first, though. He just bent down and looked in, seeing the linen wrappings. Peter then arrived and went into the tomb. He saw "the linen wrappings lying there, and the cloth that had been on Jesus' head, not lying with the linen wrappings , but rolled up in a place by itself". Only then does the other disciple go in.[21]

Peter, generally in John's gospel, has some catching up to do. Notably, a couple of chapters before, he has denied Jesus twice.[22] If he is to be taken seriously as a church leader he needs to be rehabilitated. The story of the race is the story of Peter not only catching up with the other disciple (and not any old disciple – the one most precious to Jesus), but going one step further and becoming the first authoritative witness of the central mystery of Christianity. The race is a metaphor: Peter might have failed before but now, when it really matters, he is there on the front line while the other disciples are still snoring in their beds. He is not merely rehabilitated: he is invested with authority to lead. After a deeply unpromising start, he has won the race.

After the race comes the curious business of the graveclothes. This is important. Indeed, it cuts to the heart of John's credibility. It is one of the little touches always cited as evidence that John is an eye-witness. "Why make it up?", comes the question. But we have already answered the question: it was made up precisely because it is one of the little touches that tend to boost credibility. How do we know it is made up? Because it makes no historical sense. The possible variants of first-century Jewish graveclothes have been described in Chapter 4. There is no record of any separate cloth ever being used on the head.

There is another reason for suspecting that the graveclothes are not historical. This is that they seem to have been symbolically important in some way known to the early church but now lost to us. Those graveclothes, lying in the way that they were, convinced "the other disciple". He went in and "saw and believed".[23] Why should anybody "believe" anything about Christianity on the basis of an empty tomb and a pile of clothes? The empty tomb itself is, as will be conceded, not sufficient evidence of the resurrection. We must be looking here at some ancient code, written in the symbolic language of folded clothes. The beloved disciple read the code, and believed in the message that it contained.

Explanations for the empty tomb

Jesus was never in it

Perhaps he was just slung on a rubbish dump or in a shallow grave. This has been discussed in Chapter 4.

The temporary burial hypothesis: Jesus had been in the tomb, but by the Sunday morning had been moved to a permanent burial place

This again has been discussed in Chapter 4. There is no reason to suppose that Joseph of Arimathea would have told the women or the disciples what he or his associates had done with the body after moving it from the tomb (probably after the end of the sabbath on Saturday).

And why didn't anyone say where Jesus' body was? John Dominic Crossan sums up the thesis neatly: "With regard to the body of Jesus, by Easter Sunday morning, those who cared [about the whereabouts of the body] did not know, and those who knew did not care."[24]

The body was stolen

The theft hypothesis is not currently fashionable. But that is not to say that it is unarguable.

Grave robbing was rife in first century Palestine. In 1878 a marble slab was shipped from Nazareth to France. Its original provenance is unknown, but it was almost certainly from somewhere in

Palestine. It is now in the Bibliotheque Nationale in Paris. It has on it a Greek inscription which reads:

1. EDICT OF CAESAR
2. It is my decision [concerning] graves and tombs... whoever has made
3. them for the religious observances of parents, or children, or household
4. members... that these remain undisturbed forever. But if anyone legally
5. charges that another person has destroyed, or has in any manner extracted
6. those who have been buried, or has moved with wicked intent those who
7. have been buried to other places, committing a crime against them, or has
8. moved sepulchre-sealed stones, against such a person, I order that a
9. judicial tribunal be created. Just as [is done] concerning the gods in
10. human religious observances, even more so will it be obligatory to treat
11. with honour those who have been entombed. You are absolutely not to
12. allow anyone to move [those who have been entombed]. But if
13. [someone does], I wish that [violator] to suffer capital punishment under
14. the title of tomb-breaker.[25]

Its date is unclear. Some have said that it was an edict either of Tiberius (AD 14–37) or Claudius (AD 41–54).[26] Others put it at somewhere between 50 BC and AD 50.[27] Its relevance here is that it shows that grave robbing was a problem at approximately the right time and in approximately the right place.[28]

Matthew, of course, agrees with this. He did not laugh off the possibility of grave robbery in the way that modern Christian apologists do. He thought that it was necessary to occupy a big chunk of the space that he gives to the whole burial and empty tomb story dealing with it.[29]

If the body was taken, who was the culprit? Various candidates have been suggested. The Christians, setting up straw men so that they can knock them impressively down, love saying that neither the disciples, the Jewish authorities nor the Romans[30] could have taken the body. And that is probably right. But there are other people in the frame.

Think back to Chapter 4: non-burial or dishonourable burial was, in the ancient world, a catastrophe. Jesus' family may have wanted to do the decent thing for him. We know that some of them, at least (notably his brother James), were not easily convinced of his messianic credentials. Perhaps some who were not convinced took the body and buried it in a family tomb? And perhaps they didn't bother to scotch the resurrection rumours because they weren't "Christians" themselves, and had no truck with all those hysterical people who were making bizarre claims about a risen Jesus.

Or perhaps more orthodox, mercenary robbers were responsible. It is true that Jesus would not have been buried, Tutankhamun-like, with a mass of priceless artefacts, but there were other valuable commodities.

Corpses were sometimes moved for use in magic. Tacitus records how human remains were found along with other magical kit in the quarters of Germanicus.[31] Papyri belonging to Greek necromancers state how a corpse could be interrogated by putting an inscribed scroll into its mouth.[32] Whatever you believed about Jesus, his account of life post-mortem might be particularly interesting and valuable to anyone so inclined. The "heart of one untimely dead" was central to another ritual recorded in the papyri.[33]

The Roman poet, Lucan (AD 39–65) tells us about a witch who used to steal bodies from tombs and raise them to life. He paints a vivid picture of her. Note that she seems to have been particularly interested in crucified corpses. It may well have been someone like her who slunk into the garden, rolled the stone away, and crept off with the body of Jesus.

> …deserted tombs, her dwelling-place, from which, darling of hell, she dragged the dead…
> …Funeral pyres she loves to light, and snatch the incense from the flaming tomb…

> the pyre
> Yields to her shameless clutch still smoking dust
> And bones enkindled, and the torch which held
> Some grieving sire but now, with fragments mixed
> In sable smoke and ceremental cloths

Singed with the redolent fire that burned the dead.
But those who lie within a stony cell
Untouched by fire, whose dried and mummied frames
No longer know corruption, limb by limb
Venting her rage she tears, the bloodless eyes
Drags from their cavities, and mauls the nail
Upon the withered hand: she gnaws the noose
By which some wretch has died, and from the tree
Drags down a pendent corpse, its members torn
Asunder to the winds: forth from the palms
Wrenches the iron, and from the unbending bond
Hangs by her teeth, and with her hands collects
The slimy gore which drips upon the limbs.[34]

The riposte will surely be: but what about the graveclothes left behind? It is a fair point – assuming that they were. But there may be an explanation. If John is right, a massive amount of very valuable spices was interred with Jesus. The disciples denounced a woman at Bethany for pouring a single pot of ointment over Jesus' head shortly before his death. It was very valuable, they said: the money should have been spent on the poor.[35] If that was costly, the hundred pounds of spices must have been extortionate. And it was all lying there, waiting to be taken.

It is not clear from John how those spices would have been used. The issue is discussed in Chapter 3. But if they were in powder form, perhaps they were wound into the graveclothes. In which case the graveclothes would have to be unbound to remove them. A prudent robber would know that he would get a good price for the body from the local witches and a good price too for the spices.

But perhaps there was an even stranger culprit with a much more benign motive. Tertullian, repeating in the second century the old story that the disciples stole the body, adds another possibility. If the disciples hadn't moved the body, it might have been the gardener, "that his lettuces might come to no harm from the crowds of visitants".[36] This might sound ridiculous, but remember that according to John this was Mary's first thought too. She thought that Jesus was the gardener, and asked him if he had taken the body away.[37] The whole massive structure of Christianity which has dominated world history for the best part of 2,000 years might have been built on a smallholder's concern for his lettuces. It is Monty Python at its best.

The wrong tomb?

Anyone who has been to Jerusalem will have looked over from the Old City towards the Mount of Olives. They will be looking across the Kidron Valley, on the east side of which is the Arab village of Silwan. There are some spectacular monuments in the Kidron Valley – notably the so-called tombs of Absalom and Zachariah. But beneath and around the big monuments there are dozens of smaller tombs. The rock on which Silwan is built is honeycombed by tombs.

It was probably something like that wherever Jesus was first interred. The area around the Holy Sepulchre Church – which may well be the site of the tomb – was probably full of first-century tombs. A Jewish burial chamber (first century BC/first century AD) still survives in the Syrian chapel in the precincts of the Holy Sepulchre (see Fig 29). It is perhaps 40 yards from the alleged tomb of Jesus. Jerome Murphy O'Connor comments that its relationship to the tomb of Christ "is best explained by postulating a catacomb…"[38] It is known that there were other tombs fairly nearby.[39]

The best possible Christian case is that some of the women saw where Jesus' body had been put. (There are grounds to be suspicious about that: the statements that they saw the whereabouts of the tomb are slightly too deliberate; they look as if they have been inserted deliberately to deal with the possibility that the subsequent visits were to the wrong tomb.)[40] But on any view the women were extremely distressed: their whole world had fallen apart. The light may have been fading.

On the Sunday morning, all the accounts agree that the women came early. In John, Mary Magdalene (who of course comes alone – increasing the chance of mistake), comes when it was still dark.[41]

It is perfectly possible that they were just looking at the wrong hole in the rock. There is no suggestion that Joseph's tomb was in any way distinctive. There is no suggestion that, of Jesus' company, anyone other than the women knew where the tomb was. The later arrival of the men does not constitute independent corroboration of the contention that the women had earlier got the right tomb.

Scotching the resurrection rumour: A pre-emptive strike

If Jesus wasn't really raised, say the Christians, why didn't the people who knew where the body was just produce it and put an end to the resurrection preaching?

It's a fair point, but easily answered. First, it presumes that the body was not in the hands of someone who had taken it illegally. No grave robber was going to risk execution by owning up to the theft. Second, from what we can see from the book of Acts, the preaching of the resurrection didn't start for seven weeks after the resurrection. By then any body would have decomposed wholly beyond recognition. Third, it assumes that scotching the rumour mattered to whomever knew where the body was. This is far from obvious. It is hard to underestimate the significance of Christianity at its start. Jesus was an obscure provincial teacher – one of many to come to town with new ideas about what Judaism meant. He had few followers at the best of times. After his death most of those took fright and vanished into the Jerusalem woodwork. Even when they did start preaching, they didn't, at first, get much of a following. And the following that they got wasn't a worry to the Roman authorities who were responsible for civil order. If the Romans knew where the body was, there's no reason why they should bother to produce it. If yet another obscure Jewish sect set up shop in Jerusalem, that would have been fine by them. If the Jews knew where the body was (for example in the graveyard of the condemned), again there is no reason (outside Matthew's gospel) to suppose that they would have taken the trouble to contradict definitively a superstition which, like most superstitions, they could expect would quickly die away. They may have thought that to produce the body might give credence to the Christians. It might have given out the message that they were really worried about the allegations of resurrection and were taking it seriously. The Christians would simply have said, if Jesus' body had been produced: "That's not him." And whatever had been produced would have been too decomposed to contradict them.[42]

Tomb veneration

There is no known very early tradition of veneration of the tomb of Jesus, although tomb veneration was a very common form of religious devotion at the time. This, say the Christians, indicates that the tomb of Jesus was indeed empty: there was therefore nothing to venerate. Had he been in the tomb, they say, thousands of pilgrims would have beaten their way to his door.

This contention rather flies in the face of the notion that resurrection was right at the heart of the Jesus movement, and it is also wholly at odds with Christian practice ever since the supposed tomb was discovered. Go to the Holy Sepulchre Church in Jerusalem now: it is packed with believers in busy and ecstatic veneration of a tomb that they expressly believe to be empty. The same is true of the Garden Tomb – or Gordon's Calvary – a Protestant version of the Holy Sepulchre, which looks far more authentic but is certainly not the tomb of Jesus.[43] If worshippers throng these sites now (as they have done ever since they were identified), would they not have thronged to the known site of Jesus' tomb whenever it was identified? The fact that there is no known early tradition of tomb veneration therefore tends to suggest that the early church simply didn't know where the tomb was. And why should that be? Back to Chapter 4: jackals or the temporary-burial hypothesis.

The empty tomb: References outside the gospels

This is very simple: there aren't any. It will no doubt be suggested that the historical resurrection was at the heart of, and the principal driving force behind, the early church. If that's true, why isn't the empty tomb worth a mention in the sermons of Peter or the letters of Paul? We'll return to this.

Part 2: Y

> A young atheist cannot guard his faith too carefully; dangers lie in wait for him on every side.
>
> C. S. Lewis, *Surprised by Joy*

The significance of the empty tomb

X is right: if the tomb was not empty, or was empty as a result of some non-supernatural cause, the Christians are plainly wrong. Their faith is in vain. If the tomb was empty, though, the Christians still have some work to do. The empty tomb, in other words, is a necessary but not sufficient condition of Christianity being true.

The finding of the empty tomb: Discrepancies in the canonical gospel accounts

Yes, there are discrepancies. Harmonisation is hopeless. X says that the differences speak eloquently for themselves. And he is right. But what they say is, as before, that the early church showed huge restraint and integrity. We have materially unedited accounts, which deserve for that reason to be taken all the more seriously.

X fairly summarises the discrepancies. But what he concludes from those discrepancies is wide of the mark.

Elaboration continues: The story in the gospel of Peter

The gospel of Peter is indeed helpful. Remember its status. It has never been canonical. It has always been regarded as a late, legendary development. Read it[44]: it shows no restraint. It shows what happens when human imagination gets to work on the basic gospel story. It shows what the gospels would have looked like if they were not genuine efforts to tell the unvarnished historical truth. Human beings are innately curious creatures. They dislike mystery: they like to know the full story. They like solving puzzles.

And that is what the gospel of Peter does. The writer couldn't bear not to deal with the moment of resurrection. You can almost feel his brain itching. And so he deals with it in a dramatic, spectacular way. The canonical writers no doubt felt the same itch. Probably more so, in fact, because they were much nearer to the events than the novelist who concocted Peter. But they refused to add materially to what they knew. Yes, there may sometimes be some interpretation of the events – some exposition; but never mere concoction.

Getting rid of Mark

X's contention (that Matthew, Luke and probably John depend crucially on Mark) has been made by him before. And answered. But in brief and in general, before going to the particulars:

(a) The contention isn't remotely arguable in relation to John, as X appeared to acknowledge in Chapter 2, but now seems to have forgotten.
(b) The contention in relation to Matthew and Mark has some force before you get to the passion/burial/resurrection accounts. After that, it really doesn't. Tom Wright has done the arithmetic:

> ...a glance at the Greek synopsis for even the start of the Easter story – Mark 16:1–8 and its parallels – shows that one could be forgiven for thinking that the evangelists had set out to see how *different* from one another they could possibly be.
>
> I regard it as a more or less fixed point of synoptic criticism that Luke

used Mark. But at this point he has told the story very much in his own way: a total of only sixteen words out of the 123 in Luke 24:1–9 correspond to equivalents in the 138 words of Mark 16:1–8. Nor are the parallels particularly significant: "on the first day of the week"; "to the tomb", "when they arrived", "you are seeking", "he is not here, he is risen." If Luke has "used" Mark, we must conclude either that he has done so very freely or that he has had another source alongside, which he has almost exclusively preferred. Or maybe "using" in this case means that he had the scroll of Mark on the table but was so accustomed to telling the story in his own way that he glanced at it, decided he could do without it, pushed it to one side and got on without further reference to it.

The relationship between Mark and Matthew is a little closer. There are moments when it sounds as though we are listening to a version of the same text, though from this passage alone it would be impossible to say which of them has used the other. Even so, out of 136 words in the equivalent Matthew passage (28:1–8), there are only thirty-five which are matched in Mark. As for putting Matthew and Luke side by side, there are a bare ten or a dozen matching words, depending what we count as exact parallels. It is, though, worthy of note from this brief glance at the synopsis that there is solid agreement on the words of the angel to the women: he is not here, he is risen (literally "he has been raised", egerthe)...[45] (Original emphasis.)

Mark is using an ancient template

First, says X, Mark was drawing a parallel between Jesus and Elijah. X sees echoes of the story in 2 Kings 2 in which Elijah's body is taken up by the chariot of fire, and 50 men search vainly for the body for three days in the hills of Judea.

The parallel is fanciful. It is ironic that X accuses Mark of literary creativity, while looking at Mark's simple story through such sophisticated eyes.

Mark, first of all, is the most bluff of all the writers. He has a distinct Yorkshire streak about him. If he'd meant to say that Jesus had been taken bodily into heaven like Elijah, he'd have said so. The idea that "Mark is very keen on Elijah" and is "keen to put Jesus into Elijah's company whenever he can" is simply inaccurate. Mark mentions Elijah three times. On the first occasion, it is to deal with the gossip of the crowd: some were saying that Jesus was John the Baptist; some that he was a prophet; some were saying that he was Elijah.[46] On the second occasion, the Transfiguration, Jesus is indeed in Elijah's company. But part of the point of that story is to assert that Jesus himself will rise from the dead – a very different matter from being whipped off to heaven in a chariot.[47] On the third occasion, some of the bystanders watching Jesus on the cross hear him calling out "My God, my God, why have you forsaken me?", and say: "Listen, he is calling for Elijah." The bystanders, giving him wine to drink, say: "Wait, let us see if Elijah will take him down."[48] Take him down, note: not let him hitch a lift up to the heavens in that chariot. Nowhere in any of this is there the remotest hint of any *parallel* between Jesus and Elijah. And in fact Jesus expressly says that he and Elijah will have wholly different post-mortem fates.

As to that, Mark is completely clear: "After I am risen", Jesus says, "I will go before you into Galilee."[49] The young man at the empty tomb rams the point home: "…tell his disciples and Peter that he goes before you to Galilee: there you will see him, as he said to you…"[50] I'll ram the point home, too, in case it is necessary. Taken together, these verses amount to Jesus saying: "If you are wondering what will happen to me after my death, I can tell you that it will be completely different from what happened to Elijah. He seems never to have died, but was snatched straight up by the fiery chariot. I, on the other hand, am going to die and then rise. Then I will see you in Galilee." A story more different from the Elijah story it is difficult to imagine.

There are no other parallels. No symbolic "50 strong men"[51] searched for Jesus' body. The most exuberant expository imagination can't turn that ragbag group of bemused women and baffled disciples into 50 men. And there was no search for three days. There's a limit to the number of ways that you can say that one thing is not like another, and so I'll stop.

Mark's abrupt ending

It's not creatively abrupt. It's just abrupt. It doesn't make dark post-modernist sense. Mark simply didn't write like that. He's brutally artless everywhere else in his gospel, and he doesn't, right at the end, get a sudden dose of Nabokov.

What's happened here is much more prosaic. The end has gone missing. The beginning and the end of papyrus scrolls were notoriously vulnerable. Mark plainly intends the risen Jesus to meet the disciples in Galilee: the relevant passages are cited above.

The last authentic verse of Mark that we have is verse 8: "[The women] went out and fled from the tomb, for terror and amazement had seized them; and they said nothing to anyone, for they were afraid." There is every reason to believe that this silence was temporary. If they had kept silence for ever, chapter 16:1–8 could never have been written. It clearly has the taste of eyewitness testimony. Note too that in the verse immediately before, the "young man" specifically commands the women to "tell the disciples and Peter that [Jesus] is going ahead of you to Galilee; there you will see him, just as he told you". It is immensely improbable that the women disobeyed. If they had disobeyed, the disciples might have stayed in Jerusalem and missed the chance of seeing again the man they loved most – but this time risen from the dead. The women too presumably wanted to see Jesus again. Very much indeed, in fact. What were they to do? Go up to Galilee by themselves, in the hope of seeing Jesus there? What sort of a reception could they expect there? Presumably something along the lines of: "Wonderful to see you, but why did you not pass on the message I specifically gave you? It is rather important that I see the disciples."

Remember that Mark is writing this gospel because he believes that Jesus is the Son of God, and there is good news to tell about him.[52] Without the resurrection, which Mark clearly believed in, Jesus would have no claim to be the Son of God, and there would be no good news to tell. What was in the missing part? Who knows: obviously appearances of the risen Jesus at least in Galilee. We don't know, either, when the original ending got lost.

The strange young man in white

X postulates that the young man in white was Mark only because he thinks that the gospel ended at verse 8, that the women kept silence for ever, and that the only evidence of the material in verses 1–8 must have come from the only other person there – the young man. As noted above, the thesis about the women's silence and the abrupt end at verse 8 is utterly implausible.

Just remember, too, what X said at the beginning about the consensus on the authorship and sources of Mark. Mark is said to have drawn his story principally from Peter. Well, the young man can't be Peter. Peter, in Mark's story, doesn't go to the tomb; the women knew Peter very well, and Peter went on to preach the resurrection of Jesus with great power – a position entirely incompatible with the theory being promulgated by X. So who does X think that this

"Mark" was? Someone the women didn't recognise, who knew the real (presumably non-supernatural) explanation of the empty tomb, who lied to the women about the resurrection of Jesus and Jesus' intention to meet them in Galilee, and who went on to write a history (assisted at least by Peter) of this Jesus figure, which clearly suggests that Jesus was the Son of God and was going to rise from the dead? It doesn't make any sense at all, and it is bizarre that the suggestion has been made between the covers of serious books.

What were the women thinking of?

We shouldn't get too analytical here. These were desperate, bereaved women, come to give the only service they thought they could give. Possibly they weren't thinking rationally about how they could get into the tomb. Few people do think rationally when they are in situations like this. Perhaps, if Matthew is right about the guard, they thought that the guard could help them to roll back the stone. According to Mark, of course, they did realise the difficulty. X's snipe at Mark is unworthy of him. He's petulant because his objection has been anticipated and therefore defused by Mark, and is trying to turn that petulance into a serious evidential objection. If Mark hadn't put in the line about the women realising the difficulty, X would be crowing. Since the line is there, X can't crow quite so loudly, and he shouldn't be crowing at all.

Even if the women knew that Jesus' body had already been anointed on the Friday night (and there is no evidence that they knew it had), they knew that he hadn't been anointed by *them*, which was the important thing. X has a tendency to talk about first-century Jewish burial laws as if we know everything about them, and as if they were kept to the letter by everyone. It has been suggested that there was a mandatory obligation to go to the tomb on the third day and check the body – a safeguard against permanent burial of people who were still alive.[53] But even if this was not the case, there is certainly no known prohibition against a second anointing. Where there was doubt about whether or not a body had been anointed, relatives and friends would have felt a positive obligation to anoint, just in case. We have seen that in the case of dishonourable burial, anointing would not be forbidden.

The other gospels: Craven dependence on Mark and shameless divergence from him

Having just accused Mark of the forensic trick of trying to escape criticism by acknowledging an inevitable objection, X starts his next section by doing precisely that. He can't sensibly criticise Matthew, Luke and John in one breath for following Mark, and criticise them in the next breath for not. And indeed he doesn't *sensibly* criticise.

Matthew: Power, glory, earthquakes and fake guards

In the previous chapter I acknowledged and dealt with the general problems relating to Matthew. Identical comments apply here, and there is no point in reiterating them.

Before looking at the detailed criticisms, though, it is worth observing that denunciation of Matthew's elaboration implies acceptance of the basic empty-tomb story which is said to be elaborated.

The guard story is interesting. It is regularly rubbished by anti-Christian authors, but it warrants a close look. It is perfectly true that only Matthew mentions the guard. And it looks like apologetics. Let's suppose, for the sake of argument, that it is purely apologetic fiction. Why is a guard being mentioned at all? Answer: to dispose of the suggestion that the body was stolen. The Jews were (according to Matthew) suggesting that it had been. But here's the significant thing: why were they suggesting that it had been stolen? Answer: because it had gone missing. What the Jews weren't suggesting, and what nobody in the first century was ever saying, was that the body was still there. The tomb was empty. The question is: *why* was it empty?

Why shouldn't there have been a guard of some sort? It might have been a Roman guard; it might have been a Jewish guard.[54] The text is ambiguous. But it doesn't matter. The Jewish Temple guard was disciplined and effective. Either a Roman guard or a Jewish guard could expect serious punishment for dereliction of duty.[55] That punishment may have been particularly severe if the dereliction involved breach of a seal.

The guard story continues with the story of the bribery of the guards.[56] The final word is Matthew's statement that the corruptly engendered story about the disciples stealing the body "is commonly reported among the Jews to this day".[57] This is very interesting indeed. It would have been a stupid thing to write if it were not true, because it could so easily have been contradicted. "No it isn't," the riposte would go, "I've never heard that before." It would have been foolish, too, to implant in readers' minds a scurrilous suggestion of which they might never otherwise have heard (that the disciples stole the body), unless Matthew was wholly convinced that the story was ridiculous. And it tells us, as before, that no one in first-century Jerusalem was contending that the body might still be in the tomb. Again, all were evidently agreed that the tomb was empty. The question on everyone's lips was: where was the body?

Matthew says that the tomb was sealed. We do not know what this means. It may mean that there was a cord stretched across the door, which was embedded in clay. The clay may have been marked with the imprimatur of a high authority. In the Daniel story (to which we will come), the sealing account reads: "A stone was brought and laid on the mouth of the den, and the king sealed it with his own signet and the signet of his lords, so that nothing might be changed concerning Daniel."[58] To allow breach of a seal was an affront against the authority whose mark was on the seal. If the guard was Roman, the mark on the seal may have been that of the Emperor, or the local authority to whom he had delegated power. If the guard was Jewish, any seal would presumably have been that of the Temple authorities.

X has suggested that even if there was a diligent guard, the tomb might have been empty on the Sunday morning because the body had been taken out sometime between the Friday night and whenever it was on the Saturday that the guard was posted. This implies criminal stupidity on the part of the guard. They knew when the body had been put in the tomb. If the whole purpose was to stop the body being taken, they would surely have checked to see that it was still there before they sealed the tomb at the start of their watch. However big the stone was, a group of soldiers would be able to move it, just as Joseph and Nicodemus had been able to do on the Friday night.

Now to the Daniel story. Of course there are parallels; X has pointed them out. But there are far more non-parallels. Daniel was in the den for one night only. There is no one consistently corresponding to the king in the empty-tomb story. Daniel's survival is testimony of his blamelessness. Jesus' blamelessness was never in doubt. Daniel's accusers and their wives and children are killed. Jesus' guards are stunned: his accusers presumably get away scot free. Daniel needs the help of the angel to shut the lions' mouths. Jesus needs no help from anyone. As to the angels in Daniel, the one who helps out in the lions' den is never described – just mentioned after the event. The angel with the face "like lightning" appears (as X acknowledges) in a completely different, entirely lion-free context – a dramatic vision on the bank of the River Tigris.[59] X jumps too quickly to conclusions: to establish a parallel is not to establish plagiarism.

Luke: An introduction to the primacy of Peter

If Luke's objective was sycophancy towards Peter he did a pretty pathetic job. Far better, for a start, to have edited out Peter's denial of Jesus. When it comes to the empty-tomb scene, Luke hardly sets Peter's name in lights. All that Peter did there was run to the tomb, see the graveclothes and leave, wondering what was going on. A dishonestly obsequious Luke would at the very least make Peter the first witness to the risen Jesus. Instead that honour goes to two immensely obscure followers of Jesus; Cleopas and a man whose name we do not even know.[60]

When Jesus eventually does appear among the bulk of the disciples, Peter's name is not even mentioned.

John: Strange graveclothes and a race for power

X opens his assault on John with an assertion that the race between Peter and the "beloved disciple" is a metaphorical statement about primacy in the early church. It makes Peter the first authoritative witness, and begins Peter's rehabilitation after his scandalous denial of Jesus.

But again this will not do. If the story were dishonestly making Peter the centre of attention, it would have made Peter the first witness of the risen Jesus. But it doesn't: Mary is – and that's after Peter has been in the area.[61] Peter, if anything, has been passed over by Jesus. If the race was a metaphorical one, why have Peter come second? And apparently Peter is not the first to be convinced by the evidence of the empty tomb and the graveclothes: the first is the "beloved disciple".[62] If there is supposed to be an element of rehabilitation in the story, John plainly doesn't think that it was enough: Peter is thoroughly and expressly rehabilitated later on in Galilee.[63]

But, most importantly, this cannot be a "primacy" story because the race is between the wrong people. The big dispute about the direction of the early church was between Peter (who took Paul's side) and the faction led by James. A race between Peter and James might raise suspicions of a metaphorical primacy story. A race between Peter and "the beloved disciple" does not. "The beloved disciple" is generally thought to be John himself. There is no evidence at all that John was associated with the James party. If he was, he evidently turned later to the Peter faction, as indicated by his writing of this self-effacing story. One would have expected Peter's camp to make a good deal in the surviving literature of a propaganda coup like the recruitment of John. But there is no whisper of it.

X is very dogmatic about the type of graveclothes that were used in first-century Jerusalem. In fact we don't really know what the practice and its variants were. The gospel accounts themselves are the best primary source of information about Jewish funerary practices in that time and that place. There may have been many variants. But we can say two things: first, John's assertions about the graveclothes being in two parts (linen body wrappings and then a separate head cloth) don't seem themselves to serve any obvious apologetic purpose: a single set of linen wrappings would have made the genuine apologetic point here just as well as the two-part set. And, second, the early readers and hearers of John's account would have known perfectly well what the funerary practices were. They would have spotted an anomaly. So it seems unlikely that there is any fabrication here.

There is nothing mysterious about "the beloved disciple" being convinced when he saw the folded graveclothes. X hints at a code that would cross a cabbalist's eyes. True, the empty tomb by itself is not sufficient evidence of resurrection. Nor, by themselves, are folded clothes. But taken together, the two strands of evidence do amount to a compelling case. The disciple, standing in the tomb, was mentally running through the possible explanations for the two facts: the empty tomb and the folded clothes. We will run through them in a moment. Like many after him, he realised that the folded clothes make wholly fanciful a non-supernatural explanation for the absent body.

Women as witnesses in the ancient world

All four canonical gospels make women the first witnesses of the empty tomb, and Matthew and John make women the first witnesses of the risen Jesus. This is incompatible with a dishonest intention to write an untrue but convincing account, because of the lowly status of women as witnesses in the ancient world.

This point has often been overstated by Christian apologists. It is not true that women could not be witnesses. They could be legal witnesses to matters within their knowledge if there was no male witness available.[64] The gospel accounts, anyway, were not written as submissions to a court, so the legal position is rather otiose. Outside the law courts the testimony of women was regularly used. Josephus cites women as his only witnesses on what happened inside Masada and at the battle at Gamala[65]; Pliny the Younger, in his letter to the Emperor Trajan, says that female deacons were the highest-ranking representatives of the church that he could find to interrogate.[66]

But nonetheless the point remains a strong argument for the integrity of the empty-tomb accounts. Women were definitely second-best witnesses. Anyone wanting artificially to bolster an untrue account would make sure that the account was given by a hairy, legally compellable male.

Explanations for the empty tomb

Jesus was never in it

This has already been dealt with and discounted in Chapter 4.

The temporary burial hypothesis: Jesus had been in the tomb, but by the Sunday morning had been moved to a permanent burial place

This, again, has been dealt with and discounted in Chapter 4. We can now add another piece of evidence: the graveclothes. Let's suppose, for the sake of argument, that Joseph's tomb was merely a temporary resting place, and that the intention was to move Jesus' body out to the graveyard of the condemned as soon as the sabbath was over on the Saturday. Joseph and/or his men duly arrive to move the body. There is absolutely no reason at all for them to take the body out of whatever graveclothes it was in. They would not carry a naked body to its final resting place. Not only would it have been disrespectful and obscene; it would have been extremely messy. Blood and worse would have been oozing everywhere. Can one conceive of circumstances in which the body might have been unwrapped and decanted into some sort of bag for its final journey? Well, no. But if for some reason that did happen, the motive could only have been to preserve (and presumably wash and reuse or sell), the original graveclothes. But they weren't preserved. They were left in the tomb. It makes no sense at all.

The body was stolen

The Nazareth inscription doesn't help either way. Its provenance (other than Palestine) and date are unclear. There is no evidence to indicate that it was a response to the missing body of Jesus. All it shows is that in approximately the relevant historical period grave robbing was taken seriously. But draconian penalties don't abolish crime.

Who then could have taken the body? X rightly concedes that neither the disciples nor the Jewish authorities could be responsible. He makes three alternative suggestions: Jesus' family; grave robbers; and the gardener.

For all three categories the presence of the graveclothes, folded in the empty tomb, makes the suggestion immensely improbable. This issue has already been discussed above. There is nothing in the suggestion that the graveclothes could have been unwound to remove valuable spices bound up inside them. Robbers wanting both the body and the spices would thank the original anointers for having made their job easier by binding the body and the spices neatly together, and just move body, clothes, spices and all. The spices would be removed later when the body was taken to a safe place. No robbers would leave the clothes – they presumably had some commercial value when washed. And if for some reason they did leave them, they certainly wouldn't bother folding them. The same goes for anyone nefariously making off (for some strange reason) with a naked body.

The high point of X's case about theft by or for magicians is the citation of Lucan's Pharsalia. All the other references in X's copiously referenced passage are references to the use of body parts – not of whole corpses. It's a lot easier to make off with a hand or an ear than a whole body. The Lucan reference is unabashed poetry. It is interesting that X, the rationalist, feels that he has to enlist corpse-raising necromancers to support him. He is in uncomfortable company. Not only is Lucan a poet, but he's a poet writing about events in a wholly different place (Thessaly) and a wholly different culture. There is no evidence whatever that the theft of bodies for magic was a problem in first century Palestine.

Quite apart from the graveclothes, the family can be excluded for another reason. It is true that the family was apparently slow to be convinced that Jesus was who he said he was. John notes that "not even [Jesus'] brothers believed in him."[67] But they were ultimately convinced – and convinced, it seems, by what happened after Jesus' death.[68] According to Paul, the risen Jesus appeared to James[69] (who was the brother of Jesus[70]) and Jesus' mother and brothers devoted themselves to prayer, along with the apostles, after Jesus' ascension.[71]

James became a leader in the Jerusalem church[72], and, according to Josephus, caused such trouble to the Jewish authorities that he was stoned to death.[73] The second-century writer Hegesippus says that James was martyred by being thrown from the wall of the Temple, and then finished off by the angry crowd.[74]

The point of all this is that James and at least several other members of his and Jesus' family were wholly convinced by the evidence that Jesus had died and risen. Of that family, at least James was martyred for his belief. It is hard to believe that if other (more distant) members of the family had gone to the trouble and danger of retrieving and burying Jesus' body they would not have told the (wrongly) believing ones, and spared them a lot of embarrassment, trouble and ultimate martyrdom.

The wrong tomb?

This is unlikely. As X has noted, the synoptic gospels specifically mention that the women saw where the body had gone. X's moan that this is too obviously apologetic to be true is the sort of churlishness we've come to expect. If there were no such mentions he would be gleefully saying that the absence of any mention was clear evidence that the women had gone to the wrong tomb. When Jesus was laid in the tomb the light would still have been good. It was still the Friday afternoon before the start of Shabbat. The apparent fact that Peter and "the beloved disciple" were able to run there without needing directions suggests that they also knew which was Jesus' tomb.

If there was a guard, per Matthew, of course there was no possibility at all of getting the wrong tomb. But even if there wasn't, the strange stories relating to the finding of the empty tomb make it inconceivable that this was a case of mistaken identity. How many tombs in that rough area would have had angels standing around at that time on the Sunday morning? How many tombs would have folded graveclothes just left lying there? Most tombs, anyway, would have had several dead occupants. New tombs (as this one was) would have been scarce.

The suggestion in any case betrays an important misunderstanding of the nature of first-century Jewish tombs. The door to the tomb is a door to a tomb chamber. Off the tomb chamber, usually on two or three sides, are either body benches, as apparently in the case of Joseph's tomb, or *kokhim* – niches going off at right angles to the wall of the chamber, in each of which a body would be laid. Because there are benches or *kokhim* to the sides of the tomb chamber, the individual tomb chambers, even in areas heavily populated with tombs, are quite a distance apart from one another. If they are not, the *kokhim* of adjacent tombs tend to break into one another. *Kokhim* do indeed sometimes breach one another; it was no doubt a source of great angst. If one looks at the plans of busy first-century Jewish burial areas one can get the impression of one massive complex of interconnecting tombs. The best example is the Five Tombs complex on Mount Scopus in Jerusalem: see Fig 16. But (and here is the point) the *entrances* to the tombs (which of course are the markers that any outside observers would use) are well separated.[75]

Scotching the resurrection rumour: X's pre-emptive strike

As soon as the empty-tomb rumour got around (long before the 40-day period up to Pentecost, when preaching really started in earnest), the authorities to whom it mattered wanted to put an end to it. They had tried to pre-empt it by posting the guard[76], and they tried to stop it spreading by bribing the guard.[77] Yes, these stories are only in Matthew, but it would have been crazy for him to invite contradiction by writing them down within the lifetime of many people who would be able to say that he was talking nonsense.

To begin with the Jesus movement was small, but that does not mean it was insignificant. Jesus' execution had mattered a good deal to the Jewish establishment; they had sat through the night to convict him. If they had the body, it would certainly have been produced. Violent though Jerusalem was, it wasn't awash with the bodies of men bearing the telltale marks of crucifixion – marks that would persist for a very long time.

Similarly if the Romans had the body: their concern was for civil order, which was being compromised. There is some force in the point that the Christians didn't start to get really troublesome until after Pentecost, but there was really nothing to stop the resurrection story from being rubbished after that. The disciples didn't want to be martyred. An alternative explanation for the empty tomb would have taken the wind out of the sails of the movement, but there is no suggestion of any alternative explanation even in the writings of the most virulent opponents of Christianity.

X is of course right that if a grave robber had taken the body, acting in the most curious way a grave robber has ever acted, he wouldn't broadcast it from the rooftops.

Tomb veneration

The early church appeared to know, and enshrine in tradition, the location of the tomb. There was, it is true, no tradition of veneration of the tomb. This issue is discussed in detail in Chapter 6.

The empty tomb: References outside the gospels

X flippantly asserts that there aren't any. He is too quick and too superficial. The point is dealt with in detail in Chapter 7.

Sunday observance

Many think that the first Christians changed their day of worship from Saturday to Sunday very soon after the resurrection, and that this is evidence for the truth of the resurrection accounts. I'm afraid I can't agree. The evidence about when Sunday observance started is unclear (at least to me), and I think it would be unsafe to hang anything on it.

Preaching in Jerusalem

When the first Christians started preaching the resurrection of Jesus, they did it in Jerusalem, the city where it was all supposed to have happened, under the noses of the very people who would have been able (and more than willing) to contradict their assertions if they were untrue. If the Christians had doubts about the historicity of their case (but for some reason still wanted to preach), it would have been far better to do it well away from Jerusalem and contradiction. The fact that the Christians preached first of all in Jerusalem, and so soon after the resurrection, denotes tremendous confidence in their case.

CHAPTER 6

The post-resurrection appearances

Sources

Mark

No resurrection appearances in the original manuscripts.

Matthew 28

8So they left the tomb quickly with fear and great joy, and ran to tell his
disciples. 9Suddenly Jesus met them and said, "Greetings!" And they
came to him, took hold of his feet, and worshipped him. 10Then Jesus
said to them, "Do not be afraid; go and tell my brothers to go to Galilee;
there they will see me."

11While they were going, some of the guard went into the city and told
the chief priests everything that had happened. 12After the priests had
assembled with the elders, they devised a plan to give a large sum of
money to the soldiers, 13telling them, "You must say, 'His disciples came
by night and stole him away while we were asleep.' 14If this comes to the
governor's ears, we will satisfy him and keep you out of trouble." 15So
they took the money and did as they were directed. And this story is still
told among the Jews to this day.

16Now the eleven disciples went to Galilee, to the mountain to which
Jesus had directed them. 17When they saw him, they worshipped him; but
some doubted. 18And Jesus came and said to them, "All authority in
heaven and on earth has been given to me. 19Go therefore and make disciples of all nations, baptizing them in the name of the Father and of the
Son and of the Holy Spirit, 20and teaching them to obey everything that
I have commanded you. And remember, I am with you always, to the end
of the age."

Luke 24

13Now on that same day two of them were going to a village called Emmaus, about seven miles from Jerusalem, [14]and talking with each other about all these things that had happened. [15]While they were talking and discussing, Jesus himself came near and went with them, [16]but their eyes were kept from recognizing him. [17]And he said to them, “What are you discussing with each other while you walk along?” They stood still, looking sad. [18]Then one of them, whose name was Cleopas, answered him, “Are you the only stranger in Jerusalem who does not know the things that have taken place there in these days?” [19]He asked them, “What things?” They replied, “The things about Jesus of Nazareth, who was a prophet mighty in deed and word before God and all the people, [20]and how our chief priests and leaders handed him over to be condemned to death and crucified him. [21]But we had hoped that he was the one to redeem Israel. Yes, and besides all this, it is now the third day since these things took place. [22]Moreover, some women of our group astounded us. They were at the tomb early this morning, [23]and when they did not find his body there, they came back and told us that they had indeed seen a vision of angels who said that he was alive. [24]Some of those who were with us went to the tomb and found it just as the women had said; but they did not see him.” [25]Then he said to them, “Oh, how foolish you are, and how slow of heart to believe all that the prophets have declared! [26]Was it not necessary that the Messiah should suffer these things and then enter into his glory?” [27]Then beginning with Moses and all the prophets, he interpreted to them the things about himself in all the scriptures.

28As they came near the village to which they were going, he walked ahead as if he were going on. [29]But they urged him strongly, saying, “Stay with us, because it is almost evening and the day is now nearly over.” So he went in to stay with them. [30]When he was at the table with them, he took bread, blessed and broke it, and gave it to them. [31]Then their eyes were opened, and they recognized him; and he vanished from their sight. [32]They said to each other, “Were not our hearts burning within us while he was talking to us on the road, while he was opening the scriptures to us?” [33]That same hour they got up and returned to Jerusalem; and they found the eleven and their companions gathered together. [34]They were saying, “The Lord has risen indeed, and he has appeared to Simon!” [35]Then they told what had happened on the road, and how he had been made known to them in the breaking of the bread.

36While they were talking about this, Jesus himself stood among them and said to them, “Peace be with you.” [37]They were startled and terrified, and thought that they were seeing a ghost. [38]He said to them, “Why are

you frightened, and why do doubts arise in your hearts? 39Look at my
hands and my feet; see that it is I myself. Touch me and see; for a ghost
does not have flesh and bones as you see that I have." 40And when he had
said this, he showed them his hands and his feet. 41While in their joy they
were disbelieving and still wondering, he said to them, "Have you anything here to eat?" 42They gave him a piece of broiled fish, 43and he took
it and ate in their presence.

44Then he said to them, "These are my words that I spoke to you while
I was still with you – that everything written about me in the law of
Moses, the prophets, and the psalms must be fulfilled." 45Then he opened
their minds to understand the scriptures, 46and he said to them, "Thus it
is written, that the Messiah is to suffer and to rise from the dead on the
third day, 47and that repentance and forgiveness of sins is to be proclaimed in his name to all nations, beginning from Jerusalem. 48You are
witnesses of these things. 49And see, I am sending upon you what my
Father promised; so stay here in the city until you have been clothed with
power from on high."

50Then he led them out as far as Bethany, and, lifting up his hands, he
blessed them. 51While he was blessing them, he withdrew from them and
was carried up into heaven. 52And they worshipped him, and returned to
Jerusalem with great joy; 53and they were continually in the temple blessing God.

Acts 1

In the first book, Theophilus, I wrote about all that Jesus did and taught
from the beginning 2until the day when he was taken up to heaven, after
giving instructions through the Holy Spirit to the apostles whom he had
chosen. 3After his suffering he presented himself alive to them by many
convincing proofs, appearing to them over the course of forty days and
speaking about the kingdom of God. 4While staying with them, he
ordered them not to leave Jerusalem, but to wait there for the promise of
the Father. "This", he said, "is what you have heard from me; 5for John
baptized with water, but you will be baptized with the Holy Spirit not
many days from now."

6So when they had come together, they asked him, "Lord, is this the
time when you will restore the kingdom to Israel?" 7He replied, "It is not
for you to know the times or periods that the Father has set by his own
authority. 8But you will receive power when the Holy Spirit has come
upon you; and you will be my witnesses in Jerusalem, in all Judea and
Samaria, and to the ends of the earth." 9When he had said this, as they
were watching, he was lifted up, and a cloud took him out of their sight.
10While he was going and they were gazing up towards heaven, suddenly

two men in white robes stood by them. 11They said, “Men of Galilee, why
do you stand looking up towards heaven? This Jesus, who has been taken
up from you into heaven, will come in the same way as you saw him go
into heaven.”

John 20 and 21

Chapter 20:

11But Mary stood weeping outside the tomb. As she wept, she bent over
to look into the tomb; 12and she saw two angels in white, sitting where the
body of Jesus had been lying, one at the head and the other at the feet.
13They said to her, “Woman, why are you weeping?” She said to them,
“They have taken away my Lord, and I do not know where they have laid
him.” 14When she had said this, she turned round and saw Jesus standing
there, but she did not know that it was Jesus. 15Jesus said to her, “Woman,
why are you weeping? For whom are you looking?” Supposing him to be
the gardener, she said to him, “Sir, if you have carried him away, tell me
where you have laid him, and I will take him away.” 16Jesus said to her,
“Mary!” She turned and said to him in Hebrew, “Rabbouni!” (which
means Teacher). 17Jesus said to her, “Do not hold on to me, because I
have not yet ascended to the Father. But go to my brothers and say to
them, ‘I am ascending to my Father and your Father, to my God and
your God.’” 18Mary Magdalene went and announced to the disciples, “I
have seen the Lord”; and she told them that he had said these things to
her.

19When it was evening on that day, the first day of the week, and the
doors of the house where the disciples had met were locked for fear of
the Jews, Jesus came and stood among them and said, “Peace be with
you.” 20After he said this, he showed them his hands and his side. Then
the disciples rejoiced when they saw the Lord. 21Jesus said to them again,
“Peace be with you. As the Father has sent me, so I send you.” 22When
he had said this, he breathed on them and said to them, “Receive the
Holy Spirit. 23If you forgive the sins of any, they are forgiven them; if you
retain the sins of any, they are retained.”

24But Thomas (who was called the Twin), one of the twelve, was not
with them when Jesus came. 25So the other disciples told him, “We have
seen the Lord.” But he said to them, “Unless I see the mark of the nails
in his hands, and put my finger in the mark of the nails and my hand in
his side, I will not believe.”

26A week later his disciples were again in the house, and Thomas was
with them. Although the doors were shut, Jesus came and stood among
them and said, “Peace be with you.” 27Then he said to Thomas, “Put your
finger here and see my hands. Reach out your hand and put it in my side.

Do not doubt but believe." 28Thomas answered him, "My Lord and my God!" 29Jesus said to him, "Have you believed because you have seen me? Blessed are those who have not seen and yet have come to believe."

30Now Jesus did many other signs in the presence of his disciples, which are not written in this book. 31But these are written so that you may come to believe that Jesus is the Messiah, the Son of God, and that through believing you may have life in his name.

Chapter 21:

After these things Jesus showed himself again to the disciples by the Sea of Tiberias; and he showed himself in this way. 2Gathered there together were Simon Peter, Thomas called the Twin, Nathanael of Cana in Galilee, the sons of Zebedee, and two others of his disciples. 3Simon Peter said to them, "I am going fishing." They said to him, "We will go with you." They went out and got into the boat, but that night they caught nothing.

4Just after daybreak, Jesus stood on the beach; but the disciples did not know that it was Jesus. 5Jesus said to them, "Children, you have no fish, have you?" They answered him, "No." 6He said to them, "Cast the net to the right side of the boat, and you will find some." So they cast it, and now they were not able to haul it in because there were so many fish. 7That disciple whom Jesus loved said to Peter, "It is the Lord!" When Simon Peter heard that it was the Lord, he put on some clothes, for he was naked, and jumped into the lake. 8But the other disciples came in the boat, dragging the net full of fish, for they were not far from the land, only about a hundred yards off.

9When they had gone ashore, they saw a charcoal fire there, with fish on it, and bread. 10Jesus said to them, "Bring some of the fish that you have just caught." 11So Simon Peter went aboard and hauled the net ashore, full of large fish, a hundred and fifty-three of them; and though there were so many, the net was not torn. 12Jesus said to them, "Come and have breakfast." Now none of the disciples dared to ask him, "Who are you?" because they knew it was the Lord. 13Jesus came and took the bread and gave it to them, and did the same with the fish. 14This was now the third time that Jesus appeared to the disciples after he was raised from the dead.

15When they had finished breakfast, Jesus said to Simon Peter, "Simon son of John, do you love me more than these?" He said to him, "Yes, Lord; you know that I love you." Jesus said to him, "Feed my lambs." 16A second time he said to him, "Simon son of John, do you love me?" He said to him, "Yes, Lord; you know that I love you." Jesus said to him, "Tend my sheep." 17He said to him the third time, "Simon son of

John, do you love me?" Peter felt hurt because he said to him the third time, "Do you love me?" And he said to him, "Lord, you know everything; you know that I love you." Jesus said to him, "Feed my sheep. [18]Very truly, I tell you, when you were younger, you used to fasten your own belt and go wherever you wished. But when you grow old, you will stretch out your hands, and someone else will fasten a belt around you and take you where you do not wish to go." [19](He said this to indicate the kind of death by which he would glorify God.) After this he said to him, "Follow me."

20Peter turned and saw the disciple whom Jesus loved following them; he was the one who had reclined next to Jesus at the supper and had said, "Lord, who is it that is going to betray you?" [21]When Peter saw him, he said to Jesus, "Lord, what about him?" [22]Jesus said to him, "If it is my will that he remain until I come, what is that to you? Follow me!" [23]So the rumour spread in the community that this disciple would not die. Yet Jesus did not say to him that he would not die, but, "If it is my will that he remain until I come, what is that to you?"

24This is the disciple who is testifying to these things and has written them, and we know that his testimony is true. [25]But there are also many other things that Jesus did; if every one of them were written down, I suppose that the world itself could not contain the books that would be written.

Part 1: X

It is certain that the resurrection of Jesus is a fact which belongs to the domain of the spiritual and psychic life, and which is not related to outward corporeal existence in such a way that the body which was laid in the grave could have shared therein…

Albert Schweitzer, *Quest of the Historical Jesus*

Introduction: Do we really need to start?

For any half competent cross-examiner, dealing with the post-resurrection accounts is like shooting rats in a barrel.

John, as has been conceded already, can't simply be dismissed. The weight of his testimony might be diminished by his tendency to theologise, but his account is detailed, internally coherent and may have some eyewitness evidence at its root.

Mark is the basic source for both Matthew and Luke, but he stops at the empty tomb. Without Mark to guide them, Matthew and Luke are hopelessly at sea, and their accounts diverge so radically that it is impossible, even with the most strenuous intellectual gymnastics, to begin to harmonise them.

Disposing of Matthew

Surely everyone would prefer Luke to Matthew. Matthew emerges from the examination of his empty-tomb story with his credibility in tatters. Loquacious there, he is astonishingly curt when he comes to subsequent happenings. He is supposed to be writing a history of the most important thing that has happened in the history of the world, but he can only spin out his post-empty-tomb story for twelve verses. He seems almost embarrassed to be talking about the resurrection. He seems to want to get it over with as soon as possible. In the course of those twelve verses Jesus meets the women once, telling them to expect to see Jesus in Galilee (the perfect basis for hysterical suggestion). Of the twelve verses, five are given over to an account of a Jewish conspiracy to pervert the course of justice – and are really about the empty tomb, not the resurrection at all. The disciples get to see Jesus only four verses from the end of the book, when Jesus does nothing but give them the final commission. Here is the first man to be raised from the dead: there's no description of how he looked, how they first came to see him, how long he was visible, how and when he left. And so on. This should be the climax of Matthew: 27 chapters and 15 verses have been building up to it. Then the star of the show is on for four verses, and then mysteriously off again. Even then, Matthew's risen Jesus doesn't convince them all: "When they saw him, they worshipped him; but some doubted."[1] If some of the people who were there were not convinced, how can *we* possibly be?

Matthew perhaps gives us a coded clue to what he thinks the appearance signified. It was on a mountain, he says[2] – a detail not mentioned by the other writers. Mountains are places of special spiritual revelation.[3] Perhaps the disciples did have a special spiritual experience on a mountain. Perhaps it compelled them to go out into the world pursuant to Jesus' commission. But it was not a physical appearance of a man who had recently been dead. The details are too sparse for that.

Apart from the meeting with the women at the tomb on the day of the resurrection, the only post-mortem appearance is in Galilee.

Matthew's version doesn't wash. So we are really left with comparing Luke and John.

Luke and John: Two irreconcilably different accounts

Before diving into the detail, it is worth standing back and looking at the broad picture:

(a) In John, Jesus appears first to Mary Magdalene, as she is standing weeping by the tomb.[4] In Luke, Jesus does not appear to any of the women.

(b) In John, Jesus appears first in Jerusalem (to Mary Magdalene and then to the disciples). This was on the Sunday morning.[5] The disciples then stay in Jerusalem for a week, and Jesus appears again: this is the famous confrontation with Thomas.[6] The book then looks as if it is about to end.[7] Many commentators think that it did, and that what follows was added later. This issue is discussed in Chapter 2. The story then jumps to Galilee, and remains there until the end of the book.

(c) In Luke's gospel, Jesus only ever appears in Jerusalem or the Jerusalem area. He never goes to Galilee. What's more, he commands the disciples to stay in Jerusalem "until you have been clothed with power from on high."[8] Presumably they obeyed. All the appearances in Luke's gospel were evidently on the Sunday.[9] The ascension also seems to be on the same day.[10]

(d) True, Luke in the book of Acts corrects the impression that the risen Jesus was only around for a day: "After his suffering [Jesus] presented himself alive to [the apostles] by many convincing proofs, appearing to them during 40 days and speaking about the Kingdom of God."[11] But he underlines his original assertion: that Jesus appeared to the apostles only in Jerusalem: "While staying with them, [Jesus] ordered them not to leave Jerusalem, but to wait there for the promise of the Father." Again, they presumably did as they were told.

(e) Only Luke mentions the ascension. From his account it was a dramatic, Cape Canaveral-type experience.[12] Present at the ascension were, it seems, "the apostles"[13] or possibly "the eleven" plus or minus Cleopas and the other traveller on the Emmaus road.[14]

Historical improbabilities in Luke

Luke begins his account of the resurrection appearances with the walk to Emmaus. We don't know where Emmaus was: it may never have existed.

The men joined by Jesus on the Emmaus road were Cleopas[15] and another unnamed man. It is not clear who they were.[16] Presumably they had been wandering round Palestine with Jesus for quite a time, and yet they walk with him for hours without recognising who he is. When do they find out who he is? When he has given them a scripture lesson[17] and taken bread, blessed it, broken it and given it to them.[18] The words used to describe this meal are identical to those used in Luke's description of the Last Supper.[19] The point is obvious. It's a tale about how, in the new order after Jesus' death, we are connected with him through the scriptures and the Eucharist. It is interesting that Luke omits the wine-drinking part of the Eucharist in this Emmaus metaphor. He's still trying to pass this off as history, and it wouldn't do to have two of his main witnesses staggering back to Jerusalem drunk.

Then Jesus suddenly appears amongst his disciples in Jerusalem.[20] He doesn't apparently use the door, the window, the chimney, or any other conventional way of getting into a room. But he goes on to make ostentatious displays of his physicality: he invites them to touch him; he gets some fish; says "Watch this", and eats it as they watch. If he simply appeared, he didn't have a physical body: physical bodies don't do that. And if he had a merely spiritual body, all the stuff about touching and fish-eating must have been added later to contradict the people who were saying that the resurrection appearances weren't physical. Indeed their very ostentation makes them look exactly like that.

Luke, if he's a historian at all, is an odd sort of historian. There's no doubt about his chronology at the end of the gospel: Sunday sees the first and the last appearance. And then, in direct and apparently unembarrassed contradiction in Acts 1, Jesus has 40 days to do various things (none of which are apparently worth reporting). How can we take him seriously?

The ascension is an embarrassment for any apologist. If it really happened, it was one of the most spectacular events of any apostolic career. And yet it warrants not a word in any other account. Perhaps the real explanation is a stylistic one. The other gospels never really end properly: they just peter out. Luke has undertaken to write an "orderly account".[21] He certainly has a beginning; he certainly has a middle; perhaps he just wanted a proper end too. The truth might have read something like: "Some of us thought for a while that Jesus was in a sense still alive. We thought we felt his presence, and it was sometimes so intense that we thought he was physically there. Gradually though, as you'd expect, those feelings went away."

Historical improbabilities in John

The curious business of chapter 21

The barn-door point about John is the addition of chapter 21. What was thought to be so inadequate about chapter 20? What has chapter 21 got that chapter 20 has not? The answer is, four things: Galilee; assurance of evangelistic success; Peter's final rehabilitation; and unequivocal evidence about the physical nature of the resurrection body. The addition of this chapter says a lot about the integrity of John as a historian. It massively enhances his reputation as a crafter of parables: both chapters 20 and 21 are full of them.

Galilee in John: A damage-limitation exercise

But first, and most significantly, chapter 21 has Galilee. John's original gospel has appearances only in Jerusalem. Imagine John sitting in Ephesus, or wherever his gospel was written. He may well know (even if he does not have the documents themselves in front of him) that there are three other gospels already in circulation. One of these, Mark, has no resurrection account at all. Matthew puts Jesus just in Galilee. Luke puts him just in Jerusalem. What is the natural thing for someone in John's position to do? He is anxious to increase Christianity's credibility. He cannot recall and pulp the existing gospels, replacing them with one of his own. But he can do his (rather ham-fisted) best to stop Matthew cutting Luke's throat, and vice versa. And that is what he does. Both Matthew and Luke are right: Jesus was in both places. In *Fiddler on the Roof*, Tevye is anxious to keep the peace between two factions. One says: "We need to know what is happening in the outside world." "You are right," says Tevye. "No," says another, "the lesson is the opposite: we need to keep ourselves even more to ourselves." "You are right," says Tevye. And then a third says: "But they cannot both be right." Tevye ponders for a moment: "You are also right," he says. John is doing what Tevye did, and it is as endearing and logically insupportable as Tevye.

You will succeed

Chapter 20 provides the basic doctrinal raw material for mission, and the disciples are sent out to spread the word.[22] But the disciples, and the gospel's readers, might be forgiven for thinking, this is a daunting task: how can we be sure that we will be able to fulfil such a commission? By the time that John wrote his gospel it was perfectly clear that the commission was indeed a daunting and a deadly dangerous one. The Christians needed all the encouragement they could get. That need wasn't adequately met by chapter 20: it is (as millions have subsequently found) splendidly met by chapter 21. Throw your (metaphorical) net obediently over the side, says the chapter (remembering, of course, that you are fishers of men), and the net will burst with fish. That was just what the beleaguered congregations needed to hear – and hear from the highest authority.

The highest authority on earth

The highest authority is of course Jesus himself. But he is not around any longer in the same way that he was at that Galilee lakeside. Some delegation is therefore needed. At the time that John was writing his gospel there may still very well have been dispute in the church about who was highest in the apostolic pecking order. This mattered, as the most superficial glimpse at the book of Acts shows. Two-headed organisations don't work. Yes, there had been cryptic indications in chapter 20 that Peter should have primacy, but readers not used to esoteric puzzles might well have missed the point. One can imagine John asking an associate to read through the first draft of his gospel – chapters 1–20. "It's very good", the associate might say, "but I wonder if you might make the point about Peter just a bit more clearly." Which is what chapter 21 does. Nobody could miss it now. Peter denied Jesus three times: he gets three chances to undo the denial, and he takes them.[23] What is his reward? Jesus tells him: "Feed my sheep." Be the shepherd in my place, in other words. Jesus has already said that he (Jesus) is the good shepherd, who gives his life for the sheep. Well, Peter is now the shepherd, walking, crook in hand, in Jesus' footsteps. The parallel is explicit. It even contains a dark prophecy that Peter will have to give his life for the sheep too.[24] This is inspirational stuff, but inspirational stuff that was written merely to inspire. It is great literature, but it's not history.

The physicality of the resurrection body

At first sight, chapter 20 looks as if it contains the quintessential proof of the physicality of the resurrection body. Thomas is the most famous sceptic in the world. He is a dramatic invention, of course: his gesture of doubt is not mentioned in any other gospel. And he is not as easily swayed as his soft-headed companions: "Unless I see the nail marks in his hands, and put my finger into the nail marks, and put my hand into his side, I won't believe this cock-and-bull story."[25] His attitude so far would delight the sternest materialist. But in fact he's not as robust an empiricist as he makes out. Jesus appears and offers Thomas precisely the evidence he has asked for: "Put your finger here: see my hands: reach out your hand and put it into my side."[26] But John does not record that Thomas availed himself of the opportunity. Instead (apparently without touching), Thomas disappoints the materialists and goes over to the side of the supernaturalists: "My Lord and my God", he says.[27] It is one of the greatest stories of all time, but it is not any sort of proof that the resurrection body was solid.

The nature of the resurrection body came to matter to the early church – probably mainly in the battle against the Gnostics: see Chapter 2. And when it began to matter, one can imagine that same editorial associate of John saying: "Again, very good, but couldn't you put something in to confound the Gnostics?" John may have seen or heard Luke's account of the risen Jesus eating a fish[28], and thought that that was a good way to demonstrate physicality. Chapter 21, after all, has a fishy theme. Hence John's culinary, anti-docetic fairy-story[29], in which it is hinted, but not asserted, that Jesus joined the disciples in eating the fish he had cooked. The whole story reeks, not of real smoke from the fire that Jesus had made, but of eucharistic and evangelistic parable.

So what did happen?

At the end of the section "Historical improbabilities in Luke", it was suggested that there is no need to suppose that there were any appearances at all. What the disciples may have felt was a vague sense of Jesus' presence, which they later dramatised for public consumption. It's not very impressive, when you're on a soapbox in Turkey, surrounded by baying crowds, to say: "We sort of felt that he was still around, in a way." The message had to be repackaged.

But perhaps we are being unfair to the disciples. Perhaps they genuinely felt that Jesus had appeared to them, in some way similar to those recorded in the gospels. What then? Then the hallucination thesis is the obvious explanation.

This is another currently unfashionable thesis. The Jesus Seminar (a consortium of scholars who oppose the orthodox Christian view of Jesus and the resurrection) seems rather embarrassed about it. But it is arguable, and needs to be examined.

The hallucination hypothesis

Jesus and Elvis

Whatever you think about him, Jesus was a remarkable man. He made a deep impression on everyone who met him. In those close to him he inspired devotion so intense that it is accurately characterised as hysterical. His execution was unthinkable. So unthinkable, in fact, that it was un-thought. The disciples were under colossal psychological pressure to believe that it hadn't really happened: that he wasn't really dead. And, helped by some hints from Jesus himself, that is what they did think.[30]

This is not so remarkable. There have been umpteen post-mortem "sightings" of Elvis Presley. Scholars do not take them seriously; nor do clerics build theologies on them. But they are no different in kind from the alleged "sightings" of the risen Jesus.

Mass hallucinations: Do lots of mistakes make a correct answer?

The Christians always say: "But Jesus appeared to many people at one time", as if that were a fatal objection. It is not, as evidenced by many examples from the Christian tradition itself.

In Portugal in 1917, three young children claimed to be getting visions of Mary. Mary, they said, had promised a miracle. Several thousand expectant people gathered in the countryside. And of course the miracle happened. Many people saw the sun approach the earth. Similar stories are repeated in Christian communities everywhere. Statues weep; icons bleed; the coagulated blood of saints flows freely again. And all the scepticism of science cannot dent the conviction of the faithful. The conviction is wholly immune to the evidence.

Are there "hallucinators" and "non-hallucinators"?

There is general agreement in the psychiatric literature that some people hallucinate more than others. Slade and Bentall express the consensus:

> One of the most obvious features that emerges from the literature on hallucinations, whether experimentally induced hallucinations in normal individuals or occurring spontaneously in pathological states, is the observation of individual differences. Some people hallucinate under specifiable conditions and others do not.[31]

How common are hallucinations in the general population?

It rather depends which population you look at. The issue of cultural influence is hugely important, and is discussed below. It is also worth noting that psychiatric impairment of some kind is so common as to be the norm. Psychiatrically "normal" people are *ab*normal.[32]

The first big, systematic study was in 1894. 7.8% of men and 12% of women reported at least one hallucinatory experience in their lifetime.[33] In a 1948 study, 14.3% reported having experienced hallucination. Again, hallucinations were more commonly reported by women than by men.[34] In both studies, visual hallucinations were more common than auditory, and multimodal hallucinations were quite rare.[35] [36] [37]

What personal characteristics do hallucinators tend to have?

At least when talking about schizophrenics, hallucinators tend to be significantly less intelligent than non-hallucinators[38], and (again among schizophrenics) neurotic people and those having interpersonal problems such as paranoia and aggression tend to hallucinate more. It is unclear whether, and if so to what extent, these observations can be extrapolated to the general population.[39]

The relationship between hallucination and gullibility

Hallucinators seem more susceptible than non-hallucinators to instructions to hear or see non-existent events.[40] This was demonstrated dramatically using "the 'White Christmas' test. Secretarial students were asked to close their eyes and listen to the record "White Christmas". The record was not played. About 5% of apparently normal subjects believed that it was.[41] When the experiment was repeated with a group of hallucinating schizophrenics, non-hallucinating schizophrenics and normal controls, 75% of "hallucinators" "heard" the record.[42]

Does the intensity of the suggestion matter? Well: yes and no. When white noise was played to a group of hallucinating schizophrenics, non-hallucinating schizophrenics and hallucinating alcoholics, and it was suggested to them all that they heard voices, the strength of the suggestion increased the frequency with which hallucinatory voices were heard, but did not increase the quality of the hallucination.[43]

What other conditions affect the incidence of hallucination?

Culture is important to the incidence of hallucination. Culture generates expectancy, and expectancy generates hallucination. A person coming from a culture that expects to see ghosts is more likely to see them.[44] Guilt, too, is a factor – interacting in rather obvious ways with the power of expectation. Mohawk Indians have a taboo that says that they must not eat game that they themselves kill. If they do they are haunted by the spirits of the game until appropriate reparation is made.[45] There we have a psychologically explosive cocktail: guilt for the taboo-breaking and expectation that the taboo-breaking will lead to haunting.

Hope may generate visions: miners trapped in darkness for several days saw visions of doorways, stairs and the Pope.[46] No doubt enthusiastically Protestant miners would not see the Pope: people see what they think will help them.

And various sorts of stress can conjure hallucinations. Hostages, isolated and threatened, see various things, from strange geometric shapes to complex images.[47] Similarly, soldiers deprived of sleep for long periods see things that objectively aren't there.[48]

Supremely, bereavement is a factor.

The special case of bereavement

In 1971 an English general medical practitioner, Dr Dewi Rees, published a paper reporting that of 227 widows and 66 widowers, 46.7% had post-bereavement hallucinations. 39.2% had an illusion of feeling the presence of the dead spouse: 13.3% had auditory hallucinations; 14% had visual hallucinations. More than 10% had spoken to the dead spouse, and 2.7% had had a feeling of being touched by the dead spouse.[49]

There are similar findings in most cultures. Again, expectancy and violation of taboos increase the incidence of bereavement hallucinations.[50]

What conditions affect the nature of hallucinations?

Again, culture seems to be a factor. Thus: while multimodal hallucinations are rare in the West, 50% of hallucinations in diagnosed schizophrenics in Saudi Arabia were multimodal – both auditory and visual.[51] Similar results have been reported from Africa.[52]

From the psychiatric literature to the gospels

Everything in the modern literature indicates that the disciples might have been hallucinating. They came from a culture in which ghosts wandered around so routinely that they barely warranted a comment. They were bereaved, having lost a man who they thought was the most important one who ever lived – who was the meaning of their lives. They were highly stressed, and their own lives were in danger. They were sleep-deprived: look at how in the garden of Gethsemane they were so exhausted that they could not stay awake even though Jesus had specifically asked them to.[53] That exhausted sleep was rudely broken by Jesus' arrest in the middle of the night. After that, stress was heaped upon stress: the trial; the crucifixion; the desolation of dashed hopes. After Jesus' death the sleep of disillusioned, hunted men was hardly going to be blissful.

And they were expecting something to happen. Jesus had repeatedly said that he was going to rise from the dead.[54] He was quite explicit. According to Mark and Matthew, he even told them the place: "After I have risen I will go ahead of you into Galilee."[55] Mark's "angel" reminds the women that this is what Jesus had said: "Go, tell his disciples and Peter, 'He is going ahead of you into Galilee. There you will see him, just as he told you.'"[56] Luke's "angels" also jog the women's memory: "Remember how he told you, while he was still with you in Galilee: 'The Son of Man must be delivered into the hands of sinful men, be crucified and on the third day be raised again.'"[57] All this is a perfect, textbook basis for hallucination. And of course in Matthew the disciples do indeed see Jesus in Galilee. If it is suggested that they had somehow forgotten it, it needs to be pointed out that, according to Matthew, the chief priests and the Pharisees hadn't forgotten. If you believe Matthew, they went to Pilate saying: "We remember that while he was still alive that deceiver said, 'After three days I will rise again.'"[58] John, however, insists that when Peter and the "beloved disciple" arrived at the tomb on Sunday morning, "they still did not understand from Scripture that Jesus had to rise from the dead."[59] It seems unlikely that Jesus' enemies would recall his words and promises better than his disciples did.

But whatever the disciples remembered before the Sunday morning perhaps doesn't matter all that much, because of course the memory-jogging of those Sunday morning "angels" means that, at least after the visits to the tomb on the Sunday morning, the disciples were expecting something spectacular to happen.

Guilt, too, was a factor. Perhaps particularly in the case of Peter, whose voice is the voice of Mark (and thus of Matthew and Luke too). Peter had already been designated as the lead disciple, but he fell asleep in the garden too, failed (despite wielding his sword) to prevent Jesus' arrest, and then denied Jesus three times – twice to girls.[60] It was a truly pathetic performance, and the amount of time the gospels spend dealing with Peter's rehabilitation indicates how much it embarrassed the gospel writers. Peter psychologically needed rehabilitation; he needed to be forgiven and restored by Jesus. And so it was necessary for Peter to see Jesus again. And, surprise, surprise: that is precisely what happens. If a psychologist didn't know how the last three canonical gospels ended, he could have a pretty good stab at making it up from psychological first principles.

Paul's account of the post-resurrection appearances

1 Corinthians 15: Plum or duff?

Everyone agrees that the earliest document we have that mentions the resurrection at all is Paul's First Letter to the Thessalonians. This probably dates from around AD 50–51. But the resurrection reference is only a mention.[61] It tells us nothing of the historical grounds of the belief. The first document that does that is Paul's First Letter to the Corinthians. Most would date this around AD 54. And it is very explicit:

> Now I would remind you, brothers and sisters, of the good news that I proclaimed to you, which you in turn received… For I handed on to you as of first importance what I in turn had received; that Christ died for our sins in accordance with the Scriptures, and that he was buried, and that he was raised on the third day in accordance with the Scriptures, and

> that he appeared to Cephas, then to the Twelve. Then he appeared to more than five hundred brothers and sisters at one time, most of whom are still alive, though some have died. Then he appeared to James, then to all the apostles. Last of all, as to one untimely born, he appeared also to me. For I am the least of the apostles, unfit to be called an apostle, because I persecuted the church of God…[62]

There are many odd things about this passage. Some (such as which scriptures Paul had in mind when saying that Jesus was raised on the third day "in accordance with the Scriptures") we will put to one side.[63] Many of the important points are dealt with in a slightly different context in Chapter 6.

It is regarded by Christians as the jewel in their apologetic crown: an early, authoritative statement, tantamount to a creed, which not only states unequivocally that the early church believed in the traditional formulation of empty tomb and bodily resurrection, but also lists the witnesses, inviting sceptical readers to check with the witnesses if they don't believe Paul.[64] The passage forges a connection, they say, between Paul and the earliest apostolic witnesses: ("…I handed on to you…what I in turn had received…"). But is it really such a forensic plum? A closer look shows a good deal of duff.

What were Paul's sources?

First, some chronology. The following are reasonable assumptions: Paul had his encounter with Jesus on the Damascus road in around AD 33. After this he went away to Arabia.[65] "After three years" he went to Jerusalem "to visit Cephas [Peter] and stayed with him fifteen days; but I did not see any other apostle except James the Lord's brother…"[66] That would have been AD 36 or 37. From there he went into Syria and Cilicia[67], and "after fourteen years" he went back to Jerusalem.[68] This would have been around AD 51. He was back in Jerusalem in AD 56–57.[69]

Paul says that he got the information about the passion and resurrection of Jesus straight from the horse's mouth. He reiterates this in the letter to the Galatians, when he says that three years after his conversion he went to Jerusalem. By the time that 1 Corinthians was written, in around AD 54, Paul had been to Jerusalem twice since his conversion. The dating of Galatians is controversial[70], but certainly by the time it was written Paul had been to Jerusalem to confer with the original apostles at least once.

The problem for the Christians is this: in 1 Corinthians 15 he says that he is passing on what he received (presumably in AD 36/37 and/or 51). This is heart-warming stuff for someone who wants to say that the story Paul is telling is historical. But in Galatians he makes a point of saying that he did not get the basic story from the eyewitnesses at all. It was all handed to him directly in some supernatural way:

> ...I want you to know, brothers and sisters, that the gospel that was proclaimed by me is not of human origin; for I did not receive it from a human source, nor was I taught it, but I received it through a revelation of Jesus Christ.[71]

He later drives the point home even harder, saying expressly that after his conversion on the Damascus road he did not "confer with any human being, nor did I go up to Jerusalem to those who were already apostles before me..."[72] Instead, he says, he went to Arabia, returning later to Damascus. Three years later he did go to Jerusalem and stayed with Peter, but saw only Peter and James.

There's no comfort for the Christians in the thought that "the gospel" is merely the "spiritual bits" – the theological spin on the basic historical facts. That argument is debarred by 1 Corinthians 15 itself – which introduces the very historical averments that we are looking at with the words "the good news". Those words are usually translated "gospel".

There is no empty tomb in 1 Corinthians 15
Nor anywhere else outside the gospels, for that matter.

The list of witnesses
Lots of things can be said and have been said about this. The most striking thing is how little correlation there is with the witnesses who are named in the canonical gospels. There is, for example, no mention at all of the women. They are central to the gospel stories. The gospels mention no appearance to "more than five hundred... at one time": surely they would have mentioned such a dramatic appearance had it happened? Paul appears to suggest a special appearance to James: the gospels know of no such appearance. Paul distinguishes mysteriously between an appearance to "the Twelve" and to "all the apostles": this does not relate obviously to anything

the gospels have to say. And Paul gives a rigorous chronology: Cephas; *then* the Twelve; *then* the "more than five hundred"; *then* James; *then* all the apostles. This, again, is impossible to relate to the gospels. So the Christians have to take their pick: keep the gospels (or *a* gospel: they differ so dramatically that one really has to elect one) and ditch Paul: or keep Paul and ditch the gospels.

Was Paul inviting his readers to check with the witnesses?

Christian apologists are fond of saying so. "Some of them were still alive," they say. "And Paul was suggesting that if they didn't believe him, they could check with the witnesses themselves." But how realistic was this? No names were given. And even if they had been, would anyone in Corinth – the other side of a very dangerous sea – really bother to get on a boat and struggle all the way to Palestine? Hardly. It was a safe challenge for Paul to issue. It increased the apparent evidential force of his argument without ever being likely to be taken seriously and found wanting.

The appearance to Paul

This, again, is dealt with in detail in Chapter 6. It is worth pointing out here, though, that the accounts given by Paul of his encounter with Jesus on the Damascus road aren't accounts of visual appearances at all. According to Paul, all he saw was a blinding light. He heard a voice saying things (just what is not clear: each account gives a different version).[73] He fell to the ground and was blind until he got to Damascus and was healed.

It has been suggested that this is the classic presentation of a Conversion Disorder – the physical expression of some psychological conflict or need. Falling to the ground, it is suggested, might indicate temporary paralysis. The blindness is a common symptom of the condition. The conflict within the guilt-ridden Paul is obvious and must have been massive.[74] In terms of probability, the occurrence of a well-recognised clinical syndrome in precisely those circumstances where one would expect it to occur seems overwhelmingly more likely than Paul's own diagnosis – that he had been spoken to by a man who was long dead and buried.

If the diagnosis of Conversion Disorder is right, of course, it forces us to be more sceptical than ever about the rest of Paul's evidence. He was plainly a hysteric with a deep, unresolved guilt complex. He was, moreover, a deeply insecure one. His apostolic credentials were clearly being doubted – hence the need for the rather paranoid assurance in 1 Corinthians 15 that he worked harder than any of the other apostles.[75] He is protesting a bit too much. It sounds as if he doubted the credentials himself. And that, as he pleaded his own case to his audience and to himself, was likely to give rise to all sorts of fabrications and inconsistencies.

Part 2: Y

> …these stories have the puzzled air of someone saying, "I didn't understand it at the time, and I'm not sure I do now, but this is more or less how it was…"
>
> …Nobody was expecting this kind of thing; no kind of conversion experience would have generated such ideas; nobody would have invented it, no matter how guilty (or how forgiven) they felt, no matter how many hours they pored over the scriptures. To suggest otherwise is to stop doing history and to enter into a fantasy world of our own, a new cognitive dissonance in which the relentless modernist, desperately worried that the post-Enlightenment worldview seems in imminent danger of collapse, devises strategies for shoring it up nonetheless…
>
> Tom Wright, *The Resurrection of the Son of God*

Introduction

X is sometimes very rude. But rudeness, as so often, betrays a real misunderstanding. His opening salvo is: "dealing with the post-resurrection accounts is like shooting rats in a barrel." I can see what he means. There are some significant differences, which can only be acknowledged. Notably these relate to the places where the encounters happen: Luke: Jerusalem only; Matthew: Galilee only; John: both Jerusalem and Galilee. And there is no doubt that Jesus behaves very oddly. He appears and disappears; he doesn't need to use doors. But although he can walk through walls he can eat and drink. People who knew him for years don't recognise him at first.

But for X to say that this odd behaviour on Jesus' part suggests some sort of disorder of perception, credibility or bona fides on the part of the gospel writers is an illuminating mistake. It shows that he thinks that the resurrection is not really a resurrection at all: he thinks it is a resuscitation. He is aiming his arrows at completely the wrong target. He is approaching the story as if what happened was that Jesus' body was revived in the tomb, walked out, and wandered

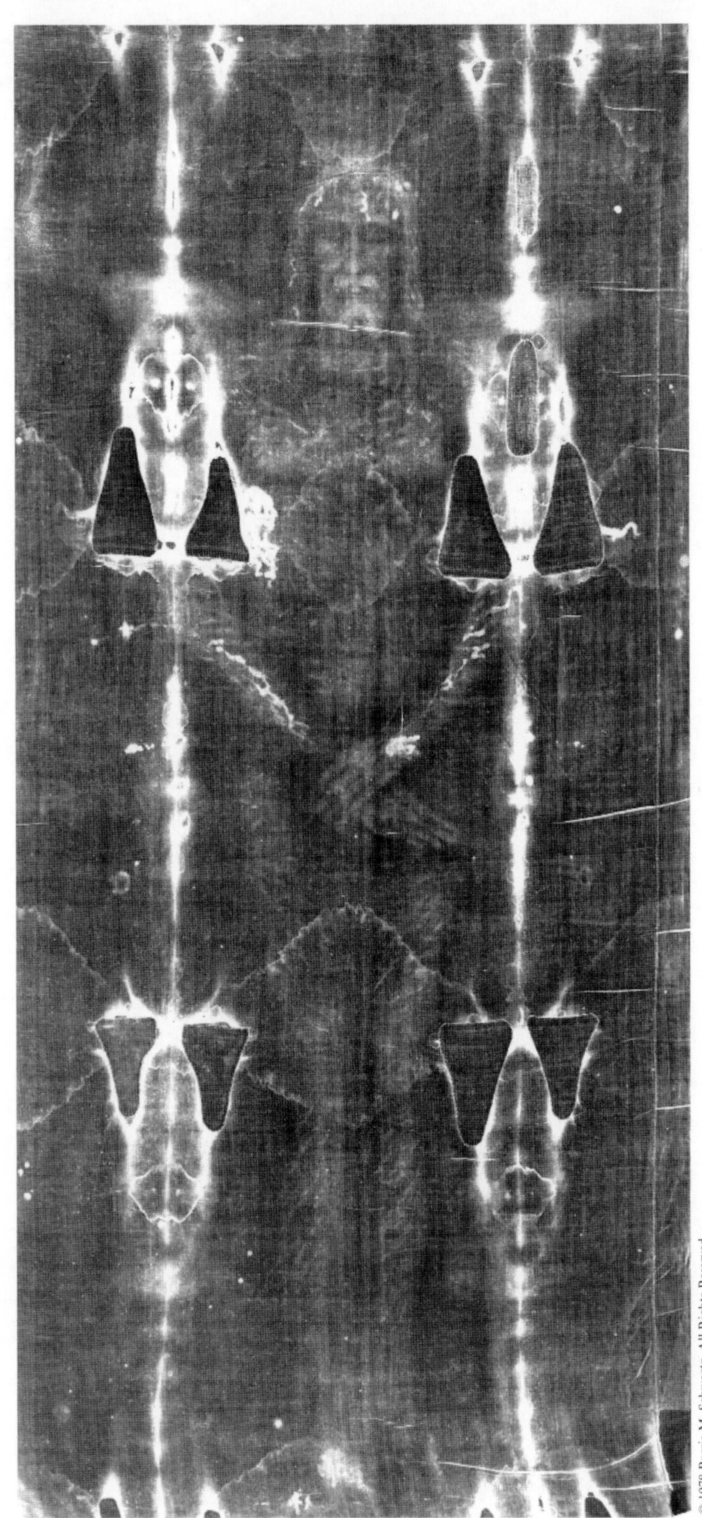

Fig 1. In the Cathedral of St. John the Baptist, Turin, is a piece of linen cloth that many believe is the shroud of Jesus. It bears a misty image of a crucified man. The process by which the image was made is obscure. It seems to have the quality of a photographic negative. The obvious marks are burn marks from a fire in 1532.

Fig 2. Aerial view of the Old City of Jerusalem from the west. Left of centre is the distinctive grey dome of the Holy Sepulchre Church, which contains the traditional sites of the death, burial and resurrection of Jesus. Towards the top of the picture, east of the Temple Mount with the golden domed Dome of the Rock, is the Mount of Olives. The Garden of Gethsemane is at the bottom of the Mount of Olives.

Fig 3. Looking towards the Garden of Gethsemane from the Jewish Cemetery on the Mount of Olives. The Garden of Gethsemane is where Jesus spent his last night and where he was arrested.

Fig 4. An ancient olive tree in the Garden of Gethsemane. Estimates of its age vary widely. The tour guides tell you that it witnessed the arrest of Jesus. This is botanically possible, but unlikely. Although there were olive groves in the area at the time of Jesus, most of these were probably cut down by Titus in AD 70.

Fig 5. Jehonanan: The crucified man of Giv'at ha-Mivtar. In 1968 building contractors working in Giv'at ha-Mivtar, one of Jerusalem's northern suburbs, found a Jewish tomb from the first century AD. In a stone ossuary (a bone box) were the remains of a man in his twenties. We know his name from the inscription on the ossuary: "Jehonanan the son of HGQWL." He had been crucified. His right calcaneum (heel bone) was pierced by an iron nail 11.5 cm long. The nail had evidently hit a knot in the wood of the cross and bent over, making it impossible to withdraw the nail from the heel when Jehonanan was taken down from the cross. This picture shows the calcaneum with the nail in situ. Next to it is a modern reconstruction which shows how the heel was fixed using a wooden washer on the outer side.

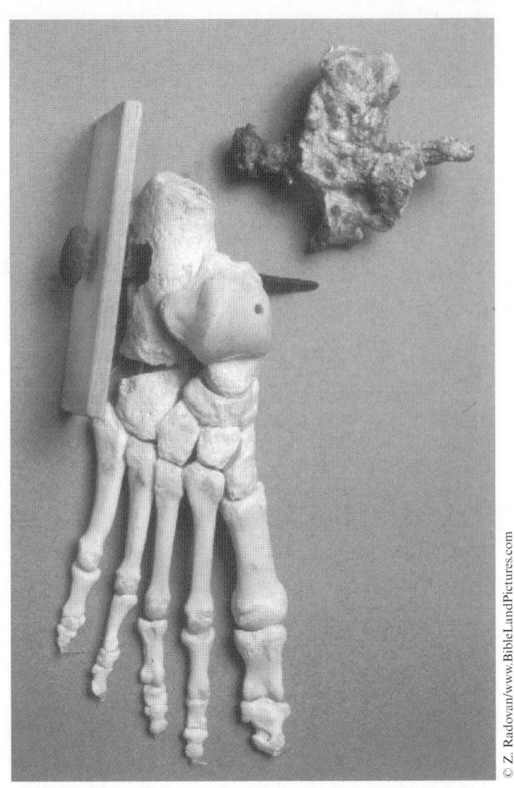

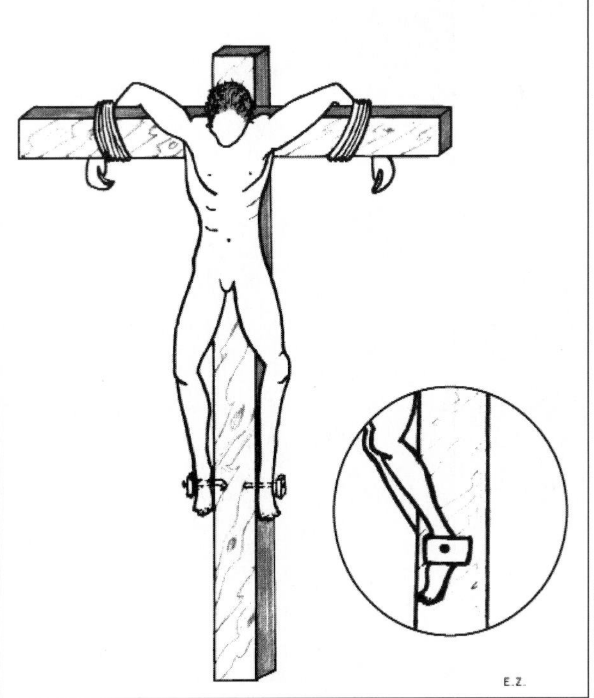

Fig 6. Reconstruction of the death of Jehonanan: There were two nails fixing the feet. The legs were astride the vertical beam and the ankles had been nailed individually to the side. The forearms had not been nailed at all. Presumably Jehonanan's arms had been tied in place.

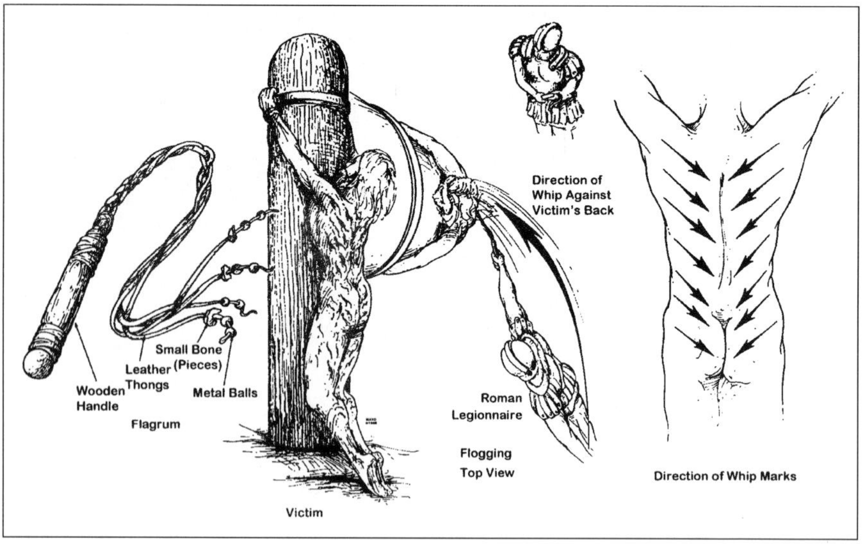

Fig 7. Left: a whip *(flagrum)* commonly used by the Romans. Centre: Naked victim tied to a scourging post. Right: Expected pattern of the scourge wounds.

Fig 8. Left: Victim carrying the *patibulum* (cross-bar) to the site of the *stipes* (upright post). Right: The low Tau cross (*crux commissa*) often used by the Romans at the time of Jesus.

© Todd Balen/Bibleplaces.com

Fig 9. Reconstruction of the area now occupied by the Holy Sepulchre Church as it was at the time of Jesus' death. The rock at the centre of the picture is Golgotha. Behind the city wall rises the Antonia Fortress. The model is at the Holyland Hotel, Jerusalem.

© Todd Balen/Bibleplaces.com

Fig 10. The top of the rock of Golgotha, the traditional site of the crucifixion of Jesus, now within the Church of the Holy Sepulchre.

Fig 11. The Sarcophagus of Yuz Asaf: Some legends say that Jesus, having survived the crucifixion, travelled east, becoming known as Yuz Asaf. Some believe that Yuz Asaf is buried in the old Khaniyar quarter of Srinagar, Kashmir. The tomb is known as the Rozabal – the "sacred tomb".

Fig 12. For many years the wax from devotional candles covered the floor next to Yuz Asaf's tomb. When it was scraped off it was seen that there were two footprints carved into the stone. There were marks on each foot said to be consistent with crucifixion wounds.

© Charles Foster

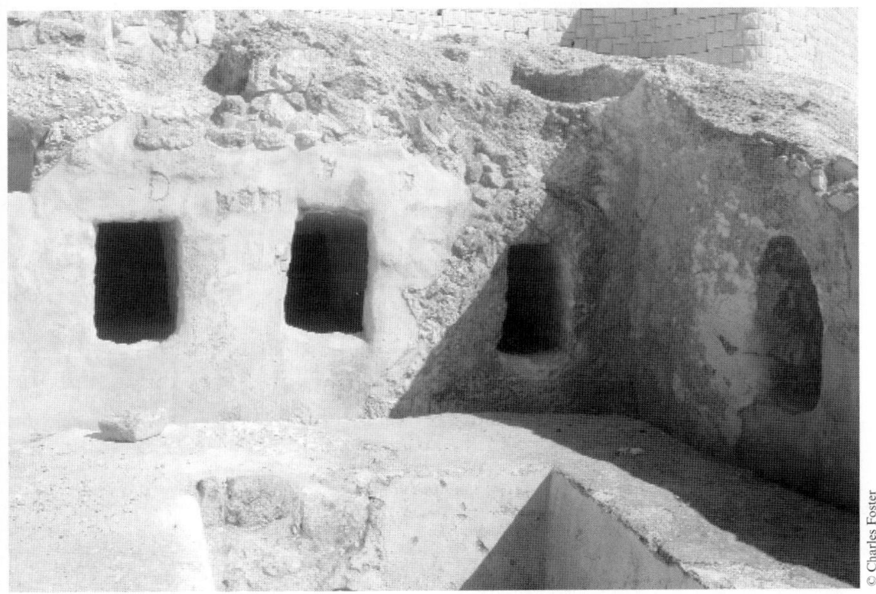

Fig 13. A first-century AD Jewish tomb on Mount Scopus, Jerusalem, showing the typical burial niches or *kokhim*, in which the bodies were placed, and the central chamber in which mourners and other members of the burial party would have stood.

© Charles Foster

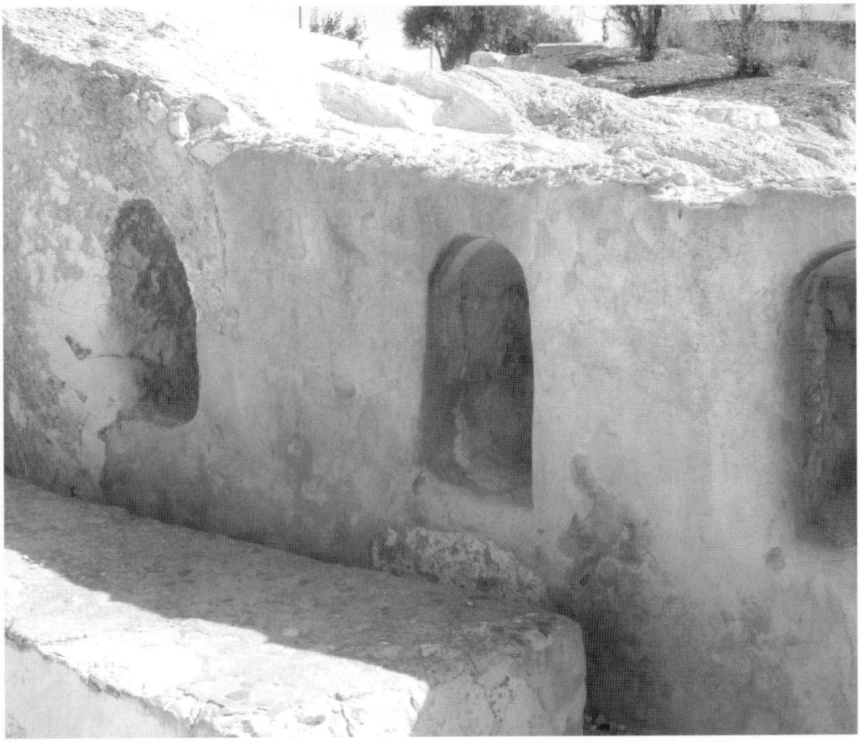

Fig 14. A first-century AD Jewish tomb on Mount Scopus, Jerusalem, showing several *kokhim* off the main chamber.

Fig 15. First-century AD Jewish tomb on Mount Scopus, Jerusalem: view of the interior of a *kokh*, or burial niche.

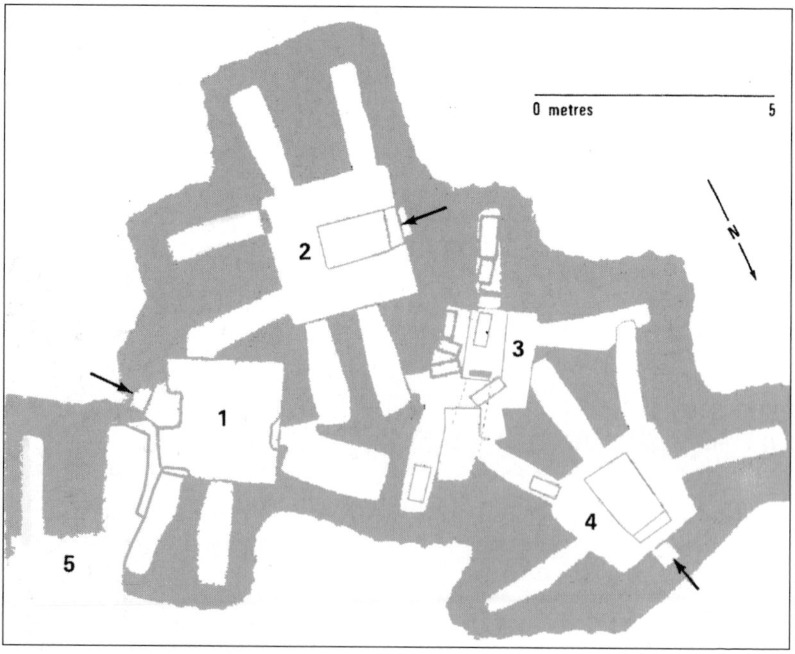

0 metres 5

N

2

3

1

4

5

Fig 16. The tomb complex on Mount Scopus, illustrated in Figs 13-15. Note how the *kokhim* of separate tombs are very close to one another, but the tomb entrances, marked with arrows, are well apart.

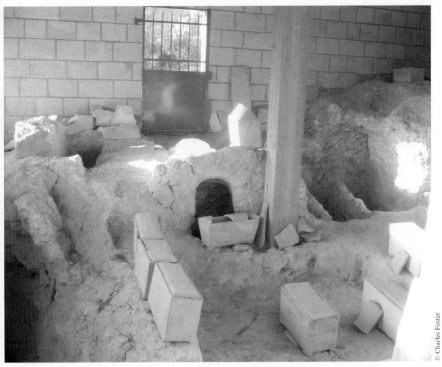

Fig 17. Ossuaries (bone boxes) in a Jewish cemetery in the grounds of the Dominus Flavit church, Mount of Olives, Jerusalem. Ossuaries are commonly found from first century BC and first century AD, primarily in Jerusalem. They were used for secondary burial. After the flesh had rotted, the bones were gathered up and placed in an ossuary. Previously the bones had often simply been mixed with other bones in the same tomb – so that the deceased would literally be "gathered to his ancestors". The burial of individuals in their own ossuaries might indicate an increasingly concrete belief in the resurrection of the individual – as distinct from the resurrection of the whole nation of Israel.

Fig 18. The tomb of Queen Helena of Adiabene, Jerusalem. A first-century AD tomb closed by a large rolling stone.

© Charles Foster

Fig 19. The tomb of Queen Helena of Adiabene, Jerusalem. View of the rolling stone from the top, showing the deep groove in which it runs.

Fig 20. The tomb of Queen Helena of Adiabene, Jerusalem. The view out of the tomb. The rolling stone can be seen to the right of the doorway.

Fig 21. Arcosolium (arched burial niche), in the tomb of Queen Helena of Adiabene, Jerusalem.

Fig 22. Herod's family tomb, Jerusalem. A Jewish tomb, probably late first century BC, closed by a rolling stone.

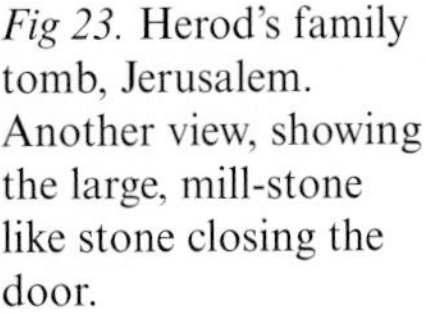

Fig 23. Herod's family tomb, Jerusalem. Another view, showing the large, mill-stone like stone closing the door.

Fig 24. The tomb complex of the Bene Hezir in the Kidron valley, Jerusalem, comprising the tomb of the Bene Hezir (left) and the 'tomb of Zechariah'. Note the doorway cut into the rock below the tomb of Bene Hezir – perhaps an Iron Age tomb. The Arab village of Silwan (Biblical Siloam), just down the Kidron valley from here, is built on rock honeycombed by simple tombs.

Fig 25. Jason's tomb, Jerusalem. A Hasmonean tomb, probably cut in the very late second century or early first century BC. The final burial in this tomb was in AD 30. Note the stone closing the entrance to the first of the tomb's courts.

Fig 26. The Garden Tomb, Jerusalem. Many (particularly Protestants), believe this to have been the tomb of Jesus. Most archaeologists consider that it is far too old to have been a "new tomb" at the time of Jesus. It probably dates to 9–6 BC. The burial benches were cut down in the Byzantine period to create rock sarcophagi.

Fig 27. The rock burial couch in the Garden Tomb.

Fig 28. "Gordon's Calvary", behind the Arab bus station in Jerusalem, and next to the Garden Tomb. When General Gordon visited Jerusalem in 1883 he thought he could see the shape of a skull in the hill. He concluded that this was where Jesus was crucified. The 'eye-sockets' of the 'skull' can clearly be seen left of centre.

Fig 29. Kokhim in a 1 BC – AD 1 tomb in the Syrian Chapel of the Church of the Holy Sepulchre, Jerusalem. This is very close to the traditional tomb of Jesus.

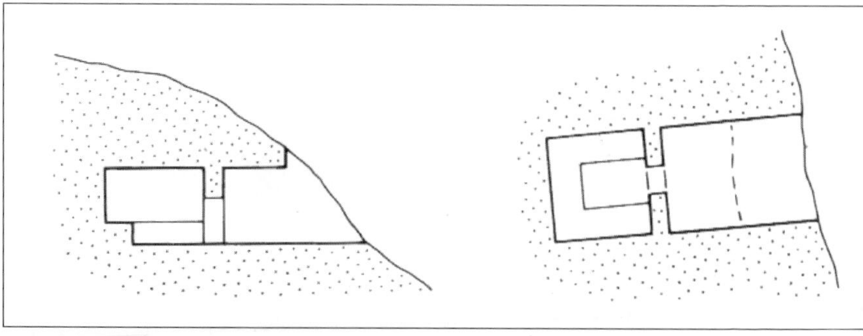

Fig 30. Reconstruction of the tomb of Jesus: Professor Martin Biddle concludes that the tomb had two components: there was an unroofed or partly covered rock-cut forecourt (3-4 metres wide and 3-4 metres deep) which opened by a low entrance into a fully enclosed square or rectangular tomb-chamber (probably about 2.8 metres square and 2 metres high) cut out of the rock.

Fig 31. A coffin lies on a waste tip in Jerusalem. Some have suggested that Jesus' body was simply slung on a tip or buried in a shallow grave, to be taken by jackals.

Fig 32. The Holy Sepulchre Church, Jerusalem, which includes the supposed sites of both Golgotha and the tomb of Jesus. The church has undergone many vicissitudes. The present structure is basically Crusader.

Fig 33. 'The disciples Peter and John running to the Sepulchre on the morning of the Resurrection'. Eugene Burnand, c. 1898.

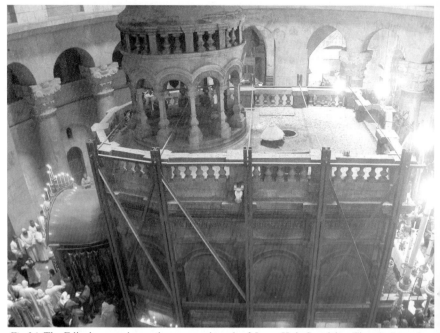

Fig 34. The Edicule erected over the supposed tomb of Jesus, Holy Sepulchre Church, Jerusalem.

Fig 35. The Nazareth Inscription: In 1878 a marble slab was shipped from Nazareth to France. Its original provenance is unknown, but it was almost certainly from somewhere in Palestine. It is now in the Bibliotheque Nationale in Paris. It records an edict of one of the Caesars making grave robbery a capital offence. Its date is unknown. It has been speculated that the edict was a response to the trouble caused by the disappearance of Jesus' body, but there is no evidence to support this.

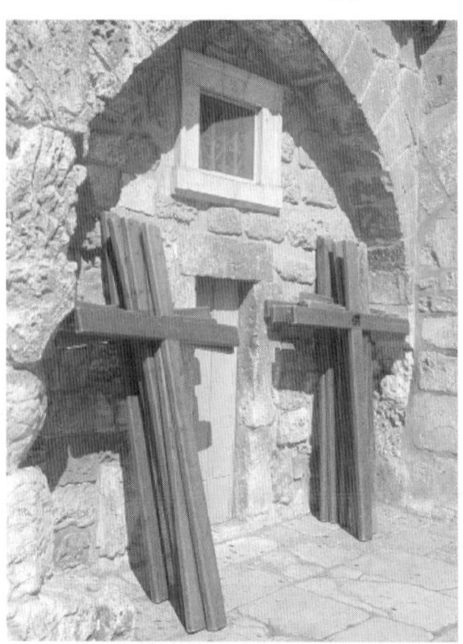

Fig 36. The triumph of piety over history on the Via Dolorosa, Jerusalem. Wooden crosses lean against a wall, waiting to be carried by pilgrims along the Via Dolorosa – the Way of Sorrows. The present-day route was only finalised in the 18th century.

around, making itself intermittently available for inspection and then finally disappearing. That has never been the Christian story, and no real Christian apologetic will try to defend it. The Christian story is far bigger and stranger, and the Christians struggle unsuccessfully for language to describe it.

The resurrection body of Jesus was like his old one in some respects. It had some continuity with the old one. It apparently bore the scars of his crucifixion.[76] It sometimes spoke with a voice that was recognisably his. It sometimes looked like him to people who had known him[77], and sometimes did not.[78] Sometimes it vanished as soon as it was recognised.[79] It could be touched[80], but sometimes, for reasons that are very unclear, he didn't want it to be.[81] Some people were so convinced that it was him that they were martyred for their conviction. But even some who saw him doubted that it was him at all.[82] It seems to have existed in more than merely our dimension at one time. Yes, it was physical, but not merely physical. It was more than physical. It could walk through walls because it was far more solid than they were, not because it was some sort of insubstantial phantasm. It wasn't bounded by space and time in the same way that we are, although if it chose it could happily occupy our space and our time in a similar way to the way we do. When it finally moved out of the range of human senses at the end of the 40 days, it was going back to a dimension that it had never totally left; which it had always occupied in some sense during those 40 days.

Understand this (or at least understand what understanding might involve), and many of X's objections to the resurrection appearances simply fall away.

Disposing of Matthew

The gist of X's attack on Matthew's account of the resurrection appearances is that it is short. That's an interesting observation, because of course the gist of X's previous attacks on him has been that he is an incurable embellisher. If Matthew's earlier credibility is in dispute because he said too much, surely his credibility here is enhanced because he says less?

Matthew is indeed very curtly factual in his final chapter. He does not give details of the way Jesus looked, and all the other things that X wants to know about. But it is misleading to suggest that his resurrection story spans only twelve verses. It starts, very explicitly and spectacularly, at verse 9 with a meeting between the women and

Jesus. They grab on to him. True, Matthew deals head on, and for five verses, with the conspiracy. It is perverse to suggest that this indicates that Matthew had no significant evidence of the resurrection (or perhaps did not believe himself in the resurrection). Those five verses are put there specifically to deal with one of the objections to the resurrection. If there were no resurrection to testify to, those five verses would be pointless. Matthew is indeed an apologist for the resurrection, and unashamedly sets out the case for it, dealing by way of pre-emptive strike with the objections that he thinks people are going to make. X tries to cast doubt on Matthew not because of his content, but because of his intention. One has to ask: how on earth did Matthew acquire the intention to defend the resurrection unless he was convinced himself? Matthew's own relatively sparse account of the resurrection appearances has to be read in that light.

X has consistently insinuated that Matthew will do anything to convince people of the Christian story. This final chapter lays that allegation finally and firmly to rest: "When they saw [Jesus]", he says, "they worshipped him; but some doubted."[83] What slick theological door-to-door salesman would make an admission like that? He has been trying to tell the truth throughout, and is doing so here.

The notion that the mention of the mountain makes this the territory of pure myth is insupportable. If it were pure myth, Matthew would have felt able to give himself a much freer literary rein than he does. You would have clouds and heavenly voices and sunbeams. You can't say on the one hand "You're creating a fable", and on the other "You're too skeletal to be believable". Matthew does seem stunned and awed by what has happened. He doesn't attempt exposition. We're all out of our depth here. But that doesn't mean that there are no demonstrable depths.

Matthew, Luke and John: Three irreconcilably different accounts?

X's analysis of the differences between Luke and John is right, with the exception of his presumption that the disciples meekly stayed in Jerusalem, as they were told. To examine that we have to go to Matthew. In Matthew and Mark, the disciples had been told that Jesus would see them in Galilee[84], and in Matthew, of course, Jesus does indeed see them in Galilee. Does the Luke/Acts version mean that the disciples could have seen Jesus in Galilee only if they had disobeyed his injunction to stay in Jerusalem? Well, not necessarily. It needs a close look.

The disciples were told to stay in Jerusalem until they had " been clothed with power from on high"[85] and until they had received "the promise of the Father"?[86] The "power" and the "promise" have generally been understood to be the gift of the Holy Spirit at Pentecost.[87] But there is plainly something funny going on with Luke's chronology. In his gospel he implies that the ascension happened on the day of the resurrection, and that on that day the command not to leave Jerusalem was given. In Acts, however, it rather looks as if the command not to leave Jerusalem could have happened shortly before the ascension, and we are further told that the ascension happened 40 days after the resurrection. Luke's gospel, then, plainly telescopes 40 days into one day. If that is right, then the disciples might have been in Galilee during some of the 40 days without any disobedience to Jesus' command to stay in Jerusalem – because the command had not at that time been given.

This is not the only example of odd inexactitude in Luke. Luke 24:12 reads: "…Peter got up and ran to the tomb; stooping and looking in, he saw the linen cloths by themselves; then he went home, amazed at what had happened." From this it sounds for all the world as if only Peter ran to the tomb. There is no other mention of any other visit to the tomb by any other disciple. But when Cleopas and the other man were talking on the Emmaus road about what had happened, Cleopas, talking to the still unrecognised Jesus, said: "Some of those who were with us went to the tomb and found it just as the women had said, but they did not see him."[88] What is happening here? There are three possibilities:

(a) Some other disciples went with Peter to the tomb, but Luke does not mention them.
(b) Some other disciples went at some other time to the tomb (but not with Peter), but Luke does not mention them.
(c) Cleopas wrongly thinks that someone other than Peter went to the tomb, and Luke is reporting Cleopas' misapprehension.

Of these, either (a) or (b) seems more likely. And this, together with the curious relationship of the end of Luke's gospel and the beginning of Acts, tells us something about how Luke, in common with many historians in the ancient world, tells history. Luke is telling the truth, and nothing but the truth, but not necessarily the whole truth, or not all at once.

Historical improbabilities in Luke

The Emmaus road

X begins by asserting that the "village called Emmaus" never existed. This used to be said a lot, but X is out of date. As on so many occasions, archaeology has been able to confirm the accuracy of the New Testament. The gospel says that Emmaus was about 60 stadia (about seven miles) from Jerusalem. For millennia its location has been a mystery. Various candidates were suggested, but none of them fitted neatly. The prime contender was Nicopolis, designated as Emmaus by the Byzantine church in the second half of the fourth century AD, and still the tourist guide's preferred site. But it is too far from Jerusalem, and in the first century was a regional capital, not a village. The twelfth-century Crusaders thought that Emmaus-Abu Ghosh, near Qiryat Yearim, was the site of Emmaus, but it was not called Emmaus in the first century. Neither was the third candidate, El Quebeibe, between Jerusalem and Ramallah.[89]

The fact that these didn't fit was used as a stick to beat Luke. And it was wielded with good effect until the archaeological excavation season of 2001. Then, just off the A1 road between Jerusalem and Tel Aviv, Emmaus rose from the dust. Jews had certainly lived there before and until AD 70. The distance was just right. It had been a wealthy, upper-class village. The excavator of Emmaus, Carsten Peter Thiede, thinks that the wealth of the village might contain a clue as to why that curiously selective chronicler, Luke, chose the Emmaus story as the centre of his resurrection narrative. Luke dedicates his gospel to the "most excellent Theophilus"[90] – presumably some sort of rich patron, and exactly the sort of man who would have had friends or relations in a place like first-century Emmaus. The gospel is full of stories about Jesus' ministry to the poor, the sick and the oppressed. But, suggests Thiede:

> ...if Luke wanted [Theophilus] to understand the message of the resurrection, what better narrative could he choose than the one where two wealthy Jerusalemite Jews return to their suburban villa and are honoured, as it were, by an appearance of the risen Christ...[91]

In Luke's account of the Emmaus road there is certainly symbolism. But that doesn't begin to mean that the events didn't happen. X seems to live in a bleak, reductionist world. Luke plainly intends us to take the story as history: if he didn't, he wouldn't have put in all the little, falsifiable details that he has, such as the name Cleopas, and indeed the location of the road where the meeting occurred. This is plainly not a cynical attempt to con someone into belief; if it were, Luke, who is no fool, would have edited out all the difficult bits – notably the failure to recognise Jesus throughout the long walk.

Luke's chronology

This has already been dealt with: see above.

The ascension

Now who is the fundamentalist? X reads the ascension story as an Apollo lift-off. He is very patronising. First-century Jews didn't have a two-tier picture of the Universe. They didn't think that heaven started vertically above the Mount of Olives, just past the clouds. They used vertical imagery to talk about heaven, because it was as good as any and better than most. But they would have found as ridiculous as X does the mediaeval Christian pictures of bamboozled apostles straining their necks to catch the last glimpse of Jesus' feet, peeping out of a cloud.

Modern physicists talk about parallel universes, and are not dismissed as crude literalists for doing so. First-century Judaism was familiar with comparable ideas, and used similar languages. They would have understood the ascension story in some terms similar to this: "There came a time when Jesus passed out of the dimension in which our limited bodies and senses could deal with him, to another dimension completely. The last time that he was accessible to us in anything like a physical human way was on the Mount of Olives, near Bethany. After that we went away and waited to see what was going to happen next."[92] All this tells us quite a lot about how we should be looking at the resurrection body.

Historical improbabilities in John

The curious business of chapter 21

X thinks that chapter 21 has been tacked on as a clear afterthought because chapter 20 was thought to be inadequate. Most of the points made by X amount to the observation: "There is teaching and encouragement in John 21, which means that the record cannot be historically reliable." We've touched on this before. It would be surprising if Jesus hadn't taught and encouraged. If John thought that it was important and helpful to pass it on, it would be surprising if he hadn't passed it on.

Chapter 21 was obviously added later. Probably not much later, though. And the author of chapter 21 was either the author of the previous chapters, or very close to him. The ham-fisted way in which chapter 21 has been added, without any attempt to smooth over the seam, is yet another indication of the integrity of the later editors, and indeed of the original author. They were all far more concerned about authenticity than tidiness.

Galilee in John: A damage limitation exercise?

X is speech-making. These points have been dealt with before.

You will succeed

Jesus is encouraging: that is hardly evidence that the words cited did not come from him.

The highest authority on earth

Well, authority is important, and Jesus knew it. It would be surprising if Jesus just left the disciples without any indication about succession.

The rehabilitation and commissioning of Peter is simply that: importantly, it is not denigration of James. If there had been an element of that there might be some grounds to suggest that the pro-Peter passages of chapter 21 were later interpolations designed to press the case of the Peter/Paul faction in its struggle with the James-ites. But there can be no such suggestion.

The physicality of the resurrection body

We have seen it several times before, and here we see it again. The gospels come up with the evidence for a particular fact (in this case the physicality – in some sense – of the resurrection body), and X says: "Ah, you have anticipated the objection so neatly that your anticipations must be later additions." It is a strange way to argue. If it is a right way to argue, no one could ever prove anything: they are damned if they don't produce evidence, and damned if they do.

He implies that the weight of the evidence of the Thomas story is diminished because John does not record that Thomas actually touched the wounds of Jesus. But isn't it the other way round? Anyone fabricating this story for anti-docetic purposes would make it perfectly clear that Thomas had touched Jesus. He'd probably embellish it further, saying that Jesus' body was warm; that Jesus' blood was all over Thomas' hands, and so on. The understatement of the story indicates that the story is real. And it indicates, too, more compellingly but more subtly than a bloody-handed story would have done, how unmistakably physical the encounter with Jesus must have been. We all know bodies when we see them. This body was more than enough for Thomas. His response is interesting: Not "Yes, that's a body all right; I've seen what I wanted to see", but "My Lord and my God."

The hallucination hypothesis

Jesus and Elvis

Apparently the occasional hysterical oddball does think that he sees Elvis wandering round a supermarket. But the supermarket Elvises behave in every way as you'd expect supermarket Elvises to act. They look consistently like Elvis to the infatuated viewer. They get in their cars and drive away. If they come back they still look more or less like Elvis, depending on how they've combed their hair and how deluded the viewer is. They don't offer themselves for verification by sceptical critics. Large groups of people don't tend to think, all at the same time, that these Elvises look like Elvis. If they do, most would just say that the Elvises "looked a bit like Elvis", and that they knew what the devotee meant by thinking that there was a likeness. The Elvises don't do anything eccentric. They don't suddenly appear in the middle of groups of previous associates. They don't talk for hours to old friends, become eventually recognised as Elvis, and then disappear. They don't give advice about what their friends should do when they go away. If they walk into the supermarket walls they fall over.

Mass hallucinations: Do lots of mistakes make a correct answer?

The mass hallucinations that are reasonably documented (assuming that they are indeed hallucinations) are of vague things. The classic example is indeed the Portugal visions of 1917, cited by X. It is true that many people reported seeing the sun "approach the earth". But many things could have been meant by this. Whether the sun approaches the earth or not is very much in the eye of the beholder – which is of course precisely X's point. One can well understand how a rumour that something as vague as "the sun is approaching the earth" might spread epidemically amongst an expectant population and translate easily into a belief that refraction from a particular cloud was indeed the sun approaching the earth. But the post-resurrection accounts are not in that class at all. They are much more concrete, much more variable, much less expected, and seen by a much less naturally receptive audience.

X's review of the psychiatric literature

All this is fair. Most headings need no further comment. Where further comments are necessary they are set out under the same headings that X uses.

How common are hallucinations in the general population?

It is simply worth highlighting here the observation that multimodal hallucinations are rare.

The relationship between hallucination and gullibility

X summarises the important "White Christmas" work of Mintz and Alpert. It was suggested to a group of hallucinating schizophrenics, non-hallucinating schizophrenics and normal controls that the record "White Christmas" was going to be played. In fact the record was not played. X concludes his summary of the paper by saying that "75% of 'hallucinators' 'heard' the record." That is true, as far as it goes. But he neglects to point out that, although 75% of the hallucinating schizophrenics "heard" the record, only 10% of them actually believed that it had been played. This is important when we come to applying these findings to the gospel accounts.

What other conditions affect the incidence of hallucination?

Hope can generate visions, true: but the stresses that do it are extreme. Some classic examples are cited by X.

The special case of bereavement

One caveat: be careful not to extrapolate too far from these data and conclude that in each case the bereaved hallucinator actually believed that there was some objective contact with the dead spouse.

From the psychiatric literature to the gospels

X is entirely wrong. Everything in the scientific literature indicates that the disciples could not have been hallucinating. Hallucinations, for a start, happen hugely more often to a rare sub-class of schizophrenic hallucinators than they do to the general population. Jesus is unlikely to have recruited his disciples from such a sub-class.

Hallucinators tend to have a lower average intelligence than the general population, and although the disciples were not bourgeois scholars (although X is keen to say of them, for some of his purposes, that they were sophisticated, artful fiction writers), their subsequent careers as preachers throughout and beyond the Roman world indicate clearly that they were no fools. Several of them appear to have had their own fishing businesses on the Sea of Galilee, which would put them surprisingly high up on the financial and intellectual ladder of first-century Jewry.

Yes, they were bereaved, but there is the world of a difference between the common type of bereavement "hallucination" and what the gospels report. The resurrection accounts are not accounts of vague feelings of the presence of the deceased; they are not mere voices in the no-man's-land between sleep and waking; they are not sensations of a hand on a shoulder in a turbulent night; they are conversations, meals and journeys. The psychiatric label "multimodal" doesn't begin to describe what the gospels describe.

Yes, no doubt the disciples felt that they had let Jesus down, but Jesus does not start off with absolution and rehabilitation. In fact that is left to the end, and is entirely in the context of the commissioning of Peter.

Yes, the disciples were stressed and relatively sleepless, but the sleeplessness wasn't of the order referred to in the Belenky trials cited by X, and the stresses weren't akin to hostage stresses. If the disciples had been more stressed and wholly sleep-deprived, the literature might suggest that they would see something like pink elephants floating in front of their eyes. There is nothing to suggest that they would see and hear (and all of them at the same time) a man delivering a theology lesson, or (weeks after the first appearance) the same man cooking fish on a beach.

X is labouring under the misapprehension that people who hallucinate think that their hallucinations are objectively there. This can happen (and particularly in people with very advanced schizophrenia), but it is very rare. The "White-Christmas" work demonstrated this. Even among the suggestible schizophrenics who heard the tune that they were told they would hear, only a small proportion actually believed that the tune had been objectively played. There is no doubt at all that most of the disciples thought that they had seen Jesus entirely objectively. Many of them subsequently died for that belief.

Did the disciples expect to see Jesus? First, the psychiatric context: there is no doubt that expectant people are more likely than non-expectant people to have a hallucinatory experience of the thing they are expecting. It is equally clear that while increasing expectancy does increase the incidence of hallucinations, it does not increase the quality of the hallucination. So if Peter (for example) was certain that he was going to see Jesus again, that would be likely to increase the chance of a vision of Jesus. It would not make Jesus' body appear more solid than it would have been if Peter was merely fairly confident that he would see Jesus, and had a vision of him. You can't explain Thomas' complete satisfaction that he had seen a particularly solid Jesus by saying that Thomas had been told in no uncertain terms by the other disciples (whom he trusted) that Jesus would appear that night (which of course is not the evidence anyway).

But the evidence does not suggest that the disciples expected to see Jesus again. X has cited those passages that indicate that Jesus told them that he would return and that they would see him in Galilee. But they seem not to have understood it – even if the Pharisees had heard it and realised the trouble it might cause. Look at Mark 9:31: Jesus has just told the disciples that he will be betrayed and killed, and will rise again on the third day. Their response? "...They did not understand what he was saying and were afraid to ask him." If they had understood it, surely they would not be cowering in Jerusalem, with Peter frightened of girls. They would not have been astonished at his appearances; they would have been standing by, waiting for further orders. There would have been no need for Jesus' swingeing denunciation on the Emmaus road of the faithlessness of the disciples: "Then he said to them: 'Oh, how foolish you are, and how slow of heart to believe all that the prophets have declared! Was it not necessary that the Messiah should suffer these things and then enter into his glory?...'"[93] If, however, the disciples (contrary to their appalling record of systematically misunderstanding almost everything Jesus said to them) had remembered and understood those words about seeing Jesus again in Galilee, or had their memories jogged by the empty-tomb angels, it cannot have been those words that led anyone to imagine that he first appeared (as Matthew, Luke and John all agree he did) in Jerusalem. The mention of Galilee would positively inoculate their psyches against any apparition in Jerusalem.

We will deal in Chapter 8 with whether or not their Jewish backgrounds would have led the disciples to expect Jesus to rise in the way that the Christians say that he did; but the brief point is that, to them, as to all other orthodox Jews, Jesus' appearance would have been the very last thing they were expecting.

Were they seeing a ghost (whatever that is)? X rightly points out that people coming from cultures that expect to see ghosts are more likely to see them, and that in first-century Palestine ghosts were two a penny. To be fair to X, the disciples' first thought on seeing the risen Jesus was that he was a ghost:

> While they were talking…Jesus himself stood among them and said to them, "Peace be with you". They were startled and terrified, and thought that they were seeing a ghost.[94]

Jesus soon puts that fear to rest:

> "Look at my hands and feet; see that it is I myself. Touch me and see; for a ghost does not have flesh and bones as you see that I have."[95]

A culture so familiar with the idea of ghosts wouldn't confuse Jesus with a ghost for long. The disciples knew perfectly well how ghosts were meant to behave, and they knew that Jesus didn't behave remotely like one.

I have dealt with X's argument so far on the presumption that if person A has a hallucination it is perfectly feasible for person B also to have the same hallucination. But, of course, it is not remotely feasible. It doesn't happen. If one stressed, tired person thought that he saw a pink elephant, an identically stressed, tired person in identical circumstances wouldn't conjure up a pink elephant too. Such a phenomenon is unknown to psychology or psychiatry. Yet if you accept X's reconstruction, not only did many of the disciples see, hear and touch a pink elephant, but they all saw, heard and touched it at the same time, and (which is something different) all believed that they had really seen, heard and touched an objective pink elephant.

The idea that hallucinations might explain the post-resurrection appearances is not seriously arguable. It is not surprising that most of Christianity's opponents, such as many of the members of the Jesus Seminar, have quietly dropped the idea from their books.

The lack of scriptural allusion in the resurrection accounts

It can't be denied that (to varying degrees) the gospel writers have been keen, in their accounts of Jesus' life and death, to view him through the Old Testamental prism. They have told us how various things about him were prophesied long ago. But when they get to the resurrection accounts, they put their Bibles down. They stop quoting. It is very dramatic. And why? Because they're at sea. Nothing like this had ever happened before. Nothing in their reading of scripture had taught them to expect anything like this.[96]

No bribery

Nowhere in the gospels is there any offer to the reader of any personal immortality. It is not suggested or implied that anyone else might under any circumstances be able to piggy-back on Jesus' resurrection. There's no apparent incentive to believe the accounts. It's as if the writers were saying: "This is how it was: take it or leave it".[97]

Paul's account of the post-resurrection appearances

1 Corinthians 15: Plum or duff?

The basic facts about this chapter are accurately summarised by X. The chapter is indeed important, for precisely the reasons identified. But, like everything else, it has to be read in its context and in its entirety.

It was, first and importantly, a letter to people who were already Christians. It was not trying to convince unbelievers. The Corinthian Christians had asked Paul in a letter[98] a number of questions about matters of Christian living and doctrine. One of the doctrinal matters was: what is meant by "resurrection"? Immortality was a familiar notion to the Greeks, but how did the Christian idea of resurrection fit with it?

When Paul, at the beginning of 1 Corinthians 15, set out so famously the summary of the evidence for the resurrection, it was not intended to be a statement of all the evidence available. That would have been completely pointless. The Corinthian Christians believed already that Jesus had risen. This was just a brief reminder – probably in the form of an ancient creed[99] – that the faith had definite historical roots. It is not a map of those roots. It is not intended to include an exhaustive witness list. It is there to set the historical scene for the theological discussion that follows, and for which the Corinthians had asked.

That early part of 1 Corinthians 15 has another agenda too. One of the particular problems in Corinth was that the Christians were splitting into factions. The divisions were not primarily doctrinal: it was just that some preferred one leader, and some another. Some were choosing, for instance, to follow Apollos (who made polished speeches) instead of Paul, who was more bluff and direct.[100]

Paul realised how catastrophic it would be if the church splintered along the fault-lines that were already becoming visible. Authority is important. Paul is therefore keen to emphasise that he brought the Jesus movement to Corinth, and that he has genuine apostolic credentials. That is why, at the end of the summary of the evidence about the resurrection appearances, he tacks on the experience that he himself had of Jesus. "I am an apostle," he says, "standing in the same line as the most significant witnesses among Jesus' most intimate associates. Listen to me, and prefer my words in the event of dispute." Since he wants to boost his own status and authority, it is hardly surprising that he name-drops. He puts himself expressly in the company of the big names: Peter; the Twelve; James; the other apostles. For the same reason it is hardly surprising that he doesn't mention the women who were the first witnesses of the resurrection. The lowly status of women as witnesses in the first-century world has already been mentioned. Their status may have been even lower among Greeks than among Jews. Women would have been unlikely to be mentioned in a creed of the sort that these early verses seem to be. Paul may not have mentioned the women because the creed didn't. In any event it would hardly boost his apostolic credibility to mention himself alongside women.

In summary, then, the famous opening section of 1 Corinthians 15 is an introduction to a discussion of the nature of the resurrection. It was written for Christians who knew the basic resurrection facts anyway; it would have been otiose to go through it all again. And (if it can be said respectfully) the passage is more about Paul's authority than it is about the resurrection itself. His authority was in question: the resurrection was not.

What were Paul's sources?

The chronology set out by X is probably right. His point is that there's a discrepancy between Paul's account of his sources in 1 Corinthians 15:3 and the account of his sources in Galatians 1:11–12. As with so many of X's points, this sounds good, but it evaporates when looked at closely.

Let's put the two passages alongside one another:

1 Corinthians 1–7:

> Now I would remind you, brothers and sisters, of the good news that I proclaimed to you, which you in turn received, in which also you stand, through which also you are being saved, if you hold firmly to the message that I have proclaimed to you – unless you have come to believe in vain. For I handed on to you as of first importance what I in turn received: that Christ died for our sins in accordance with the Scriptures, and that he was buried, and that he was raised on the third day in accordance with the Scriptures, and that he appeared to Cephas, then to the Twelve. Then he appeared to more than five hundred brothers and sisters at one time, most of whom are still alive, though some have died. Then he appeared to James, then to all the apostles…

Galatians 1:6–7, 11–12 and 15–20:

> I am astonished that you are so quickly deserting the one who called you in the grace of Christ and are turning to a different gospel – not that there is another gospel, but there are some who are confusing you and want to pervert the gospel of Christ… I want you to know, brothers and sisters, that the gospel that was proclaimed by me is not of human origin: for I did not receive it from a human source, nor was I taught it, but I received it through a revelation of Jesus Christ… When God…was pleased to reveal his Son to me, so that I might proclaim him among the Gentiles, I did not confer with any human being, nor did I go up to Jerusalem to those who were already apostles before me, but I went away at once into Arabia, and afterwards I returned to Damascus. Then after three years I did go up to Jerusalem to visit Cephas and stayed with him fifteen days; but I did not see any other apostle except James the Lord's brother. In what I am writing to you, before God, I do not lie…

Well, what, first of all, is the "gospel" which in Galatians 1 he is adamant he did not get from men? It is clear enough: it is the "grace of Christ" – the idea that Christ's death in our place reconciles us with God. It seems that this is the "good news" he is referring to in 1 Corinthians 15 too. In 1 Corinthians 15 Paul does not say from whom or where he got the various things that he "in turn had received".

There are broadly three things that he "received": the basic gospel ("that Christ died for our sins in accordance with the Scriptures…")[101]; and (quite separate from that) knowledge of the fact of the resurrection ("and that he was buried and that he was raised on the third day")[102]; and (quite separate from either of these) the evidence for the resurrection.[103] But here's the point: no one would ever confuse the gospel with the evidence for the resurrection. It would be like saying that a road traffic accident *was* the list of the witnesses who had attended the post-mortem of the victim. It would be immensely surprising if Paul had not talked with Peter and James in Jerusalem about what they and others had seen of the risen Jesus. It would be even more surprising if he had ever claimed that this amounted to "the gospel". And he didn't. He expressly says in Galatians 1 that he didn't get the gospel from men, and that's all of a piece with 1 Corinthians 15. In 1 Corinthians 15:3 he said that he received all the three elements (gospel, resurrection fact and resurrection evidence). But he doesn't say that he got them all from the same source. X needs to learn to read texts more carefully, and to distinguish between evidence and the things that are evidenced. It is pretty basic stuff.

No empty tomb in 1 Corinthians 15

Yes there is. Jesus was buried, and then he was raised. "Raised", to any first-century Jew, meant that the original body wasn't there. The tomb was empty. The expression "empty tomb" isn't used outside the gospels, but (as the later look through Acts will make clear) the disciples went around preaching what, from the gospel accounts of the empty tomb and the resurrection appearances, you'd expect them to preach. Attempts to prise Paul and the other New Testament writers away from the gospels have consistently failed.

The list of witnesses

The *point* of this witness list has already been dealt with: see above. The list itself needs to be read in the light of those comments.

It has to be acknowledged that this list is frustrating. It would have been nice to know (for example) who the "more than five hundred" were, and the circumstances of their meeting with Jesus. It has been suggested that this meeting is the one in Galilee referred to by Matthew[104], but we simply don't know. But the frustration itself is illuminating. Why does Paul not give chapter and verse? Because all this was old hat to the Corinthians. And the details of that appearance, now lost to us, were no doubt much better known in the churches then. The Corinthians weren't stupid. They would have asked questions like: "500? Really? Who were they? And when was that?" And it is reasonable to suppose that answers to those questions were available then. The Corinthians were probably bored stiff with sermons about the evidence for the resurrection. They probably dealt with the circumstances of the "five hundred" on week one of their Alpha Courses. They had written to Paul asking much deeper theological questions about the resurrection, and he wasn't going to patronise them by telling them what they already knew. Remember what this list was for. The history wasn't relevant, except as broad context.

The distinction between "the Twelve" and "the rest of the apostles"[105] is indeed obscure. The appearance to the "Twelve" is presumably that referred to by Luke[106], and the title "Twelve" is a sort of honorary one rather than a numerically accurate one: Judas and Thomas were missing. "Apostles" is clearly used loosely – probably in a way similar to the way that the word "them" is used in Luke to refer to Jesus' general close associates – who included Cleopas and the other man on the Emmaus road.[107]

Was Paul inviting his readers to check with the witnesses?

It is perfectly true that Corinth was a long way from Palestine, that Paul's Corinthian readers were unlikely to check, and that even if they wanted to they had no names. But remember that this list looks like part of a formal creed. If it was, it was probably used in other churches, some of them presumably much nearer Palestine. And, as noted above, other details of the appearance are likely to have been originally available. At the very least, inclusion of a challenge like the one implicit in the comment "most of whom are still alive" does denote remarkable historical confidence.

The appearance to Paul

We return to this in the next chapter. For the moment the allegation is simply that Paul was suffering from Conversion Disorder. This can't be right. The voice that Paul heard was heard (according to two out of the three accounts in Acts) by Paul's companions.[108] There also seems to have been something physical ("something like scales") covering Paul's eyes.[109]

CHAPTER 7

Did the early church believe in the bodily resurrection of Jesus?

Introduction

It is perfectly obvious that the early church believed in some sense in "the resurrection of Jesus". But what did they mean by that? It is important for Y to show that they meant by this that the body of Jesus was taken supernaturally from the tomb and that Jesus appeared actually to his disciples in a new resurrection body.

This is important because the early church was composed of or had extraordinary access to the people who said that they were witnesses of the relevant events. If the witnesses themselves believed in the bodily resurrection, that goes some way towards establishing that there *was* a bodily resurrection. By no means the whole way, true. Lots of people sincerely believe in plainly ridiculous things. But if the original witnesses didn't believe that they had seen a bodily resurrection, then Y's case for the historicity of the bodily resurrection is severely damaged. For all practical purposes it ends at the empty tomb, and it has already been acknowledged that the empty tomb itself is not sufficient evidence of the bodily resurrection of Jesus.

Part 1: X

> ...you ask me how I know He lives: He lives within my heart...
>
> Christian hymn

In a nutshell, these are my conclusions: First, the Easter story is not about the events of a single day, but reflects the struggle of Jesus'

> followers to make sense both of his death and their continuing experience of empowerment by him. Second, stories of the resurrected Jesus appearing to various people are not really about "visions" at all, but are literary fiction prompted by struggles over leadership in the early Church. Third, resurrection is one – but only one – of the metaphors used to express the sense of Jesus' continuing presence with his followers and friends.
>
> John Dominic Crossan, *Who is Jesus?*

Prologue

I sat down to write this section in the Armenian guest house on the Via Dolorosa in Jerusalem. As I wrote I heard a group of American pilgrims in the street below. They had just come from the Garden Tomb, which, in the teeth of all the evidence, they devoutly believed was the tomb of Jesus. They were talking excitedly about the findings of Ron Wyatt at the Garden Tomb. Ron Wyatt said that he had found the blood of Jesus there, and it had only 24 chromosomes instead of the normal human complement of 46. This, said Wyatt, was because Jesus had no human father, and so his chromosomes lacked the normal paternal contribution.[1] The pilgrims found this moving and convincing.

Then they set off to walk the length of the Via Dolorosa, which they believed was the original route of Jesus' final journey to Calvary. Their belief was undaunted by the fact that the present-day Via Dolorosa route was not fixed until the eighteenth century, and by the fact that it ends at the Holy Sepulchre Church, which, being Protestants of a certain type, they did not think was the real site of Calvary.

As they set off they burst into song: "He lives, he lives," they sang, "Christ Jesus lives today. He walks with me, and talks with me, along life's narrow way… You ask me how I know he lives." No one was asking, but they told the world anyway: "He lives within my heart." For once, I thought, they were reflecting authentic Christianity. For that was almost exactly what the early church believed.

The strange silence of the early church on matters of resurrection history

Apart from Paul's brief allusion to the post-resurrection appearances in 1 Corinthians 15 (of which much more later), the early church seems remarkably uninterested in a physical resurrection.

Outside the gospels there is no mention of the empty tomb, of the stone rolled away or (bar 1 Corinthians 15) of those post-resurrection appearances which you would have thought would be seared into the apostles' memories and at the forefront of their preaching.

You can suggest (and Y *will* suggest) many elaborate reasons why this should be. But there is one simple one: the early church didn't believe in the physical resurrection of Jesus at all. Peter, Paul and the rest of the early movers and shakers of the Jesus movement would have been astonished and horrified to see the way that the poor old Bishop of Durham, Dr David Jenkins, was pilloried by the evangelical world for suggesting that the resurrection was a "spiritual" event which didn't necessarily involve the translocation or transformation of a lump of carrion.

The ambivalence of the gospel accounts

The canonical gospels, in their original form, are non-committal about the nature of the resurrection body of Jesus. The passages that seem clearly to assert that that body was physical are outnumbered by those that suggest it was not, at odds with those that suggest it was not (a body can't be both physical and non-physical), and are in any event too obviously apologetic to be taken seriously: they must be later additions.

In most of the post-resurrection accounts, the body of Jesus behaves weirdly. People who had known Jesus intimately for years didn't recognise him. He simply appears and disappears: he doesn't have to go through doors like normal people do. For a lot of the time that Luke tells us (in Acts) that Jesus was around after his resurrection, he doesn't seem to be in the company of the apostles or indeed visible at all. One would have thought that if the purpose of those 40 days was to convince people that he was really alive he would have made himself more consistently available. And not just to the disciples (whose impartiality was always going to be questioned), but to genuinely independent witnesses.

The ostentatiously physical passages (eating fish, and so on) have already been commented on: see Chapter 6. They are simply too good to be true. They are of great historical value, but the history they teach is not that Jesus had a truly physical resurrection body, but that the church at the time that these accounts were written down was in the middle of a bitter campaign against the docetic heretics who asserted that Jesus was never (either before or after his death) properly physical.

Did Paul believe in a physical resurrection?

It doesn't seem so. The main evidence comes from 1 Corinthians 15. To understand it fully we will have to know a bit of Greek.

Bear in mind that 1 Corinthians 15 is the earliest written teaching that we have about the resurrection. All mainstream theologians agree that it pre-dates the writing-down of the canonical gospels.

Paul's meeting with Jesus all of a piece with the other post-resurrection appearances

Look at the opening of 1 Corinthians 15. Paul lists the post-resurrection appearances that he thinks it is important to mention. He doesn't mention some mentioned in the gospels (notably the women), and does mention some not mentioned in the gospels (notably the appearance to the "five hundred"). This list has already been discussed in Chapter 6, and the debate about its reliability won't be reopened here. The important thing for the moment is to notice that Paul mentions in the same list, in the same breath, and with the same tone, Jesus' "appearance" to him on the Damascus road. He appears to be saying that that Damascus road apparition was, so far as he understood it, of the same nature and quality as the appearances to Peter, to the Twelve and to the others whom he has called as witnesses of the resurrection.

What, then, did Paul think had happened to him on the Damascus road? The book of Acts has three descriptions of it.[2] They are all slightly, but probably not materially, different. The most important thing to note is that Paul never sees Jesus at all. He hears a voice and he sees a blinding light. We are a million miles away from eating fish and putting hands into wounds. And yet, says Paul in this earliest of resurrection documents, this was an experience of the risen Jesus like that of Peter, Thomas and the rest. The word he uses for his experience and for all the other appearances is *ophthe*. This can mean straightforward optical seeing, but it can also mean seeing with the inner eye. We can't say that Paul didn't have a clear idea of what Peter and co. had actually seen: he makes a point of saying that he had been to Jerusalem to chat to Peter and James. Presumably they didn't talk merely about the weather.

What can we conclude? It seems clear that Peter and James had not given Paul an account of physical confrontation with the risen Jesus anything like the one that the canonical gospels give. Paul therefore felt perfectly comfortable in saying not only that his unashamedly non-physical encounter with Jesus should be placed in the list of the resurrection appearances along with the others, but also that it qualified him to be an apostle, just like the others. Sometimes people try to dismiss this passage as simply Paul trying to re-establish his authority over the Corinthian church by whipping out his apostolic credentials. There is no doubt an element of truth in that. But it hardly helps the Christians. Quite apart from amounting to a serious slight on Paul's integrity and the whole corpus of scripture that flows from his pen, it also indicates what was thought necessary to establish apostolic credentials. And the answer is: a vaguely spiritual, but clearly non-physical encounter with Jesus after his death.

Paul thinks that our resurrection body will be like Jesus' resurrection body: And both are "spiritual"

Later in 1 Corinthians 15 Paul talks about the nature of our resurrection body. The clear implication is that it will have the same nature as that of Jesus because our body will be raised only because of his resurrection.[3] Jesus is the first fruit: we will be fruits of a similar colour and taste, having been plucked from the same theological tree. And the nature of our resurrection body is clear: it is spiritual: "It is sown a physical body, it is raised a spiritual body."[4] Jesus is the second Adam; he has triumphed over corruptible physicality, and we can hope to do so too. The contrast between the first and the second Adam couldn't be clearer:

> "Thus it is written: The first man, Adam, became a living being"; the last Adam became a life-giving spirit. But it is not the spiritual that is first, but the physical, and then the spiritual. The first man was from the earth, a man of dust; the second man is from heaven. As was the man of dust, so are those who are of the dust; and as is the man of heaven, so are those who are of heaven. Just as we have borne the image of the man of dust, we will also bear the image of the man of heaven…flesh and blood cannot inherit the kingdom of God, nor does the perishable inherit the imperishable…[5]

Paul is getting excited, but his central point can't be missed. He's got a clear distaste for ponderous physicality. But we won't be burdened with it for ever, he says. Trust in Jesus and you will get a new body. This one will be a spiritual one. It won't eat fish on beaches. Flesh and blood don't inherit heaven. An earthly body for earth: a spiritual body for heaven. If the gospels were trying to say that Jesus' body was in any sense physical, Paul plainly disagrees.[6]

Some in the early church were plainly embarrassed by this. It was a gift to the Gnostics. "Heretics", complained Irenaeus, "always quote this passage." Unlike most modern Christians, though, someone at least had the intellectual honesty to acknowledge the obvious discordance between Paul and the gospels. One might not approve, however, of the way he tried to deal with it. He wrote an entirely bogus Third Epistle to the Corinthians, which said on these matters everything that a properly orthodox Paul would have said.[7]

It will be said, though, that "spiritual" is a mistranslation. And so we have to dive into the Greek. What is transformed into what? Well, what is sown is a *soma psychikon*: what is raised is a *soma pneumatikon*.[8] The *psychikon* comes first, and is followed by the *pneumatikon*.[9]

Psychikon is the adjective derived from the noun *psyche* – which is generally translated "soul". *Pneumatikon* is the adjective derived from the noun *pneuma* – generally translated "spirit". Thus the Holy Spirit is the Holy *pneuma* – the quintessential spirit. There is nothing *embodied* about the Holy Spirit. A "soulish" body is sown: a spiritual one is raised. This is very strange. It is not the dichotomy we would expect. It is certainly not the dichotomy of most Easter hymns. What can he mean? There is one main clue.[10]

Wherever Paul uses *pneumatikos* (the adverb from *pneumatikon*), he uses it in contrast to blatantly material things.[11] And so there is every reason to suppose that he is using it in the same way in this curious contrast between soulish and spiritual. Whatever *pneumatikon* is, it is the opposite to *psychikon*. We know from the context that a *soma psychikon* must be made of flesh: it is our physical bodies that are "sown" in the grave. And so it follows that a *soma pneumatikon* must not be made of flesh.[12]

It might be said, of course, that 1 Corinthians 15 was a temporary aberration on the part of Paul. But it seems not. For he had a chance to put it right, and not only did not take that chance, but took the opportunity to reiterate the teaching that the Gnostics so loved. Perhaps the Corinthians were baffled by the resurrection teaching in the first letter. One can hardly blame them. So Paul wrote again on the same subject:

> So we do not lose heart. Even though our outer nature is wasting away, our inner nature is being renewed day by day. For this slight momentary affliction is preparing us for an eternal weight of glory beyond all measure, because we look not at what can be seen but at what cannot be seen; for what can be seen is temporary, but what cannot be seen is eternal.[13]

That's clear enough. Our inner, spiritual nature, which we can't see, is going to endure. What we can see (and notably our bodies) is all going to be food for worms. It is the invisible things that last. On this reasoning Jesus' resurrection body, if it could really have been seen by the disciples and touched by Thomas, would be bound to go literally the way of all flesh. It could survive only if it were not made of physical stuff at all.

He goes on:

> For we know that if the earthly temple we live in is destroyed, we have a building from God, a house not made with hands, eternal in the heavens. For in this tent we groan, longing to be clothed with our heavenly dwelling – if indeed, when we have taken it off, we will not be found naked… So we are always confident; even though we know that while we are at home in the body we are away from the Lord…we would rather be away from the body and at home with the Lord…[14, 15]

The "earthly temple", of course, is the body. When that is destroyed, what happens to the faithful Christian? He goes "home" to be with the Lord. But not, and this is the point, with a body. Paul makes this a matter of definition. If you've still got a body, you are not with the Lord. For Paul, bodies are wholly redundant in heaven. It's a sensible enough position. You need a body for eating, excreting and making love. You won't be doing any of those things in the ethereal bliss that is Paul's afterlife. And since Paul in 1 Corinthians 15 is so emphatic about the relationship between Jesus' resurrection body and our body in the afterlife, we can be sure that Jesus didn't have a remotely physical body after his death. Before leaving this point, look too at what Paul says in Colossians. Talking about what Jesus has done to effect salvation, he says that reconciliation has been brought about "in [Jesus'] fleshly body through death...".[16] The clear implication is that death is an end of Jesus' "fleshly" body.[17]

What about the other New Testament writers?

Was Paul off on a philosophical frolic of his own? He might have departed heretically from the resurrection dogma of the canonical gospels, but was he joined by any of the other canonical New Testament writers?

It seems that he had some company – notably the author or authors of the First and Second Letters of Peter.

Here is a bit from 1 Peter:

> You have been born anew, not of perishable but of imperishable seed, through the living and enduring word of God. For: "All flesh is like grass, and all its glory like the flower of grass. The grass withers, and the flower falls, but the word of the Lord endures for ever." That word is the good news that was announced to you.[18]

Whoever wrote that appears to agree with Paul. Flesh, of the sort that bears wounds and sits down to eat in taverns in Emmaus, has no place in the eternal scheme. What then endures? Not bodies, but intangible, spiritual news.

As well as these positive indications that the resurrection body of Jesus was regarded as a spiritual rather than a material one, there are many occasions where the New Testament writers pass up obvious opportunities to tell the physical resurrection story. They make it hard for the Christians to maintain with a straight face the common contention that the early church was propelled by an unshakeable conviction that Jesus had risen bodily from the tomb and appeared to his disciples, who had then subjected him to a detailed examination in which his physicality was established beyond doubt.

Look, for instance, at the Second Letter of Peter. Again, it seems unlikely that this was written by the apostle Peter, but it is unimpeachably canonical. The New Revised Standard Version puts this passage under the revealing, and accurate, heading "The Grounds of Christian Hope". The author writes:

> For we did not follow cleverly devised myths when we made known to you the power and coming of our Lord Jesus Christ, but we have been eyewitnesses of his majesty.[19]

We expect this to be an introduction to a systematic but enthusiastic statement of the evidence for the resurrection. We expect a robust repudiation of the claim that the notion of the resurrection is a "cleverly devised myth". But no:

> For he received honour and glory from God the Father when that voice was conveyed to him by the Majestic Glory, saying: "This is my Son, my Beloved, with whom I am well pleased." We ourselves heard this voice come from heaven, while we were with him on the holy mountain.[20]

The crucial eyewitness evidence turns out to be nothing whatever to do with the resurrection. It's all about the transfiguration. There's not a word about the resurrection in the whole of the letter.

Nor, for that matter, in James, Jude, 1 and 2 John, Titus or Philemon. There's no need to labour the point.[21]

Apparent belief in a bodily resurrection: A pre-emptive strike

But it can't be denied that there are places in the New Testament outside the gospels where the bodily resurrection does indeed appear to be asserted. The book of Acts provides a number of examples, and they will no doubt be deployed by Y. It will no doubt be said, too, that the apostles appear to have been persecuted, many of them to martyrs' deaths, for believing in the resurrection. Their evangelistic zeal cannot be questioned. What can be said about all this?

Dashed hopes are powerful: Flying saucers and energetic evangelism

In the American Midwest in the 1950s a woman believed that she was getting messages from outer space. She had quite a band of followers. One message was particularly important. It said that America would be destroyed by an apocalyptic flood. Times and dates were given.

The flood didn't happen. One might have thought that this would be the end of the group. The woman had made fools of them all. It was now obvious that her messages were bogus. But no: far from it. The group grew in confidence and numbers. The original members were aggressive and successful evangelists. The thesis now was that God had saved the world because of this group. The planned flood had been cancelled or postponed because of the existence of this faithful remnant. If human beings were rational animals the group should have dissipated in despair. But they are not.

Researchers concluded that the group had sought converts not despite the original gospel having been exposed as nonsense, but *because* it had been exposed. The evangelists psychologically couldn't face the abandonment of everything that they had lived with and for for years. They needed the encouragement that came from conversions. If more converts signed up, this would make the group's claims, in the members' own eyes and psyches, credible. Intense evangelism wasn't evidence of the truth of their gospel; it was evidence of the dependence of the disciples on the original conviction.[22]

It was the same for the apostles. Jesus had instilled great hope. They thought that he was a Messiah-figure. They thought that with him they could all change the world. And then it all went terribly wrong. He let them down. He was executed in the most brutal way. What were they to do? The flying-saucer disciples of the American Midwest explain perfectly the picture painted by the book of Acts. The energy behind those exhaustingly impressive maps of first- and second-century missionary expansion was the energy of dashed hopes sublimated.

The evidential value of martyrdom

True, many of the early Christians, including those who were supposed eyewitnesses of the death and resurrection of Jesus, were martyred. They kept their faith in the face of appalling suffering. Their courage must be saluted. But that courage must not artificially inflate their status as witnesses.

Two things must be said. First: so far as we know, they were dying for their belief in the Jesus movement in general – not for a specific belief in the physical resurrection of Jesus. And second: people are prepared to die for all sorts of beliefs. We do not take the death of a suicide bomber in Iraq as proof of the validity of the reactionary Islam that has made him immolate himself.

The merger of a tomb and a feeling of forgiveness

It has been suggested that after the death of Jesus the early Christians had an experience of grace or forgiveness. This might have been psychologically inevitable, and may have been a consequence of the guilt that at least some of them felt for having let Jesus down. That sort of burden either crushes or is lifted. When it is lifted the relief is likely to be so intense that a supernatural label is likely to be slapped on the cause. If the Christians were cultically devoted to visiting the tomb of Jesus, the experience of forgiveness could have become associated with the tomb (and therefore with the death of Jesus). Putting two and two together, the early Christians made about 397. The result was the fully-fledged Christian doctrine of atonement. For present purposes it is enough to say that their reasoning may have gone along these lines: dead bodies don't normally produce feelings of relief and grace like those we have experienced. Jesus must therefore have risen. If, at the same time, they believed that the tomb was empty, they were not far from belief in a physical resurrection body.[23]

Part 2: Y

> ...Peter, standing with the Eleven, raised his voice and addressed them: ...God raised [Jesus] up, having freed him from death... (Acts 2: 14 and 24)

The curious silence of the early church on matters of resurrection history

It is true that the empty tomb is not mentioned as such outside the gospels. But several things have to be borne in mind:

(a) Most of the New Testament outside the gospels consists of letters to people who were already Christians. They didn't need to be convinced of the truth of the resurrection. To set out the evidence again and again would be pointless: it would be teaching grandmothers to suck eggs. This issue has been examined in detail in the context of 1 Corinthians 15. Look at what the letters are about. The church had moved on. It never for one moment abandoned its faith in the resurrection, but it didn't need to dwell all the time on the historicity of the resurrection. It was interested in working out the consequences of the faith that had been vindicated by the resurrection.

(b) Almost always, whenever the apostles preached to the unconverted, they talked about the resurrection. Many examples from Acts, cited below, make this point.

(c) When first-century Jews talked about resurrection, they meant bodily resurrection. That means an empty tomb. This issue is dealt with in Chapter 8.

(d) It is conceded by X that the gospels talk unequivocally about an empty tomb. The stories that are now written down in the gospels were certainly circulating at the time that the apostles (whose experiences the written gospels and their orally circulated predecessors contained) were preaching the resurrection. It seems immensely improbable that those apostles meant by the resurrection something that did not involve the empty tomb. Is X really suggesting that the early resurrection preaching (which started 40 days after the resurrection, and in Jerusalem)[24] did not presume the empty tomb?

There is certainly no silence on the matter of Jesus' resurrection. The apostles couldn't be stopped from bellowing it from the rooftops. They spoke of the fact of it, the nature of it, and their personal knowledge of it. Most of the proper speeches or sermons in Acts have the resurrection at their heart. Threats of violence and death didn't mute the disciples one bit. A quick flick through Acts shows it well. This is a long and fairly tedious list. Its length and repetitiveness tell their own very obvious story.

(a) Being "a witness to the resurrection" was the job description of an apostle. When Judas' replacement was being sought, the candidates were sought from among "the men who have accompanied us throughout the time that the Lord Jesus went in and out among us, beginning from the baptism of John until the day when he was taken up from us – one of these must become a witness with us to his resurrection."[25]
(b) The very first sermon of the Christian church was preached by Peter in Jerusalem on the day of Pentecost. Jesus, he said "...you crucified and killed by the hands of those outside the law. But God raised him up, having freed him from death, because it was impossible for him to be held in its power".[26] He went on: "Fellow Israelites, I may say to you confidently of our ancestor David that he both died and was buried, and his tomb is with us to this day...David spoke of the resurrection of the Messiah, saying: 'He was not abandoned to Hades, nor did his flesh experience corruption.' This Jesus God raised up, and of that all of us are witnesses..."[27]

    Here, of course, clearly implicit, is the empty tomb and the physical resurrection.

(c) Slightly later, in Jerusalem, Peter addresses the people, saying: "…you killed the author of life, whom God raised from the dead. To this we are witnesses."[28]

(d) Peter and John upset the Sadducees because "they were teaching the people and proclaiming that in Jesus there is the resurrection of the dead…" It led to their arrest.[29]

(e) Under arrest, and testifying before the Jewish authorities, Peter said: "Let it be known to all of you, and to all the people of Israel, that [a man whom they had healed] is standing before you in good health by the name of Jesus Christ of Nazareth, whom you crucified, whom God raised from the dead."[30]

(f) Peter and John were told to shut up. They refused, saying: "We cannot keep from speaking about what we have seen and heard."[31] They are emphasising the evidence – not merely promulgating a belief.

(g) Describing what the apostles spent their time doing, Acts says: "With great power the apostles gave their testimony to the resurrection of the Lord Jesus…"[32]

(h) The apostles were arrested, brought before the Council and denounced for disobeying the order not to preach. "Peter and the apostles" answered: "…The God of our ancestors raised up Jesus, whom you had killed by hanging him on a tree…we are witnesses to these things…"[33]

(i) Peter, speaking in Caesarea, said: "We are witnesses to all that [Jesus] did both in Judea and in Jerusalem. They put him to death by hanging him on a tree, but God raised him on the third day and allowed him to appear, not to all the people but to us who were chosen by God as witnesses, and who ate and drank with him after he rose from the dead."[34]

(j) Paul, speaking in the synagogue in Antioch, said: "Even though they found no cause for a sentence of death, they asked Pilate to have him killed. When they had carried out everything that was written about him, they took him down from the tree and laid him in a tomb. But God raised him from the dead; and for many days he appeared to those who came up with him from Galilee to Jerusalem, and they are now his witnesses to the people… As to [God] raising [Jesus] from the dead, no more to return to corruption, [God] has spoken in this way: 'I will give you the holy promises made to David.' Therefore he has also said in another psalm, 'You will not let your Holy One experience corruption.'

For David, after he had served the purpose of God in his own generation, died, was laid beside his ancestors, and experienced corruption; but he whom God raised up experienced no corruption."[35]

How much clearer could it be? David rotted in his tomb: Jesus didn't.

(k) In Thessalonica, Paul went into the synagogue on three sabbath days and argued, "explaining and proving that it was necessary for the Messiah to suffer and to rise from the dead, and saying 'This is the Messiah, Jesus whom I am proclaiming to you.' "[36]

(l) In Athens, some of the philosophers who debated with Paul thought that he was a "proclaimer of foreign divinities". "This was because he was telling the good news about Jesus and the resurrection."[37] Before the Areopagus, Paul made his speech, tailored to the intellectual proclivities of the Athenians, and concluded: "...of this [God] has given assurance to all by raising [Jesus] from the dead."[38] The response to this was as it has always been everywhere: "When they heard of the resurrection of the dead, some scoffed; but others said: 'We will hear you again about this.' "[39]

(m) Back in Jerusalem, Paul was hauled in front of the Council. He cunningly sought to exploit the theological division between the Pharisees and Sadducees: "When Paul noticed that some were Sadducees and others were Pharisees, he called out in the council, 'Brothers, I am a Pharisee, a son of Pharisees. I am on trial concerning hope and resurrection.' "[40]

(n) Paul found himself in Caesarea. He went before the Roman governor, accused by the high priest's barrister, Tertullus, of all sorts of disruptive behaviour. He defended himself robustly: "...let these men here tell me what crime they had found when I stood before the Council, unless it was this one sentence that I called out while standing before them. 'It is about the resurrection of the dead that I am on trial before you today.' "[41]

(o) Paul remained in prison for years. A new governor, Festus, was appointed. Festus summarised Paul's case to King Agrippa, and is clearly rather baffled by it all: "When the accusers stood up, they did not charge him with any of the crimes that I was expecting. Instead they had certain points of disagreement with him about their own religion and about a certain Jesus, who had died, but whom Paul asserted to be alive..."[42]

(p) Paul gets a chance to put his case to Agrippa: "Why is it thought incredible by any of you [Jews]", he asks, "that God raises the dead?"[43] "...I stand here", he went on, "testifying to both small and great, saying nothing but what the prophets and Moses said would take place: that the Messiah must suffer, and that by being the first to rise from the dead, he would proclaim light both to our people and to the Gentiles."[44]

(q) Paul then found himself in Rome, where he lived under house arrest, and where most think that he was eventually killed for his faith.

The ambivalence of the gospel accounts

X says that the gospels are equivocal about whether Jesus' resurrection body was physical or not. They are not equivocal. They merely describe what the witnesses saw. The nature of that resurrection body has been discussed in detail in Chapter 6. X's big mistake was pointed out there. His arguments are directed towards establishing that Jesus' body was not resuscitated. He needn't bother. No Christian has ever said that it was. The resurrection body of Jesus was far stranger than that. You expect it to be described in strange ways in the gospel accounts, and so it is.

Did Paul believe in a physical resurrection?

X says not, and relies on 1 Corinthians 15 to establish this. He has some arguable points. He wisely, though, doesn't go outside 1 Corinthians 15: if he did (and particularly if he ventured into Romans)[45], he would see that there is not the slightest doubt that Paul believed that Jesus had risen at least physically. And in fact more than physically. X's inability to understand this last cryptic comment lies at the root of a great deal of his miscomprehension.

Is Paul's meeting with Jesus all of a piece with the other post-resurrection appearances?

We have seen in the previous chapter the purpose and context of 1 Corinthians 15. One of the purposes is to establish Paul's authority. "I am a kosher apostle," he is saying. "Listen to what I am saying."

Is he really saying that his Damascus-road experience of Jesus is of the same quality as that in all the other apostolic and other encounters that he has mentioned? It is true that he uses the same word, "*ophthe*", to describe the appearance to him as he does to describe the other appearances. But "*ophthe*" is an elastic, general-purpose word. It doesn't imply anything about the quality of the appearance. And nor does he say: "The quality of my experience was identical to that of the others I have mentioned." His experience is in the same list as the others, true; but that is as far as is gets. If A is in the same list as B it doesn't begin to imply that it has the same nature as B. Bread and red wine were both on our shopping list today. That doesn't mean that bread and red wine are qualitatively similar, let alone identical.

In fact Paul is at pains to distinguish his experience from that of the others: "Last of all, as to one untimely born, he appeared also to me."[46] He is distinguishing it not only in time, but also in nature. "...as to one untimely born..." is the language of Caesarean section: a child born by Caesarean section has a qualitatively different experience of birth from a child born vaginally.

Paul must have talked to Peter and James about their resurrection experiences and those of the other apostles. Indeed, there is a suggestion that his visit may have involved some sort of systematic inquiry into the appearances.[47] There is no reason to suppose that they gave him an account different from that in the gospels, and every reason to suppose that they gave him an account corresponding to that in the gospels. Paul knew very well that his experience was different in several respects: he made no bones about it; see, for example, his accounts in Acts.[48] Is X really saying that Paul thought that all the original apostolic encounters with Jesus involved blinding light, audible voices, falling to the ground and scales on the eyes? If X is saying this, he certainly gets no support from 1 Corinthians 15.

Paul thinks that our resurrection body will be like Jesus' resurrection body: And both are "spiritual"

These are deep waters. The first thing to remember is what the gospels say about the nature of the resurrection body of Jesus. This was dealt with in Chapter 6. The resurrection body is certainly physical in some ways: it can be touched; it can eat fish. But it is equally clearly not merely physical in the way that we understand physical things to be. When a merely physical thing hits another merely physical thing there is a collision. But when Jesus' resurrection body hit a wall it went through it. But this was no ghost. He was not less substantial than the door: he was far more substantial than the door.

He wasn't less physical than the door; he was more physical. Heaven and heavenly things, says C.S. Lewis, will be far more solid and far heavier than the insubstantial mistiness of hell.[49] But here words begin to fail us. Tom Wright, acknowledging the limitations of language, has coined his own word to describe the nature of the resurrection body: it is *transphysical*.[50] If our resurrection bodies are going to be like that, it bodes well for a supra-sentient, supra-physical afterlife. You don't need any kind of body, let alone a supra-physical one, for a resurrection life that doesn't involve doing and sensual enjoyment. Resurrected Christians are no wraiths.

But does Paul agree? There is no doubt that Paul's teaching in 1 Corinthians 15 is difficult and troublesome. There are three ways to deal with it. The first is to say that Paul is no theologian, but a great mystical poet.[51] It is sometimes tempting to agree. The second is to despair of making any sense of the passage, blaming Paul for being irredeemably incoherent. I have often found comfort in C. S. Lewis's observation:

> I cannot be the only reader who has wondered why God, having given [St Paul] so many gifts, withheld from him (what would to us seem so necessary for the first Christian theologian) that of lucidity and orderly exposition…[52]

Indeed you are not, Professor Lewis. The writer of 2 Peter was (as Lewis again observed) sometimes stumped by the Pauline epistles.[53] But it is as well to remember that Lewis did not stop there. He thought that Paul's opacity might serve a purpose; that the opacity might be due to some inadequacy of our own spiritual optics.[54]

Which brings us to the third option: to grapple with the difficulties, hoping that some sense can be squeezed out of them. And I think it can. But it is a strange, elusive sense. You can see why the "orderly exposition" I would have wanted would have struggled to convey it. We are over the edges of eternity, and it is not surprising that normal grammar and vocabulary strain queasily to cope.

Remember the argument: a *soma psychikon* is sown; a *soma pneumatikon* is raised. The King James Version translates these respectively a "natural body" and a "spiritual body". That's not bad, but not particularly good either. Incomprehensibly worse is the Revised Standard Version, which renders the terms "physical body" and "spiritual body". This has led to a great deal of misunderstanding.

X's misunderstanding is one variant. X is right, though, to point out that *psychikon* derives from *psyche* – generally translated "soul". "*Pneuma*" (from which *pneumatikon* derives) is indeed usually translated "spirit". A better literal translation would say that a "soulish body" is sown and a "spiritual body" arises. There are now four steps to follow:[55]

(a) Both "*psyche*" and "*pneuma*" seem insubstantial things. You would think that neither would make much impression on a wall with which it collided. But that is a modern misunderstanding. A first-century reader of New Testament Greek would certainly, if weighing "*psyche*" in one hand and "*pneuma*" in the other, think that *pneuma* was immeasurably heavier and more substantial than *psyche*. Collision between *pneuma* and a wall would be conceptually tricky for a first-century Greek, but if it happened, *pneuma* would get the better of it. And what is true of the nouns is true of their adjectives.

(b) Paul uses the same idea in 1 Corinthians 2: there he contrasts the *psychikos* man with the *pneumatikos* man. One doesn't get the gifts of the Spirit: the other does. Both are of course living, breathing men who walk round and eat things. You wouldn't find a *pneumatikos* man floating somewhere in the ether. Anyone who doubts that this is what Paul had in mind should go to Romans 8:9: "You are not in the flesh; you are in the Spirit [*pneumati*], since the Spirit [*pneuma*] of God dwells in you." Well, the Christians to whom Paul was writing were very much alive. In that sense they were very much "in the flesh". Being "in the spirit" isn't something that just happens after you die.

(c) Now another bit of Greek: if somebody was said to be "*pneumatikos*", the sense would be not that they were made of "*pneuma*" but that they were *driven* by "*pneuma*": that *pneuma* was the wind in their sails.

(d) Finally, back to 1 Corinthians 15: *soma* is a very physical word. One would not normally expect a *soma* to be simply an ethereal thing. It is an odd word to use of a "spiritual body" if the idea is just of a wraith-like presence or influence. You expect a *soma* to be able to bump into things.

We also have to remind ourselves of the strange resurrection body of Jesus in the gospels. Its nature has been discussed at length here.

There are plenty of Greek words that Paul could have used to describe a merely physical resuscitated body. But they would have been simply inaccurate. The reality was much more complex, much more promising and much more wonderful. In an attempt to describe it, Paul takes refuge in the nuances of New Testament Greek. Those nuances would not have been lost on those Greek Corinthian readers who had begged him for an exposition of the resurrection. He told them that the resurrection bodies that they would have would be like that of Jesus: they would be far more solid than their present ones; their present bodies would look transparent in comparison. And the new bodies would be powered by the spirit of God.

What about the other New Testament writers?

The view of the early church is demonstrated compellingly and unmistakably by the review of Acts, but X has some points to make from some of the other books.

He focuses on 1 and 2 Peter. "All flesh is grass", says 1 Peter. "The grass withers, and the flower falls, but the word of the Lord endures for ever."[56] It is not clear why X has cited this. This isn't a passage about the resurrection at all. It is a passage about the transience of material things (Christians know that human and animal bodies decompose), and the durability of other things. The writer is simply trying to get his audience's priorities right. An essay on the resurrection body would have been hopelessly confusing in this context. It is confusing enough in the right context, as we have seen.

X then goes on to criticise the author of 2 Peter for passing up an opportunity to talk about the resurrection.[57] If X had been writing 2 Peter, the argument goes, he would have mentioned the resurrection rather than the transfiguration. X wants us to conclude from this that whoever wrote 2 Peter either didn't know about or didn't believe in the resurrection. It is as logical as saying that a man doesn't acknowledge that he is married if, in every letter to his wife, he doesn't refer specifically to their wedding day.

A similar comment applies to X's other citations. There are several New Testament books that don't explicitly talk about the resurrection. But every line of them assumes it. It is true that Christianity is nothing without the resurrection, but it doesn't follow that there is nothing to say about Christianity and its practice that can't be said without an express mention of the resurrection. The books X cites aren't about the resurrection. It is odd to say that the Christians didn't believe in the resurrection because they wrote and read books that weren't entirely about it. It is like looking solely at *Henry IV Part II* and saying that Shakespeare wasn't interested in, and didn't believe in, the events contained in *Henry IV Part 1*.

Apparent belief in a bodily resurrection: X's pre-emptive strike

Dashed hopes are powerful: Flying saucers and energetic evangelism

X says that there is a useful parallel between a flying-saucer cult in the American Midwest and the disciples following the death of Jesus. The saucer-ites prophecy had been confounded. This was a big psychological problem: the cult *was* the cult members' lives. It was psychologically necessary to seek reassurance by being successful evangelists. Their energetic evangelism, far from confirming the truth of the message, was generated precisely by its failure.

That's what happened, says X, with Christianity: he says that you can't point to the preaching of the early church as evidence of the truth of its contentions.

In the case of Christianity, though, there was no resurrection expectation to dash. The disciples had lived with a rabbi they believed was mortal. And, if you end the story with the crucifixion scene, he indeed proved to be mortal. If the story had ended there, it would have coincided with the disciples' expectation. There was no reason to stop the ministry of the Jesus movement. Jesus had said some very worthwhile things. After his death, teach his message, by all means. Circulate the poetry of the sermon on the mount. Publish the kingdom parables. Tell the world that Jesus had been a great teacher. But that is precisely what the disciples did not do. They went to their deaths saying that they had been completely surprised by the next phase of the story. They said that they had been completely wrong in their expectation. They said that Jesus had risen, and that was the core of their preaching. Excise the resurrection from the teaching of the early church and you have no teaching and no early church at all.

We will look below at the ordeals of the disciples, but it is worth looking briefly, through the eyes of the early chroniclers, at how the resurrection movement spread. Islam, of course, spread impressively too. Within a very few years of the Prophet's death great swathes of the globe were under his flag. But Islam's conquest was a military conquest. It triumphed because of the death of its enemies. Christianity's conquest was a peaceful one: it triumphed because of the death of its followers.

Tertullian (c. AD 155–225) wrote that "the extremities of Spain, the various parts of Gaul, the regions of Britain which have never been penetrated by Roman arms, have received the religion of Christ". In AD 230, Origen of Alexandria wrote (slightly overstating the case, true): "The divine goodness of our Lord and Saviour is equally diffused among the Britons, the Africans and other nations of the World." Arnobius wrote in about AD 300: "So swiftly runs the word of God that though in several thousand years God was not known except among the Jews, now within the space of a few years his word is concealed neither from the Indians in the East nor from the Britons in the West." St Jerome, writing from Bethlehem in AD 378, declared: "From India to Britain, all nations resound with the death and resurrection of Christ." The Patriarch of Constantinople, Chrystotom, wrote in AD 402 about the British Isles: "The British Isles, which are beyond the sea, and which lie in the ocean, have received the virtue of the Word. Churches are there founded and altars erected. Though you should go to the ocean, to the British Isles, there you will hear all men everywhere discoursing matters out of the Scriptures, with a different voice indeed, but not another faith; with a different tongue, but the same judgment."

The evidential value of martyrdom

Before turning to X's points, let's look at what happened to the Apostles. Many of the stories are contained in ancient traditions, and references are not given for these.

Matthew: He is said to have preached in Egypt and Ethiopia, and tradition says that he was martyred by being speared in Nadabah, Ethiopia, in AD 60.

John: He is said to have preached in Asia Minor and Samaria. He is the only one of the Twelve to have died a natural death. Tradition says that he died in Ephesus in around AD 101.

Peter: Eusebius says that he preached in Pontus, Galatia, Bithynia, Cappadocia and Asia. Early tradition says that he was crucified upside down (claiming that he was not worthy to die in the same way as Jesus) in Rome around AD 64–68.

James, son of Alphaeus:
His career is obscure. There is a late legend of his martyrdom in Persia.

James the son of Zebedee:
He is said to have preached in Samaria, Judea and Spain. He was martyred around AD 43–44 when he was put to the sword by Herod.[58]

Bartholomew: He is said to have preached in India, Mesopotamia, Persia, Egypt, Armenia, and the shores of the Black Sea. Tradition says that on an uncertain date he was flayed alive and crucified at Albanopolis, Armenia, as punishment for having converted Armenia to Christianity.

Philip: Tradition says that he preached in France, southern Russia and Asia Minor, and that he was martyred in Hierapolis, Turkey.

Andrew: He is said to have been a missionary in Macedonia, Greece, Scythia, Asia Minor, Russia, and possibly in eastern and central Europe. Tradition says that he was crucified by order of the Governor at Patrae in Achaia in AD 60. The story says that he took two days to die on the cross, and he preached to and encouraged the people who gathered round.

Thomas: He is said to have preached in Parthia, Persia and India. He is said to have been speared to death in India around AD 72.

Jude/Thaddaeus: He is said to have preached in Syria, Mesopotamia and Persia. There are two conflicting traditions about his death. One says that he was beaten to death by magicians in Persia some time before the

	end of the first century. Another says that he was crucified in Edessa, Turkey, in AD 72.
Matthias:	He preached for more than 30 years in Judea, Cappadocia and Ethiopia. Tradition says that he was stoned to death.
Simon Zealotes:	He is said to have preached in Egypt, Mauritania, Africa, Libya and Britain, and some traditions say that he was crucified in Britain in AD 74.
Paul:	We don't know how Paul died. He is last heard of under house arrest in Rome. Early traditions say that he was executed in Rome in AD 67, but before that he may have gone on a fourth missionary journey – perhaps, some say, as far as Spain.

X acknowledges the bravery of these men. But he says that it wasn't the resurrection (as opposed to a general belief in Christian truth) that drove them. And he points out that the fact that people martyr themselves for a cause doesn't prove the truth of that cause.

Both points are unsustainable. We have seen what the early preaching was about. No resurrection: no Christianity. "If Christ has not been raised," wrote Paul, "your faith is futile."[59] These men died gladly because they knew that what they were saying about the risen Jesus was true.

There is no parallel with the suicide bombers. They are in no position to *know* whether or not the cause for which they die is true. They simply believe it passionately and pathologically. To die for what you believe to be true is one thing: to die for what you know to be untrue is quite another. These early martyrs, remember, were the witnesses of what they were preaching. If the tomb was not really empty, they knew. If the resurrection appearances did not occur, they knew. If the resurrection appearances "occurred" only in a subjective sense, inside the heads and psyches of the individuals, they knew. If Christianity was bogus or evidentially shaky, they knew.

The merger of a tomb and a feeling of forgiveness

There is no evidence at all that there was a cultic practice of visiting the tomb. The nearest we get to establishing this is based on the fact that in AD 325/6, when Bishop Makarios of Jerusalem sought the site of Jesus' tomb, he excavated a site (the present site of the Church of the Holy Sepulchre) and uncovered a tomb that he believed was the tomb of Jesus. Why he believed this is unclear: it has been suggested that there was some sort of mark on it.[60]

The area of the tomb, originally outside the city walls, was included within the city by the "Third Wall" built by Herod Agrippa in AD 41–43. The contents (if any) of the tombs would have been removed at this time.[61] The conventional view has been that in the period after AD 135 the site was levelled and that on the top of it a temple complex dedicated to Venus was built. In this view, from around AD 135 at the latest, the tomb was inaccessible. It may very well have been inaccessible from AD 41–43 onwards. The city was of course destroyed in AD 70. It has fairly recently been suggested that the site was levelled not around AD 135 in preparation for the building of Venus' temple, but some time shortly after AD 70, in preparation for the building of the fortress of the Tenth Legion.[62]

There is almost complete agreement among scholars that the present site of the "Tomb of Christ" in the Church of the Holy Sepulchre could be the real Tomb of Jesus. If it is, then Bishop Makarios got the right spot in AD 325/6. If he did, then Christians remembered the spot, which by then had been beneath a pagan temple from around AD 135, possibly beneath the designated site of the legionary fortress from shortly after AD 70, and possibly inaccessible from around AD 41–43. Knowledge of the position of something does not begin to imply cultic devotion to it. There is not a single mention in any of the early Christian literature of tomb devotion. And why should there be? The tomb's only significance was that it was empty. Only the piety of later ages made it a place of pilgrimage. It was its very inaccessibility that made it devotionally desirable.

X says that the disciples felt a sense of forgiveness. They connected it with their tomb cult and, hey presto, the doctrine of atonement. Quite apart from the complete lack of historical evidence for any of this, it is psychologically highly improbable. X has built a lot of his earlier hypotheses on the assumption that the early Christians felt crushing guilt. Now they are feeling liberatingly guilt-free. Surely something *happened* to produce this transformation?

Standing back

There has been a mass of detail in this chapter. Many hypotheses have been mooted. It is easy to lose sight of the wood because of all the extremely interesting trees. We have looked at lots of questions about what the earliest witnesses of the central resurrection events actually believed about the resurrection. But all this, of course, begs the central and crucial question: how did they ever get to think that they should be discussing the theology of the resurrection in relation to the death of Jesus of Nazareth? The most probable explanation is that Jesus rose.

CHAPTER 8

Where did the Christians get their idea of resurrection?

Part 1: X

> Your dead shall live, their corpses shall rise. O dwellers in the dust, awake and sing for joy! (Isaiah 26:19)

> In antiquity the civilised nations of Western Asia and Egypt pictured to themselves the changes of the seasons, and particularly the annual growth and decay of vegetation, as episodes in the life of gods, whose mournful death and happy resurrection they celebrated with dramatic rites of alternate lamentation and rejoicing.
>
> Sir James George Frazer, *The Golden Bough*

Christianity didn't burst into a religious and cultural vacuum, infecting only theological virgins. The eastern Mediterranean in the first century reeked of religion. False messiahs were a dime a dozen; the latest apocalyptic predictions took the place of the football results in the chatter of the masses. In Palestine, resentment of Roman rule had done for Judaism what oppression tends to do for all religious movements: made it thrive. Suffering is a greenhouse for fundamentalism.

The Jesus movement started talking about the resurrection of the man Jesus. Where did their ideas come from?

The obvious answer, from the gospels, is that the ideas came from Jesus. We are told that he predicted his own resurrection. But he was a Jew, marinated like his followers in the Torah and rabbinic teaching. His ideas about resurrection were orthodox Jewish ones. The primary contention, then, is that we need look no further than Judaism to find the seeds of Christian belief about the resurrection. If other candidates are needed, there are two obvious ones: contemporary beliefs about dying and rising gods, and Hellenistic beliefs about resurrection.

Did Christianity lift its resurrection beliefs from Judaism?

The Old Testament

In the Old Testament there are clear references to Judaism. The most notorious examples are in Isaiah, Hosea, Ezekiel and Daniel.

(a) Isaiah

Isaiah chapters 24–27 have a good deal to say about resurrection. The point is made dramatically in chapter 26:

> O Lord our God, other lords besides you have ruled over us, but we acknowledge your name alone. The dead do not live; shades do not rise – because you have punished and destroyed them, and wiped out all memory of them. But you have increased the nation, O Lord, you have increased the nation; you are glorified; you have enlarged all the borders of the land. O Lord, in distress they sought you, they poured out a prayer when your chastening was on them. Like a woman with child, who writhes and cries out in her pangs when she is near her time, so were we because of you, O Lord; we were with child, we writhed, but we gave birth only to wind. We have won no victories on earth, and no one is born to inhabit the world. Your dead shall live, their corpses shall rise. O dwellers in the dust, awake and sing for joy! For your dew is a radiant dew, and the earth will give birth to those long dead.[1]

It all sounds gloomy at first. But repentance, coupled with the grace of God, changes the picture completely. Then the tombs open.

(b) Hosea

There are two passages of particular interest:

First the general position, immortalised by Handel:

> Shall I ransom them from the power of Sheol? Shall I redeem them from Death? O Death, where are your plagues? O Sheol, where is your destruction?[2]

If one is being strictly exegetical, the answer in Hosea to the first two rhetorical questions is probably "No." There's not in fact much hope in Hosea. But it may well not have been read like that by everyone, and it apparently wasn't read that way by Paul.[3]

And then to details:

> Come, let us return to the Lord; for it is he who has torn, and he will heal us; he has struck down, and he will bind us up. After two days he will revive us; on the third day he will raise us up, that we may live before him.[4]

This speaks very eloquently for itself. It is all there: not only resurrection, but resurrection on the third day.

(c) Ezekiel

The important passage is the famous one: the valley of the dry bones. Familiarity has done it no favours. It deserves to be read again.

> The hand of the Lord came upon me, and he brought me out by the spirit of the Lord and set me down in the middle of a valley; it was full of bones. He led me all round them; there were very many lying in the valley, and they were very dry. He said to me, "Mortal, can these bones live?" I answered, "O Lord God, you know." Then he said to me, "Prophesy to these bones, and say to them: O dry bones, hear the word of the Lord. Thus says the Lord God to these bones: I will cause breath to enter you, and you shall live. I will lay sinews on you, and will cause flesh to come upon you, and cover you with skin, and put breath in you, and you shall live; and you shall know that I am the Lord."
>
> So I prophesied as I had been commanded; and as I prophesied, suddenly there was a noise, a rattling, and the bones came together, bone to its bone. I looked, and there were sinews on them, and flesh had come upon them, and skin had covered them; but there was no breath in them. Then he said to me, "Prophesy to the breath, prophesy, mortal, and say to the breath: Thus says the Lord God: Come from the four winds, O breath, and breathe upon these slain, that they may live." I prophesied as he commanded me, and the breath came into them, and they lived, and stood on their feet, a vast multitude.
>
> Then he said to me, "Mortal, these bones are the whole house of Israel. They say, 'Our bones are dried up, and our hope is lost; we are cut off completely.' Therefore prophesy, and say to them, Thus says the Lord God: I am going to open your graves, and bring you up from your graves,

> O my people; and I will bring you back to the land of Israel. And you shall know that I am the Lord, when I open your graves, and bring you up from your graves, O my people. I will put my spirit within you, and you shall live, and I will place you on your own soil; then you shall know that I, the Lord, have spoken and will act, says the Lord."[5]

It couldn't be clearer. Graves open; bones are clothed with new flesh; resurrection bodies stand up.

(d) Daniel

> At that time Michael, the great prince, the protector of your people, shall arise. There shall be a time of anguish, such as has never occurred since nations first came into existence. But at that time your people shall be delivered, everyone who is found written in the book. Many of those who sleep in the dust of the earth shall awake, some to everlasting life, and some to shame and everlasting contempt. Those who are wise shall shine like the brightness of the sky, and those who lead many to righteousness, like the stars for ever and ever.[6]

One can go straight from there to Paul or, for that matter, to Calvin. Resurrection happens to the elect. It is an awakening. Since everyone knew that bodies decomposed, there must be some sort of bodily reconstruction inherent in the idea. And note the stars. The Romans thought that their god-emperors became stars. Paul in 1 Corinthians 15 seems to be teetering on the edge of saying that resurrection bodies are like stars.[7] The parallels are too close to be accidental.

The period between the Testaments

It is acknowledged that the Old Testament did not speak with one voice on the question of resurrection. The Old Testament as a whole was agnostic. But the mood changed during the inter-testamental period. In 2 Maccabees, for instance, resurrection is clearly promised to martyrs for Judaism, and equally clearly denied to the ungodly. Here are three examples:

Seven Jewish brothers are killed most horribly. The second brother says to his killers with his last breath:

> You accursed wretch, you dismiss us from this present life, but the King of the Universe will raise us up to an everlasting renewal of life, because we have died for his laws.[8]

The fourth brother's final testament is similar:

> One cannot but choose to die at the hands of mortals and to cherish the hope God gives of being raised again by him. But for you [his killers] there will be no resurrection to life![9]

The third brother is particularly interesting. The torturers, before killing him, cut out his tongue and hack off his hands.

> When it was demanded, he quickly put out his tongue and courageously stretched forth his hands and said nobly: "I got these from Heaven", and because of his laws I disdain them, and from him I hope to get them back again.[10]

So not only is there resurrection for the faithful and obedient, but there is also the hope of a restored body. Whatever the afterlife holds for that brave young Jew, he will evidently need a body to enjoy it.

By the time of Jesus, most Jews, bar the ruling Sadducees, believed in resurrection. The gospels themselves, dealing with the period before Jesus' death, are full of it.

Is it surprising that the Christians believe in resurrection?

Of course not. Most of the disciples were faithful, orthodox Jews. It would be surprising if they didn't believe in resurrection. They saw Jesus as (at least) a martyr for a righteous cause. They would expect him to share the fate of the martyred boys in 2 Maccabees. He could validly, on good scriptural authority, hope for resurrection. And they no doubt hoped with him. And no doubt hope became expectation. And expectation eventually became conviction.

Did Christianity lift its resurrection beliefs from the myths of dying and rising gods?

The first-century eastern Mediterranean was awash with dying and rising gods. Some of them had long and distinguished ancestries, and any half competent anthropologist can trace the connection between them. The roll call is more or less endless if you include the various names given to obviously identical deities, but anyone would include Isis and Osiris, Dionysus, Tammuz, Attis, Mithras, Persephone, Orpheus, Cybele, Adonis and so on. "There is only a difference in names between the festivals of Bacchus and those of Osiris, between the Mysteries of Isis and those of Demeter," wrote Diodorus, overstating the case slightly, but helpfully.

There have been many attempts, with varying degrees of scholarship, to say that the Jesus resurrection myth is part of the same genus.[11]

Three examples demonstrate the credibility of the thesis: the story of Isis and Osiris; the story of Dionysus; and the story of Romulus.

Isis and Osiris

There are many versions of this myth, but the basic story is as follows: Osiris, a popular ruler, was married to his sister, Isis. His brother, Set, was jealous of his popularity, and planned to kill him. Set made a magnificent coffin to his brother's measurements, and then organised a feast to which Osiris and many others (the number is usually given as 72) were invited. During the feast Set produced the coffin and announced that he would give it to whomever it fitted. All the guests tried it. None fitted, until, finally, Osiris stepped inside. Set slammed the coffin shut, sealed it and threw it into the Nile.

Isis was devastated. She searched the world for the coffin, finally finding it in the roots of a huge tree. She returned the coffin to Egypt, intending to give her husband-brother a decent burial, and hid it in the marshes next to the Nile.

Set found the coffin. He was incensed, and chopped Osiris' body into pieces, which he scattered throughout Egypt.

Isis eventually managed to collect all the body parts except (in some versions of the myth) his penis. She reassembled the body and wrapped it in bandages. In some versions of the myth Isis breathed life back into Osiris, miraculously (considering the still missing part) conceiving Horus as she did so.

Horus then set out to avenge his father. Neither Horus nor Set won a decisive victory. Osiris was proclaimed king of the underworld, Horus king of the living, and Set the ruler of the deserts.

The myth is a very, very old one. It existed in Egypt in Old Kingdom times, and was introduced to Rome in the first century

BC. The Christian parallels are clear. Osiris is emphatically dead, and emphatically resurrected. He becomes judge of the world of the dead, just as Jesus is said to do.[12] Some have seen more precise parallels. Osiris was sealed in his coffin by 72 conspirators: the Sanhedrin that condemned Jesus comprised 71 men. Add Judas, and you have 72. And Osiris, like Jesus, died on the day of a full moon and was resurrected on the third day.[13]

Dionysus/Bacchus

Dionysus (also known as Bacchus), the Thracian god of wine, was borrowed by the Greeks and elevated, rather late in the day, to the pantheon of Olympus,[14] where he (a god of passion and intuition) was bound to find himself opposing the god Apollo, who represented reason and order. When they joined forces (as their cults sometimes did – notably at the great temple at Delphi), they were a mighty force in the Hellenistic world. Dionysus' father was Zeus, king of the gods; his mother was (depending on which story you read) either Semele (a mortal woman) or Persephone (queen of the underworld). In any event he was illegitimate, because Zeus' wife was the notorious Hera. She was furious to hear of her husband's infidelity. In the Semele story, Hera persuades the pregnant Semele to look upon Zeus. This, for a mortal, meant death, and Semele indeed died. The fetal Dionysus was rescued by Zeus, however, who sewed Dionysus into his thigh. Dionysus was born from the god's thigh a few months later. In one version of the story Dionysus descends to the underworld to bring Semele back, but this, like the Persephone version, is a late variant. Dionysus' connections with the underworld are dubious.

In the Persephone story, Hera sends Titans to rip Dionysus to bits. They do so, eating everything but Dionysus' heart. The heart is saved, and implanted by Zeus in the womb of Semele, or eaten by her in order to reconceive Dionysus. Whatever the mechanism, it works, and Dionysus is reborn.

It is said that the Dionysiac myths prefigured and influenced the Christian myth in three main ways. First, Dionysus, like Jesus, had an unnatural birth: Jesus came from a virgin; Dionysus came from a god's thigh. Second, Dionysus, like Jesus, died and came to life again. Third, Dionysus was eaten, like Jesus is metaphorically eaten at the Eucharist. Other parallels have been suggested, but are embarrassing to most mainstream scholars.[15]

Dionysiac cults flourished in the Greek and Roman world. They were often related to the Orphic cult (Orpheus seems to have acted as a sort of Dionysiac high priest), and (whether or not the link with the original myth is obvious or logical) devotees may have engaged in a eucharistic meal in which the body and blood of the god were eaten and drunk.

Romulus

Plutarch, a priest of the Delphic Oracle, tells us in his *Lives* about Romulus, who, with his brother, Remus, founded Rome. In his death, and in what followed, there are very striking parallels with the Jesus story. There was a Senate conspiracy, according to Plutarch, and Romulus was murdered. Jesus was murdered as a result of a conspiracy of the ruling Jewish establishment. At the death of Romulus, darkness covered the earth, just as it did during the crucifixion of Jesus. Then the body of Romulus vanished. So did the body of Jesus. People wanted to search for Romulus, but the Senate told them not to: he had been taken up to the gods. Jesus, according to the Christians, had gone to his equivalent of "the gods". Most people in the Romulus story were happy with that explanation, but "some doubted" – just as "some doubted" when faced with the evidence of the risen Jesus. Proculus, a close friend of Romulus, met him walking along the road. The parallel with the Emmaus-road story in Luke is obvious. Romulus told Proculus that he (Romulus) had been a god all along, had come to earth to establish a kingdom, and now had to return to his home in heaven. Jesus is constantly talking about the kingdom of heaven, and eventually tells his disciples that he has to go away again. If the Romans are virtuous, says Romulus, Rome will be a great empire. Jesus gives his disciples authority, promises them the gift of the Holy Spirit, and commissions them as his witnesses to the ends of the earth.

Dying and rising gods: Conclusion

What are we to make of all this? Only that there was ample raw material to fuel and provide metaphors for a resurrection belief very similar to the one held by the early Christians. We need not credit the early followers of Jesus with great theological creativity. The resurrection story was old news.

Did Christianity lift its resurrection belief from other elements of Hellenistic beliefs?

If Judaism will not do as a source, and the dying and rising gods will not do as a source, then there are still umpteen other myths on which the early Christians could have drawn.

Resurrection was not something that happened only to gods. Of course from Homer onwards mortals are constantly talking with the dead.[16] But not just talking. Sometimes they go to the realm of the dead. Odysseus famously goes to Hades, and so, very significantly, does Orpheus. His story is examined below. Achilles talks to the shade of the warrior Patroclus, fallen at Troy. Sometimes redemption and resurrection myths are woven together – notably in the tale of Alcestis and Admetus. That story too is below, along with the fascinating story of Callirhoe, contained in a Greek and Latin novel of uncertain date (but which most would put in the middle or second half of the first century AD). Christianity is just another such tale.

Orpheus

He was a mythical poet and musician who features regularly in the classical literature from the sixth century BC onwards. He joined the Argonauts on their expedition, and on his return married Eurydice. She was killed by a snake bite, and Orpheus was devastated. He went to the land of the dead to find her. His music charmed the guardians of the River Styx (the ferryman Charon and his dog Cerberus), and he was allowed over. Hades, king of the underworld, was moved by his grief and his music, and allowed Orpheus to take Eurydice back with him to the land of the living. There was one condition: neither of them must look back. They climbed together towards the light. Orpheus, delighted at the sight of the sun, looked back to share his joy with Eurydice. He had been warned: she vanished.

There are a number of different accounts of Orpheus' own death, but they tend to agree that he was killed by the women of Thrace. The earliest account is that of Aeschylus. He says that the women were followers of Dionysus, and that Dionysus had urged them to tear Orpheus to pieces because Orpheus worshipped Apollo rather than Dionysus. Still singing, his head floated off to Lesbos. His limbs were collected and buried by the Muses; his lyre became a constellation in the heavens.

By the fifth century BC there was an Orphic mystery religion, served by travelling priests. Its rites are obscure, but part of the ritual is said to have included the mimed or actual dismemberment of a victim representing Dionysus. Having been dismembered, Dionysus was then reborn. When a believer died, the religion taught, the soul was freed from its prison (the body). It thus tesselated well with Platonism.

The Christian parallels are again fairly obvious. Orpheus has a trip to the underworld, but returns, like Jesus. The relation with Dionysiac religion engages all the eucharistic motifs of Dionysiac cult. Summarising the Orphic view, Socrates says: "In reality we are just as if we are dead. In fact I once heard the wise men say we are now dead, and the body is our tomb."[17] The empty tomb in Mark, for some, is thus a mere Orphic metaphor for the body. If one believes this, there is no need for any historical dismissal of the empty tomb story.[18]

Some would say that there are other suggestions that Mark (from whom the others drew their accounts) is speaking in Orphic riddles. In the 1970s a gold leaf was discovered at Hipponion in southern Italy. It describes what happens when an Orphic initiate enters the world of the dead.[19] On the right-hand side will be "a white cypress". Beyond the cypress the guardians of the sacred waters will ask the initiate "What are you looking for in the land of the dead?" It has been suggested that a similar pattern occurs in Mark's gospel[20]: when the women enter the tomb they see a "young man, dressed in a white robe, sitting on the right side..."[21] Is he in the place of the white cypress? He tells them: "...you are looking for Jesus of Nazareth..."[22] That is not so far from a question about what they are looking for. And indeed, in John, Jesus asks Mary directly: "Whom are you looking for?"[23]

Alcestis and Admetus

Admetus asked for Apollo's help in wooing Alcestis, the beautiful daughter of Pelias. Apollo did help, and Admetus duly won the great prize. But he made a dreadful mistake. Before marrying Alcestis he omitted the customary sacrifice to Artemis. The goddess was quick to punish him for his negligence. After the wedding festivities he went to the bridal chamber, expecting to find Alcestis waiting for him. Instead, hissing on the bed, was a tangled knot of snakes. Admetus went screaming to Apollo, who agreed to intervene on his behalf with Artemis. Apollo was an effective negotiator. Not only was Artemis' immediate wrath assuaged, but Artemis promised that when the day of Admetus' death arrived, he would be spared if a member of his family died voluntarily for love of him.

That day arrived surprisingly quickly. Admetus begged his elderly parents to give up their lives for him. They had had long and good lives, he said; surely it was a sacrifice worth making. They both refused, saying that they still thoroughly enjoyed life, and that he should be happy with his allotted span. But Alcestis loved him more. To save him, she took poison. Her ghost went to Tartarus, but Persephone, queen of the underworld, thought it wrong that a wife should die for a husband and sent her back up to the light. In a different version, Alcestis is rescued from the underworld by Hercules.

Here we have almost every element of Christian theology. Love compels the lover to die. The death saves the beloved, and death itself can have no hold on the lover, who is disgorged from Hades back to the world.

Callirhoe

Callirhoe was a beautiful woman. In the opening scene she was married to Chaereas. He wrongly believed that she was unfaithful, and kicked her. She seemed to be dead. She was buried. She was not dead, however, and woke up in the tomb as grave robbers were breaking in. The robbers took her, along with all the grave goods, to Miletus. Meanwhile, Chaereas arrived at the tomb at dawn. He was astonished to find that the stones that blocked the entrance had been moved, and that the entrance was wide open. He was seized by a "fearful bewilderment". Rumours spread and others arrived at the tomb. Chaereas and others finally went into the tomb and confirmed that the body was not there. Chaereas speculated loudly about what had happened, wondering if a god, jealous of Callirhoe's beauty, had carried her off. Or perhaps, he thought, she was a goddess. There are many other twists in the plot. They do not matter for these purposes.[24] The couple were eventually happily united.

There is no need to labour the parallels with the New Testament story; no one could miss them. The central motif (although not the striking gospel-like details), appear in other, earlier tales.[25]

Christianity and Hellenistic tales: Conclusion

Again, there is no need to think that the disciples were great novelists. The market-day chat of first-century Jerusalem would have given their imaginations everything necessary to generate the resurrection story, even if their own Jewish backgrounds had for some reason failed to do so.

Part 2: Y

> [Jesus] was teaching his disciples, saying to them, "The Son of Man is to be betrayed into human hands, and they will kill him, and three days after being killed, he will rise again." But they did not understand what he was saying… (Mark 9:31–32)

Did Christianity lift its resurrection beliefs from Judaism?

X has cited several passages from the Old Testament that talk about resurrection. But they are not at all typical. They are famous and interesting precisely because they are unusual. The general tone of the Old Testament is distinctly: no resurrection. Two examples make the point:

> The dead know nothing; they have no more reward, and even the memory of them is lost. Their love and their hate and their envy have already perished; never again will they have any share in all that happens under the sun…[26]

This is the gist of the main strand of Old Testament teaching on the fate of the dead. The dead are dead.

"Do the shades rise up to praise you?" asks the Psalmist. "Is your steadfast love declared in the grave…"[27] And the clear answer that most of the Old Testament gives to both questions is: "No".

When Israel was facing particular trauma, though, there were sometimes whispers of resurrection. That is the context of each of the passages from Isaiah, Daniel, Ezekiel and Hosea. In each, Israel was facing judgment or was in exile.

It is unclear in the passages cited by X whether the references to redemption are metaphorical references to the redemption of Israel as a people, or to the redemption of individuals. They have been taken both ways. But perhaps the distinction is an unhelpful one: the idea of community was such that individual resurrection was often regarded as meaningless, if not downright offensive, without the resurrection of the whole of Israel.

It is true, though, that by the first century the idea of resurrection had taken hold. Most first-century Jews believed in resurrection. And it was undoubtedly a physical resurrection that they believed in. But here's the thing: it was, as it had always been, a resurrection of *all* as a result of the mercy of God. It was sometimes equated with, sometimes conflated with and sometimes confused with, the resurrection of Israel. But, whatever it was, it was an apocalyptic event, marking the end of the age. When resurrection happened, everything else stopped. The graves might open, but they would all open together, at the end of time.

It cannot be said, either, that resurrection was associated with the Messiah. There were plenty of messianic ideas, and plenty of messianic contenders, but you will search the literature in vain for any suggestion that the Messiah would be the first fruit, or that there could be occasional exceptions to the rule that resurrection was apocalyptic.

The notion that Jesus, three days after his death, would rise alone – the first fruits of the dead – was completely unprecedented in Jewish thought. It would never have occurred in the wildest dreams of the most eccentric first-century Jew. The only rational way to explain its appearance in the New Testament is that it actually happened.

Did Christianity lift its resurrection beliefs from the myths of dying and rising gods?

The first, rather cheap, observation is that this argument almost always comes from people who say that the Christians didn't, at first, say that Jesus was God, and that that understanding was a much later development. They can't have it both ways. They can't say in one breath: "Belief in dying and rising gods explains a belief in the resurrection of Jesus" and in the next: "But Christians didn't, for decades after they were proclaiming the resurrection of Jesus, think he was God." This observation doesn't help much, of course, if one adheres to the basic Christian belief that belief in Jesus' divinity was a result of belief in the resurrection, and (for most people) sprang into being at about the same time as belief in the resurrection. So on to the substantive points.

The objection doesn't explain how the first disciples came to believe in the resurrection. This is so obvious a point that it is often missed. Even if they later came to see Jesus as standing squarely in the tradition of Isis and Osiris, one still has to ask: "But why on earth should they begin to think that?" Once the story of a rising Jesus had emerged, it is easy enough to postulate what the imagination of people, marinated for millennia in the legends of crop and sun cycles, might do with that story. But what that collective imagination did with the story once it had emerged doesn't help to explain how the story emerged in the first place. True, Christians appropriated pagan midwinter festivals. True, there are parallels between the story of Dionysus and the story of Jesus. True, dying and rising gods were symbols of the cycles of the sun and the harvest. But how did anyone ever start to think that the death of an itinerant Galilean peasant should be in any way equated with the emergence of crops or the annual return of the sun? So, as an argument against the historicity of the resurrection, this doesn't even start to get off the ground.

First-century Palestine was a fairly cosmopolitan place. No doubt travellers from Syria, the Aegean and Egypt brought, along with wine and spices, tales of the mystery religions. But, without wanting to patronise them, the disciples really don't seem the sort to let such exotic stuff lodge in their heads. They are (for Jesus) frustratingly slow and parochial. And these religions never had much of a hold in Palestine. The Orphic mysteries aren't recorded in Palestine until the late first century at the earliest. Once the Temple was destroyed and monotheistic Judaism's ability to inoculate Palestinians against it had diminished, the mystery cults appear. But not before.

The realm of the dying and rising gods of the Mediterranean is obviously the realm of myth. Nobody ever pretended otherwise. That is why they were, and are, so durable. They never held themselves up to be proved or disproved. No Dionysiac reveller, either in the heat of the orgy or in the reflective calm of the hangover, actually thought he had eaten his incarnate god. The most devout priests knew that the power they wielded was the potent power of metaphor. Whatever you think the disciples were seeing, it wasn't metaphor or symbol. Metaphors don't eat fish for breakfast. The disciples weren't historically conditioned or literarily equipped to make a myth like that.

In dealing with Isis and Osiris, Dionysus and Romulus, X has done his best, although he has unerringly grasped the wrong end of whatever mythological sticks have been brandished at him. He has set out the details of the stories. I am not going to trawl through them all, pointing out the differences. There are some arguable parallels. There are some blindingly obvious differences. In the case at least of the Romulus story, it is likely that Plutarch (c. AD 45–125 – a priest of the Delphic Oracle) borrowed some of the themes from Christianity, rather than the other way round. But there is a broader and more important point.

Christianity is a myth. But it is a true myth. It is not surprising that there are echoes of the Christian truths in the great myths of the world. As human beings grope towards the truth, they don't get nowhere. They get somewhere. As they strain their ears for divine music, they get faint, distant, broken melodies. But then Christianity comes, and suddenly the melodies are all there, played so clearly and so sweetly that it breaks the heart. For many of the listeners the response will be: "I've heard something like that before; I've been looking for this all my life." That is why the ancient myths of men and the True Myth sometimes sound alike.

Christianity borrowed the notion of resurrection from Hellenistic beliefs about the fate of the dead

Again, all the supposedly comparable Greek stories cited by X are unapologetically myths. Nobody has ever reverenced the tomb of Odysseus, although we all in a sense admire him. Why? Because he doesn't have a tomb; he almost certainly never existed. And if you could find someone who thought that he did, they wouldn't think that he'd actually been to Hades and back.

But, perhaps more importantly, none of these stories is talking about resurrection in anything like the sense that the Christians talk about it. "I believe in the resurrection of the body," goes the Creed. By that the Christians mean that a man who had been dead and buried was suddenly neither dead nor buried. He had a body which had some continuity with the one that he had had on earth. That body was sometimes, but not always, recognisable as that of Jesus, and apparently bore the wounds he had sustained on the cross. It had left its graveclothes behind, but apparently had acquired and wore new ones. It ate and drank. It was at pains to underline its physicality. But at the same time the body had some other attributes that regular bodies do not have. It could walk through doors, for instance, and appear out of nowhere. It seemed to exist sometimes in the same dimension as the disciples, and relate to them there in the old ways, and sometimes (possibly simultaneously) to exist in some other dimension (for which its more unusual attributes were presumably more appropriate). Whatever you say about him, he wasn't a ghost.

All this has no parallel in ancient myth. For Homer, the dead were tragic, grey, insubstantial shades, locked in the underworld. Yes, Achilles spoke to Patroclus, but he didn't doubt for a moment that Patroclus was dead. That's the whole point of the Patroclus story: Achilles is speaking to the *dead*. Again, it's so obvious that it is easy to miss. When you are dead in the Homeric world, you don't stop being dead: you might, exceptionally and myth-makingly, be allowed a poignant sojourn in the light, but you're a ghost when you do, and it won't be long before you are beckoned back into the darkness.

Moving into the Platonic world, the afterlife becomes potentially a more cheerful place than in the Homeric Bronze Age (particularly if you have intelligently devoted your life to Platonic philosophy under a decent, approved teacher), but it's an afterlife of the soul. The body is a wretched encumbrance. You get rid of it if you die well. The very last thing you'd want after you died would be to be reunited with it.

Alcestis looks more like a real bodily resurrection. She was dead, and then she wasn't. But she "rose" only to die again. Hers was a sort of resuscitation, like that of Lazarus. And hers was only a fairy story, retailed to Athenian audiences to make a number of ethical points. She never existed. She never had any cult. No funerary inscription invokes her hopefully. She is the exception that points up the general Homeric and Platonic rule: the dead don't rise.

How many times do we have to labour the point about these stories not even pretending to be comparable to the Christian ones? Callirhoe is a character in a novel, for goodness' sake. It is quite likely that Christianity gave the novelist the story.

It is sometimes said that first-century Palestine was a credulous place. They were always talking about ghosts and things there. This is no doubt true. And surely it strengthens the Christian contentions. The disciples knew what ghosts were supposed to be like. Jerusalem undulated with ghosts. And ghosts don't behave like the curiously undead carpenter behaved.

Conclusion

The eastern Mediterranean was a mythologically busy place. It loved stories. Many of those stories had religious themes. Some of them have echoes in or were borrowed from the Christian story. But none of them claimed to be historically true in any sense whatever. Christianity does. It says that it is the true, prototypic myth. And the historical case for that assertion is very strong.

APPENDIX 1

The cause of death

Introduction

There is a massive amount of literature speculating, with widely varying degrees of medical literacy, about the medical circumstances of Jesus' death.[1] The overwhelming conclusion of the mainstream literature, even that written by virulent opponents of Christianity, is that Jesus did indeed die on the cross. The very few exceptions are not really medical papers at all. The most recent illustrative example is *Did Jesus Christ die of pulmonary embolism? A rebuttal.*[2] The author is apparently an Ahmadiyya or someone sympathetic to the Ahmadiyya sect. He believes that Jesus survived. He assumes that the Turin Shroud was the shroud of Jesus and that its existence and nature indicates that Jesus did not die. He notes that some people are known to have survived crucifixion, and cites the physical nature of Jesus' resurrection body and Jesus' assertion that he was not a ghost as evidence of survival. He concludes by observing that "there is historical evidence that Jesus migrated toward the east". His final line is a curious one for a medical journal: "Jesus would have failed in the task he had been given to save the lost tribes of Israel if he did not survive the cross."

Stresses prior to the crucifixion

Jesus was presumably fairly fit. He was a youngish man – probably around 33 at the time of his death. He walked long distances; he had come to Jerusalem for Passover from Galilee, about five days' walk to the north.

On the night before he died he was in the garden of Gethsemane (at the foot of the Mount of Olives) with his disciples. He seems to have known what was about to happen to him, and asked his disciples to stay awake with him. They failed to do so, but, if Luke's gospel is to be believed, someone was evidently sufficiently awake at some time during the night to see Jesus praying. Something odd happened as he prayed: "In his anguish he prayed more earnestly, and his sweat became like great drops of blood falling down on the ground."[3] This has no obvious prophetic resonance. Luke is said to have been a doctor, and he might have recorded this because of its mere medical strangeness.

This may have been a (very rare) condition called haematidrosis, in which blood is expressed from the sweat glands. The abstract of the most comprehensive review article on the subject reads as follows:

> In order to verify the accuracy of the commonly used statement, "I sweat blood," a survey of the literature in the subject of hematidrosis was made. Seventy-six cases were studied and classified into categories according to the causative factor. These were components of systemic disease, vicarious menstruation, excessive exertion, psychogenic, and unknown. The psychogenic were further subdivided into those that occurred only one time, those that recurred and the stigmatics. Acute fear and intense mental contemplation were found to be the most frequent inciting causes. Hematidrosis is an extremely rare clinical phenomenon with only few instances reported to have occurred within the twentieth century.[4]

The most frequent inciting causes would seem to have been present in Jesus. Actual blood loss through haematidrosis would have been insignificant, but if present it was an indicator of extreme stress.

Jesus was arrested in the garden and taken for trial that night before the Jewish court. The accounts of the abuse he received there are as follows:

(a) Matthew: "they spat in his face and struck him; and some slapped him…"[5]
(b) Mark: "…some began to spit on him, to blindfold him, and to strike him… The guards also took him over and beat him…"[6]

(c) Luke: "…the men who were holding Jesus began to mock him and beat him; they also blindfolded him…"[7]
(d) John: "…one of the police standing nearby struck Jesus on the face…"[8]

From the Jewish court he was taken to Pilate. The accounts of the abuse he received there are as follows:

(a) Mark: Jesus was flogged.[9] Soldiers twisted some thorns into a crown and put it on him. They struck his head with a reed and spat upon him.[10]
(b) Matthew: Jesus was flogged.[11] The soldiers twisted some thorns into a crown and put it on his head. They spat on him and hit him on the head with a reed.[12]
(c) Luke: Jesus was apparently flogged, although the gospel talks just about Pilate's intention to have him flogged.[13]
(d) John: Pilate had Jesus flogged, and the soldiers put a crown of thorns on his head.[14] The Roman soldiers "kept coming up to him, saying 'Hail, King of the Jews', and striking him on the face."[15]

He had done a fair amount of walking, presumably bound and buffeted by various guards. Jerusalem is a hilly place. There is dispute about the exact location of the places where he was tried, but he must have walked miles. He had not slept.

There would have been some blood loss from the thorns in his head. Head wounds are notorious for bleeding copiously. There is a lot of discussion about the type of thorn likely to have been used, and the shape of the "crown". Summing up this discussion: we simply don't know the answers.

The flogging is likely to have been medically significant. It is likely that Jesus was stripped naked and tied to a post. The whip used was called a *flagrum* – a two- or three-thonged whip with twinned *plumbatae* – bone or metal pellets – at the end of the lashes. The harrowing flagellation scene in the film *The Passion of the Christ* is probably not far from the historical mark. Eusebius, writing in the third century, said of the scourging of those destined for execution: "the veins were laid bare, and…the very muscles, sinews and bowels of the victim were open to exposure…"[16]

Before the crucifixion, then, Jesus was in a bad way.

The crucifixion

Getting to Calvary

The normal practice was for the victim to carry to the site of the crucifixion not the whole cross, but the cross-bar – known as the *patibulum*. The weight of the patibulum has been variously estimated at between 22 and 57 kg. Again, there is no real science in these estimates. But the wood most easily available was probably olive wood, which is a fairly dense wood. Jehohanan, the crucified man of Givat ha'Mivtar, certainly had his ankle nailed through an olive-wood washer.

For some reason, though, Jesus did not carry his *patibulum* all the way to Calvary. Whether he carried it at all is unclear. At some point the synoptic gospels say that it was carried by a man called Simon. And indeed they perhaps imply that he carried it all the way.[17] John does not mention Simon, saying instead that "carrying the cross by himself, [Jesus] went out to [Calvary]."[18] Certainly none of the gospels has any room for the notion that Simon took the cross from Jesus because Jesus was exhausted, or for the tradition that Jesus fell on the way to Calvary. We do not know why Simon carried the cross, if indeed he did. We cannot conclude from the Simon of Cyrene story anything about Jesus' medical condition.

The route of the final journey to Calvary is again unclear. It seems likely that his confrontation with Pilate (and presumably his flogging) was at the Citadel, on the west side of the Old City, next to Jaffa Gate. This was Herod's palace, where Pilate normally stayed when in Jerusalem away from his usual seat in Caesarea. It is quite likely that the site of Calvary was the site of the Holy Sepulchre Church. Accordingly, the most logical route of the real Via Dolorosa would have been along David Street, north on the Triple Suk, and then west to Golgotha.[19] The Via Dolorosa of modern pilgrims is itself a modern creation. Its present route was fixed in the eighteenth century, and several of the present stations of the cross were fixed only in the nineteenth.[20]

How did Jesus die?

The mechanism of crucifixion is discussed in Chapter 2.

By the time he arrived at Calvary Jesus would have been highly stressed, exhausted and probably dehydrated, and is likely to have sustained fairly significant blood loss.

The resurrection accounts clearly indicate that the disciples thought that he had been nailed to the cross through his hands/wrists/forearms and his feet or ankles, although that was not invariable.

There is a tendency among some writers to assume that crucifixion was carried out according to some inflexible, internationally agreed protocol. This is certainly not the case. Josephus, writing about Roman crucifixions during the First Jewish Revolt of AD 66–73, notes: "The soldiers, out of rage and hate, amused themselves by nailing their prisoners in different positions."[21] But the basic pattern is clear enough. That basic pattern has led to a bizarre sub-specialty: studies in experimental crucifixion. Dr Pierre Barbet nailed cadavers to crosses and made various medical observations.[22] He was keen to correlate the mode of crucifixion and the cause of death with the appearance of the Turin Shroud.

When he passed nails through the middle of the palms of freshly amputated hands he found that they tore through the skin between the fingers at a pull of about 88 pounds. He calculated from this that if the body is suspended with the arms at an angle of about 68 degrees with the upright, there is a pull on each hand greater than the entire weight of the body.

He postulated (from what he believed was present on the Shroud) that there were two basic positions assumed by Jesus on the cross, and that in the lower of these two positions Jesus would have been unable to breathe out. Jesus would therefore have had to push up with his feet in order to breathe out. He then assumed that the practice of *crucifragium* (leg breaking) resulted in death by preventing this upward movement with the feet, and so causing asphyxiation.

He concluded:

(a) That Jesus was nailed through an area of the wrist called Destot's space, bounded by the capitate, the semilunar, the triquetral and the hamate bones: not through the palm of the hand.
(b) That death was due to asphyxiation.

These findings have been bitterly criticised, notably by Frederick Zugibe.[23] He thought that Barbet's calculations were wrong, and that the most plausible region for the nail-entry site was the upper part of the palm. He thought that this was compatible with the Shroud.

Zugibe's own studies in experimental crucifixion, using live volunteers (not nailed to the cross), led him to conclude that the cause of death was shock. He thought (on the basis of experimental work on animals by other workers) that the scourging would produce hypovolaemia and pleural effusion. Having detailed the other traumas leading up to crucifixion he went on:

> The large square iron nails driven through both hands into the cross would damage the sensory branches of the median nerve resulting in one of the most exquisite pains ever experienced by people... The nails through the feet would also elicit a great deal of pain. Both of these would cause additional traumatic shock and hypovolaemia. The hours on the cross, with pressure of the weight of the body on the nails through the hands and feet would cause episodes of excruciating agony every time the *crucarius* moved. These episodes and the unrelenting pains of the chest wall from the scourging would greatly worsen the state of traumatic shock and the excessive sweating induced by the ongoing trauma and by the hot sun, would cause an increasing degree of hypovolaemic shock... Shock...is defined "as a constellation of syndromes all characterised by low perfusion and circulatory insufficiency, leading to an imbalance between the metabolic needs of vital organs and the available blood flow". It is "a state of inadequate perfusion of all cells and tissues, which at first leads to reversible hypoxic injury, but if sufficiently protracted or grave, to irreversible cell and organ injury and sometimes to the death of the patient..."

The medical evidence was reviewed again in a much-criticised article by Edwards *et al.*[24] They thought that the weight of the body would interfere markedly with normal respiration – and particularly exhalation. With increasing exhaustion, they thought, each respiratory effort would become increasingly difficult, leading eventually to asphyxia. They noted, considering crucifixion in general, before turning to the specific case of Jesus, that: "the actual cause of death by crucifixion was multifactorial and varied somewhat with each case, but the two most prominent causes probably were hypovolaemic shock and exhaustion asphyxia. Other possible contributing factors included dehydration, stress-induced arrhythmias, and congestive heart failure with the rapid accumulation of pericardial and perhaps pleural effusions..."

The nature and significance of the flow of blood and water from the spear wound has been much discussed. It has been suggested that it was ascites[25] or urine (resulting from a perforation of the bladder).[26]

Edwards *et al.* noted that the Greek word used to describe the site of the spear wound was *pleuran*.[27] They thought that this indicated laterality and often implied the ribs. They concluded, therefore, that the wound was in the thorax and well away from the abdominal midline. The wound has traditionally been depicted on the right side, although John is silent as to the side. They thought that a right-sided wound was likely: "…a large flow of blood would be more likely with a perforation of the distended and thin-walled right atrium or ventricle than the thick-walled and contracted left ventricle…"

They acknowledged the medical difficulty of explaining how water could have flowed out of the wound before blood, but thought that this was just explained in terms of what the observer thought was most important. This is plausible. They concluded that:

> …the water probably represented serous pleural and pericardial fluid, and would have preceded the flow of blood and been smaller in volume than the blood. Perhaps in the setting of hypovolemia and impending acute heart failure, pleural and pericardial effusions may have developed and would have added to the volume of apparent water. The blood, in contrast, may have originated from the right atrium or the right ventricle or perhaps from a hemopericardium.

They thought that the fairly quick death of Jesus, and the fact that he "cried out in a loud voice" and then died

> …suggests the possibility of a catastrophic terminal event. One popular explanation has been that Jesus died of cardiac rupture. In the setting of the scourging and crucifixion, with associated hypovolemia, hypoxemia, and perhaps an altered coagulable state, friable non-infective thrombotic vegetations could have formed on the aortic or mitral valve. These then could have dislodged and embolized into the coronary circulation and thereby produced an acute transmural myocardial infarction. Thrombotic valvular vegetations have been reported to develop under analogous acute traumatic conditions. Rupture of the left ventricular free wall may occur, though uncommonly, in the first few hours following infarction.

They thought, however, that:

> The actual cause of Jesus' death, like that of other crucified victims, may have been multifactorial and related primarily to hypovolemic shock, exhaustion asphyxia, and perhaps acute heart failure. A fatal cardiac arrhythmia may have accounted for the apparent catastrophic terminal event.

Edwards *et al.* concluded:

> it remains unsettled whether Jesus died of cardiac rupture or of cardiorespiratory failure. However, the important feature may be not how he died but rather whether he died. Clearly, the weight of historical and medical evidence indicates that Jesus was dead before the wound to his side was inflicted and supports the traditional view that the spear, thrust between his right ribs, probably perforated not only the right lung but also the pericardium and heart and thereby ensured his death…

The most recent hypothesis is that Jesus died of pulmonary embolism. Multiple trauma, says this hypothesis, would have led to significant activation of the coagulation system, mainly by tissue factor. Jesus would have been significantly dehydrated. The nailing to the cross would have resulted in further release of tissue factor and increased procoagulant activity. "A crucified individual could not move his ankles and this prolonged immobilization in the upright position resulted in increase of the prothrombotic risk." Heat from the sun, stress and rapid shallow breathing greatly increased dehydration. It is suggested that Jesus inherited a hypercoagulable state, since thrombophilia, particularly factor V Leiden, and prothrombin mutation are common in Israel, particularly in Jewish people in the Galilee area.[28]

APPENDIX 2

The Turin Shroud

In the Cathedral of St John the Baptist, Turin is a piece of linen cloth which many believe is the shroud of Jesus. It bears a misty image of a crucified man between 5 feet 11 inches and 6 feet 1 inch tall. He has long hair, which at the back appears to be in the form of an unplaited ponytail. There are also red stains that correspond with the expected blood flow from the wounds of crucifixion, from the spear wound mentioned by Luke, and from wounds inflicted by thorns or other spikes driven into the head. A wound is visible in the wrist – not the palm, as most mediaeval artists envisaged. Over 100 marks are visible on the chest and much of the dorsal side, consistent with scourging with the sort of whips known to be used by first-century Romans. The legs appear to be unbroken. The right shoulder is noticeably higher than the left, as if it has been dislocated. The arms are folded over the body, with the hands across the genitals. Reconstructions suggest that the position of the arms is unnatural, but entirely what one would expect if one was forcibly folding arms that were locked in rigor mortis. Rigor mortis comes on very quickly in circumstances such as those in which Jesus was supposed to have died.

The cloth itself is 14 feet 3 inches by 3 feet 7 inches long. The "body" was apparently laid lengthwise on the cloth, and the cloth was then folded over the head and back to the feet. There are images of the front of the body on the front of the cloth and of the back of the body on the back of the cloth. The cloth was not folded symmetrically over the body: the front section falls a little short of the end of the feet and the longer dorsal section is therefore folded up over the feet.

No competent apologist either for or against the resurrection of Jesus would make the Shroud a bulwark of their argument. If the Shroud were proved to be a fake, those who say that the resurrection never happened would be in no stronger a position. And those who contend that the Bible tells the truth about the resurrection would be no worse off. No one is ever going to be able to prove that the Shroud was indeed the Shroud of Jesus, or that that mysterious image was caused by his resurrection. Protestants, historically wary of treating relics with anything other than pious contempt, have tended to keep out of the controversy.

Is the Shroud a mediaeval fake? The carbon-dating evidence

In 1988, headlines in all the papers screamed that the Shroud had been proved to be a mediaeval fake. An evidently expert team had carbon-dated the Shroud to the period AD 1260–1390. This accorded neatly with an observation made in 1389 by the then Bishop of Troyes. The image on the Shroud had been painted, he said. The Roman Catholic Church has been coy ever since of making extravagant claims about the origin of the Shroud. The 1988 findings seemed to empty the Shroud of all its mystery. The Church made some carefully scripted comments about how it had never said the Shroud was genuine, and the debate went quiet. But only for a while.

The 1988 results have now been comprehensively discredited. There are four main lines of criticism. First: linen, for some unknown reason, generally gives a much more recent carbon-date than other substances of identical age. If you carbon-date the linen wrappings from a mummified pharaonic cat, the cat will appear much older than the linen. This effect was not taken into account in the 1988 testing.

Second: many substances, including linen, acquire over the years a patina of bacterial contamination. Over centuries that patina can amount to a significant proportion of the mass of the total sample tested. Obviously the patina will have, on average, a lower age than the base on which it lies. To obtain a meaningful carbon-dating result the patina needs to be washed off before testing starts. It seems unlikely that this was done properly in 1988.

Third: the samples tested in 1988 came from an area of the Shroud that is likely to have been heavily contaminated. The Shroud has been an object of adoration and study for at least many centuries. Every adorer and student who has touched it has left some of his DNA, some of his sweat and some of his cells on it. Mediaeval illustrations show the Shroud being held up for display. They make it clear that over centuries the part of the Shroud held in ungloved hands was precisely that part analysed in 1988. One could hardly select a more predictably unreliable sample than that used.

Fourth: the Shroud was almost destroyed by fire in 1532, and the fire left dramatic burn marks on it. How this would have affected carbon 14 dating is anyone's guess. There also remains the possibility that whatever process produced the image skewed the dating.

There is widespread agreement that the carbon 14 dating needs to be repeated. In the meantime there are some very strange things about the Shroud which it is at least interesting to look at.

Photographic characteristics of the image

In 1898, Secondo Pia took the first photograph of the Shroud. The result was astonishing. It showed that the image on the Shroud was actually a negative. If you look at a negative image of the Shroud's image, in other words, you see a positive image.

It later emerged that the Shroud's image is a three-dimensional image. If you paint your face with ink and then press a cloth onto it, the image on the cloth does contain three-dimensional information. But if you then flatten the cloth out, the facial image will of course be extremely distorted. But the Shroud's image is not distorted. It has not been created by ordinary contact with the original. Subsequent computer analysis has deepened the mystery. The technology for producing images of such quality is not available now: it was certainly not available in the Middle Ages.

How was the image created?

This is straightforward: nobody knows. Suggestions that the image was painted on have been rubbished. It is true that analysis has shown pigments of the sort used by mediaeval painters, but they are present in no higher a concentration over the image parts of the Shroud than over the non-image parts. It is well documented that pilgrims would press icons against the Shroud in the hope that its holiness would rub off. Perhaps it did. What is certain is that some of the icon's pigments rubbed off.

Other theories include an imprinting by vapour rising from the mingled sweat and moisture of the body and the aloes and other compounds used to anoint the body, but this effect is archaeologically unknown and experimentally irreproducible. More recently, there has been speculation about a massive burst of radiation from the body. Again, there are great difficulties with this, but if radiation really is the answer it would seem to be more of a problem for the sceptics than for the advocates of the Shroud's authenticity. Such images are unknown on other shrouds from antiquity. There is only one known parallel, and it is a poor parallel. It comes, bizarrely, from a hospice in Liverpool. In March 1981 a 44-year-old man died there. When the nurses came to strip his bed they found imprinted on the nylon mattress cover an image, complete with skin-crease details, of one arm, one leg and buttock and part of the jaw.[1]

The curious business of the bloodstains

There is certainly blood on the Shroud. It is of primate origin. It has been grouped as AB – a group relatively rare in the general population but common in Galileans. There is probably nothing in the grouping, though: there is a tendency for blood of all groups to test AB after a time. As already noted, its distribution is consistent with the wounds that the gospels say Jesus had.

It has often been said that the "blood" on the Shroud is too red to be genuine. It is true that blood stains tend to darken to brown with the passage of time. But haemolysed blood does not. When red blood cells are smashed up, haemoglobin is released, and the red staining it produces persists. The circumstances of Jesus' scourging and death would have played havoc with the walls of his red blood cells, and the strangely red stains are precisely what one would expect.

But the strangest and perhaps most significant thing about the blood stains is their position relative to the image itself. There are some changes, caused by something or other, in the linen fibres in the area of the image. But the blood stains are *under* those transmuted image fibres. The blood stains, in other words, were on the cloth before the image was. That seems an odd and immensely difficult thing for a faker to do.

Botanical evidence

There are large quantities of pollen on the Shroud. Some say that in the region of the head there are some imprints of flowers. To cut a long and complex story short, some contend that some of these flowers come from the environs of Jerusalem, and flower around the time of Passover.[2]

The history of the Shroud

One of the arguments traditionally mounted against the Shroud's authenticity is that it suddenly springs into history, free of provenance, in the Middle Ages. This is not a fair representation of the evidence, but the counter arguments are complex and outside the scope of this book.

Where does this leave us?

There is a good case that the Shroud is that of a scourged and crucified man bearing the wounds the gospels described Jesus as having (and siting the crucifixion wounds in the position supported by archaeology rather than subsequent artistic tradition). It has at some stage been in the Jerusalem area (and probably was at the time the flower images were produced, which seems to be at the same time as the body image was produced). The flowers most represented by the pollen sampling flower around Passover. The Shroud may date from around the first century AD. The body image operates as a photographic negative. It contains coded three-dimensional information which cannot be produced by any known technology. The way in which the image was put onto the cloth is wholly mysterious. However it found its way there, the blood stains were there first.

Normal dead bodies don't do this. It would be unsafe to say more than that.

APPENDIX 3

The Gospel of Peter

From *The Apocryphal New Testament*, M.R. James, Oxford: Clarendon Press, 1924

I. 1 But of the Jews no man washed his hands, neither did Herod
nor any one of his judges: and whereas they would not 2 wash,
Pilate rose up. And then Herod the king commanded that the Lord
should be taken into their hands, saying unto them: All that I commanded you to do unto him, do ye

II. 3 Now there stood there Joseph the friend of Pilate and of the
Lord, and he, knowing that they were about to crucify him, came
unto Pilate and begged the body of Jesus for burial. And Pilate
sending unto Herod, begged his body. 5 And Herod said: Brother
Pilate, even if none had begged for him, we should have buried him,
since also the Sabbath dawneth; for it is written in the law that the
sun should not set upon one that hath been slain (murdered).

III. 6 And he delivered him unto the people before the first day of
(or on the day before the) unleavened bread, even their feast. And
they having taken the Lord pushed him as they ran, and said: Let us
hale the Son of God, now that 7 we have gotten authority over him.
And they put on him a purple robe, and made him sit upon the seat
of judgement, 8 saying: Give righteous judgement, thou King of
Israel. And one of them brought a crown of thorns and set it upon
the 9 Lord's head; and others stood and did spit in his eyes, and others buffeted his cheeks; and others did prick him with a reed, and

some of them scourged him, saying With this honour let us honour (or at this price let us value) the son of God.

IV. 10 And they brought two malefactors, and crucified the 11 Lord between them. But he kept silence, as one feeling no pain. And when they set the cross upright, they wrote 12 thereon: This is the King of Israel. And they laid his garments before him, and divided them among themselves and 13 cast the lot upon them. But one of those malefactors reproached them, saying: We have thus suffered for the evils which we have done; but this man which hath become the 14 saviour of men, wherein hath he injured you? And they were wroth with him, and commanded that his legs should not be broken, that so he might die in torment.

V. 15 Now it was noonday, and darkness prevailed over all Judaea: and they were troubled and in an agony lest the sun should have set, for that he yet lived: for it is written for them that the sun should not set upon him that hath been 16 slain (murdered). And one of them said: Give ye him to drink gall with vinegar: and they mingled it and gave him 17 to drink: and they fulfilled all things and accomplished 18 their sins upon their own heads. And many went about with 19 lamps, supposing that it was night: and some fell. And the Lord cried out aloud saying: My power, my power, thou hast forsaken me. And when he had so said, he was taken up.

20 And in the same hour was the veil of the temple of Jerusalem rent in two.

VI. 21 And then they plucked the nails from the hands of the Lord and laid him upon the earth: and the whole earth was shaken, and there came a great fear on all.

22 Then the sun shone forth, and it was found to be the ninth 23 hour. And the Jews rejoiced, and gave his body unto Joseph to bury it, because he had beheld all the good things which 24 he did. And he took the Lord and washed him and wrapped him in linen and brought him unto his own sepulchre, which is called the Garden of Joseph.

VII. 25 Then the Jews and the elders and the priests, when they perceived how great evil they had done themselves, began to lament and to say: Woe unto our sins: the judgement and the end of Jerusalem is drawn nigh.

26 But I with my fellows was in grief, and we were wounded in our minds and would have hid ourselves; for we were sought after by them as malefactors, and as thinking to set 27 the temple on fire. And beside all these things we were fasting, and we sat mourning and weeping night and day until the Sabbath.

VIII. 28 But the scribes and Pharisees and elders gathered one with another, for they had heard that all the people were murmuring and beating their breasts, saying: If these very great signs have come to pass at his death, behold how 29 righteous he was. And the elders were afraid and came unto 30 Pilate, entreating him and saying: Give us soldiers that we (or they) may watch his sepulchre for three days, lest his disciples come and steal him away and the people suppose 31 that he is risen from the dead, and do us hurt. And Pilate gave them Petronius the centurion with soldiers to watch the sepulchre; and the elders and scribes came with them unto 32 the tomb, and when they had rolled a great stone to keep out (al. together with) the centurion and the soldiers, then all 33 that were there together set it upon the door of the tomb; and plastered thereon seven seals; and they pitched a tent there and kept watch.

IX. 34 And early in the morning as the Sabbath dawned, there came a multitude from Jerusalem and the region roundabout to see the sepulchre that had been sealed.

35 Now in the night whereon the Lord's day dawned, as the soldiers were keeping guard two by two in every watch, 36 there came a great sound in the heaven, and they saw the heavens opened and two men descend thence, shining with (lit. having) a great light, and drawing near unto the sepulchre. 37 And that stone which had been set on the door rolled away of itself and went back to the side, and the sepulchre was

X. 38 opened and both of the young men entered in. When therefore those soldiers saw that, they waked up the centurion and the elders (for they also were there keeping 39 watch); and while they were yet telling them the things which they had seen, they saw again three men come out of the sepulchre, and two of them sustaining the other (lit. the 40 one), and a cross following, after them. And of the two they saw that their heads reached unto heaven, but of him that 41 was led by them that it overpassed the heavens. And they 42 heard a voice out of the heavens saying: Hast thou (or Thou hast) preached unto them that sleep? And an answer was heard from the cross, saying: Yea.

XI. 43 Those men therefore took counsel one with another to go and report these things unto Pilate. And while they yet thought thereabout, again the heavens were opened and a 45 man descended and entered into the tomb. And they that were with the centurion (or the centurion and they that were with him) when they saw that, hasted to go by night unto Pilate and left the sepulchre whereon they were keeping watch, and told all that they had seen, and were in great agony, saying: Of a truth he was the son of God.

46 Pilate answered and said: I am clear from the blood of 47 the son of God, but thus it seemed good unto you. Then all they came and besought him and exhorted him to charge the centurion and the soldiers to tell nothing of that they had 48 seen: For, said they, it is expedient for us to incur the greatest sin before God, rather than to (and not to) fall into 49 the hands of the people of the Jews and to be stoned. Pilate therefore charged the centurion and the soldiers that they should say nothing.

XII. 50 Now early on the Lord's day Mary Magdalene, a disciple (fem.) of the Lord – which, being afraid because of the Jews, for they were inflamed with anger, had not performed at the sepulchre of the Lord those things which women are accustomed to do unto them that die and are 51 beloved of them – took with her the women her friends and 52 came unto the tomb where he was laid. And they feared lest the Jews should see them, and said: Even if we were not able to weep and lament him on that day whereon he was 53 crucified, yet let us now do so at his tomb. But who will roll away for us the stone also that is set upon the door of the tomb, that we may enter in and sit beside him and perform 54 that which is due? for the stone was great, and we fear lest any man see us. And if we cannot do so, yet let us cast down at the door these things which we bring for a memorial of him, and we will weep and lament until we come unto our house.

XIII. 55 And they went and found the sepulchre open: and they drew near and looked in there, and saw there a young man sitting in the midst of the sepulchre, of a fair countenance and clad in very bright raiment, which said unto them: 56 Wherefore are ye come? whom seek ye? not him that was crucified? He is risen and is departed; but if ye believe it not, look in and see the place where he lay, that he is not here: for he is risen and is departed thither whence he was sent. 57 Then the women were affrighted and fled.

XIV. 58 Now it was the last day of unleavened bread, and many were coming forth of the city and returning unto their 59 own homes because the feast was at an end. But we, the twelve disciples of the Lord, were weeping and were in sorrow, and each one being grieved for that which had befallen 60 departed unto his own house. But I, Simon Peter, and Andrew my brother, took our nets and went unto the sea: and there was with us Levi the son of Alphaeus, whom the Lord…" [there the fragment ends]

Bibliography

Abubak, Ben. Ishmael, Salahuddin. *Evidence of Jesus in India* (Review of Religion, April 2002).

Acharya, S. *The Christ Conspiracy* (Kempton, Ill, Adventures Unlimited Press, 1999).

Alpert, M. *The Signs and Symptoms of Schizophrenia* (Comprehensive Psychiatry, 26, 1985).

Anderson, Norman. *Jesus Christ: The Witness of History* (Downers Grove, Ill: IVP, 1985).

Baigent, Michael, Leigh, Richard and Lincoln, Henry. *The Holy Blood and the Holy Grail* (London. Arrow, 2nd ed., 1996).

Baraka, A. *Historical Aspects of Opium* (Middle East J Anesthesiol, 2000; 15).

Barber, T.X. and Calverley, D.S. *An Experimental Study of "Hypnotic" (Auditory and Visual) Hallucinations* (Journal of Abnormal and Social Psychology 66, 1964).

Barbet, P. *Les Cinq Plaies du Christ* (Paris. Procure du Carmel de l'Action de Graces, 2nd ed., 1937).

Barbet, P. *A Doctor at Calvary* (New York: P.J. Kennedy and Sons, 1955: Image Books, 1963).

Belenky, G.L. *Unusual Visual Experiences Reported by Subjects in the British Army Study of Sustained Operations* (Exercise Early Call. Military Medicine 144, 1979).

Bentall, P.D. and Slade, R.P. *Sensory Deception: A Scientific Analysis of Hallucination* (London, Croom Helm, 1988).

Betz, Hans Dieter. *The Greek Magical Papyri in Translation* (Chicago, University of Chicago Press, 1986).

Biddle, Martin. *The Tomb of Christ* (Stroud, Sutton Publishing, 1999).

Booth, M. *Opium – A History* (New York, St Martin's Griffin, 1998).

Bourguignon, E. *Hallucinations and Trance: An Anthropologist's Perspective: W. Keup* (British Medical Journal, 2 October 1971).

Brenner, B. *Did Jesus Christ die of pulmonary embolism?* (J Thromb Haemost 2005: 3, 2130–1).

Brown, Dan. *The Da Vinci Code* (New York, Bantam, 2003).

Brown, Raymond. *The Death of the Messiah* (New York, Doubleday, 1998).

Burch, G.E., De Pasquale, N.P. *Death by Crucifixion* (Am Heart J, 1963).

Burke, Omar Michael. *Among the Dervishes* (London, Octagon Press, 1976).

Calvin, John. *A Harmony of the Gospels, Matthew, Mark & Luke* (Grand Rapids, Michigan, Eerdmans 1995).

Carrier, Richard C. *The burial of Jesus in light of Jewish law:* in *The Empty Tomb: Jesus Beyond the Grave* (Robert Price and Jeffrey Jay Lowder [eds], New York, Prometheus Books, 2005).

Carrier, Richard C. *"Craig's Empty Tomb and Habermas on the Post-Resurrection Appearances of Jesus"* (Secular Web, 1999).

Carrier, Richard, *The Nazareth Inscription*: *http://www.infidels.org/library/modern/richard_carrier/nazarethlaw.html* (2000)

Carrier, Richard C. *The plausibility of theft* in *The Empty Tomb: Jesus Beyond the Grave* (Robert Price and Jeffrey Jay Lowder [eds], New York, Prometheus Books, 2005).

Carrier, Richard C: *The spiritual body of Christ and the legend of the empty tomb*, in *The Empty Tomb: Jesus Beyond the Grave* (Robert Price and Jeffrey Jay Lowder [eds], New York, Prometheus Books, 2005).

Clark, C.C.P. *What was the physical cause of the death of Jesus Christ?* (Med Rec 1890, 38:543).

Cochrane, R. and Stopes-Roe, M. *Factors affecting the distribution of psychological symptoms in urban areas of England* (Acta Psychiactrica Scandinavica 61, 1980).

Cohen, M.M. *The history of opium and opiates* (Tex Med, 1969).

Comer, N.L., Madow, L. and Dixon, J.J. *Observations of sensory deprivation in a life-threatening situation* (American Journal of Psychiatry 124, 1967).

Craig, William Lane. *Assessing the New Testament Evidence for the Historicity of the Resurrection of Jesus, Studies in the Bible and Early Christianity* 16 (Lewison, NY: Edwin Mellen, 1989).

Craig, William Lane. *Reasonable Faith: Christian Truth and Apologetics* (Wheaton, Ill Crossway, 1994).

Craig, William Lane (with Gerd Ludemann). *Jesus' Resurrection: Fact or Figment?* (Downers Grove, IL: Inter Varsity, 2000 – eds Paul Copan and Ronald K. Tacelli).

Crossan, John Dominic. *The Birth of Christianity: Discovering What Happened in the Years Immediately after the Execution of Jesus* (San Francisco: Harper Collins, 1998).

Crossan, John Dominic. *The Historical Jesus: The Life of a Mediterranean Jewish Peasant* (San Francisco: Harper Collins, 1991).

Crossan, John Dominic. *Who Killed Jesus?* (San Francisco, Harper Collins, 1996).

Currie, George. *The Military Discipline of the Romans from the Founding of the City to the Close of the Republic* (Indiana: Graduate Council of Indiana University, 1928).

Danin, Avinoam, Whanger, A.D, Baruch, Uri and Whanger, M. *Flora of the Shroud of Turin* (St. Louis, Missouri: Botanical Garden Press, 1999).

Davis, C.T. *The crucifixion of Jesus: The passion of the Christ from a medical point of view* (Ariz Med 1965, 22).

Dawood, N.J. (Trans.) *The Koran* (Harmondsworth: Penguin, 1990).

de Kruijf, T.C. *"More Than Half a Hundredweight" of Spices: Abundance and Symbolism in the Gospel of John* (Bijdragen 43, 1982).

de Pasquale, N.P. and Burch, G.E., *Death by Crucifixion* (Am Heart J, 1963).

de Zulueta, F. *Violation of sepulture in Palestine at the beginning of the Christian era* (Journal of Roman Studies 22, 1932).

Dohrenwend, B.P. and Dohrenwend, B.S. *Psychiatric disorders in urban settings* (In S. Arietti and G. Caplan [eds] American Handbook of Psychiatry, Vol. 2: New York: Basic Books, 1974).

Duarte, Danilo Freire Duarte. *Opium and opioids: A brief history* (Rev. Bras. Anestesiol. vol. 55 no. 1 Campinas Jan./Feb. 2005).

Edwards W.D., Gabel, W.J. and Hosmer, F.E. *On the physical death of Jesus Christ* (JAMA 1986 255).

Eusebius. *Against Apollonius of Tyana by Philostratus* (In *The Life of Apollonius of Tyana, the Epistles of Apollonius and the Treatise of Eusebius*. F.C. Conybeare [ed.], Cambridge, MA: Harvard University Press, 1912: Vol. 2).

Eusebius. *Epistle of the Church in Smyrna.*

Eusebius. *Onomast.*

Evans, Craig A. *Jesus and the Ossuaries: What Jewish Burial Practices Reveal about the Beginning of Christianity* (Waco: Baylor University, 2003).

Festinger, Leon. *A Theory of Cognitive Dissonance* (Stanford, California: Stanford UP, 1957).

Festinger, Leon, Riecken, H. and Schachter, S. *When Prophecy Fails* (Minneapolis: University of Minnesota Press, 1956).

Fida Hassnain. *A Search for the Historical Jesus* (Bath: Gateway Books, 1994).

Freke, Timothy and Gandy, Peter. *The Jesus Mysteries: Was the Original Jesus a Pagan God?* (London: Harper Collins, 2000).

Gansfried, Solomon. *Code of Jewish Law (Kitzur Shulchan Aruch)* (Trans. Hyman E. Goldin) (New York: Hebrew Publishing Company, 1927, Vol. IV, Ch. CXCVII: Laws pertaining to Purification [Tahara], numbers 9 and 10).

Gibson, Shimon and Taylor, Joan E. *Beneath the Church of the Holy Sepulchre, Jerusalem: The Archaeology and Early History of Traditional Golgotha* (London: Palestine Exploration Fund, 1994).

Green, Michael. *The Books the Church Suppressed* (Oxford: Monarch, 2005).

Green, Michael. *Man Alive* (Leicester: IVP, 1968).

Haas, N. *Anthropological Observations on the skeletal Remains from Gi'vat ha-Mivtar* (Israel Exploration Journal 20, 1970).

Harpur, Tom. *The Pagan Christ* (London: Thomas Allen, 2005).

Hegesippus, *Commentaries on the Acts of the Church, Book 5* (Trans. Roberts-Donaldson).

Hengel, Martin. *Crucifixion in the Ancient World and the Folly of the Message of the Cross* (Philadephia: Fortress, 1977).

Herodotus. *Histories* (Oxford: Oxford University Press [Trans. Robin Wakefield], 1998).

Hewitt, J. *The Use of Nails in Crucifixion* (Harvard Theological Review 25, 1932).

Holoubek, J.E. and Holoubek A.B. *Blood, Sweat and Fear: A Classification of Hematidrosis* (J Med. 1996, 27 3–4).

James, M.R. *The Apocryphal New Testament* (Oxford: Clarendon Press, 1924).

Johnson, R.L. and Miller, M.D. *Auditory hallucinations and intellectual deficit* (Journal of Psychiatric Research 33, 1965).

Josephus. *Jewish Antiquities* ([Trans. Louis H. Feldman] Cambridge, MA: Harvard University Press, The Loeb Classical Library, 1963).

Josephus. *Jewish War* ([Trans. William Whiston] In *The Works of Josephus Flavius*, Grand Rapids, Michigan: Associated Publishers, 1860).

Josephus. *Life* ([Trans. William Whiston] In *The Works of Josephus Flavius*, Grand Rapids, Michigan: Associated Publishers, 1860).

Joyce, Donovan. *The Jesus Scroll* (New York: Doubleday, 1973).

Kent, Jack A. *The Psychological Origins of the Resurrection Myth* (London: Open Gate Press, 1999).

Kersten, Holger. *Jesus Lived in India* ([Trans. T. Woods-Czisch] Longmead, Shaftesbury: Element Books, 1986).

Kersten, Holger and Gruber, Elmar R. *The Jesus Conspiracy: The Turin Shroud and the Truth About Resurrection* (New York: Element Books, 1995).

Kirby, Peter. *The case against the empty tomb*. In *The Empty Tomb: Jesus Beyond the Grave* (Robert Price and Jeffrey Jay Lowder [eds], New York: Prometheus Books, 2005).

Kloner, Amos. *"Did a rolling stone close Jesus' tomb?"* (Biblical Archaeology Review 25:5, Sept/Oct 1999).

Kloner, A. *A monument of the second temple period west of the Old City of Jerusalem* (Eretz-Israel, 1985) 18 (Hebrew with an English summary).

Knox, J. *Chapters in a Life of Paul* (New York: Abingdon-Cokesbury, 1950).

Kritikos, P.G. *The history of opium in antiquity* (J Am Pharm Assoc, 1968, 8).

Kritikos, P.G. and Papadaki, S.P. *The history of poppy and opium and their expansion in antiquity in the eastern Mediterranean area* (Bull. Narcotics, 1967, 19).

Le Camus, E. *The Life of Christ* (Vol. III, New York: The Cathedral Library Association, 1908).

Lewis, Clive Staples. *Letters of C.S. Lewis* [ed. W.H. Lewis] (London: Geofrrey Bles, 1966).

Lewis, Clive Staples. *Reflections on the Psalms* (London: Geoffrey Bles, 1958).

Lewis, Clive Staples. *The Great Divorce: A dream* (London: Geoffrey Bles, 1945).

Liebowitz, H. *Jewish burial practices in the Roman period* (The Mankind Quarterly 22) (1981–82).

Lowder, Jeffrey Jay. *Historical evidence and the empty tomb*. In *The Empty Tomb, Jesus Beyond the Grave* (Robert Price and Jeffrey Jay Lowder [eds]. Prometheus Books, NY: 2005).

Ludemann, Gerd. *The Resurrection: A Historical Inquiry* (Amherst, New York: Prometheus Books, 2004).

Macht, D.I. *The history of opium and some of its preparation and alkaloids* (JAMA, 1915, 64).

Magness, Jodi. *What did Jesus' tomb look like?* (Biblical Archaeology Review, 2006) 32:1.

Matchett, W.F. *Repeated hallucinatory experiences as part of the mourning process among Hopi Indian women* (Psychiatry 35, 1972).

McCane, Byron. *Roll Back the Stone: Death and Burial in the World of Jesus* (New York, Trinity Press International, 2003).

McDonald, W.S. and Oden, C.W. Aumakua: *Behavioural direction visions in Hawaiians* (Journal of Abnormal Psychology 86, 1977).

McDowell, Josh. *Evidence that Demands a Verdict* (Nashville: Thomas Nelson, 1999).

McKellar, P. *Experience and Behaviour* (Harmondsworth: Penguin, 1968).

Meacham, William. *Authentication of the Turin Shroud: An issue in archaeological epistemology* (Current Anthroplogy, Vol. 24, No. 3, June 1983).

Merrillees, R.S. *Highs and Lows in the Holy Land: Opium in Biblical Times* (Eretz-Israel 20, 1989).

Meshorer, Y. *Ancient Jewish Coinage II: Herod the Great through Bar Cochba* (New York, 1982).

Mikulicz-Radecki, F.V. *The chest wound in the crucified Christ* (Med News, 1966; 14:30–40).

Mintz, S. and Alpert, M. *Imagery vividness, reality testing and schizophrenic hallucinations* (Journal of Abnormal Psychology, 79, 1972).

Mir Khawand bin Badshah, *Rauza-tus-Safa* (Bombay, 1852).

Murphy, H.B.M., Wittkower, E.D., Fried, J. and Ellenberger, H.A. *A cross-cultural survey of schizophrenic symptomatology* (International Journal of Social Psychiatry, 9, 1963).

Murphy-O'Connor, Jerome. *The Holy Land* (Oxford: OUP, 1998).

Murphy-O'Connor, Jerome. *Paul: A Critical Life* (Oxford: OUP, 1997).

O'Rahilly, A. *The Burial of Christ* (IER 58, 1941, 310).

Philo. *Embassy to Gaius.*

Philostratus. *Life of Apollonius* ([Trans. G.W. Bowerstock] Penguin Books, 1970).

Pliny the Younger. *Epistles 10:96.*

Price, Robert. *Apocryphal apparitions*. In *The Empty Tomb: Jesus Beyond the Grave* (Amherst, New York: Prometheus Books, 2005).

Price, Robert. *The empty tomb: The second life of Jesus*. In *The Empty Tomb: Jesus Beyond the Grave* (Amherst, New York: Prometheus Books, 2005).

Price, Robert and Lowder, Jeffrey Jay [eds]. *The Empty Tomb: Jesus Beyond the Grave* (Amherst, New York: Prometheus Books, 2005).

Primrose, W.B. *A Surgeon Looks at the Crucifixion* (New York: Hibbert, 1949).

Prioreschi, P., Heaney, R.P. and Brehm, F. *A quantitative assessment of ancient therapeutics: Poppy and pain in hippocratic corpus* (Med Hypothese, 1998, 51).

Posey, T.B. and Losch, M.E. *Auditory hallucinations of hearing voices in 375 normal subjects* (Imagination, Cognition and Personality 2, 1983).

Radcliffe G. Edmonds. *Myths of the Underworld Journey in Plato, Aristophanes and the "Orphic" Gold Tablets* (Cambridge: Cambridge University Press, 2004).

Ragg, Lonsdale and Ragg, Laura. *The Gospel of Barnabas* (Oxford: Clarenden Press, 1907).

Ridley, Sir Edward. *The Pharsalia of Lucan* (London: Longmans, Green and Co., 1896).

Schillebeeckx, Edward. *Jesus: An experiment in Christology* (New York: Seabury Press, 1979).

Schonfeld, Hugh. *The Passover Plot* (New York: Bantam, 1969).

Semahot 13.5, 10.8, *The Tractate "Mourning"* (trans Dov Zlotnik, Yale Judaica Series 18, 1966).

Siegel, R.K. *Hostage hallucinations: Visual imagery induced by isolation and life-threatening stress* (Journal of Nervous and Mental Disease 172, 1984).

Sidgewick, H.A. *et al. Report of the Census of Hallucinations* (Proceedings of the Society for Psychical Research 26, 1894).

Srole, L., Sanger, T., Michael, S., Opler, M.K. and Rennie, T.A.C. *Mental Health in the Metropolis: The Midtown Manhattan Study* (New York: McGraw-Hill, 1962).

Stewart, Robert S. (ed.). *The Resurrection of Jesus: The Crossan-Wright Dialogue* (Minneapolis: Fortress, 2006).

Strobel, Lee. *The Case for Christ* (Grand Rapids: Zondervan, 1998).

Tacitus. *Annals: 6.*

Tallmadge, C.K. *Some anaesthetics of antiquity* (J Hist Med Allied Sci, 1946, 1).

Talmud *Beitzah* 6a, 22a; *Sanhedrin* 26 b.

Talmud, *Sanhedrin* 35a–35b, *Yevamoth* 7a, *Baba Bathra* 100b, *Shabbath* 150–51.

Talmud Jmmanuel, Edauard A. Meir (Schmidruti Switzerland, 1978).

Tenney, S.M. *On death by crucifixion* (Am Heart J 1964, 68).

Tertullian. *De Spectaculis.*

Thiede, Carsten Peter. *The Emmaus Mystery* (London: Continuum, 2005).

Thiering, Barbara. *Jesus and the Riddle of the Dead Sea Scrolls: Unlocking the Secrets of His Life Story* (San Francisco: Harper Collins, 1992).

Thorburn, Thomas James. *The Resurrection Narratives and Modern Criticism* (London: Kegan Paul, Trench, Trubner and Co., 1910).

H. Ur. Rehman. *Did Jesus Christ die of pulmonary embolism? A rebuttal* (J. Thromb Haemost 2005; 3: 2131–3).

van Campenhausen, Hans. *Tradition and Life in the Church: Essays and Lectures in Church History* (Trans. A.V. Littledale – Philadelphia: Fortress Press, 1968).

Wenham, John. *Easter Enigma: Are the Resurrection Accounts in Conflict?* ([2nd ed.] Grand Rapids, MI: Baker, 1992).

West, D.J. *A mass observation questionnaire on hallucinations* (Journal of the Society for Psychical Research 34, 1948).

Wilson, A.N. *Paul: The Mind of the Apostle* (London: Pimlico, 1998).

Wilson, Ian and Schwartz, Barrie. *The Turin Shroud* (London: Michael O'Mara, 2000).

Wright, D.A. *The history of opium* (Med Biol Illus, 1968, 18).

Wright, N.T. *Resurrection of the Son of God* (London: SPCK, 2003).

Zarroug, E.A. *The frequency of visual hallucinations in schizophrenic patients in Saudi Arabia* (British Journal of Psychiatry 127, 1975).

Zias, Joe. *Health and healing in the land of Israel* (Mikhmanim, Spring 1999).

Zias, J. and Sekeles, E. *The crucified man from Giv'at ha-Mivtar: A re-appraisal* (Israel Exploration Journal 35, 1985).

Zugibe, Frederick T. *Pierre Barbet Revisited* (Sindon. N.S. Quad No. 8, December 1995).

Website References

http://www.geocities.com/Athens/Delphi/1340/jesus_in_india.htm
www.tombofjesus.com
www.barnabas.net
www.encyclopediaofauthentichinduism.org/articles/52_the_dynasties_of.htm
www.tombofjesus.com/core/majorplayers/the-tomb/the-tomb-p3.htm
www.jewsforjudaism.org/web/faq/faq092.html
www.infidels.org/library/modern/richard_carrier/indef/4e.html
www.infidels.org/library/modern/richard_carrier/nazarethlaw.html
www.textexcavation.com/nazarethinscription.html

References

Chapter 1: Does all this matter?

1 Ludemann, Gerd, *The Resurrection: A Historical Inquiry*, Amherst, New York, Prometheus Books, 2004, p. 114.

Chapter 2: The sources

1 John 20:31.
2 John 20:30 and 21:25.
3 See Luke 1:3 and Acts 1:1.
4 Although it is possible that Theophilus was not an individual at all. Some first-century authors dedicated their books to entirely non-existent patrons.
5 Luke 1:1–4.
6 Errors would be most obvious in Acts. Most modern biographers of Paul have made it an express (and unsurprising) principle to prefer Paul's own version of Paul's life (as set out in the letters) to Luke's version of those same events, if they differ. See, for example, Jerome Murphy-O'Connor, *Paul: A Critical Life*, Oxford, OUP, 1997: he cites and uses the methodological principle of Knox: "A fact only suggested in the letters has a status which even the most unequivocal statement of Acts, if not otherwise supported, cannot confer. We may, with proper caution, use Acts to supplement the autobiographical data of the letters, but never to correct them" (Knox, J., *Chapters in a Life of Paul*, New

York, Abingdon-Cokesbury, 1950: 32, cited in Murphy-O'Connor). That said, though, neither Murphy O'Connor, Knox nor anyone else actually shows that Luke got it wrong. He might differ from Paul on matters of emphasis; he might have been more helpful and given a fuller account; he might sometimes telescope two stories into one. But there are no blatant errors.

7 John 19:35.

8 John 21:24.

9 John 20:30–31.

10 Origen, Eusebius and Theodoret.

11 The arguments are summarised in Wright, N.T. *Resurrection of the Son of God* (London: SPCK, 2003) pp. 594–596.

12 Annals XV, 44.

13 Anderson, Norman, *Jesus Christ: The Witness of History*. 2nd ed. Downers Grove, Ill: IVP, 1985, 20.

14 1 Thessalonians 1:10.

15 Lives of the Caesars, 26.2.

16 Sanhedrin 43a.

17 See, for example, Deuteronomy 21:23; Galatians 3:13; Luke 23:39.

18 Chronography, 18.1.

19 Josephus: *Jewish Antiquities* (Trans. Louis H. Feldman, Cambridge, Harvard University Press, The Loeb Classical Library, 1963).

20 Brown, Dan, *The Da Vinci Code*, New York, Bantam, 2003.

21 The only arguable exception is so-called "Secret Mark". The most credulous scholars are merely agnostic about Secret Mark. Most are outright disbelievers.

22 On this, see Michael Green, *The Books the Church Suppressed*, Oxford, Monarch, 2005.

23 Argument rages about whether Gnosticism sprang from pre-Christian paganism. But no existing Gnostic documents can be dated before the rise of Christianity.

24 See Green, ibid., pp. 41–92.

25 Acts 1:21–22.

26 Price, Robert, *The Empty Tomb: The Second Life of Jesus*, p. 15: In *The Empty Tomb: Jesus Beyond the Grave*, Price, R.M. and Lowder, J.J., Prometheus Books, Amherst, New York, 2005, p. 15.

27 For a discussion of the way that fading memory might have affected the version of events accepted by the early Church, see John Dominic Crossan, *The Birth of Christianity: Discovering What Happened in the Years Immediately after the Execution of Jesus*. San Francisco, Harper Collins, 1998: pp. 59–68.

28 1 Corinthians 9:22.

29 Colossians 3:22. See also 1 Peter 2:18.

30 Attempts to date the pre-Markan passion narrative are technical and beyond the scope of this book. Some of the issues relating to the dating arise in the course of argument. But here are two: Mark never names the high priest at the time of Jesus' death. We know that it was Caiphas. He was high priest from AD 18–37. Thus, one argument goes, the tradition relied on by Mark must be prior to AD 37: see William Lane Craig, *Assessing the New Testament Evidence for the Historicity of the Resurrection of Jesus*, Studies in the Bible and Early Christianity 16 (Lewison, NY: Edwin Mellen, 1989), p. 361. Not necessarily, goes the counter-argument: Mark might have been written so late that the writer didn't know who the relevant high priest was. Another argument relates to Mark's reference to the "first day of the week" (Mark 16:2) – the day he says that the tomb was found to be empty. This has all the hallmarks of a very early formulation, says William Lane Craig. It must predate even the very early creed in 1 Corinthians 15 (which refers to the "third day"). The empty-tomb narrative is therefore too old to be legendary: Legends just don't develop that fast: see Craig, *Assessing the New Testament*, ibid., p. 363; and William Lane Craig, *Reasonable Faith: Christian Truth and Apologetics* (Wheaton, ILL: Crossway, 1994), p. 275. Not so, says (e.g.) Lowder: Mark is probably just contrasting the first day of the week with the last (i.e. the sabbath, when the women, because of Jewish law, were prevented from preparing the body). Jeffrey Jay Lowder: *Historical Evidence and the Empty Tomb*, in Price and Lowder, ibid., pp. 278–280.

31 2 Timothy 3:16.

32 See Mark 14:68 and 14:72.

Chapter 3: The death

1 Some of the objections outlined here are based on *Challenging the Verdict*, by Earl Doherty: Ottawa, Age of Reason Publications, 2001.
2 John 19:33.
3 John 19:34.
4 John 19:36–37: see too Psalm 34:20; Exodus 12:46; Numbers 9:12; Zechariah 12:10.
5 Mathew 27:51.
6 Matthew 27:52.
7 Matthew 27:53.
8 *The Koran*, Sura 4:157–158: Trans. N.J. Dawood, Harmondsworth, Penguin, 1990.
9 Available online at www.barnabas.net
10 "Accordingly they led Judas to Herod, who of a long time had desired that Jesus should go to his house… Now when Judas had been led thither, Herod asked him of many things, to which Judas gave answers not to the purpose, denying that he was Jesus… Then Herod mocked him, with all his court, and caused him to be clad in white as the fools are clad, and sent him back to Pilate… Thereupon, in mockery they clad him in an old purple garment, saying: 'It is fitting to our new king to clothe him and crown him': so they gathered thorns and made a crown, like those of gold and precious stones which kings wear on their heads. And this crown of thorns they placed upon Judas' head, putting in his hand a reed for sceptre, and they made him sit in a high place. And the soldiers came before him, bowing down in mockery, saluting him as King of the Jews. And they held out their hands to receive gifts, such as new kings are accustomed to give; and receiving nothing they smote Judas, saying: 'Now, how art thou crowned, foolish king, if thou wilt not pay thy soldiers and servants?'… Verily I say that the voice, the face, and the person of Judas were so like to Jesus, that his disciples and believers entirely believed that he was Jesus… Jesus replied, embracing his mother: 'Believe me, mother, for verily I say to thee that I have not been dead at all ; for God hath reserved me till near the end of the world.'… And though I have been innocent in the world, since men have called me "God," and "Son of

God," God, in order that I be not mocked of the demons on the day of judgement, hath willed that I be mocked of men in this world by the death of Judas, making all men to believe that I died upon the cross. And this mocking shall continue until the advent of Mohammed, the messenger of God, who, when he shall come, shall reveal this deception to those who believe in God's law… And he reproved many who believed him to have died and risen again, saying: 'Do ye then hold me and God for liars? for God hath granted to me to live almost unto the end of the world, even as I said unto you. Verily I say unto you, I died not, but Judas the traitor. Beware, for Satan will make every effort to deceive you… Then before their eyes the four angels carried him up into heaven." (The Crucifixion Of Jesus According To The Gospel of Barnabas.)

11 Ibid.

12 John 19:41.

13 *The Holy Blood and the Holy Grail*, Michael Baigent, Richard Leigh and Henry Lincoln, New York, Arrow, 1996, p. 377.

14 Matthew 27:23–24; Mark 15:10; 15:14, 15; Luke 23:4, 23:14–23; John 18:38–39, 19:4–6, 19:12.

15 Matthew 27:19.

16 e.g. John 19:10.

17 See, for example, Kersten, Holgar and Gruber, Elmar R. *The Jesus Conspiracy: The Turin Shroud and the Truth About Resurrection* (New York, Element Books, 1995) and Schonfeld, Hugh. *The Passover Plot* (New York Bantam,1969).

18 Josephus, Life: 76.

19 Haas, N. 1970. *Anthropological observations on the skeletal remains from Gi'vat ha-Mivtar*. Israel Exploration Journal 20:38–59.

20 Zias, J. and Sekeles, E., 1985. *The crucified man from Giv'at ha-Mivtar: A re-appraisal*. Israel Exploration Journal 35:22–27.

21 Hewitt, J. (1932), *The use of nails in crucifixion*. Harvard Theological Review 25:29–45.

22 Luke 24:39: "Look at my hands and my feet."

23 John 20:20: "…he showed them his hands and his side…" 20:25: Thomas says: "Unless I see the mark of the nails in his hands, and put my finger in the mark of the nails and my

hand in his side, I will not believe." 20:27: Jesus says to Thomas: "Put your finger here and see my hands. Reach out your hand and put it in my side...".

24 See Appendix 1, and the disagreement between Barbet and Zugibe.

25 Mark 15:34–37.

26 Matthew 27:45–50.

27 John 19:28–30.

28 Barbara Thiering has suggested that it might be snake poison: see her book *Jesus and the Riddle of the Dead Sea Scrolls*: San Francisco, Harper Collins, 1992, p. 116.

29 *Opium and Opioids: A Brief History*, Danilo Freire Duarte Rev. Bras. Anestesiol. vol.55, no.1 Campinas Jan./Feb. 2005; Booth M., *Opium – A History*, New York, St Martin's Griffin, 1998. Cohen M.M., *The history of opium and opiates*. Tex Med, 1969, 65:76–85; Baraka, A., *Historical aspects of opium*. Middle East J. Anesthesiol., 2000, 15:423–436. Kritikos, P.G., *The history of opium in antiquity*. J Am Pharm Assoc, 1968, 8:446–447; Kritikos, P.G., Papadaki, S.P., *The history of poppy and opium and their expansion in antiquity in the Eastern Mediterranean Area*. Bull. Narcotics, 1967, 19:5–10. Macht, D.I., *The history of opium and some of its preparation and alkaloids*. JAMA, 1915, 64:477–461; Prioreschi, P., Heaney, R.P., Brehm, F. *A quantitative assessment of ancient therapeutics: Poppy and pain in the Hippocratic Corpus*. Med Hypothese, 1998, 51:325–331; Wright, D.A., *The history of opium*. Med Biol Illus, 1968, 18:62–70; Tallmadge, C.K., J Hist Med Allied Sci, 1946, 1:515–520.

30 See Joe Zias, *Health and healing in the land of Israel*, Mikhmanim, Spring 1999.

31 Meshorer, Y., *Ancient Jewish Coinage II: Herod the Great through Bar Cochba*, New York, 1982.

32 Merrillees, R.S., *Highs and Lows in the Holy Land: Opium in Biblical Times*, Eretz Israel 20:149–152, 1989.

33 See the Visuddhi Magga: Harvard Classics. 1909–14.

34 Mark 15:44–45.

35 Meacham, William, *Authentication of the Turin Shroud: An Issue in Archaeological Epistemology*: Current Anthroplogy, Vol. 24, No. 3, June 1983.

36 Surah 23:50: *The Koran*, Trans. N.J. Dawood, Harmondsworth, Penguin, 1990.

37 There is a vast literature on this subject. The more exotic variants on the basic theme are not dealt with here, but it is worth mentioning *Talmud Jmmanuel*, ed. Edauard A. Meir, (Schmidruti, Switzerland, 1978) – a text said to have been found by Meir in a tomb south of the Old City of Jerusalem, but subsequently lost. It details Jesus' post-crucifixion eastern wanderings, but its credibility is not enhanced by Meir's insistence that six years before it was discovered he had been told by his extra-terrestrial handlers (who came regularly to Earth in their spaceship from the Pleiades), that he would find it. The same ETs apparently guided the rest of his research into the subject.

38 One example: Burke, studying Sufism in Herat, Afghanistan in the 1970s, found a thousand-strong sect of Yuz Asaf devotees. They knew Yuz Asaf also as Issa, son of Maryam, and believed that having escaped the cross in Palestine, he travelled to India, settling in Kashmir. See Omar Michael Burke, *Among the Dervishes*, London, Octagon Press, 1976, 107.

39 Mir Khawand bin Badshah, *Rauza-tus-Safa*, Bombay, 1852: Vol. 1, 132–13.

40 Thus, for example, Al-Shaikh Al-Said-us-Sadiq Abi Jaffar Muhammad Ibn-i-Ali Ibn-i-Hussain Ibn-i-Musa Ibn-i-Baibuyah al-Qummi, who died in Khorasan in 962, wrote that Yuz Asaf had come to Kashmir. He records one of Yuz Asaf's parables. It is strikingly similar to the parable of the sower.

41 Mullah Nadri, Tarikh -I-Kashmir: 1420: "During this time Hazrat Yuz Asaf having come from Bait-ul Muqaddas [the Holy Land] to this holy valley proclaimed his prophethood. He devoted himself, day and night, in [prayers to] God, and having attained the heights of piety and virtue, he declared himself to be a Messenger [of God] for the people of Kashmir. He invited people [to his religion]. Because the people of the valley had faith in this Prophet, Raja Gopadatta referred the objection of Hindus to him [for decision]. It was because of this Prophet's orders that Sulaiman, whom Hindus called Sandeman, completed [the repairs of] the dome. [The year was] Fifty and four. Further, on one of the stones of the stairs

he [Sulaiman] inscribed: 'In these times Yuz Asaf proclaimed his prophethood,' and on the other stone of the stairs he also inscribed that he [Yuz Asaf] was Yusu, Prophet of the Children of Israel…I have seen in a book of Hindus that this prophet was really Hazrat Isa [Jesus], the Spirit of God, on whom be peace [and salutations] and had also assumed the name of Yuz Asaf. The real knowledge is with God. He spent his life in this [valley]. After his departure [his death] he was laid to rest in Mohalla Anzmarah. It is also said that lights of prophethood used to emanate from the tomb of this Prophet. Raja Gopadatta having ruled for sixty years and two months, [then] died…"

42 Originally published in Urdu as *Masih Hindustan Mein*, and republished by Islam International Publications, 1989. Available online at htttp://www.geocities.com/Athens/Delphi/1340/jesus_in_india.htm

43 The most coherent modern account of the evidence for Jesus being in India is by Abubak Ben Ishmael Salahuddin, *Evidence of Jesus in India*, Review of Religion, April 2002, 48–68.

44 There is a comprehensive website giving details of the tomb's alleged history: www.tombofjesus.com

45 Fida Hassnain, *A Search for the Historical Jesus*, Bath, Gateway Books, 1994: 201–203.

46 Holger Kersten, *Jesus lived in India*, trans. T. Woods-Czisch, Longmead, Shaftesbury, 1986: 200.

47 Third Khanda of the Pratisarga parvan of the Bhavishya Mahapurana, vv 16–33, from the translation at http://www.tombofjesus.com/core/majorplayers/the-tomb/the-tomb-p3.htm

48 Philostratus, *Life of Apollonius*. Trans. G.W. Bowerstock: Harmondsworth, Penguin Books, 1970.

49 See the story of the raising of Jairus' daughter, Matthew 9:23–25.

50 See Eusebius: *Against 'Apollonius of Tyana' by Philostratus*. In *The Life of Apollonius of Tyana, the Epistles of Apollonius and the Treatise of Eusebius*, F.C. Conybeare (ed.), Cambridge, MA, Harvard University Press, 1912: Vol. 2, 485–605.

51 *Against Heresies*: Vol. 22: Ch. 22:5: The whole of the relevant passage reads: "They, however, that they may establish their

false opinion regarding that which is written, 'to proclaim the acceptable year of the Lord,' maintain that He preached for one year only, and then suffered in the twelfth month. [In speaking thus], they are forgetful to their own disadvantage, destroying His whole work, and robbing Him of that age which is both more necessary and more honourable than any other; that more advanced age, I mean, during which also as a teacher He excelled all others. For how could He have had disciples, if He did not teach? And how could He have taught, unless He had reached the age of a Master? For when He came to be baptized, He had not yet completed His thirtieth year, but was beginning to be about thirty years of age (for thus Luke, who has mentioned His years, has expressed it: 'Now Jesus was, as it were, beginning to be thirty years old,' when He came to receive baptism); and, [according to these men,] He preached only one year reckoning from His baptism. On completing His thirtieth year He suffered, being in fact still a young man, and who had by no means attained to advanced age. Now, that the first stage of early life embraces thirty years, and that this extends onwards to the fortieth year, every one will admit; but from the fortieth and fiftieth year a man begins to decline towards old age, which our Lord possessed while He still fulfilled the office of a Teacher, even as the Gospel and all the elders testify; those who were conversant in Asia with John, the disciple of the Lord, [affirming] that John conveyed to them that information. And he remained among them up to the times of Trajan. Some of them, moreover, saw not only John, but the other apostles also, and heard the very same account from them, and bear testimony as to the [validity of] the statement. Whom then should we rather believe? Whether such men as these, or Ptolemaeus, who never saw the apostles, and who never even in his dreams attained to the slightest trace of an apostle?"

52 Joyce, Donovan. *The Jesus Scroll*: New York, Doubleday, 1973.

53 Ibid., p. 378.

54 John 19:31–37.

55 John 19:35.

56 N.T. Wright, *The Resurrection of the Son of God*, ibid., pp. 632–636.
57 Wright, ibid., pp. 633–634.
58 Wright, ibid., p. 636.
59 See, for example, Lonsdale and Laura Ragg, *The Gospel of Barnabas*, Oxford: Clarendon Press, 1907.
60 Possibly *Gnostic*, *Ebionite* or *Diatessaronic*.
61 This, and the citation used by X, is from verses 16–33 of the Third Khanda of the Pratisarga parvan of the Bhavishya Mahapurana, from the translation at http://www.tombofjesus.com/core/majorplayers/the-tomb/the-tomb-p3.htm
62 See, for example, http://www.encyclopediaofauthentic hinduism.org/articles/52_the_dynasties_of.htm

Chapter 4: The burial

1 Suetonius. *Augustus* 13:1–2: cited in Byron McCane, *Roll Back the Stone: Death and Burial in the World of Jesus*. New York, Trinity Press International, 2003.
2 Tacitus: *Annals*: 6.29.
3 *Satyricon* 111–12.
4 For a detailed discussion of this, see John Dominic Crossan, *Who Killed Jesus?* San Francisco, Harper San Francisco, 1996, pp. 163–164.
5 See Sanhedrin 6.4 h-p.
6 Sanhedrin 6.4 q-r.
7 Jewish Wars 4: 202, 260.
8 Jewish Wars 4: 317.
9 The polemic website Jews for Judaism, which seeks to answer Christian missionaries, asks: "How would the Jewish authorities have treated Jesus' corpse?" And it gives the answer: "To bury the body of a crucified individual (or anyone else) was a matter of obeying God's commandments. Joseph of Arimathea (or whatever his correct name) was probably the Sanhedrin burial agent whose task it was to take care of the crucified once they had died. The approach of the sabbath and the concern that a corpse not be left hanging after sunset (Deuteronomy 21:23) added to Joseph's concern to get the body of Jesus (and the other two victims) buried

before sunset. Perhaps there was a Roman concession to local religious custom concerning a corpse hanging overnight, especially at the onset of the Sabbath or a festival. Joseph complied with the Torah's requirement even though he may have had no personal reason to honour the crucified individual. One may assume that if it is true that two other individuals were crucified along with Jesus and died that same day that Joseph also asked for their bodies and buried them as well." http://www.jewsforjudaism.org/web/faq/faq092.html

10 Talmud, Sanhedrin 35a–35b, Yevamoth 7a, Baba Bathra 100b, Shabbath 150–51: see the discussion in Carrier, ibid., pp. 382–383.

11 Talmud Beitzah 6a, 22a; Sanhedrin 26 b: also Carrier, ibid., pp. 382–383.

12 Luke 23:56.

13 See Liebowitz, H., *Jewish Burial Practices in the Roman Period.* The Mankind Quarterly 22 (1981–82), 108.

14 John 11:44.

15 Semahot 1:2–5. See McCane, ibid.: pp. 31–32 and p. 94.

16 See Solomon Gansfried, *Code of Jewish Law (Kitzur Shulchan Aruch)*, Trans. Hyman E. Goldin, New York, Hebrew Publishing Company, 1927, Vol. IV, Ch. CXCVII: Laws pertaining to Purification (Tahara), numbers 9 and 10: pp. 51–4. Those who see the Turin Shroud as genuine believe that the Shroud is a classic example of a sovev.

17 "Entylissein" in the Greek: see Raymond Brown, *The Death of the Messiah*, New York, Doubleday, 1998, Vol. 2, p. 1252 and 1255.

18 "Enelein" in the Greek.

19 Researchers working on the Turin Shroud often refer to themselves as "sindonologists".

20 Brown, ibid., 1244–1245.

21 For a detailed discussion of this, see Brown, ibid., pp. 1264–1265.

22 Mark 14:64; Matthew 26:65–66; John 19:7.

23 The idea of dishonourable burial goes back a long way. In 1 Kings 13:21–22 a prophet who disobeys God is told: "Your body shall not go into the tomb of your fathers." In Jeremiah 22:18–19 God threatens Jehoiakim: "They shall not lament for him…with the burial of a donkey he shall be buried –

dragged off and thrown out beyond the gates of Jerusalem." Mishnah *Sanhedrin* (c. AD 200) makes the point explicitly: criminals condemned by a Jewish court must not be buried "in the burial place of their fathers" but in separate graveyards of the condemned kept by the court specifically for that purpose. Grieving must be private: "The kinsmen came and greeted the judges and the witnesses as if to say: 'We have nothing against you in our hearts, for you have judged the judgment of truth.' And they used not to make open lamentation, but they went mourning, for mourning has its place in the heart" (6:6). See too *Sanhedrin* 2:6 – mourning should not be observed for criminals condemned by a Jewish court. For discussion of the issue of dishonourable burial, see McCane, ibid., pp. 95–106.

24 See Richard C. Carrier, *The Burial of Jesus in Light of Jewish Law*: In Price and Lowder, ibid., pp. 380–382.

25 See McCane, ibid., pp. 101–106. Amos Kloner, a noted authority on first-century Jewish funerary practices, notes: "During the Second Temple period and later, Jews often practised temporary burial…a borrowed or temporary cave was used for a limited time, and the occupation of the cave by the corpse conferred no rights of ownership upon the family…[and] Jesus' interment was probably of this nature": Amos Kloner, *Did a Rolling Stone Close Jesus' Tomb?* Biblical Archaeology Review 25:5, Sept/Oct 1999, p. 29). He cites the Semahot: "Whoever finds a corpse in a tomb should not move it from its place, unless he knows that this is a temporary grave." The Semahot gives an example: "Rabban Gamliel had a temporary tomb in Yabneh into which they brought the corpse and locked the door upon it.": Semahot 13.5, 10.8, trans. Dov Zlotnik, *The Tractate "Mourning"*, Yale Judaica Series 18, 1966, p. 84, 74). Martin Hengel, *Crucifixion in the Ancient World and the Folly of the Message of the Cross*: Philadelphia: Fortress, 1977: Craig A Evans, *Jesus and the Ossuaries: What Jewish Burial Practices reveal about the beginning of Christianity*: Waco; Baylor University, 2003.

26 e.g. William Lane Craig, *Jesus' Resurrection: Fact or Figment?* (with Gerd Ludemann), eds Paul Copan and Ronald K. Tacelli (Downers Grove, IL: Inter Varsity, 2000).

27 See Semahot 6:1 and the discussion in McCane, ibid., at 37–38.
28 Mark 15:47; Matthew 27:61.
29 Luke 23:55.
30 Mark 15:43.
31 Matthew 27:57.
32 Luke 23:50–51.
33 John 19:38.
34 See, for example, John Dominic Crossan in *Who Killed Jesus*, ibid., pp. 172–173.
35 See Jeffrey Jay Lowder, *Historical evidence and the Empty Tomb*, in Price and Lowder, ibid., at p. 268.
36 Philo, *Embassy to Gaius*, 302.
37 Josephus: *Jewish Antiquities*, 18:56.
38 Josephus, *Jewish War*, 2.171.
39 Josephus, *Jewish Antiquities*, 18:60–62.
40 Brown, ibid., pp. 1234–34.
41 John 3:1–21.
42 John 7:50–51.
43 John 19:39.
44 John 19:40.
45 Summarised by Brown, ibid., at 1261–1264.
46 At the burial of Herod the Great, 500 servants were needed to carry the spices: Josephus: War 1.33.9.
47 John 19:19–20. In Jeremiah 34:5, God promised King Zedekiah: "…as spices were burned for your ancestors, the earlier kings who preceded you, so they shall burn spices for you and lament for you…"
48 Or are they? Brown, ibid., p. 1219, suggests that a variant reading of John 19:38 ("So they came and took away his body"), continues the story begun in John 19:31, and that accordingly 19:38 is saying that "the Jews" came and took away the body.
49 Acts 13:27–29. Brown, ibid., points out that Justin, in Dialogue 97:1, says this: "For the Lord too remained on the tree almost until evening, and towards evening they buried him." The suggestion there, according to Brown, is that "they" might again be the Jews rather than the disciples. The Gospel of Peter, at 6.21, states: "And then they [the Jews] drew out the nails from the hands of the Lord and placed him

on the earth." Crossan, ibid., at pp. 170–171, thinks that this part of Peter formed part of the original, ancient passion narrative ("the Cross Gospel"), and that the clear implication is that the writer was saying that the people who crucified Jesus and drew the nails out of his hands also buried him. This, thinks Crossan, "does not seem to be based on any knowledge of what actually happened but is rather a hope for what surely must have happened. Jesus' companions had fled after his arrest and were not there to see what happened. Their ultimate terror was that he was left unburied. So the process of negating that awful possibility began. It began, as early as we can see it, with the crucifiers' burial of Jesus by sunset, according to Deuteronomy 21:22–23. It began with hope. But hope, for all its humanity, is not history."

50 Matthew 27:33, Mark 15:22; John 19:17; see too Hebrews 13:12–13.

51 John 19:20.

52 John 19:41.

53 Matthew 27:60; Mark 15:46; Luke 23:53.

54 Matthew 27:60; Mark:15:46.

55 Mark 16:4; Matthew 27:60.

56 John 20:5.

57 John 20:6–8.

58 John 20:12.

59 Mark 16:5; Luke 24:3.

60 Mark 16:5.

61 Luke 24:4.

62 Mark 15:46.

63 Mark 16:3.

64 Mark 16:4.

65 Matthew 27:60.

66 Matthew 28:2.

67 Luke 24:2.

68 John 20:1.

69 Richard Carrier says that mention of a round rolling stone is an anachronism: "…that would not have been the case in the time of Jesus, yet it was often the case after 70 CE, just when the gospels were being written." Richard C. Carrier. *Craig's Empty Tomb and Habermas on the Post-Resurrection Appearances of Jesus*: Secular Web, 1999: http://www.infidels.

org/library/modern/richard_carrier/indef/4e.html. This is simply wrong. Round stones were never common, but they appear to have been as common at the time of Jesus' death as later.

70 Kloner, A. (1985), *A monument of the Second Temple period west of the Old City of Jerusalem*. Eretz-Israel, 18, 58–64 (Hebrew with an English summary).

71 Notably from Josephus' accounts of multiple crucifixions at the times of the Jewish Wars.

72 *Against Flaccus* 83: cited in Crossan, ibid., p. 167.

73 See Jodi Magness, *What did Jesus' tomb look like?* Biblical Archaeology Review, (2006) 32:1/ pp. 38–49.

74 It may be Ramathain (see Josephus: *Antiquities* 13.4:9). Eusebius identifies Arimathea with the birthplace of Samuel – Ramah or Ramathain-zophim, near Lydda (Eusebius: Onomast. 144:28 and 1 Samuel 1:19). Other suggestions include er-Ram and el-Birah-Ramallah – both north of Jerusalem. The mosaic Madaba map lists Armathem and Arimathe.

75 It is worth noting that, if Joseph was merely fulfilling Jewish law, it doesn't follow that he should have buried all three. We don't know what the others were crucified for. It wasn't crucifixion that forbade Jews burial with their families. It was only people condemned under the religious law who were liable to "dishonourable burial". For all we know the other two condemned that day might have had families waiting by to give splendid funerals followed by interment in the family tomb. They would have no need for the assistance that a Joseph figure could give. Jesus was, after all, quite a long way from home.

76 John 19:39.

77 A.N. Jannaris, *Exp Tim* 14 (1902–3), 460.

78 As it is in John 12:3.

79 O'Rahilly, A. *The Burial of Christ*, IER 58 (1941), 310: cited in Brown, ibid., p. 1260.

80 de Kruijf, T.C., *"More than half a hundredweight" of spices: Abundance and symbolism in the Gospel of John*: Bijdragen 43 (1982), 234–39: cited in Brown, ibid., p. 1260.

81 See Luke 23:50–54.

82 The shape of the stone is considered by Shimon Gibson and Joan E. Taylor in *Beneath the Church of the Holy Sepulchre, Jerusalem: The Archaeology and Early History of Traditional Golgotha*. London, Palestine Exploration Fund, 1994. p. 88, note 31: "The blocking stone is mentioned in a number of sources dating from the mid-4th to 9th centuries AD… The blocking stone is referred to as rectangular in shape even in publications of the 17th and 18th centuries…".

83 Martin Biddle, *The Tomb of Christ*, Stroud, Sutton Publishing, 1999, pp 116–118.

84 Martin Biddle, ibid., p. 55.

Chapter 5: The empty tomb

1 Note, though, that in Mark 15:47 (the verse immediately preceding Mark 16:1, where these women are named), Mary Magdalene and Mary the mother of Joses are the ones who see where the body is laid. Some argue, mainly as a result of this, that the pre-Markan passion narrative and the empty tomb narrative are independent of one another. If chapter 15 (death and burial) and chapter 16 (empty tomb) had been part of a continuous narrative the names in 15:47 and 16:1 would have been the same.

2 Luke 24:9–10.

3 The issue of the dependence of all the other gospels on Mark is well reviewed in Peter Kirby, *The Case against the Empty Tomb*, in Price and Lowder, ibid., at pp. 234–237.

4 See Mark 9:2–13.

5 2 Kings 2:6–18.

6 See the discussion in Kirby, ibid., at p. 237.

7 For a detailed discussion of the significance of the ending of Mark – and an argument that the silence was intended to be permanent – see Kirby, ibid., at pp. 238–240.

8 See Gerd Ludemann, in Paul Copan and Ronald K. Tacelli, eds, *Jesus' Resurrection: Fact or Figment: A Debate between William Lane Craig and Gerd Ludemann*, Downers Grove, ILL: IVP, 2000, 154.

9 "The desire to anoint 'on the third day' a dead body already buried and wrapped in linen cloths, is, however it be explained, not in accordance with any custom known to us."

Hans Van Campenhausen, *Tradition and Life in the Church; Essays and Lectures in Church History*, trans. A.V. Littledale, Philadelphia: Fortress Press, 1968, p. 58, cited in Kirby, ibid., at p. 243.

10 See John Dominic Crossan, *Who Killed Jesus?* (ibid.): pp. 177–181.

11 Matthew 27:62–66.

12 Matthew 27:62–66.

13 Matthew 28:11–15.

14 As does the empty-tomb account itself.

15 See, for example, John Calvin, *A Harmony of the Gospels: Matthew, Mark and Luke*. Eerdmans, 1995, 220–226.

16 For a detailed analysis of the historicity of the guard story, see Raymond Brown, ibid., pp. 1310–1313.

17 See Richard C. Carrier, *The plausibility of theft*. In Price and Lowder (eds), ibid., 360–364. For the Daniel story, see Daniel 6:10–24.

18 Daniel 10:6.

19 Matthew 27:62–66.

20 Luke 24:11–12.

21 John 20:3–8.

22 John 18:15–18 and 25–27.

23 John 20:8.

24 Crossan, John Dominic, *The Historical Jesus: The Life of a Mediterranean Jewish Peasant*, San Francisco: Harper Collins, 1991, p. 394.

25 Trans. Billington, Clyde E., *The Nazareth Inscription: Proof of the resurrection of Christ?* In *Artifax*, Spring 2005

26 Green, Michael. *Man Alive*: Leicester, IVP 1968, p. 36.

27 See F. de Zulueta: *Violation of sepulture in Palestine at the beginning of the Christian Era*, Journal of Roman Studies 22 (1932), pp. 184–97.

28 For a comprehensive review of the significance of the inscription, see Richard Carrier, *The Nazareth Inscription* (2000), http://www.infidels.org/library/modern/richard_carrier/nazarethlaw.html

29 Matthew's account of Jewish suspicions is repeated in the apocryphal Gospel of Nicodemus: Acts of Pilate: 1:13; in the Diatessaron, and in Justin's Trypho: cited in Richard Carrier, *The Plausibility of Theft*, Price and Lowder , ibid., p. 351.

30 It has sometimes been suggested that the Romans might have been responsible for moving the body. Their motive, on this thesis, would have been to promote the cause of the benign Messiah, Jesus, who urged Jews to pay their taxes to Caesar and generally be good citizens. There were plenty of other alternative Messiah candidates. Many of them had troublesome Jewish-nationalist tendencies, and saw the restoration of Israel as involving the violent expulsion of Rome. The idea is not discussed in detail here because of its intrinsic implausibility. There are three main reasons to dismiss it. First, if the Romans wanted to promote Jesus, it seems hugely more likely that they would have kept him alive. Second; the idea of the personal resurrection of the Messiah formed no part of Jewish thought. The Romans would never have thought that a story about Jesus' arising alone on the third day would ever catch on; and third, there is the business of the grave clothes.

31 Tacitus, *Annals* 2.69, cited in Richard Carrier, *The Plausibility of Theft*, Price and Lowder, ibid., p. 350.

32 Papyri Graecae Magicae 4:2140–44, 4.207 ff: Hans Dieter Betz, *The Greek Magical Papyri in Translation*: Chicago, University of Chicago Press, 1986, p. 76: Cited in Carrier, ibid., at p. 350.

33 Papyri Graece Magicae 4:2574–2601, 4.2643 ff: Cited in Carrier, ibid., at p. 351.

34 Lucan: Pharsalia, 608–609; 624; 633–649. Trans. Sir Edward Ridley: see *The Pharsalia of Lucan*, London, Longmans, Green and Co., 1896.

35 Matthew 26:6–13.

36 Tertullian, *De Spectaculis* 30.

37 John 20:15.

38 *The Holy Land*, ibid., p. 53. He notes: "…such kokhim graves are typical of the C1 BC and the C1 AD, and these could not have been dug after the quarry was incorporated into the city in AD 41–43… Constantine's engineers would have cut away all save the outermost chamber, in which the body of Christ had been laid…"

39 *Beneath the Church of the Holy Sepulchre: The Archaeology and Early History of Traditional Golgotha*, Shimon Gibson

and Joan Taylor, London, Palestine Exploration Fund, 1994, p. 63.

40 See Mark 15:47; Matthew 27:61; Luke 23:55.

41 John 20:1.

42 It has even been suggested that it would not have been possible under Jewish law to identify the body more than three days after death. These suggestions are based on the following passage from the Mishnah: "You cannot testify to [the identity of a corpse] save by the facial features together with the nose, even if there are marks of identification in his body and garments: again, you can testify only within three days (of death)." Mishnah Yehamot 16.3a–e. This is of course from considerably after the time of Jesus. What law and practice were at the material time is unknown.

43 It is far too old. It probably dates from the ninth to the sixth centuries BC. In the Byzantine period the body benches inside were cut down to create rock sarcophagi. The Byzantines clearly did not think that this could have been the tomb. The Crusaders used the site as a stable. The site was popularised in 1883 by General Charles Gordon. He thought that he could see the shape of a skull in the hill behind the tomb (above the present Arab bus station). Indeed it is easy to see why he thought this. The site conforms in many ways to the expectations raised by the gospel accounts. It is outside the present city walls; there is a beautiful garden; it is next to a green-(ish) hill (just like in the hymn).

44 It is at Appendix 3.

45 Tom Wright, *The Resurrection of the Son of God*, ibid., pp. 589–590.

46 Mark 6:14–15.

47 Mark 9:2–13.

48 Mark 15:34–36.

49 Mark 14:28.

50 Mark 16:7.

51 See 2 Kings 2:16.

52 See Mark 1:1.

53 Joe Zias: Personal communication, 2005.

54 Le Camus, E., *The Life of Christ*, Vol. III, New York: The Cathedral Library Association, 1908, p. 392; Thorburn, Thomas James, *The Resurrection Narratives and Modern*

Criticism, London: Kegan Paul, Trench, Trubner and Co., 1910, p. 179–82. Both cited in Josh McDowell, *Evidence that Demands a Verdict*, Nashville, Thomas Nelson, 1999, pp. 235–237.

55 There has been a lot of speculation about what the punishment would in fact be. The authorities conflict. But it would be well worth avoiding. The subject is exhaustively discussed by George Currie in *The Military Discipline of the Romans from the founding of the City to the Close of the Republic*. An abstract of a thesis published under the auspices of the Graduate Council of Indiana University, 1928.

56 Matthew 28:11–15.

57 Matthew 28:15.

58 Daniel 6:17.

59 Daniel 10:2–6.

60 Luke 24:13–35.

61 John 20:14–17.

62 John 20:8.

63 John 21:15–17.

64 As the Mishnah makes clear: see Yebamoth 16:7; Ketuboth 2:5; Eduymoth 3:6: cited by John Wenham in *Easter Enigma: Are the Resurrection Accounts in Conflict?* 2nd ed. Grand Rapids, MI: Baker, 1992, pp. 150–151.

65 Jewish War 7.389 and 4.81.

66 Pliny the Younger: *Epistles* 10:96. Both the Josephus and Pliny references are cited by Jeffrey Jay Lowder, *Historical Evidence and the Empty Tomb*: in Price and Lowder, ibid., pp. 283–284.

67 John 7:5.

68 Robert Price, in *Apocryphal Apparitions*, in *The Empty Tomb*, Price and Lowder, ibid., at pp. 82–84, takes issue with this view, saying that Luke "strongly implies that the Holy Family were doers of Jesus' word from the beginning", and that accordingly James "was not 'turned round' by an appearance of the Risen Jesus…" No authority he cites seems to me to support those propositions.

69 1 Corinthians 15:7.

70 Matthew 13:55; Mark 6:3; Galatians 1:18–19.

71 Acts 1:12–14.

72 Acts 12:12; Acts 12:17; Acts 15:13–21; Galatians 2:9–10.

73 Josephus: Antiquities 20:9.

74 "[The 'Jews, scribes and Pharisees']…came, therefore, in a body to James, and said: "We entreat thee, restrain the people: for they are gone astray in their opinions about Jesus, as if he were the Christ. We entreat thee to persuade all who have come hither for the day of the Passover, concerning Jesus. For we all listen to thy persuasion; since we, as well as all the people, bear thee testimony that thou art just, and showest partiality to none. Do thou, therefore, persuade the people not to entertain erroneous opinions concerning Jesus: for all the people, and we also, listen to thy persuasion. Take thy stand, then, upon the summit[5] of the temple, that from that elevated spot thou mayest be clearly seen, and thy words may be plainly audible to all the people. For, in order to attend the Passover, all the tribes have congregated hither, and some of the Gentiles also."

The aforesaid scribes and Pharisees accordingly set James on the summit of the temple, and cried aloud to him, and said: "O just one, whom we are all bound to obey, forasmuch as the people is in error, and follows Jesus the crucified, do thou tell us what is the door of Jesus, the crucified." And he answered with a loud voice: "Why ask ye me concerning Jesus the Son of man? He Himself sitteth in heaven, at the right hand of the Great Power, and shall come on the clouds of heaven."

And, when many were fully convinced by these words, and offered praise for the testimony of James, and said, "Hosanna to the son of David," then again the said Pharisees and scribes said to one another, "We have not done well in procuring this testimony to Jesus. But let us go up and throw him down, that they may be afraid, and not believe him." And they cried aloud, and said: "Oh! oh! the just man himself is in error." Thus they fulfilled the Scripture written in Isaiah: "Let us away with the just man, because he is troublesome to us: therefore shall they eat the fruit of their doings." So they went up and threw down the just man, and said to one another: "Let us stone James the Just." And they began to stone him: for he was not killed by the fall; but he turned, and kneeled down, and said: "I beseech Thee, Lord God our Father, forgive them; for they know not what they do."

And, while they were thus stoning him to death, one of the priests, the sons of Rechab, the son of Rechabim, to whom testimony is borne by Jeremiah the prophet, began to cry aloud, saying: "Cease, what do ye? The just man is praying for us." But one among them, one of the fullers, took the staff with which he was accustomed to wring out the garments he dyed, and hurled it at the head of the just man.

And so he suffered martyrdom; and they buried him on the spot, and the pillar erected to his memory still remains, close by the temple. This man was a true witness to both Jews and Greeks that Jesus is the Christ". *Hegesippus, Commentaries on the Acts of the Church*, Book 5. Trans. Roberts-Donaldson.

75 This is likely to be the case even if the tomb was one of a parallel series of simple tombs with burial couches instead of *kokhim*. Sufficient room is likely to have been left between adjacent tombs to allow the fashioning of later *kokhim*.

76 Matthew 27:62–66.

77 Matthew 28:11–15.

Chapter 6: The post-resurrection appearances

1 Matthew 28:17.

2 Matthew 28:16.

3 E.g. the giving of the law on Mount Sinai, and the revelation of Jesus' status alongside Moses and Elijah in the Transfiguration.

4 John 20:14–17.

5 See John 20:19.

6 John 20:24–29.

7 See John 20:30–31.

8 Luke 24:49.

9 See Luke 24:1, 13, 29, 33, 36, 50.

10 See Luke 24:50.

11 Acts 1:3.

12 Luke 24:51; Acts 1:9–10.

13 See Acts 1:2–9.

14 See Luke 24:33–53: note the constant repetition of "they".

15 Luke 24:18.

16 Luke is very unclear: He says that the women had told their story to "the eleven and all the rest" in Luke 24:9 and, then,

in 24:10, to "the apostles". Apparently referring back to these references, 24:13 says: "…two of them were going to a village called Emmaus…"

17 Luke 24:25–27.

18 Luke 24:30.

19 Luke 22:19.

20 See Luke 24:36–43.

21 Luke 1:3.

22 See John 20:21.

23 John 21:15–17.

24 John 21:18–19.

25 John 20:25, slightly adapted.

26 John 20:27.

27 John 20:28.

28 Luke 24:42–43.

29 John 21:9–13.

30 This thesis is articulated in many places: See, for example, Jack A. Kent, *The Psychological Origins of the Resurrection Myth*: London, Open Gate Press, 1999.

31 Bentall, P.D. and Slade, R.P., *Sensory Deception: A Scientific Analysis of Hallucination*: London, Croom Helm, 1988, p. 93.

32 Note the famous Midtown study in Manhattan in late 1950s: only about a quarter of all those interviewed were considered to be completely free from psychiatric impairment: Srole L., Langner, T.S, Michael, S.T, Opler, M.K. and Rennie, T.A.C., *Mental Health in the Metropolis: The Midtown Manhattan Study*, McGraw-Hill, New York, 1961. Similar results have been found in other communities: Dohrenwend, B.P and Dohrenwend, B.S. (1974), *Psychiatric disorders in urban settings*. In S. Arietti and G. Caplan (eds), *American Handbook of Psychiatry*, Vol. 2: New York, Basic Books; Cochrane, R. and Stopes-Roe, M. (1980) *Factors affecting the distribution of psychological symptoms in urban areas of England*. Acta Psychiactrica Scandinavica, 61, 445–460.

33 Sidgewick, H.A., *et al.*, 1894, *Report of the census of hallucinations. Proceedings of the Society for Psychical Research*, 26, 259–394: This study involved 7,717 men and 7,599 women.

34 West, D.J., 1948, *A mass observation questionnaire on hallucinations*. Journal of the Society for Psychical Research, 34, 187–196: This involved 1,519 subjects.

35 11.6% multimodal per Sidgewick: 8.4% per West.

36 There are other, smaller, studies too. See, for example, McKellar, *Experience and Behaviour*, Harmondsworth, Penguin, 1968. Of 500 subjects, 125 reported at least one hallucinatory experience.

37 These figures are significantly lower than those reported in Posey, T.B. and Losch, M.E. (1983) *Auditory hallucinations of hearing voices in 375 normal subjects*. Imagination, Cognition and Personality, 2: 99–113: This was a (small) study of 375 college students. A remarkable 71% reported some experiences of voices. 39% said that they had heard their thoughts spoken out loud. 5% had had conversations with their hallucinations.

38 Johnson, R.L. and Miller, M.D. (1965) *Auditory hallucinations and intellectual deficit*. Journal of Psychiatric Research, 3:37–41.

39 Bentall and Slade, ibid., pp. 94–97.

40 See Bentall and Slade, ibid., pp. 97–99.

41 Barber, T.X. and Calverley, D.S. (1964) *An experimental study of "hypnotic" (auditory and visual) hallucinations*. Journal of Abnormal and Social Psychology, 66, 589–597.

42 Mintz, S. and Alpert, M. (1972) *Imagery vividness, reality testing and schizophrenic hallucinations*. Journal of Abnormal Psychology, 79, 310–316.

43 Alpert, M. (1985) *The signs and symptoms of schizophrenia*. Comprehensive Psychiatry, 26, 103–112.

44 See Bentall and Slade, ibid., pp. 223–224.

45 Bourguignon, E., *Hallucinations and trance: An anthropologist's perspective*: In W. Keup (ed.) *Origin and Mechanisms of Hallucinations*, New York, Plenum Press, 1970.

46 Comer, N.L., Madow, L. and Dixon, J.J. (1967) *Observations of sensory deprivation in a life-threatening situation*. American Journal of Psychiatry, 124, 164–169.

47 Siegel, R.K. (1984) *Hostage hallucinations: Visual imagery induced by isolation and life-threatening stress*. Journal of Nervous and Mental Disease, 172, 264–272. hostages: 8/31.

48 Belenky, G.L. (1979) *Unusual visual experiences reported by subjects in the British Army study of sustained operations, Exercise Early Call.* Military Medicine, 144, 695–696.

49 British Medical Journal. 2 October 1971. Interestingly, although hallucinations generally seem to be more common in women than in men, more men than women had bereavement hallucinations: 50% as opposed to 45.8%. These observations were at odds with those reported at the Spring 1995 meeting of the Jesus Seminar, mentioned by John Dominic Crossan in *The Birth of Christianity: Discovering What Happened in the Years Immediately after the Execution of Jesus*: San Francisco, Harper Collins, 1998, pp. xvi–xvii. He notes that 50–80% of people feel "an intuitive, sometimes overwhelming presence or spirit of the lost person", and that significantly more women than men report this.

50 See, for example, McDonald, W.S. and Oden, C.W. (1977) *Aumakua: Behavioural direction visions in Hawaiians*. Journal of Abnormal Psychology, 86, 189–194: Two male Hawaiian students suffered from hallucinations of dead relatives. Conventional psychological techniques failed to stop the hallucinations. It then emerged that in this culture about 40% of people had confrontations with dead ancestors. These confrontations typically resulted from the violation of a cultural taboo. When amends were made, the hallucination stopped. Also Matchett, W.F. (1972) *Repeated hallucinatory experiences as part of the mourning process among Hopi Indian women*. Psychiatry, 35, 185–194: Reports that the Hopi Indians of North America often hallucinate the presence of a recently deceased family member.

51 Zarroug, E.A. (1975) *The frequency of visual hallucinations in schizophrenic patients in Saudi Arabia*, British Journal of Psychiatry, 127, 553–555.

52 Murphy, H.B.M, Wittkower, E.D, Fried, J. and Ellenberger, H.A. (1963) *A cross-cultural survey of schizophrenic symptomatology*. International Journal of Social Psychiatry, 9, 235–249.

53 See Matthew 26:36–45.

54 Mark 8:31; Mark 9:30–31; Mark 10:33–34; Luke 9:22; Luke 13:32–34; Luke 18:31–34.

55 Mark 14:28; Matthew 26:32.

56 Mark 16:7.
57 Luke 24:6–7.
58 Matthew 27:63.
59 John 20:9.
60 Mark 14:66–72; Matthew 26:69–75; Luke 22:55–61; John 18:17–27.
61 1 Thessalonians 4:14: "…since we believe that Jesus died and rose again…"
62 1 Corinthians 15:1–9
63 This remains a mystery. There are various suggestions, including Hosea 6:2 and Jonah 1:17.
64 That is what Christians say is implicit in the comment in verse 6, "…most of whom are still alive…"
65 Galatians 1:17.
66 Galatians 1:18–19.
67 Galatians 1:21.
68 Galatians 2:1.
69 For details of the chronology of Paul's life, see Jerome Murphy O'Connor, *Paul: A Critical Life*, Oxford, OUP, 1996, 1–31.
70 Some think that it is the earliest of Paul's letters (AD 48–49); others put it in the mid 50s. The issue is not crucial for this argument.
71 Galatians 1:11–12.
72 Galatians 1:15–17.
73 See Acts 9:1–9; 22:1–21; 26:2–23.
74 See Kent, ibid., p. 49 *et seq.* He cites the *Diagnostic and Statistical Manual of Mental Disorders*, 3rd ed. (American Psychiatric Association) – commonly known as DSM III. This has now been replaced by DSM IV. The diagnostic criteria for conversion disorder in DSM IV are:
A. One or more *symptoms* or deficits affecting voluntary motor or sensory function that suggest a neurological or other general medical condition.
B. Psychological factors are judged to be associated with the symptom or deficit because the initiation or exacerbation of the symptom or deficit is preceded by conflicts or other stressors.
C. The symptom or deficit is not intentionally produced or feigned (as in *Factitious Disorder* or *Malingering*).

D. The symptom or deficit cannot, after appropriate investigation, be fully explained by a general medical condition, or by the direct effects of a *substance*, or as a culturally sanctioned behavior or experience.
E. The symptom or deficit causes clinically significant distress or impairment in social, occupational, or other important areas of functioning or warrants medical evaluation.
F. The symptom or deficit is not limited to pain or sexual dysfunction, does not occur exclusively during the course of *Somatization Disorder* and is not better accounted for by another *mental disorder*.

75 1 Corinthians 15:10.
76 Luke 24:40; John 20:24–28.
77 e.g. Matthew 28:9.
78 e.g. Luke 24:13–31.
79 Luke 24:31.
80 e.g. Matthew 28:9; John 20:27.
81 John 20:17.
82 Matthew 28:17.
83 Matthew 28:17.
84 Matthew 26:32; Mark 14:28.
85 Luke 24:49.
86 Acts 1:4.
87 Acts 2.
88 Luke 24:24.
89 Carsten Peter Thiede, *The Emmaus Mystery*, London, Continuum, 2005, p. 15.
90 Luke 1:3.
91 Thiede, ibid., p. 204.
92 See Luke 24:50–52 and Acts 1:9–14.
93 Luke 24:25–26.
94 Luke 24:36–37.
95 Luke 24:39.
96 See Wright, ibid., pp. 599–602. Note particularly his comment on how John Dominic Crossan, who is very ready to say of just about everything in the gospels “that’s historicized prophecy”, is stumped by the resurrection accounts, and changes tack completely.
97 See Wright, ibid., pp. 602–604.
98 See 1 Corinthians 7:1; 1 Corinthians 16:7.

99 In Lee Strobel, *The Case for Christ*, Grand Rapids, Zondervan, 1998, p. 229, it is suggested that "received" and "delivered" are rabbinic terms indicating tradition. There is the parallelism and the stylised content of a formal creed. The original text uses "Cephas" for Peter. Cephas is the Aramaic form. The use of the Aramaic itself indicates very early origin. The pattern and vocabulary are said to be similar to that of Aramaic and Mishnaic Hebrew.
100 See 1 Corinthians 1:12; 1 Corinthians 3:4; 1 Corinthians 4:6.
101 1 Corinthians 15:3.
102 1 Corinthians 15:4.
103 1 Corinthians 15:5–7.
104 Matthew 28:10 and 16.
105 1 Corinthians 15:5 and 7.
106 Luke 24:34–36.
107 Luke 24:13.
108 See Acts 9:1–9; Acts 22:1–21.
109 See Acts 9:18.

Chapter 7: Did the early church believe in the bodily resurrection of Jesus?

1 See http://www.wyattarchaeology.com/ark.htm
2 See Acts 9:1–9; 22:1–21; 26:2–23.
3 1 Corinthians 15:20–57.
4 1 Corinthians 15:44.
5 1 Corinthians 15:45–50.
6 See Richard Carrier, *The spiritual body of Christ and the legend of the empty tomb*, in Price and Lowder, ibid., pp. 105–231.
7 3 Corinthians 5:24–35. The Third Epistle to the Corinthians is canonical in the Armenian Orthodox Church.
8 1 Corinthians 15:44.
9 1 Corinthians 15:46.
10 Carrier, ibid., at pp. 128–139, has several other arguments based on 1 Thessalonians and 1 Corinthians 2:14–15. They seem to me, on proper analysis, to weaken rather than improve his case, and so I have left them out here. The arguments appear in Y's section.

11 See Romans 7:14; Romans 15:27; 1 Corinthians 10:3–4; Ephesians 6:12. See Carrier, ibid., at pp. 128–129.
12 Carrier, ibid., pp. 128–129.
13 2 Corinthians 4:16–18.
14 2 Corinthians 5:1–8.
15 X acknowledges that the section that he has missed out here does not fit very neatly with his thesis: "…we will not be found naked. For while we are still in this tent, we groan under our burden, because we wish not to be unclothed but to be further clothed, so that what is mortal may be swallowed up by life. He who has prepared us for this very thing is God, who has given us the Spirit as a guarantee. So we are always confident…"
16 Colossians 1:22.
17 Carrier, ibid., p. 105 *et seq.*, says that the evidence suggests that Paul believed in the "two-body hypothesis": this meant that the identity of Jesus left one body to enter another. He had received a new, more glorious body, made of the stuff of the stars. There is no doubt, he says, that the two-body hypothesis was around in second-Temple Judaism: see, e.g. Josephus' famous speech against suicide. He says that the subsequent gospel accounts, which do emphasise a physical raising of the body, are a legendary development of the two-body belief. But how does this hypothesis fit with the empty tomb? And the empty tomb? How does this fit with the two-body hypothesis? Carrier says (pp. 155–156) that all the gospel writers clearly used Mark (in the case of Matthew and Luke), or had access to Mark (in the case of John). The empty tomb in Mark "…was not historical, but symbolic: it represented the resurrection of Jesus, with a powerful symbol pregnant with meaning – not only 'elucidating' the core gospel inherited from Paul (e.g. 1 Cor. 15:3–5, which is ambiguous as to whether Jesus rose in the flesh or the spirit), but also maintaining Mark's own narrative theme of 'reversal of expectation'. The empty tomb was for Mark like the Exodus for Philo: educational fiction, whose true meaning was far more important than any historical claim ever could be." And where did Mark get this idea from? There are many possibilities, says Carrier (p. 158 *et seq.*). They include Homer and contemporary ascension mythology, both pagan and

Jewish, but most likely are the Psalms: notably Psalms 22, 23, 24. This issue is dealt with in the next chapter.

18 1 Peter 1:23–25.

19 2 Peter 1:16.

20 2 Peter 1:17–18.

21 Of the non-canonical early Christian writers, some (e.g. Ignatius of Antioch, in his Letter to Smyrna) clearly affirm the bodily resurrection. Ignatius, on his way to martyrdom in Rome in the first decade of the second century, says: "For I know and believe that after the resurrection [Jesus] was in the flesh." Others do not appear to touch on the issue at all. Others arguably do. The whole subject is reviewed comprehensively in Wright, ibid., at pp. 480–552.

22 See Festinger, Leon, *A theory of cognitive dissonance.* Stanford, California. Stanford UP, 1957; Festinger, Leon, Riecken, H., and Schachter, S., *When Prophecy Fails.* Minneapolis; University of Minnesota Press, 1956. See too the commentary on this in Wright, ibid., pp. 697–701.

23 Schillebeeckx, Edward, 1979. *Jesus: An Experiment in Christology*. New York, Seabury Press. Cited in Wright, ibid., pp. 701–706.

24 Acts 2.

25 Acts 1:21–22.

26 Acts 2:23–24.

27 Acts 2:29–32.

28 Acts 3:15.

29 Acts 4:2–3.

30 Acts 4:10.

31 Acts 4:20.

32 Acts 4:33.

33 Acts 5:30–32.

34 Acts 10:39–41.

35 Acts 13:29–37.

36 Acts 17:3.

37 Acts 17:18.

38 Acts 17:31.

39 Acts 17:32.

40 Acts 23:6. The New RSV renders this "concerning the hope of the resurrection of the dead".

41 Acts 24:20–21.

42 Acts 25:19.
43 Acts 26:8.
44 Acts 26:22–23.
45 Romans 8:9 is discussed below. Note, too, for example, Romans 1:4: when indicating to his readers who Jesus is, the resurrection is the defining characteristic. Cf. Romans 4:24–25; Romans 6:4–9. Look, too, at 1 Thessalonians, the oldest letter in the New Testament. There Paul writes about waiting for God's Son from heaven "whom he raised from the dead – Jesus…" (v. 10). Also 2 Tim. 2:8: "Remember Jesus Christ, raised from the dead…"
46 1 Corinthians 15:8.
47 In Galatians 1:18 Paul uses the word "historesai" to describe his visit to Peter. It is suggested in Lee Strobel, *The Case for Christ*, Zondervan, Grand Rapids, 1998, pp. 229–230, that this implies a systematic inquiry.
48 Acts 9:1–9; 22:1–21; 26:2–23.
49 See *The Great Divorce: A Dream*, London, Geoffrey Bles, 1945.
50 Wright, ibid.
51 The view taken by A.N. Wilson in *Paul: The Mind of the Apostle*, London, Pimlico Press, 1998.
52 C.S. Lewis, *Reflections on the Psalms*, London, Geoffrey Bles, 1958.
53 See 2 Peter 3:15–16; C.S. Lewis, *Letters of C.S. Lewis*, ed. W.H. Lewis, London, Geofrrey Bles, 1966 (letter of 3 August 1953).
54 Lewis went on: "It may be that what we should have liked would have been fatal to us if granted. It may be indispensable that Our Lord's teaching, by that elusiveness (to our systematising intellect), should demand a response from the whole man, should make it so clear that there is no quesiton of learning a subject but of steeping ourselves in a Personality, acquiring a new outlook and temper, breathing a new atmosphere, suffering Him, in His own way, to rebuild in us the defaced image of Himself. So in St Paul. Perhaps the sort of works I would wish him to have written would have been useless. The crabbedness, the appearance of inconsequence and even of sophistry, the turbulent mixture of petty detail, personal complaint, practical advice, and lyrical rapture,

finally let through what matters more than ideas – a whole Christian life in operation – better say, Christ Himself operating in a man's life. And in the same way, the value of the Old Testament may be dependent on what seems its imperfection. It may repel one use in order that we may be forced to use it in another way – to find the Word in it, not without repeated and leisurely reading nor without discriminations made by our conscience and our critical facilities, to re-live, while we read, the whole Jewish experience of God's gradual and graded self-revelation, to feel the very material through which it works. For here again, it is our total response that has to be elicited." Reflections on the Psalms, ibid.

55 For steps (a) to (c), see Wright, ibid., pp. 347–356.
56 1 Peter 1:23–25.
57 2 Peter 1:16–18.
58 Acts 12:2.
59 1 Corinthians 15:17.
60 Martin Biddle, *The Tomb of Christ*, Stroud, Sutton Publishing, 1999, pp. 65–66.
61 See *Beneath the Church of the Holy Sepulchre: The Archaeology and Early History of Traditional Golgotha*, Shimon Gibson and Joan Taylor, London, Palestine Exploration Fund, 1994, xix.
62 Discussed in Biddle, ibid., at pp 57–58.

Chapter 8: Where did the Christians get their idea of resurrection?

1 Verses 13–19.
2 Hosea 13:14.
3 See 1 Corinthians 15:54.
4 Hosea 6:1–2.
5 Ezekiel 37:1–14.
6 Daniel 12:1–3.
7 See, for example, 1 Corinthians 15:40–41 and 47–49.
8 2 Maccabees 7:9.
9 2 Maccabees 7:14.
10 2 Maccabees 7:10.
11 Two of the latest are *The Pagan Christ*, by Tom Harpur, London, Thomas Allen, 2005, and *The Jesus Mysteries: Was*

the Original Jesus a Pagan God? by Timothy Freke and Peter Gandy, London, Harper Collins, 2000.

12 Tom Harpur, ibid., suggests that Jesus was actually a Horus rather than an Osiris figure.

13 See Richard Carrier, *The spiritual body of Christ and the legend of the empty tomb*, in Price and Lowder, ibid., p. 159.

14 Herodotus writes, in *Histories* 2:146: "…the Greek story has it that no sooner was Dionysus born than Zeus sewed him up in his thigh and carried him away to Nysa in Ethiopia beyond Egypt; and as for Pan, the Greeks do not know what became of him after his birth. It is therefore plain to me that the Greeks learned the names of these two gods later than the names of all the others, and trace the birth of both to the time when they gained the knowledge."

15 Freke and Gandy, ibid., and S. Acharya (in *The Christ Conspiracy*, Kempton, Ill., Adventures Unlimited Press, 1999) make a number of other suggestions, for instance that Dionysus, like Jesus, rode in a triumphal procession on an ass: and indeed there are depictions of Dionysus riding on an ass. Words like "So what?" spring to mind. Likewise they suggest that Dionysus changed water into wine, as Jesus did at the wedding at Cana. But Dionysus didn't. At his behest, empty jars were indeed filled with wine flowing from a spring, as one might expect from a wine-god. They suggest too that Dionysus was identified with the Ram or the Lamb. Jesus was of course known as "the Lamb of God". Many metaphors were used to describe Dionysus. The main one was the Bull. Others include "tiger", "panther", "lion" , "lynx" and even "dolphin". But not, in fact, the lamb. It is further suggested that the Dionysus/Jesus link is implied by the fact that in Euripides' famous play about Dionysus, *The Bacchae*, one of the characters, Pentheus (Dionysus' arch-enemy), is killed when he is "lifted up on a tree" (supposedly a parallel to the crucifixion), and that in a Sicilian myth about Dionysus another enemy is crucified. Do these really have to be answered? It is difficult to see how the death of enemies in any way might suggest anything about the death of a person whose life is supposed to parallel that of Dionysus. And, in any event, the "lifted up on a tree" scene wasn't anything to do with crucifixion. Dionysus tricked Pentheus into grabbing

the top of a tree which he (Dionysus) had bent down to the earth. Dionysus then let go of the tree, and Pentheus found himself at the top. Dionysus' crowd of manic women followers, the Maenads, start hurling sticks and stones at Pentheus, but they cannot reach him. Eventually they rip the tree up by the roots. Pentheus falls to the ground and is dismembered by the women. We are a long way from Calvary.

16 Achilles and Patroclus, for example.
17 Plato, *Georgias*, 493a (cited in Carrier, ibid., at p. 162).
18 See Carrier, ibid., at pp. 161–163.
19 For a detailed discussion of its significance, see Radcliffe G. Edmonds, *Myths of the Underworld Journey in Plato, Aristophanes and the "Orphic" Gold Tablets*, Cambridge University Press, 2004.
20 Carrier, ibid., pp. 162–163.
21 Mark 16:5.
22 Mark 16:6.
23 John 20:15.
24 They are summarised in Wright, ibid., pp. 70–71.
25 Reviewed by Wright, ibid., pp. 72–74.
26 Ecclesiastes 9:5–6.
27 Psalm 88:10–11.

Appendix 1: The cause of death

1 Some of the many papers, apart from those dealt with specifically in this Appendix, include Mikulicz-Radecki, F.V., *The chest wound in the crucified Christ*, Med News, 1966:14:30–40; Davis, C.T., *The crucifixion of Jesus: The passion of the Christ from a medical point of view*: Ariz Med. 1965; 22:183–187: Tenney, S.M., *On death by crucifixion*. Am Heart J 1964; 68:286–287: De Pasquale, N.P., Burch, G.E., *Death by crucifixion*, Am Heart J, 1963; 434–435.
2 H. Ur. Rehman, J. Thromb Haemost 2005; 3:2131–3.
3 Luke 22:44.
4 Holoubek, J.E., Holoubek, A.B., *Blood, sweat and fear: A classification of hematidrosis*. J Med. 1996; 27(3–4):115–33.
5 Matthew 26:67.
6 Mark 14:65.
7 Luke 22:63–64.

8 John 18:22.
9 Mark 15:15.
10 Mark 15:17–19.
11 Matthew 27:26.
12 Matthew 27:28–30.
13 Luke 23:16 and 22.
14 John 19:1–2.
15 John 19:3.
16 Eusebius, *Epistle of the Church in Smyrna*.
17 Mark 15:21; Matthew 27:32; Luke 23:26.
18 John 19:17.
19 Jerome Murphy-O'Connor, *The Holy Land*, Oxford, OUP, 1998, pp. 35–36.
20 Murphy-O'Connor, ibid., p. 35.
21 Josephus: *Jewish Wars*. 5.11–451.
22 See Barbet, P., *Les Cinq Plaies du Christ*, 2nd ed. Paris. Procure du Carmel de l'Action de Graces, 1937; Barbet, P., *A Doctor at Calvary*, New York: P.J. Kennedy and Sons, 1955: Image Books, 1963.
23 See Zugibe, Frederick T., *Pierre Barbet Revisited*, Sindon, N.S. Quad No. 8, December 1995.
24 *On the physical death of Jesus Christ*, Edwards, W.D., Gabel, W.J., Hosmer, F.E., JAMA 1986; 255:1455–1463.
25 Primrose, W.B., *A Surgeon Looks at the Crucifixion*. New York, Hibbert, 1949, pp. 382–388.
26 Clark, C.C.P., *What was the physical cause of the death of Jesus Christ?* Med Rec 1890; 38:543.
27 John 19:34.
28 Brenner, B., *Did Jesus Christ die of pulmonary embolism?* J Thromb Haemost 2005; 3:2130–1.

Appendix 2: The Turin Shroud

1 See Wilson, Ian and Schwartz, Barrie, *The Turin Shroud*, London, Michael O'Mara, pp. 119–120.
2 Danin, Avinoam, Whanger, A.D, Baruch, Uri and Whanger, M. *Flora of the Shroud of Turin*, St Louis, Missouri, Botanical Garden Press, 1999.

Index

[*A citation in a footnote is indicated by 'fn'. Figures are indicated by their Fig numbers, rather than by a page number*].

"If your parents were divorced, you need to read this compelling book. *Breaking the Cycle of Divorce* acts like an inoculation against the divorce epidemic, preventing its spread from generation to generation. It will assure you that your marriage *can* be for a lifetime and give you a very practical road map to get you there."

SHAUNTI FELDHAHN, author of *For Women Only*

"Dr. John Trent is honest. He is vulnerable, and he is right! Adult children of divorce (like me) *can* begin a new cycle of successful marriage in their family. I know because I've been married 41 years! Start reading, because this book gives you practical steps to take you to a lifelong love."

LINDA DILLOW, author of *Calm My Anxious Heart* and co-author of *Intimate Issues*

"While acknowledging the detrimental influence of parental divorce on children, this book gives compelling evidence that the negative power of parental example can be broken. John Trent is 'living proof' that the insights of this book can lead to a successful marriage."

GARY D. CHAPMAN, PH.D., author of *The Five Love Languages* and *The Four Seasons of Marriage*

"John Trent takes the family portrait of divorce and changes the frame to one of hope. He shows us how to paint over the broken lines of divorce with brushstrokes of enduring love, gives us the tools to break the cycle, and shares how to create a legacy of love for a lifetime."

SHARON JAYNES, author of *Becoming the Woman of His Dreams* and *Becoming a Woman Who Listens to God*

Also by John Trent

The Blessing
The Gift of Honor
The Language of Love
Love Is a Decision
The Two Sides of Love
Home Remedies
The Hidden Value of a Man
Leaving the Lights On
(all with Gary Smalley)
LifeMapping
Seeking Solid Ground
A Love for All Seasons
Go the Distance
The Making of a Godly Man Workbook
Choosing to Live the Blessing
Leading from Your Strengths
Parenting from Your Strengths
The Light of Home
The Dad's Everything Book for Sons
The Dad's Everything Book for Daughters
Heart Shift
The Two-Degree Difference

Books for Children

The Treasure Tree
There's a Duck in My Closet!
I'd Choose You!
Spider Sisters
Two Trails
The Black & White Rainbow

breaking the cycle of divorce

FOCUS ON THE FAMILY

breaking the cycle of divorce

how your marriage can succeed even if your parents' didn't

JOHN TRENT, PH.D.
WITH LARRY K. WEEDEN

Tyndale House Publishers, Inc.
Carol Stream, Illinois

Breaking the Cycle of Divorce

A Focus on the Family book published by
Tyndale House Publishers, Carol Stream, Illinois 60188

Editors: Mick Silva, Kathy Davis
Cover design by: Stephen Vosloo. Author photograph by Hayes Button Photography.

Published in association with the literary agency of Alive Communications, Inc., 7680 Goddard Street, Suite 200, Colorado Springs, CO 80920, www.alivecommunications.com

Library of Congress Cataloging-in-Publication Data
Trent, John T.
Breaking the cycle of divorce : how your marriage can succeed even if your parents' didn't / by John Trent, with Larry Weeden.
p. cm.
"A Focus on the Family book."
978-1-58997-141-7
1. Divorce—Religious aspects—Christianity. 2. Marriage—Religious aspects—Christianity. I. Weeden, Larry K. II. Title.
BT707.T74 2006
646.7'8—dc22

2005034854

Printed in the United States of America
1 2 3 4 5 6 7 8 9 / 15 14 13 12 11

In loving memory of Zoa L. Trent, beloved mother and a world-class example of someone who used God's love to "reverse the curse" for her children and many others

Contents

Acknowledgments

My thanks go to Cecil Price, professional researcher par excellence, for his help in finding statistics and other material used in this book.

I'd also like to thank my friend Jim McGuire, who served as a technical go-between when my e-mail and that of my co-writer didn't want to get along with each other. I'm glad Jim was up some late nights to get chapter attachments from one of us to the other.

As always, my agent, Lee Hough at Alive Communications, was a great help in pulling together the pieces of the project and looking out for my best interests.

On the personal side, my wife, Cindy, and our daughters, Kari and Laura, deserve praise for their loving support and encouragement. I couldn't do the work I do if I didn't have them all solidly in my corner. They're my biggest fans, and that means more to me than I can say.

My brothers, Jeff and Joe, are likewise a source of great encouragement as I work on writing projects. In this book, they're also a part of the cast of characters.

Finally, my thanks go to the Focus on the Family team of professionals who have worked so hard to help shape, package, and present this book in an outstanding way.

Introduction

The Challenge

Children of divorce have no idea how to create and maintain a healthy relationship themselves. Typically, therefore, the idea of getting married fills them with both joy and dread at the same time.

Imagine growing up in a big city in the eastern United States, having never set foot outside the "concrete jungle." One day a person you care for a great deal asks you to paint a picture of the Arizona desert in spring bloom, with flowering cacti of various kinds and a brightly colored carpet of wildflowers covering the sand—a scene you've never witnessed or even viewed in photographs.

Would you be able to do it?

Almost certainly you'd find it impossible, even if you had artistic talent. How could you hope to paint a landscape you had never seen? You might worry about hurting your loved one's feelings; you might wish desperately that you could satisfy the request. But you'd find yourself asking, "What does one kind of cactus look like, let alone a dozen different kinds? And since when do cacti bloom? And while we're at it, what's a wildflower?"

Adult children of divorce who are considering the possibility of marriage—or who are already married and struggling to keep it together—face a challenge that seems nearly as inconceivable. Like every human being, they want to be loved and accepted. Like most people, they long to find those things in a marriage relationship that will be strong and thriving and mutually fulfilling "for as long as we both shall live."

Unfortunately, those adult children of divorce have never seen such a marriage relationship. They have no idea what it looks like. Their only experience is with a relationship that, for any of a thousand reasons, didn't last. In their experience, when the going gets tough, men and women bail out of a "bad" marriage.

A number of surveys and studies have discovered that adult children of divorce are far more likely to get divorced themselves than are the adult children of intact families (i.e., families in which Mom and Dad did not divorce).

So these children of divorce very often have no idea how to create and maintain a healthy relationship themselves. Typically, therefore, the idea of getting married fills them with both joy and dread at the same time. As Judith Wallerstein, one of the leading researchers on the effects of divorce, puts it, "When children of divorce become adults, they are badly frightened that their relationships will fail, just like the most important relationship in their parents' lives failed. They mature with a keen sense that their growing-up experiences did not prepare them for love, commitment, trust, marriage, or even for the nitty-gritty of handling and resolving conflicts. . . . [T]hey are haunted by powerful ghosts from their childhoods that tell them that they, like their parents, will not succeed."[1]

Those fears are well founded. A number of surveys and studies have discovered that adult children of divorce are far more likely to get divorced themselves than are the adult children of intact families (i.e., families in which Mom and Dad did not divorce).[2] Depending on the survey, the child of divorce is at least two to four times more likely to divorce.

As if the divorce statistics weren't scary enough, the children of divorce are also more prone to other problems. For instance, they are twice as likely as children from intact homes to drop out of high school. They're twice as likely to become teen parents and unmarried parents. They're also far more likely to become dependent on welfare as adults.[3]

THERE IS HOPE

If you're reading this as an adult child of divorce, you're probably familiar with those statistics and the fear they produce.

You may be wondering, as I suggested at the beginning, how you can possibly be expected to paint a picture of something you've never seen—how you can have a strong, intact marriage when your own parents' marriage failed. And you're probably wondering whether this book can really help.

To you, the anxious reader, I have two things to say here at the outset. *First and foremost, yes, it is possible to break the cycle of divorce.* You *can* learn to create and maintain a healthy, strong, lasting marriage relationship. You *can* learn to paint that picture of something you haven't yet seen. There is real hope for your future and your marriage.

Second, it may encourage you to know that I don't address this topic as an academic who simply thought it would make for an interesting study. No, this book is rooted in my own experience and grows out of my own passion and need to know. You see, I, too, am an adult child of divorce. My father actually went through three divorces, my mother through two.

So, like you, as I met and fell in love with the person of my dreams, I had to wonder whether I could enjoy a healthy marriage. When conflicts arose after the wedding, I had to consider whether we could work through our differences.

Could I succeed where my parents had failed, or was I doomed to repeat their mistakes, their choices, . . . their patterns?

Because I was privileged to marry the most wonderful woman in the world, because of lessons I've learned along the way (from my mom and others), and especially because of God's grace, I will have been married for 27 years by the time this book releases, and the future looks even brighter than the past. My wife, Cindy, and I are living proof that the cycle of divorce can be broken. My parents' marital failure does *not* have to dictate the fate of our relationship, and your parents' divorce doesn't have to doom your marriage either.

You, an adult child of divorce, can create a strong, lasting marriage. When conflicts arise between you and your spouse, the two of you can work through them and find healthy resolution. In the face of other challenges (health issues, the everyday trials of life, etc.), you and your mate can draw closer together rather than drifting apart.

Walk with me through the pages of this book and let me show you how to start a new cycle in your family. It all begins, as we'll see in chapter 1, with recognizing that because you grew up in a home of divorce, you also grew up facing a greater challenge than you may have imagined. For, realize it or not, even in the twenty-first century, you're facing the effects of a curse.

Questions for Reflection and Application

1. As a child of divorce, what is your greatest fear in getting or being married yourself?

2. What do you think a healthy marriage should look like? Why?

3. Right now, on a scale from 1 (no confidence at all) to 10 (absolutely certain), how confident are you that you can break the cycle of divorce and build a strong and lasting marriage?

Chapter One

Under the Curse

The picture is clear that children and adults whose parents divorce really are living under a curse. And the curse spreads from generation to generation until someone manages to break it and establish new patterns.

In the introduction, I had you imagine being asked to paint a landscape that you'd never seen. Now let me give you another word picture to help you understand what adult children of divorce (ACODs) are up against.

Today, when we hear the word *curse*, we envision a horror movie or an image out of a Stephen King–type novel of someone standing in a graveyard at midnight, shaking a bloody chicken leg at us. Those are imaginary pictures that may haunt us but don't really touch us. But the "curse" you and I grew up with, if you're from a divorced family, is real.

In the Bible, when it speaks of someone's being "under a curse," the image is that of a stream that has been dammed up. Much of the Holy Land is arid. So streams flowing with fresh, life-giving water—when they can be found—are vitally important.

Imagine, then, that you're stumbling through a desert, exhausted and thirsty. Your water gave out days ago, and your mouth feels as dry as the sand. The relentless sun bakes your brain and blinds your eyes. The bleached-white bones of a long-dead camel remind you of how perilous your own situation is.

What keeps you going? What gives you hope? You know that somewhere up ahead—not too far now—is a spring-fed stream. Even in the driest times, this stream is known to keep flowing. If you can just get to it, this water will give you new strength and energy, refreshing you enough to complete your return to civilization.

At last, the stream comes into view as you crest a hill! At first you're afraid it might be a mirage. But as you lurch down the far side of the hill, gathering speed as you go and drawing closer and closer, you recognize that it is, indeed, the stream you've been counting on to keep you alive.

Stumbling to the stream's edge, you want to just wade in and immerse yourself in the cooling water. As you plunge in, though, the realization hits you—there is no water! Finding yourself in the middle of a dry, rocky creek bed, it dawns on you that you had heard no sound of running water as you approached.

What could have happened? Where's the water?

Driven by your thirst, you head "upstream" to search for the problem. You know that the spring feeding the stream is not supposed to be all that far away. Staggering with weakness and fatigue, you move out.

Before long, your journey takes you around a hill and up a small valley. And there you find the problem. A short distance from where the water springs out of the hill, before it has had a chance to grow into a stream, someone has built a tall, solid dam. The flow of water down the hill, into the valley, and then into the familiar stream has been cut off.

And there you have a picture of what the Bible means when it says someone is under a curse. The flow of life-giving love and encouragement has been cut off. The person is without hope in a "dry" land.

Everyone and everything below the dam is now without water in a dry and barren land.

And there you have a picture of what the Bible means when it says someone is under a curse. The flow of life-giving love and encouragement has been cut off. The person is without hope in a "dry" land. It's a picture of life-giving water, dammed up and out of reach.

ACODs like me grew up under this kind of curse. The flow of love, support, and good modeling of a healthy marriage that should have been theirs from two parents while growing up was instead cut off. And they live with the effects of that curse every day of their lives.

Perhaps you're thinking that *curse* is too strong a word to use in describing the impact when parents divorce. Don't try telling that to Allison.

ALLISON'S STORY

As a young girl, Allison watched her parents fight constantly. Her mom took to drinking, and Allison became the de facto parent. Then one day her dad caught her mom in bed with another man, and the marriage was over.

Allison now found herself torn in half. She loved both parents, but any loyalty she showed toward one of them was seen by the other as treason. Her father sued for custody and got it, but it soon became clear that he was only using her to get revenge on her mother.

When Allison went to spend time with her mom, Mom's new boyfriend saw Allison as competition for Mom's time and attention. So he berated her, kept her under his thumb, and generally tried to make her life miserable.

At age 15, Allison came to the realization that the guidance and care she still desperately needed from loving parents were never going to be hers. She was on her own.

Not surprisingly, Allison developed a chronic mistrust of relationships. How could she believe anyone who claimed to love her (as her parents had)? How could she trust that others wouldn't try to manipulate her? And how was she supposed to get over the anger? She became convinced that if she ever did marry, she was doomed to repeat her parents' history.[1]

Life Under the Curse

Allison's case highlights what life under the curse of being an ACOD is like. Seeing her parents divorce makes an Allison wonder if any marriage can survive. Knowing that one of her parents committed infidelity makes her doubt that any marital partner can ultimately be trusted. Or maybe, she thinks, she herself will eventually follow her mother's example, even though that's the last thing she would intend right now.

In addition, if Allison marries but feels that her spouse doesn't understand her anxieties and so can't offer the support she needs, that, too, could become a source of constant tension in the home.

Statistically, studies have shown that children of divorce suffer from more depression, anxiety, low self-esteem, feelings of rejection, drug and alcohol abuse, delinquency, poor interpersonal relationships, and criminality than children from intact homes.[2] Sixty-five percent of children from divorced families will never build a good post-divorce relationship with their fathers. Thirty percent will be unable to develop a good post-divorce relationship with their mothers.[3]

As cited in the Introduction, ACODs are also at least two

to four times as likely to divorce as are adult children of intact homes. (And if both spouses come from divorced homes, the odds that they will divorce increase by *189* percent.[4])

The effects of divorce on childhood happiness may be more pronounced than the effects of death and may have deeper consequences on quality of life or emotional health.

Statistics like these led one expert on the impact of divorce to write, "The effects of divorce on childhood happiness may be more pronounced than the effects of death and may have deeper consequences on quality of life or emotional health."[5]

As further evidence of the dramatic impact of parental divorce, consider the case of Frank and Betty. They met at college and became romantically and sexually involved. Then Betty discovered she was pregnant. They lived together until they graduated, then got married shortly afterward. But it was an unhappy marriage, marked by emotional abuse, constant fighting, and failure to resolve conflicts. After eight years of this, the relationship ended in divorce.

And not one bit of that was surprising.

Why? Because 20 years earlier, Frank's parents had met in college, become romantically involved, and gotten pregnant.

Then they had married and fought amid emotional abuse and unresolved conflict. Finally, after 10 years of contention, they had divorced.[6]

I could go on and on, but the picture is clear that children and adults whose parents divorce really are living under a curse. And the curse spreads from generation to generation until someone manages to break it and establish new patterns.

My Story

I, too, should have been one of those stories of living under the curse of divorce and the aching thirst it creates. My mother had been divorced once before meeting my father. My dad left my mom and divorced her when their three boys were all still under the age of three. He would go on to divorce twice more.

My own marriage, therefore, should have been a train wreck waiting to happen. To say I was a mess growing up would be putting the case mildly. As a young boy and then a teen, I longed for my dad's presence in my life. I was painfully aware—especially in my high school years—that other guys had dads who played catch with them, helped with their homework, attended their ball games to cheer them on, and then took them out for burgers afterward. *Am I really such a rotten kid,* I wondered, *that my dad couldn't stand to be here and do those things for me (and my brothers)?*

Like any child of divorce, I grew up asking all the "why" questions. I grew up with a model of marriage that said it's not permanent. I grew up with anger and frustration and got in trouble as a result. Early in dating, I broke off my relationships with girls whenever the girls started to get serious, because I didn't want to be hurt again.

By God's grace and with the help of a number of people, however, I beat the odds. I've been able to break the curse and avoid the wreck. I have a strong marriage, and I've worked hard at being a loving father to my two girls. I'm far from perfect in any way, but I have discovered that there's a way to "reverse the curse" and move toward the commitment and caring you and I really long for.

This book is designed to help you break the pattern, or cycle, of divorce as well—the curse you grew up with—and experience success in life and in marriage. To begin, let's look at some of the common manifestations of living under the curse in case you have any doubts about whether you're still under its spell.

QUESTIONS FOR REFLECTION AND APPLICATION

1. How well can you relate, as an ACOD, to the word picture of thirsting for life-giving water, water that was cut off by your parents' divorce? Why?

2. In your own words, why are ACODs so prone to repeating their parents' mistakes and getting divorced themselves?

3. How important is it to you that I, though a fellow ACOD, am able to write from the experience of having built a lasting marriage? Why?

Chapter Two

Manifestations of the Curse, Part I

Logically, of course, there's no way that kids are responsible for their parents' divorce. . . . But the heart can stubbornly resist even what its own brain tells it, and nowhere is this more true than in children who eventually grow into ACODs.

I've stated and illustrated that adult children of divorce are under a "curse," meaning they've grown up with life-giving elements "dammed up" or missing from their lives. Does that mean, however, that their parents were "evil" or purposely set out to create a deficit and life-shaping need in their lives? Of course not. As you'll see later in this book, my mother's steady, consistent love was a key to eventually reversing the curse in my life. Good people can and do divorce.

My mother didn't want my brothers and me to come up to a dry stream—but it happened, and it happens to ACODs today. Let's look at a number of reflections of the "curse" we can grow up under. What are some of the common negative effects, or manifestations, of this curse? Learning more about them can help you to better understand just how deeply you have been touched personally by the scourge of divorce in your family.

Gaining that understanding is vital. Why? *Because these manifestations, if left unchecked, can be the very things that will wreck your own marriage and continue the cycle of divorce in your family.*

From my own experience and research, I've identified 12 common manifestations of the curse. We'll take a brief look at each of them in these next three chapters. Then, in chapter 5, we'll see how to overcome these problems, *reverse the curse*, and build a strong and lasting marriage.

Isolation

People in prison are there because they've been convicted of doing something wrong, something illegal. They're sent to prison as punishment for their crimes, and prison life is harsh, indeed. But what do the guards do to punish inmates who cause trouble, who break the rules or get into fights and so earn the *strictest* treatment?

They put them into solitary confinement.

Prison officials know that short of physical torture, "solitary" is about the harshest thing they can do to a person. Oh, the prisoner might actually like it at first. He may feel safer, calmer, and glad to be away from other prisoners who were irritating or even threatening him. But that attitude soon changes.

Before long, the inmate starts to feel lonely. Whether he

realizes it or not, he was created for human contact. And the more time he spends in isolation, the more he will crave that contact. If he stays alone for weeks or months because he's considered dangerous to guards or other prisoners, he may begin to suffer serious consequences. One psychiatrist who studied inmates in solitary said that he saw effects ranging from "memory loss to severe anxiety to hallucinations to delusions and, under the severest cases of sensory deprivation, people go crazy."[1]

These manifestations, if left unchecked, can be the very things that will wreck your own marriage.

All of that to say that isolation is punishment for human beings, pure and simple. There's no worse feeling than to feel that you're all alone in facing life and its struggles. Scripture affirms this when it says, "Two are better than one. . . . If one falls down, his friend can help him up. But pity the man who falls and has no one to help him up!"[2]

Yet, sadly, ACODs often put themselves in just such a prison of their own making. They withdraw from others emotionally, psychologically, and physically—even from their own spouses and children.

Why? They've been badly hurt by one or both of the most important people in their early lives (Mom and Dad), and they're afraid of being hurt badly again if they let someone else get close. Or they fear they may repeat the hurtful behaviors of their parents and end up harming loved ones themselves. Or because they grew up in homes of divorce, where they saw a powerful example of how *not* to build a healthy relationship, they may simply not know how to connect with other human beings in positive ways (my isolation of choice for years).

Of course, it's possible for the husband and wife to grow isolated from each other in any marriage. They get busy with work, hobbies, and social activities in their off hours. They may focus on their children, making less and less time for each other as the years go by. And nowadays, one or both may spend several hours a day surfing the Internet away from the family. But they don't usually set out to grow isolated.

With ACODs, however, while their isolation may not be consciously planned, it *is* intentional, for one or all of the reasons described above.

To get a better sense of whether you have a tendency to isolate yourself from friends and loved ones, answer the questions in the following self-test.

Isolation Self-Test:

- Whenever you have conflict with someone close to you, is your first impulse to "run away and hide"?

- Do you feel that it's emotionally dangerous to share your feelings, fears, and hopes with your spouse?
- Do you believe, even if you never say it aloud to anyone, that your friends and spouse will abandon you sooner or later?

If your answer to any one of those questions is *yes*, you probably have a tendency to isolate yourself. If your honest answer to any two or all three is *yes*, you almost certainly are prone to isolation.

UNHEALTHY FAMILY SECRETS

Another closely related problem commonly experienced by children of divorce is the tendency to be secretive about certain details of family life. Many times, children who grow up in broken homes learn that hiding embarrassing family information is better, in order to keep up appearances. In this case, the truism holds: Things are not always as they seem.

Certainly you know of some examples of "secrets" that are actually well-known, and kept with a wink and a nod. Al Capone, for example—the famous Chicago gangster from the 1920s—carried a business card that identified him as a used furniture dealer, even though everyone in the city knew his real occupation.

Then there are other secrets that are carefully hidden but

need to be revealed. There was, for instance, the case of the youth leader who was loved and respected by all in his parish, yet he turned out to be a child molester. Unfortunately, that terrible secret didn't come to light until after many children had been hurt.

Families are good at keeping unhealthy secrets, too. In one family, the wife and mother carried on an affair with a neighbor man. To say that she and her husband had a strange marriage would be an understatement, but the fact is that within their family, her relationship with the neighbor was known by all (though never discussed), including their four children. This secret was never revealed to the world outside the family, however, and so it and the affair persisted for years. (Eventually, the husband and wife did divorce.)

ACODs are highly prone to keeping unhealthy family secrets. And marital infidelity is just one of the dark secrets they may keep—secrets that likely contributed to their parents' breakup. Other all-too-common secrets include: the fact that their parents fought all the time. The fact that one parent is/was an alcoholic or drug abuser. The fact that one parent is/was a sexual abuser. The fact that one parent battered the other. The fact that the family struggled financially or was poor.

Why do ACODs tend to keep such terrible secrets? One obvious answer is shame. If a parent did something that led to divorce, like have an affair, there's naturally some embarrassment for all the family members. They understandably would just as soon not have the rest of the world be aware of what happened. It's the same situation when any loved one has done something to bring disgrace to the family.

The habit of keeping unhealthy secrets is usually learned from one or both parents.

A second reason is that, like most habits, the habit of keeping unhealthy secrets is usually learned from one or both parents. Chances are that they tried to keep secret whatever problems they had, including those that led to their divorce. So their children learned that that's the way to handle problems, and the habit carried over into adulthood.

Finally, ACODs keep unhealthy secrets because they, themselves, have things to hide. They may have developed some of their parents' faults, or they may have problems of their own that they think they need to hide. So, in an attempt to protect their own reputation, they try to keep the truth buried away.

To gain a better understanding of whether you might have a tendency to keep unhealthy family secrets, answer the following questions:

Unhealthy Family Secrets Self-Test:

- Are you still today carrying some secret about your family of origin that you're unable to reveal to anyone else?
- Do you have any dark secrets of your own that you've never revealed to anyone?
- Do you have any person in your life—a spouse or a friend—with whom you can be completely candid?

If your answer to either of the first two questions is *yes*, you are in fact keeping unhealthy family secrets. And if your answer to the last question is *no*, you're going to have trouble overcoming this self-destructive habit.

False Guilt

Another common manifestation of the curse of family divorce is false guilt. Many are the children who, when their parents split, come to believe that they (the children) are somehow responsible. And that false sense of guilt is often carried into adulthood.

My older brother, Joe, was not quite three years old when our parents divorced. He played no part in our dad's decision to walk out on the family, yet he quickly became convinced, even by age five or six, that he was somehow at fault. All our mom's reassurances that he was not to blame failed to budge him from this conviction. (And my grandmother's coolness toward "Little Joe" because he shared our father's name and looks didn't help at all.)

I noticed another good example of this manifestation recently (actually, while I was writing this) on television. Part of the backstory on USA Network's popular detective show *Monk* is that when Adrian Monk and his brother, Ambrose, were still young children, their father abandoned the boys and their mother. In the particular episode I was watching, *both* brothers finally admitted that for more than 30 years, each had felt responsible for their father's leaving.

Now, the show is fictional, but based on my personal experience and on talking with hundreds of ACODs over the years, I know that that story line was true to life. For more than 30 years, *each* could easily have been carrying that false load of guilt.

Logically, of course, children are not the responsible parties when it comes to their parents' divorce. The decision to end a marriage is made by the adults, and they alone are accountable for it. But the heart can stubbornly resist even what the brain tells it, and nowhere is this truer than in children who eventually grow into ACODs.

Why are ACODs so prone to false guilt, beginning with the tendency to feel responsible for their parents' divorce? The first reason is a deep feeling that when something as huge and terrible as your family's getting torn apart forever happens, *someone* must be to blame. But the children, who love Mom *and* Dad and are trying desperately to cling to them both, don't want to blame their parents. They *need* to see their parents as still loving and caring for them, still willing to sacrifice for them.

And so someone else has to take the blame and be found guilty; more often than not, the children assign the role to themselves.

Not surprisingly, people who consider themselves guilty of something as awful as driving their parents apart tend to feel badly about themselves.

A second reason is that in the confused logic of children, if they're responsible for their parents' breakup—if their bad behavior or failure to somehow please the parent who left is what caused the divorce—then there's hope they can find a way to "make things right" and bring Mom and Dad back together.

If I can just be a good-enough boy so that Mom isn't always getting upset with me . . .

If I can get good-enough grades in school to convince Dad that I'm not stupid . . .

If I just take good-enough care of the house so that Mom will see how much help I could be if she came home . . .

If I can hit home runs and win all my baseball games and make Dad proud of me . . .

This is the kind of thinking that often dominates the minds of children of divorce. And thinking like this that is forged in the natural self-centeredness of childhood usually carries on into adulthood, as strong as the finest steel. It can also become generalized to feeling guilty about most anything that goes wrong.

Not surprisingly, people who consider themselves guilty of something as awful as driving their parents apart tend to feel badly about themselves. *I must be a terrible person to have destroyed my parents' marriage,* they figure. And, feeling that way, they also find it easy to consider themselves unworthy of love, undeserving of happiness.

The result: False guilt tends to drive ACODs to isolate themselves from others. Genuine guilt, in contrast—which results when you've actually, intentionally done something wrong—leads a person toward repentance and a life that changes for the better.

To assess whether you might have a tendency to struggle with false guilt, answer the following questions:

False Guilt Self-Test:

- Whenever anything goes wrong, is your first impulse to blame yourself?

- Even when an objective analysis of a negative situation shows that you're not at fault, do you still tend to think that you *must* be guilty somehow?
- Deep down, do you feel responsible for your parents' breakup?

If your answer to any one of those questions is *yes*, you probably have a tendency to feel false guilt. If your honest answer to any two or all three is *yes*, you almost certainly are prone to false guilt. And if your answer to the last question in particular is *yes*, you are *absolutely* experiencing false guilt.

Fear-Based Procrastination

Yet another common manifestation of the curse falling on ACODs is fear-based procrastination. Lots of people procrastinate, of course, and fear—especially of failure—is often the primary motivator. But ACODs are even more prone to putting things off than the norm.

Chad is a fortunate young man—he has found the woman of his dreams in Jenny. But even though he loves her dearly and likes to envision making a life and starting a family with her, he can't bring himself to actually ask Jenny to marry him. He's terrified of "taking the plunge" and making that huge commitment. Chad, not coincidentally, is an adult child of divorce.

Missy is a college sophomore, and it's time for her to

declare a major and commit to a particular course of study. But she finds herself frozen by fear and unable to make a choice. *What if I make the wrong decision and end up hating my major?* she reasons. *I'll have wasted a year or more of my life and thousands of dollars.* Missy, too, is a young adult child of divorce.

> *When you know from personal experience just how much failure can hurt, you're naturally reluctant to expose yourself to the possibility of such pain again—and far more so than someone who has never experienced a significant failure.*

Why is procrastination especially pronounced among ACODs? Let me count the ways! In a given case, it may be any one of the following reasons, or maybe a combination of some or all of them.

First, the most important relationship in the ACOD's life—the marriage of his or her parents—ended in bitterly painful failure. So the ACOD can find himself or herself afraid to start something lest it, too, end in painful failure. When you know from personal experience just how much failure can hurt, you're naturally reluctant to expose yourself to the possibility of such pain again—and far more so than someone who has never experienced a significant failure.

Along the same lines, just the whole idea of making a wholehearted commitment to something is likely to induce fear. Giving yourself completely to someone or some thing can be a mortifying prospect to the ACOD, yet it's also the key to fully enjoying a marriage relationship or most any other experience. Thus, the ACOD can find himself or herself in an agonizing dilemma.

The ACOD's fear of failure may also be rooted in concern for his or her parents. After all, they've already suffered greatly from the demise of their marriage. *If I try this [marriage, career, etc.] and fail,* the ACOD may reason, *it will be yet another bitter disappointment for Mom/Dad. I don't want to be the cause of more pain for them!*

Finally, if a young ACOD like Chad or Missy is struggling with various issues, doubts, and insecurities brought on by his or her parents' divorce, he or she may simply have a hard time concentrating on the task at hand and making steady progress. The lingering effects of the divorce may be like a persistent low-grade fever that saps strength and the will to work from a person with a mild infection.

Note that this tendency to procrastinate—like all the manifestations of the curse, really—often gets taken to one extreme or the other. An ACOD who's in the habit of procrastinating may well be one of the worst procrastinators around. Making decisions and getting things done can be a major, daily struggle for such a person.

At the other extreme, the ACOD may become almost fanatical in resisting the harmful patterns of his or her parents. A prime example is the child of an alcoholic who vows never to take a single drink—who won't even take cough syrup that contains a small amount of alcohol and who (typically) condemns even the most moderate alcohol consumption by others.

In the area of procrastination, some ACODs will reason, *My mom was always afraid to get help to stop my dad from beating her.* I'll *never hesitate to get the help I need.* Or, *I've seen how fear keeps my older sibling from making decisions, and I can understand why, but* I'm *not going to let the collapse of our parents' marriage keep* me *from doing what needs to get done. No, sir.*

To gain a better understanding of whether you might have a bent toward fear-based procrastination, answer the following questions:

Fear-Based Procrastination Self-Test:

- When you're facing a significant decision, do you tend to make it in a prudent but timely way, or do you put if off as long as possible, even well past the stated deadline?
- When you're given an assignment at work or elsewhere, are the first thoughts that enter your mind pictures of potential failure or pictures of potential success?

- When you think of making major personal commitments, is your predominant feeling one of joy or one of dread?

If you tend to put off decisions as long as you can, to automatically picture yourself failing at anything new, or to dread making personal commitments (such as marriage), you definitely have a problem with fear-based procrastination.

LIVING WITH THE CURSE

So far we've looked at four common manifestations of the curse of growing up in a home of divorce. In the next two chapters, we'll look at eight more. But don't give up hope! You *can* reverse the curse and break the cycle of divorce, as we'll see soon in chapter 5.

QUESTIONS FOR REFLECTION AND APPLICATION

1. Which of the manifestations of the curse described in this chapter do you think is potentially the most harmful? Why?

2. To which of these manifestations can you relate most personally? Why?

3. What impact is that manifestation having on your life as an individual? On your marriage (if you're already married)?

Chapter Three

Manifestations of the Curse, Part II

Whenever a marriage ends in divorce, some seriously poor choices have been made along the way, and kids always learn and usually imitate what they've seen their parents do.

As mentioned at the start of the preceding chapter, one or more of the common manifestations of the curse of growing up in a home of divorce may sink your own marriage if you're not careful. But perhaps you didn't relate to any of the four described in that chapter. Don't think you're out of the woods yet—here are four more typical traits of ACODs:

Poor Choices

Any person can make poor choices. Unfortunately, people from divorced homes can be emotionally pushed toward making some really bad choices. I know; I certainly have made my share.

From late grade school on into high school, my twin brother,

Jeff, and I chose to hang out with a rough group of guys. We were constantly getting into trouble, and it seemed that one prank led to another and another. The magnitude of our actions increased as well.

The summer before Jeff and I started high school, late one night, our "gang" decided to break into a darkened house. We thought it was empty, still under construction. But, as it turned out, the home was finished and occupied—the owners just weren't there at the time.

Well, to make a long story short, some people noticed what we were up to and called the police. We all got caught in the act. Fortunately for us, because we were juveniles, we were all let go with a stern warning and a ride home in a squad car. But that wasn't bad enough—I've never forgotten the look of shock and disappointment on our mother's face as Jeff and I climbed out of that police cruiser at two o'clock in the morning.

If our older brother, Joe, along with a few other key people, hadn't intervened and given us a push out of that group of friends (a story I'll tell elsewhere in the book), there's no telling what might have become of us. Two of those guys, who never left our "gang," later spent time in prison for drugs. Another actually died of an overdose. As Scripture says, "Bad company corrupts good character."[1]

One of the poor choices made by many ACODs today is living with someone without benefit of marriage. There's a certain logic to such a decision; after all, if your parents' divorce makes you question your own ability to build a lasting marriage, why not make a "trial run" with a willing partner?

ACODs are rebelling against the pain and sense of betrayal that they feel. They're still hurting from their parents' breakup, and they can strike out in destructive—sometimes self-destructive—choices and behaviors.

Even apart from the moral issues surrounding cohabiting, however, it's a bad idea relationally and every other way. Research has shown that such couples are markedly less happy and less healthy than married couples. If cohabiting couples eventually marry, their likelihood of divorcing will be 46 percent higher than that of couples who marry without having first lived together.[2]

So why are ACODs prone to making poor choices? As with all the manifestations of the curse, the first and foremost reason is that this is what they've seen modeled by their parents. Whenever a marriage ends in divorce, even very good people have most likely made seriously poor choices along the way, and children learn and usually imitate what they've seen their parents do.

A second reason is that ACODs are rebelling against the

pain and sense of betrayal that they feel. They're still hurting from their parents' breakup, and they can strike out in destructive—sometimes self-destructive—choices and behaviors (or like me, turn anger at their situation into "legal" ways of hitting and hurting, from boxing to "knock them out cold" football).

A third reason can be that they're hungry for acceptance and a sense of belonging. Often feeling rejected by one (usually the noncustodial) parent or even both, they may be willing to do whatever is asked of them by someone who seems to offer love. If that someone is of the wrong sort, the result can be a whole string of bad decisions.

To help you discern whether you might have a problem with making poor choices, answer the following questions:

Poor Choices Self-Test:

- Looking back on your life as objectively as you can, do you see a pattern of making major decisions poorly?
- Have other people been seriously hurt by choices you've made?
- Based on your past decisions, do you feel confident about your ability to make good choices in the future?

If your honest answer to either of the first two questions is *yes*, and especially if you answer both in the affirmative, you've likely got a problem with making poor decisions. If you also respond *no* to the third question, you've certainly got an issue with poor choices.

FALSE STARTS

On a recent episode of the TV show *Inside the Actors Studio*, in which host James Lipton interviews successful actors, actresses, and directors, he began a new line of questioning with a famous actor by saying something like, "And now we come to a recurring theme on this program, the divorce of our guest's parents." And in fact it seems that there's news of another celebrity marriage breakdown every other week.

Some of these stars are known as much for their serial relationships as they are for their on-screen or on-stage work. Names like Madonna, Rosanne, Nicholas Cage, Angelina Jolie, Britney Spears, and Tom Cruise show up in the tabloids regularly. They've all been in multiple marriages and other pairings. And they're all ACODs.

But relationships are only one area where ACODs are prone to making false starts. You'll also see it in their attempts to break bad habits or establish good ones. The tendency shows up, too, in the multiple projects at home and at work that they start but somehow never finish.

These many new relationships, projects, and attempts at self-improvement are all always started with good intentions and high hopes. There's a genuine desire to succeed "this time." Yet time after time those hopes are dashed. A scripture says, "Hope deferred makes the heart sick,"[3] and that's a succinct, on-target description of what ACODs feel every time a false start comes to a bad end.

In the area of relationships, ACODs making false starts may be so desperate for love, acceptance, and security that they grab on to the first person who appears to offer them.

Why are ACODs so liable to make false starts? For one thing, as I've stated before, they've been badly hurt and are terribly afraid of being hurt again. But if they back out of a relationship before the other person has a chance to, they think (often subconsciously) they won't be hurt as badly. If they drop a project or an effort toward self-improvement, they avoid the pain of failure.

Of course, there's also the fact that ACODs making false starts are usually imitating their parents. Once again, it's a learned trait.

In the area of relationships, ACODs making false starts may be so desperate for love, acceptance, and security that they grab on to the first person who appears to offer them. When reality sets in, the love and acceptance may be only conditional and temporary, the security an illusion.

To get a better feel for your own tendency to make false starts, answer the following questions:

False Starts Self-Test:

- On a scale from 1 (poor) to 5 (excellent), how good have you been at following through on plans and commitments you've made?
- How confident are you of your ability to follow through in the future?
- Based on your experience, does the prospect of starting a new, close relationship fill you with expectation of a bright future or of another eventual heartbreak?

If your candid response to the first question is a 1, a 2, or even a 3, and if your answer to the second question is something like "Not very," you've likely got a problem with making false starts. If your answer to the last question is also an anticipation of heartbreak, you've definitely made a habit of false starts.

BROKEN COMMITMENTS

A close cousin to false starts is broken commitments. A false start often *ends* in a broken commitment. One example of this is the sad recent trend of more and more first marriages ending within the first five years. One writer, Pamela Paul, dubbed these "starter marriages," and she herself was divorced after less than a year of matrimony (and tries to say that's a good thing).

What do you suppose is the first risk factor for experiencing a "starter marriage" that Paul listed in her book on the subject? That's right, coming from a home where your parents divorced. Affirming what I've already said a number of times in this book, Paul points out that parents who divorced did not give their children role models for building and sustaining a healthy marriage. Instead, they modeled breaking the most important commitment in your life.

Another reason ACODs are especially prone to broken commitments is that they don't really like commitments. In their experience, commitments lead inevitably to disappointment and pain. Thus there's a tendency to make commitments only when they feel pressured into it and have no choice.

When they *do* make commitments, ACODs expect the other party to break them sooner or later. So, again, by breaking those commitments first themselves, they avoid (or at least lessen) the pain.

Are you likely to be a commitment breaker? To get an idea, answer the following:

Broken Commitments Self-Test:

- Do you have a pattern in your past of failing to follow through on commitments you've made?

- Have others told you they don't trust your promises?
- When you don't fulfill a commitment for whatever reason, do you tend to keep silent and hope people don't notice, perhaps also intentionally avoiding the person to whom you had made the pledge?

If you answer *yes* to even one of those questions, you've likely got a problem with breaking commitments. If you have to honestly say *yes* to two or all three, you're definitely finding it difficult to keep commitments.

Blaming Others

Have you ever known someone who, no matter what he does wrong, is always quick to point the finger of blame at someone else? He's never at fault. He could be caught red-handed doing something wrong and still claim that he's misunderstood and persecuted.

I know a man who was like this on the job. If someone pointed out that he spent too much time making personal phone calls, that person was insensitive and exaggerating to try to hurt him.

When this man failed to meet a deadline, it was because the project was more complicated than he had expected or the deadline wasn't reasonable.

When the man neglected to let his supervisor know that he

needed help to get his work done, the problem was that the supervisor had been "unavailable."

And when this man got nowhere in finding a mate, it was because none of the women he met were good enough to meet his standards. It was *their* fault things didn't work out.

ACODs genuinely feel powerless. After all, they couldn't keep the two most important people in their world together.

Some ACODs share this same tendency to blame others when things go wrong. When the problem is at work, a boss or co-workers or suppliers have to be at fault. When there are struggles in the marriage, the spouse or the in-laws are always to blame. If there are issues with their children, those children are being disrespectful and disobedient.

Why this propensity to blame others? For one thing, ACODs facing this aspect of the "curse" can genuinely feel powerless. After all, they couldn't keep the two most important people in their world together. They couldn't control what became of themselves after their parents' divorce—where they lived and whom they lived with and where they went to school. So they grew up feeling that the most vital things in life really are beyond their authority.

For another thing, others (Mom and/or Dad) caused their

greatest pain. It's easy and natural to assume, then, that others are also to blame when pain is experienced later in life.

Further, because of the pain that ACODs have experienced for years, they're understandably inclined to try to avoid more pain. And admitting you're to blame when you've done something wrong is painful. It hurts your pride. It also opens the door to still more pain in the form of a reprimand, a damaged relationship, or a loss of esteem in the eyes of someone you love.

Are you guilty of blaming others for your mistakes? To gain some insight into whether this is an issue for you, answer the following:

Blaming Others Self-Test:

- Looking back as objectively as you can, do you see a pattern of always pointing the finger at someone else when things go wrong?
- Have others ever told you that you seem to believe you can do nothing wrong?
- When was the last time that you accepted the blame, without argument, for something that wasn't done right or on time?

If your candid answer to the first or second question is *yes*, or if your answer to the last question is "A long time ago" or

"Never," you probably have a tendency to blame others. If you give those responses to two or all three of the questions, there's no doubt that blaming others is a concern for you.

Living with the Curse II

In this chapter and the last, we've now covered eight common manifestations of the curse of growing up in a home of divorce. I wish that this exhausted the list of common problems that I've seen and experienced myself. Sadly, that's not the case. In the next chapter, we'll look at the last four of these traits that are common to ACODs before turning to hope and help.

Remember, the good news is coming. Starting in chapter 5, we'll explore how to reverse the curse and break the cycle of divorce in your family.

QUESTIONS FOR REFLECTION AND APPLICATION

1. Which of the manifestations of the curse described in this chapter do you think is potentially the most harmful? Why?

2. To which of these manifestations can you relate most personally? Why?

3. What impact is that manifestation having on your life as an individual? On your marriage (if you're already married)?

Chapter Four

Manifestations of the Curse, Part III

It's one thing to let another's words pass in one ear and out the other. But to truly take in and wrestle with that person's point of view, desires, and expectations is tough stuff for the already insecure.

We've now seen eight common manifestations of the curse of growing up in a home of divorce. These are the habits that can weaken the foundation of your own marriage if you don't do something to overcome them. And we're not done yet. In over 25 years of working with couples and singles—and in my own life—I've seen four more typical traits of ACODs that we need to explore, starting with one that can be among the most damaging:

Smoldering Anger

It takes no great insight to observe that there are lots of angry people in the world today. From road rage on the highways to teens shooting up their schools to red-faced spouses screaming at each other in the middle of the night, anger seems to be all around us. Some of those people are simply out of control, but many have good reason for their rage. And among them are the adult children of divorce.

Jerry's parents divorced when he was still in grade school. He had seen and heard them argue all his life—often and at high volume. The peace never lasted long in their home. Still, when his parents went their separate ways, it came as quite a blow to Jerry.

The breakup of their home was only the start of Jerry's struggles, however. His father soon disappeared from his life altogether. Jerry felt betrayed and abandoned. How could his own dad turn his back on him completely?

Before long, Jerry was acting out in school. He grew surly at home, when he communicated at all. As time went by, still with no contact from his father, Jerry developed into an angry young man.

Children who go through their parents' divorce—at any age—also tend to get and remain angry at those parents, especially the one perceived as having pushed for the divorce.

As with the other manifestations of the curse, one reason ACODs are prone to anger is that they often saw it demonstrated by their parents as they were growing up. Marriages that end in divorce are often loud and angry long before the final split occurs. And children observing such behavior learn that that's how conflicts get handled.

Children who go through their parents' divorce—at any age—also tend to get and remain angry at those parents, especially the one perceived as having pushed for the divorce. That parent, more than anyone else (unless the ACOD is blaming himself or herself), is responsible for destroying the ACOD's sense of security and normalcy. Many ACODs have never gotten over that feeling of betrayal.

Of course, the parent who then moved out—who became far less of a presence in the child's life and maybe even disappeared altogether (like Jerry's father)—often became an object of anger as well. And in many cases, the ACOD has never forgiven that parent, never moved beyond the intense anger. How bad is that? In God's Word we're told: "But whoever hates his brother is in the darkness and walks around in the darkness; he does not know where he is going, because the darkness has blinded him."[1] In other words, our anger can push us deeper into that desert land of the "curse," further from the life-giving love and light we need.

This anger toward a parent can also become anger toward life in general because it hasn't treated the ACOD well or given him the "breaks" that other people get. *Why couldn't my parents have stayed together like So-and-So's?* the ACOD reasons. *I'm at least as good a person as her. Why did she get to have a parent at every soccer game, a dad to walk her down the aisle at her wedding?*

If you have any doubts about whether there's anger smoldering just beneath your own surface, answer these questions:

Smoldering Anger Self-Test:

- Do you have at least occasional feelings of anger or even hatred toward one or both of your parents?
- Do you get angry with others easily, often for no apparent reason?
- Has anyone close to you suggested that you have a problem with anger?
- Do you frequently get angry with yourself?

If your answer to one or two of those questions is *yes,* you likely have an issue with anger. If your honest response to three or all four is *yes,* you have a definite problem with unresolved anger.

NOT REALLY LISTENING

Another common trait of ACODs is not really listening to others. And failing to listen can damage relationships.

I think of Matt, the man who said that at the relatively young age of 34, he had already been married three times. Why so much marital failure so quickly? He claimed that it was because he was going bald and had been since high school. "My lack of hair is ruining my life!" he insisted. (Of course, if that were true, one could ask why all three women had married him in the first place.)

The fact is, however, that Matt was told repeatedly that he was obsessing over his hair and that it wasn't that big a deal to them (his wives). But he simply wouldn't listen. He had his mind made up, and that was all there was to it. The loving and reassuring words of three different wives were like water rolling off the proverbial duck's back.

Why does a failure to listen characterize so many ACODs? Reason number one is, again, parental example. Moms and dads in troubled marriages are often consumed with their own problems. To really listen to someone else requires shifting their focus to that other person. But when they're self-absorbed, wrapped up in their own troubles, such a shift usually doesn't happen.

Another reason is that, as stated earlier, ACODs can lack self-confidence. And really listening to someone else, especially someone with an opposing point of view or a different agenda, demands self-confidence and even courage. It's one thing to let another's words pass in one ear and out the other. But to truly take in and wrestle with that person's point of view, desires, and expectations is tough stuff for the already insecure.

To gauge your own propensity to not really listen, respond honestly to the following questions:

Not Really Listening Self-Test:

- Do people regularly have to make sure they have your attention before they start talking to you?
- Does your mind usually wander when others are talking to you?
- Do you often interrupt people who are speaking to you in order to interject your own point of view?
- Do you have trouble remembering the details of a conversation five minutes after it's over?

If your candid answer to one or two questions is *yes,* you could learn to listen better. If you say *yes* to three or all four questions, you have a major issue with not really listening.

Unending Arguments

He says black; she shouts white. He wants fish; she craves steak. He longs to buy the hot new sports car; she insists on the sensible used station wagon. He wants to arrive at social events 10 minutes early; she prefers to be fashionably late. And every time they lock horns, the arguing continues until one or both of them simply run out of energy.

It seems that no matter the subject, they're at opposite ends of the spectrum, and never the twain shall meet.

All couples disagree from time to time, of course. But ACODs are inclined to argue more, and in many cases they seem to be in perpetual discord with their spouses and/or others closest to them. Why this unpleasant and relationship-wrecking tendency?

We start, once again, with parental example. Growing up in a home that breaks apart because of divorce means being exposed to a lot of arguing. It's often frequent and loud arguing. And it's a pattern that leads, in the case of ACODs, to the death of the marriage.

All couples disagree from time to time, of course. But ACODs are inclined to argue more, and in many cases they seem to be in perpetual discord with their spouses and/or others closest to them.

For ACODs, then, arguing loud and long is the normal way to handle disagreements. They often don't know how to resolve conflict in healthful ways. They've never learned to "fight" fairly and respectfully.

As noted earlier, ACODs also suffer from low self-esteem

and feelings of insecurity. This means, among other things, that they have an inordinate need to be "right" when they're at odds with someone else. If they can win the argument, they feel better about themselves, at least temporarily. If they lose, on the other hand, it only confirms their poor opinion of themselves.

Further, we've already looked in this chapter at how ACODs also tend to be angry and to not really listen to others. Those things being true, it's not surprising that they often end up in the middle of arguments. They were mad and inattentive to start with! And they're ticking off the people who live with them.

To get a handle on your own tendency to engage in endless arguments, answer these questions:

Unending Arguments Self-Test:

- When you have a difference of opinion with someone, is your first instinct to argue or to seek a meeting of the minds?
- Has anyone ever described you as "feisty" or said you're hard to get along with?
- Can you recall a day in the last two weeks when you *didn't* have at least one argument with someone?
- Based on your experience, would you say that you have good skills in resolving disagreements with those closest to you?

If your first instinct is to argue; if you answer *yes* to the second question, *no* to the third, and/or *no* to the last—these are indicators of a tendency to argue. If you give the negative response to two or more questions, this is a definite issue for you.

SEEING ONLY AN IMPERSONAL GOD

Late in the night of April 14, 1912, Third Officer Charles Victor Groves stood watch on the deck of his ship, the *Californian*, in the middle of the North Atlantic. His lumbering freighter was uneventfully going about its business of transoceanic commerce.

Then, out of the dark, came a huge, brilliantly lit apparition. Racing through the ocean at nearly full speed, the RMS *Titanic* quickly loomed larger and larger on the horizon. Even from a distance of 10 miles, the giant luxury liner on its maiden voyage from Southampton, England, to New York filled Groves with wonder.

As Groves watched in amazement, the *Titanic* seemed to fly by his ship. He remarked later, "I felt terribly small in comparison to its greatness." Neither Groves nor anyone else knew that the *Titanic* and all 2,209 souls aboard were only minutes from disaster.

As the *Titanic* flew by Groves that fateful night, its passengers and crew were seemingly unaware of his presence in the same patch of ocean. The few on board the mighty liner who noticed the *Californian* likely took little (if any) note of the nondescript cargo ship.

Many ACODs today can relate to what Third Officer Groves must have felt that evening. When they think of the mighty God of the universe, they see Him as big, impersonal, and vaguely aware of their existence at best. If He's involved in their lives at all, it's only as He "flies by" on His way to deal with matters that He considers more important.

From such painful experience, it's easy to conclude that God is uncaring or incapable of helping.

Why are ACODs prone to viewing God as cold and impersonal? Well, for starters, if they were old enough when it happened, they probably prayed to Him as their parents' marriage was breaking apart, imploring Him to keep them together. And what good did that do? Whatever else they might have prayed about in their lives, that had been their most important request, and all to no avail.

From such painful experience, it's easy to conclude that God is uncaring or incapable of helping. And if He couldn't or wouldn't help them and their families with that most urgent need, why trust that He would meet any other?

But thinking of God as uncaring or incapable can be

painful, too. If He doesn't care or can't help, we really are on our own, aren't we? So it becomes easier to think of Him as impersonal. That's just the way He is—like the *Titanic*, big and powerful and on His way to somewhere else.

That's a sad perspective because, as common sense as well as scientific studies have shown, people who believe in God and enjoy a personal, daily relationship with Him are happier and healthier, with a greater sense of purpose in life and hope for the future. They're better able to take on life's challenges and overcome its obstacles.

To gauge whether you might be looking at God as an impersonal being, answer the following questions:

Seeing Only an Impersonal God Self-Test:

- If someone asked you whether God answers prayer, would you say *yes* or *no*?
- Do you regularly pray to God about your own needs and desires?
- When your thoughts first turn to God, do you see Him as warm and personal or as cold and distant?
- Would you describe most of your experiences with God as positive or negative?

If you answer *no* to either of the first two questions, you likely view God as impersonal (no matter how you would describe your theology). If you candidly answer *no* to both, and if you also view Him as distant and/or consider your experiences with Him to be mostly negative, then you're certainly viewing Him as impersonal.

Now for Some Good News

At last we've covered all 12 of the manifestations of the curse of being an ACOD that I see most often. If you're an ACOD, the chances are good that you can relate to one or more of them. But while these last three chapters have been a necessary if long stretch of "bad" news, we're now ready for some good news.

Starting in the next chapter, we'll begin to look at how to overcome the curse, including these troublesome traits so common to us ACODs. We'll see that there *is* hope for the future and that we *don't* have to repeat our parents' marital failures. We can learn, we can grow, and with God's help we can make better choices.

I trust you'll agree that that's good news, indeed.

Questions for Reflection and Application

1. Which of the manifestations of the curse described in this chapter do you think is potentially the most harmful? Why?

2. To which of these manifestations can you relate most personally? Why?

3. What impact is that manifestation having on your life as an individual? On your marriage (if you're already married)?

Chapter Five

Reversing the Curse

We need to know that we are loved with a love that will not fade, will not weaken, and will never abandon us. But as children of divorce, life has made us afraid that such love simply does not exist. And I'm here to tell you that such love does exist.

After reading through all those common manifestations of the curse of growing up in a home of divorce, you may be thinking that as an ACOD, you're doomed to fail at marriage. That certainly was the thinking of a woman named Carrie.

"I grew up watching my parents fight constantly," Carrie said. "They divorced when I was 15." And sure enough, Carrie's own marriage ended in a messy divorce after just six years.

Funny thing, though: Carrie has a sister, Cheryl. And even though Cheryl grew up in that same acrimonious environment and witnessed the same bitter divorce of their parents, she was still happily married, at 13 years and counting, at the time Carrie made her remarks.[1]

Two sisters—twins, even—both ACODs, yet entirely different outcomes in their own marriages. What does this tell us? Well, one obvious lesson is that while the ACOD curse presents a huge obstacle to marital success, it is by no means an insurmountable obstacle. It can be overcome.

In short, you can build a strong and lasting marriage despite your parents' divorce. You *can* break the cycle.

But how can you go about that? How can you defeat the odds, reverse the curse, and achieve something that eluded your own parents? That's what this chapter and the rest of this book will show you. And it begins with grasping and making daily use of a fundamental truth.

Choose to Use Your Power

Coming out of a home of divorce, you've undoubtedly experienced a lot of pain and even trauma. You have pictures burned into your memory—of parents fighting with each other, yelling at each other, or maybe giving each other the cold, silent treatment. Perhaps you've even got pictures of your mom and dad physically abusing each other.

You are not a slave to your past. What happened to your parents' marriage does not have to happen to yours.

Maybe your pictures include one parent lying to the other, cheating on the other, expressing outright hatred to the other, or finally walking out on the other. And maybe your pictures include some of your parents' frustration and anger and pain being taken out on you and your brothers and sisters.

Whatever pictures circle around and around in your memory, and whatever ill effects they seem to have produced on your ability to sustain a healthy marriage, *the truth of the matter is that you have a choice about how you will respond.* You are not a slave to your past. What happened to your parents' marriage does not have to happen to yours.

You can pick a different outcome and make it your reality.

This power to choose how we will respond to life's challenges is one of the greatest of God's gifts to the human race. One of my favorite stories in this regard comes from the Bible; it's the true story of a young king named Josiah.

In ancient days, the kingdom of Israel was divided in two following the death of Solomon. In both the northern and southern kingdoms that resulted, the rulers who followed Solomon and his father, the great King David, were mostly evil. They turned their backs on the God of Abraham and led the people in worshiping idols. One of the worst was Manasseh, the grandfather of Josiah.

Here's part of what the Scriptures say about Manasseh: "In both courts of the temple of the LORD, he built altars to all the starry hosts. He sacrificed his own son in the fire, practiced sorcery and divination, and consulted mediums and spiritists. He did much evil in the eyes of the Lord, provoking him to anger."[2]

Not surprisingly, Manasseh's son who followed him on the throne, Amon, imitated his dad's terrible practices. Here's some of what we read about him: "He did evil in the eyes of the Lord, as his father Manasseh had done. He walked in all the ways of his father; he worshiped the idols his father had worshiped, and bowed down to them."[3]

After Amon was murdered, the people made Josiah king at the ripe old age of eight! Now, given the track record of his grandpa and his dad, we might have expected him to carry out a lot of religious depravity as well. Call it the curse of growing up in a really evil family! After all, that was the family history, the model he had seen since his earliest days, the only way of life he knew.

Instead, however, we read this about Josiah: "He did what was right in the eyes of the Lord and walked in all the ways of his father David, not turning aside to the right or to the left."[4]

I've always wondered who or what influenced Josiah to take such a different path from that of his granddad and father. Was it a devout nurse or tutor? Could it have been his mother? Perhaps it began with Josiah's seeing, even as a child, the destructive impact that idol worship had on the people and society of Judah.

Whatever the reason, Josiah *chose* to leapfrog, if you will, the evil example of his immediate forbears and identify instead with his ancestor David, called in Scripture "a man after God's own heart." Josiah refused to be bound by the corrupt beliefs and practices of the kings who preceded him. He recognized the better path—the path of truth and of national health and well-being—and resolutely set out to follow it.

This power to choose a better path despite growing up in a divorced family is yours as well. No matter what your background or your present circumstances, regardless of what life or other people have thrown at you, you can decide to think, speak, and act in ways that build up rather than tear down relationships.

You are not a slave to your family's past, any more than was Josiah.

Let me make this truth very practical for you. Let's suppose, for the sake of illustration, that as an ACOD, you often manifest the trait of smoldering anger. Whenever you and your spouse have any kind of disagreement, even over matters that seem trivial in retrospect, you're soon shouting and out of control.

You know what's wrong. You realize now, after reading chapter 4, that much of your simmering anger is rooted in your parents' divorce. But it's a deeply ingrained habit, and you've been like that ever since their breakup. Nevertheless, you can choose to change. You can choose to respond to conflict with your spouse in a more healthful way.

Certainly this isn't easy. You might feel powerless to make such a choice—and especially to follow through on it with any kind of consistency. Later in this chapter, we'll look at where the power comes from. But understand that reversing the curse begins with exercising your will and *choosing* to do so.

FACE YOUR FEARS

As we saw in chapters 2-4, we ACODs are prone to a lot of fears because of our painful experiences. They motivate many of the behaviors that we identified as manifestations of the curse of growing up in a home of divorce. To overcome those manifestations, then, we need to face our fears.

If one of our parents betrayed the other, we fear that our spouse will betray us. If one parent abandoned the other, we fear that our spouse will abandon us as well. And ultimately, since our parents failed at marriage, we're afraid that we will, too.

Or maybe we're afraid that *we're* destined to be the betrayer, the abandoner, and ultimately the one who causes the failure, as if it's in our genetic makeup or it's our destiny.

Melody was an ACOD with these kinds of fears. Only 13 when her parents divorced, she watched her father marry the woman with whom he'd had his affair. Then, just three years later, he divorced that woman as well. After that, he disappeared from Melody's life.

Twelve years later, though now "happily" married, Melody lived in fear that *this* man she loved would abandon her, too. Husband Cliff was a hard worker and devoted to their marriage, but he was also quiet and emotionally distant—just as her father had been.

Fear made Melody suspicious and contentious. Though Cliff had done nothing to earn her distrust, when he came home at night, she would grill him about where he had been, what he'd been doing, and with whom. And despite his innocence and his reassuring answers, she just couldn't shake the fear that he would one day abandon her—again, just like her dad.[5]

How do we overcome these fears? *First, we need to remember that fears grow in dark places, and they shrink in the light of day*. Our private imaginations can be such dark places. Talking openly with our spouses about our fears, along with our needs and expectations, can bring them into the light.

If Melody, for instance, would talk candidly with Cliff about her fear of abandonment and how it prompted her to conduct those nightly interrogations, it could lead to greater understanding and patience on both sides. He might agree to stay in touch throughout the day; she could agree to bite her tongue. And they could both agree to be gentle with each other when one of them slipped up on a given day.

Second, we can work to gain some objectivity about our spouse and our marriage. Rather than accept the notion that we're bound to end up like our parents, we can write out a list of the ways in which we and our spouse are *not* like our parents—especially in those faults that contributed to their divorce. Then we can write out a list of those ways in which our marriage is *not* like our parents' marriage, particularly in its troubled aspects.

It's a matter of reprogramming our thinking, of focusing on—so we can build on—the positives in our lives rather than the negatives that grow out of a legacy of divorce.

Since most of us focus on people's shortcomings—our own as well as those of our spouse—it's also good to make another list of our (and perhaps our parents') strengths. One of the top items in that list should be our commitment to our spouse and to the relationship. Then we can make a list of our spouse's strengths and other positive attributes.

After we've made these lists, it's good to post them in prominent places in the home where we'll see them several times a day. The bathroom mirror, the refrigerator, and the computer screen are just some of the possibilities. And we can make multiple copies to post if need be.

Regularly refreshing our minds with these positive truths, just by glancing at our lists throughout the day, can help to chip away at and even counteract those fears. It's a matter of reprogramming our thinking, of focusing on—so we can build on—the positives in our lives rather than the negatives that grow out of a legacy of divorce.

Third, if we still struggle with our fears, we need to be willing to seek and accept help. A good friend who can hear us out and help us look at things more objectively can be a tremendous blessing. A professional counselor—one who shares our commitment to making our marriage work and be successful—can also offer valuable assistance.

Finally, spiritual resources can offer great comfort and even freedom from fear. I'll say more about this area in the last section of this chapter.

Adjust by Two Degrees

In overcoming the manifestations of the curse in our lives—choosing not to fail like our parents, facing our fears and the other principles discussed in this chapter—our natural human tendency is to want and think we *need* to make and see huge changes virtually overnight. For example, if our tendency for years has been to procrastinate, we'd like to be able to stop stalling and become super-productive the very next day.

In most cases, however, life doesn't work that way. Pastor and author Chuck Swindoll wrote a best-selling book a number of years ago called *Three Steps Forward, Two Steps Back,* and that's the way we usually make progress toward a positive goal. Or, as I like to put it, we need to aim to make just two-degree changes. Let me explain.

If you continue to make two-degree changes, you will change where you end up.

On a compass, two degrees isn't much of a change in direction. When you consider that a normal right or left turn onto a perpendicular street is a 90-degree change, a turn of only two degrees seems inconsequential. It's hardly worth noticing.

But if you continue to make two-degree changes over an extended time and distance, the ultimate result will be a huge change in where you end up.[6]

The potential impact of small changes got impressed unforgettably on my mind one summer day in a cramped, sticky-hot 727, sitting on the tarmac at the airport in Austin, Texas. My work requires a lot of air travel, so I'm well acquainted with long delays at the ticket counter, long delays at the security checkpoint, long delays at the gate waiting for the plane to come in, long delays . . . well, you get the picture.

On this memorable day, though, my flight had actually been pushed away from the gate on schedule. *I might even get home on time*, I mused. But no. After taxiing a mere 500 yards from the terminal, heading toward the runway, we suddenly came to a stop. The pilot came on the intercom and announced, "Folks, we just found out we have a paperwork issue we have to iron out. We'll be stopping here for a few minutes."

As I said, I know all about air travel delays. So I realized that the phrase "a few minutes" could mean "anytime between now and when your youngest child graduates from college, falls in love, gets married, and gives birth to your new grandkid." And I normally stay calm and use the time in that aluminum tube to read, write, or do correspondence on my laptop. But when my battery ran out, and after sitting next to this stranger for what was becoming a very long time, I decided to strike up a conversation with my seatmate.

It turned out that he was an engineer from the Houston area. Jumping to a logical conclusion, I asked if he worked for one of the oil companies.

"No, I work for NASA," he replied.

Well, I'm sure that in the 60 minutes that followed, he came to deeply regret having told me that. As a kid growing up in the Apollo period of manned space flight, culminating in the first walk on the moon by Neil Armstrong and Buzz Aldrin, I had dreamed of becoming an astronaut. Now here I was, talking with a genuine rocket scientist who could answer all my questions about space flight!

And ask I did. To his credit, the man patiently responded, even telling me some behind-the-scenes stories that I took in like a kid watching his favorite Saturday-morning cartoon. I was having a great time!

Then I asked a question that I considered simple but that the engineer saw marked me as a real novice. "What are the tolerances you build into the trajectory for a moon flight?" I said. "For example, after you blast off, could you be off target just a little, maybe two degrees, and not have it be such a huge problem?"

The man knew the basic answer but wanted to show me exactly how crazy my idea was. So he whipped out his briefcase and pulled out his handheld calculator, which looked like a Cray supercomputer stuffed into a box the size of a paperback novel. I could just hear my laptop saying, "Wow, that's what I want to be when I grow up!"

The man punched in the "very approximate" distance from the earth to the moon of 225,740 miles, depending—of course—on the time of year and the apogee of the moon's orbit around us. Then his fingers flew over the keyboard for a bit as he plugged in the variables in some equation that I would never understand in a million years.

Finally he announced, "Be just two degrees off after

blastoff, and roughly taking the time and distance traveled into account, and you'll not only miss your point of orbital entry around the moon, but you'll actually miss the moon by about 11,121 miles." And he turned the calculator toward me so I could see he was not making this up.

Now, we've already established that I'm no rocket scientist, but even I knew that 11,000 miles and change was quite a lot! Just a two-degree error in your flight path and you could find yourself on the way to Mars instead of to the moon. Or, to state it differently in terms that apply to you and me every day, just a slight difference in direction, over time, can make a huge difference in where you end up.

This is as true in a positive sense as it is in a negative. And it gives us a great deal of hope in overcoming the manifestations of the curse.

Let's suppose, as before, that you really struggle with procrastination. Instead of doing the things you need to every day, you tend to sit for hours in front of the TV after coming home from work. Before you know it, it's time to go to bed each night, and the work remains undone. You recognize that this is a problem, and you figure you really ought to quit watching TV altogether, starting tonight.

But that's not realistic, is it? Your habit of wasting the night in front of the TV is deeply ingrained. Besides, you have some favorite shows that you really enjoy and are going to want to watch. My suggestion: Start by making a two-degree change.

Let's say you're watching four hours of TV each night. Don't expect to cut that to zero tomorrow. But how about cutting just one half-hour show out of that lineup? Surely there's at least one sitcom that you're watching more out of habit than because you really enjoy it. Turn off the TV just for that half hour, and load the dishwasher, pay some bills, or take care of some other need during that time.

Try that for a week. It's a small change, nothing too drastic, but it's movement in the right direction. And it's a lot easier to tell yourself, *I can do without one sitcom per night,* than it is to think, *I have to quit watching TV!*

At the end of that week, if you weren't able to turn the TV off for half an hour at least four or five nights, try again for another week. The more you try, the easier it will get. And as soon as you *are* able to skip that sitcom more often than not for a week, look at your viewing schedule again and see if there isn't *another* half hour of TV that you could live without each night.

Again, take your time with this. Some nights you'll fail, but more and more nights you'll succeed. That small change in direction, after a while, will add up to a major change in your procrastination-by-television habit.

I once read that we tend to *overestimate* how much we can

accomplish in the short run and *underestimate* how much we can accomplish in the long run. And I believe that that's very true. But by making just two-degree changes in our bad habits, we can eventually make major progress in overcoming them. (I'll say more about the value of two-degree changes in chapter 7.)

START WITH ONE

Consistent with the idea of making two-degree changes, there's also great wisdom in focusing on overcoming just one manifestation of the curse at a time. If you're like most of us ACODs, you probably struggle with several of the marks of the curse. Ultimately, you'd like to conquer all of them, and preferably all at once.

But just as we don't generally make drastic improvements overnight in an area that's been troubling us for years, so we also are liable to be more sorry than successful if we try to tackle multiple manifestations simultaneously. Better results usually come from focusing on one thing at a time.

Better results usually come from focusing on one thing at a time.

As I mentioned earlier, one of my "issues" from growing up in a home of divorce was anger. I continued to struggle with it (and other things) well into adulthood. And one of the ways it came out was that after my two daughters were born, when I'd get upset with them, I would point my finger at them while scolding them. It was irritating and even scary to them, definitely not a healthy habit.

Now, I could have tried to tell myself, "I'm never, ever going to get angry at my children again. Starting tomorrow, I'm always going to be calm and kind, even when they willfully disobey me or Cindy!" And that resolve, frankly, would have lasted less than a day.

Fortunately, it occurred to me that the atmosphere would start to improve between me and my girls if I could just break that habit of pointing at them menacingly while reprimanding them. So I came up with a "small" but practical way of breaking the habit. I gathered them around me one day and announced, "Girls, Daddy wants to stop pointing at you in anger when he's talking to you. So here's what we're going to do that's going to help me do that: From now on, every time I point my finger at you when I'm angry, I'm going to pay you one dollar on the spot!"

As you might imagine, Kari and Laura thought that was a great idea. Visions of kid-sized riches started dancing in their heads.

For my part, I didn't relish the idea of "throwing away" my money, so I was privately determined not to pay out a single buck. And sure enough, I suddenly found myself much more aware of when I started to point at them. That's not to say, however, that my wallet stayed shut. In fact, over the next three weeks, I paid out almost $20 in singles!

The good news is that by the end of those three weeks, I had become so attuned to when I was about to point at them that I was finally catching myself and stopping before I raised the dreaded finger. The girls had mixed feelings about that.

The even better news is that breaking that bad habit with this simple approach had a ripple effect. First, it helped me to get my anger under control quickly when I became upset with my daughters. In order not to point, I had to stop and think about what I was about to do and why. That proved to be enough of a pause for me to get a grip on myself.

Second, I found myself increasingly able to control my anger in all situations, not just when the girls did something bothersome. I was more in tune with my emotions and more aware of what it felt like to start losing control of them.

And third, I discovered that growing in this one area helped me immensely in other problem areas as well. The effort to improve in controlling my anger weakened the hold of other bad habits, too. Talk about unexpected bonuses!

Seek Accountability

What do groups that help people with habitual, even addictive behaviors—groups like Alcoholics Anonymous and Gamblers

Anonymous—have in common as a key to success? Accountability. They have found that sometimes, when a person is sorely tempted to give in to an urge, the *only* thing that keeps that person from surrendering is the knowledge that in a few days, someone whom he or she respects and does not want to disappoint is going to ask, "Did you give in to the urge this week?"

I've found the same to be true in my own life—on a simple scale, with my daughters, as described in the preceding section—in my work as a counselor, and in working with men through the group called Promise Keepers. I can't count the number of times that a man has said to me, "I was so tempted to _____ this past week"—whatever the bad habit with which he was struggling. "The only way I kept from giving in was thinking about how I would see _____"—me or someone else to whom he had made himself accountable—"in a few days and knowing he was going to ask the question and not let me fake my way through a lie."

Done right, with someone you trust and who will respect your need for confidentiality, accountability can be a powerful tool in your efforts to overcome the manifestations of the curse and build a strong marriage.

Do you tend to blame others for everything that goes wrong in your life, especially your spouse? An accountability partner can help you look at things more objectively.

Do you tend to break your commitments and make multiple false starts toward real change? Your accountability partner can call you on that and give you the nudge you need to stay the course.

In short, someone to whom you're willing to make yourself truly accountable can be a great asset in dealing with any of the manifestations of the curse.

Do you tend to stuff your negative feelings and keep secrets? An accountability partner can draw out how you really feel and help you face up to what you're thinking and doing.

In short, someone to whom you're willing to make yourself truly accountable can be a great asset in dealing with *any* of the manifestations of the curse. As suggested above, this person needs to be someone you can trust to have your best interests at heart and to protect your privacy. It also needs to be someone to whom you're willing to spill your guts. And it needs to be a person who will ask you the tough questions about how you handled your problem area(s) since you last met, and who won't let you dance around the truth when you answer.

Who might be a good candidate to become your accountability partner? It could be a friend, a member of your extended family, a clergy person, or a counselor. But wherever you can find the right individual, I encourage you to avail yourself of this tremendous source of help.

Get Professional Help When Needed

With a doctorate in counseling, it would be easy for me to just sit on that side of the room, wearing my psychologist sweater and dispensing advice to others. However, one of the best decisions Cindy and I ever made was to seek a "coach," or counselor, for a yearly tune-up. As the scripture says, "Where there is no guidance the people fall, but in a abundance of counselors there is victory."[7]

It started when my father was dying and we had to make a lot of decisions about all the issues surrounding that relationship (such as whether he should move into our home). Cindy suggested that we sit down and talk to someone. Knowing this would cost money, I pressed her to see if she was serious. She was. So I called a friend who is a counselor with a Ph.D. We scheduled three sessions to meet with him and talk through, as a couple, how to face the situation with my father. Frankly, I thought there really wasn't much to talk about and we'd finish in one session. However, after three sessions, Cindy was ready to sign up for three more weeks of coaching!

That started something that we have done, almost without

exception, for 20 years: meeting once a year for three sessions with a trained counselor to talk through whatever issues life has thrown at us that year. My travel schedule was the focus one year, along with the struggles of raising junior high kids and an unexpected job change. Later, it would be the death of my mother and the loss of Cindy's parents in the same year.

Especially when you're dealing with a really tough issue, problem, or cycle, and you don't seem to be making progress on your own, a trained professional can be a great help.

In other words, at least for my part, I will die long before I run out of issues to talk through with a trained "coach." I'm purposely using the word *coach* instead of *counselor.* In most cases that's what people, including ACODs, need: some strategic, short, positive, future-oriented coaching by a trained counselor—not years and years of in-depth meetings with a therapist.

Cindy and I would both agree that those almost yearly meetings with Dr. Retts have been a tremendous help to our marriage—and to reversing the curse. Am I saying that everyone should go to counseling? Absolutely not. However, I am saying that everyone should, as the scripture above says, seek guidance. Especially when you're dealing with a really tough issue, problem, or cycle, and you don't seem to be making progress on your own, a trained professional can be a great help.

Choose a counselor with care, though. Pick a person with outstanding faith and experience. If you can, get a referral from someone you know has been helped significantly with issues like your own. You can also get help from Focus on the Family in locating a good counselor in your area. Just call 1-800-AFAMILY.

Rest in God

Finally and most importantly, the power to do everything positive that I've discussed in this book comes by drawing on the love and power of God. All the other suggestions I've made are important, and you can follow them on your own to one extent or another, depending on your level of motivation and your strength of willpower. *But the greatest power to make lasting change comes from gaining an accurate understanding of God and His love for you, and then letting Him work in and through you.*

Imagine that I tell you about the joys of the Apple iPod and how convenient it makes it to enjoy your favorite music wherever you go. Then I describe all the steps needed to download your tunes, locate the songs you want to play, and crank up the volume. But while giving you all that help, I neglect to mention this thing called *the battery* and the role it plays and the whys and hows of keeping it charged. Your iPod will soon run out of power and become nothing more than an expensive decoration on your shelf.

Well, for me to give you the other keys to overcoming the manifestations of the curse without mentioning God would be just like that. Those other keys are important, even vital, but the most necessary truth is that God is the greatest difference-maker in individual lives and in marriages.

First, then, we need to get that better understanding of God and how He wants to relate to us. He's *not* impersonal. He's *not* unconcerned. He *hasn't* turned His back on us even though people (e.g., our parents) have hurt us or let us down with their decisions.

Here are just a few of the truths we find about God and how He feels about us in the Scriptures: "Are not two sparrows sold for a penny? Yet not one of them will fall to the ground apart from the will of your Father [God]. And even the very hairs of your head are all numbered. So don't be afraid; you are worth more than many sparrows."[8]

"Cast all your anxiety on him [God] because he cares for you."[9]

"But because of his great love for us, God, who is rich in mercy . . ."[10]

"And so we know and rely on the love God has for us. God is love. Whoever lives in love lives in God, and God in him."[11]

The psalmist wrote, "Answer me, O Lord, out of the goodness of your love; in your great mercy turn to me."[12]

"You are forgiving and good, O Lord, abounding in love to all who call to you."[13]

"For the Lord is good and his love endures forever."[14]

And then there is perhaps the best-known verse in the entire New Testament: "For God so loved the world that he gave his one and only Son, that whoever believes in him shall not perish but have eternal life."[15]

So God not only loves us—loves *you*—but He loves us enough to invite us to cast our anxieties on Him, to forgive us, and to make an unfathomable sacrifice in order to offer us eternal life. *This* is how God feels about us.

If this is a new concept to you, or if you just have trouble believing it, I encourage you to review and meditate on these truths several times a day. Dog-ear this page, and come back to it over and over. Write these passages on notecards and carry them with you so you can reread them as you go about your daily activities. Let these truths sink deep into your heart and mind.

You see, all the manifestations of the curse grow out of the fact that every human being needs—craves, can't live joyfully without—unconditional love. We *need* to know that we are loved with a love that will not fade, will not weaken, and will never abandon us. But as children of divorce, life has made us afraid that such love simply does not exist. And I'm here to tell you that such love *does* exist. It's real, and it comes from the God who made us. We must grasp and hold on to this truth and never let go—just as He will never let go of us.

When we come to accept the reality of God's love, to allow Him to fill that gaping hole in our hearts, that love will start to reverse the curse for us. Understanding that we are loved with a love that will never desert us, never violate our trust, and never disappoint us, we will feel less and less of a need to be angry, to argue, to procrastinate, to make poor choices in a desperate search for love, and so on.

I'm not saying all this will happen overnight—remember the principle of two-degree changes. But over time, as we learn to bask in God's love, we will tend less and less to live like someone under a curse.

When we embrace God's love and ask for His help, He responds.

At the same time, not only does God's *love* help to reverse the curse, but so also does His *power.* Let me explain.

When we embrace God's love and ask for His help, He responds. Remember the scripture above in which we're invited to cast our anxieties on Him. In another scripture, we see a historical example of His love and power combining to thwart a literal curse.

The people of Israel, having escaped from bondage in Egypt, were about to enter the land promised to them by God. Understandably, the people already living there (known as Ammonites and Moabites) were not keen on that idea. But they also had heard the stories about Israel's prior conquests en route from Egypt, so their leaders decided they needed more help in defeating Israel's encroachment than their armies alone could provide. They needed surefire spiritual help.

So these leaders sent for a man named Balaam. Balaam had a reputation for being connected to God. If Balaam gave someone a blessing, that person usually got blessed by God. In the same way, if Balaam spoke a curse against someone, that person normally got cursed by God. Curse Israel for us, these leaders told Balaam, and we'll pay you handsomely.

Well, Balaam went and tried to curse Israel all right—four different times. But each time, he found himself able to say only those things that God wanted him to say about Israel, which were all blessings! The leaders, and especially King Balak of Moab, got mightily upset with Balaam and told him to pack up and go home.

Later Moses, the leader of Israel, reminded the people of that incident, and he explained just what had happened: "They hired Balaam . . . to pronounce a curse on you. However, the

LORD your God would not listen to Balaam but *turned the curse into a blessing for you,* because the LORD your God loves you."[16]

Isn't that amazing? What Balak and his fellow leaders had meant to be a curse against Israel, God instead—by His power and because of His love—turned into a blessing.

Likewise God both wants to *and* can *turn the curse under which we ACODs have lived into a blessing.*

He loves us—He loves *you*—enough to do that for us.

What's more, God's power can strengthen us internally to do what we know we should in a given situation. When we don't want to turn off the TV; when we're about to start another argument; when we want to blame someone else for something that went wrong—we can ask for and receive His help to do the healthier thing instead.

We read in Scripture, "For it is God who works in you to will and to act according to his good purpose."[17] He strengthens us both in our *desire* to do what's right and in our *ability* to actually get up and do it.

And another passage tells us, "I can do everything through him [God] who gives me strength."[18] Whatever we know is good and right, something that He would want us to do, He will empower us to do.

The question is, then, will you turn to God and draw on His love and power to help you reverse the curse in your life?

REVERSING THE CURSE AND BREAKING THE CYCLE

To break the cycle of divorce in our families, to build strong marriages of our own, we need to reverse the curse that we've been living under as children of divorce. Using the principles in this chapter—and especially drawing upon the love and power of God—will do so much to help us reach that goal.

As we'll see in the next chapter, having an example to follow can also be a tremendous asset in our quest for strong and lasting marriages.

QUESTIONS FOR REFLECTION AND APPLICATION

1. Which of the principles, or strategies, offered in this chapter do you think will be most immediately helpful to you? Why?

2. What action can you take today to begin to put that strategy into practice?

3. How would you describe your relationship with God? Are you regularly seeking His help, or are you trying to live (and make your marriage work, if you're married) on your own?

Chapter Six

The Power of an Example

I went from hoping that surely I could somehow be more successful at marriage than my parents to firmly believing that this would be the case. Despite living under the curse of parental divorce, I could and would have a solid marriage.

Throughout this book, I've made the point that one of the ways in which adult children of divorce (ACODs) are under a curse is that the primary example they've seen of marriage—in many cases the *only* example—is an example of failure. The only picture they have is a picture that says marriage just doesn't last.

Conversely, adult children of healthy intact families enjoy the advantage of experiencing that marital commitment can and does last. They enjoy the blessing of *knowing*, from first-hand experience, that even when there's conflict in a home, the relationship can survive and even thrive rather than fall apart.

As an ACOD myself, I should have been cursed by the lack of a good marriage model. But by the grace of God, I was instead blessed with not just one but two powerful examples of love and lasting commitment. Let me tell you about them, and then we'll explore the specifics of how such examples can make a dramatic impact in an ACOD's life.

My Story

The first outstanding model of love and commitment that God gave me was my mom, Zoa Trent. Since she divorced twice and was a single parent for most of my life, you might wonder how she helped me to believe in the permanence of marriage. Here's how:

My mom was, in a word, a *great* mom. She loved me and my two brothers unconditionally, and we—okay, I especially—put that love to the test many times. When I acted out in anger over my father's refusal to be a part of our lives, she never gave up on me, never accepted the idea that I was beyond redemption.

When, as teens, my twin brother and I would come home after a night of carousing with our friends, she would be up and waiting for us. Because of her warmth and acceptance, we'd be eager to jump onto her bed, one on each side of her, and tell her where we'd been and what we were thinking.

Sometimes on the weekends, we got home late at night. But every time we asked if it were still okay to come into her room, she'd say, "I'll always have time to sleep, but I won't always have you boys to talk to."

As you'll see in the next chapter of this book, my mom also

went *way* out of her comfort zone to meet her boys' needs. She took small steps to help, and she took big steps to the best of her abilities. Over the years, I've met a lot of dedicated and wonderful single moms, but none tops Zoa Trent in my estimation.

Now, the reason you need to know all that is this: Though her own two marriages failed, my mom never stopped believing in the institution of marriage as God designed it. Especially after she became a Christian (which happened after her divorces), she developed the deep conviction that God wants marriage to last a lifetime and that with His help, it's not only possible but normal.

And because of the way she modeled love and commitment to us, my brothers and I had no trouble trusting her when she talked about such things.

Without an example of marital success to look at regularly, hope is hard to come by.

We weren't seeing a healthy marriage lived out before us every day. But we were seeing the kind of rock-solid, utterly dependable, and tenacious love that she told us would one day characterize our marriages. We were seeing the kind of commitment that says, "You will always be mine, and I will always be yours, no matter what." And so we had confidence that we could also enjoy such commitment to and with our wives one day.

The second great model God gave me was a man named Doug Barram. Doug was the Young Life leader at our high school, so I began to see him my freshman year. My twin brother and I were football players, and Doug was one of the few people who didn't just come to games but also to *practices.* He'd yell out words of encouragement as we ran plays or trotted past him on our way to the locker room. (He was a big man at six-foot-four and about 225 pounds, and he had played football himself.)

Before long, Doug had learned my name and seemed genuinely excited to see me each time we met. He was always open to talking about whatever we teens wanted to discuss, and he invited us to hang out at his house, with his family.

In Doug's home, for the first time I saw a strong marriage up close. The man obviously adored his wife; you could see it in the way he looked at her, spoke to her, kissed her, and helped her. And you could see that she felt the same about him. This was the husband I wanted to be in due time.

He also clearly loved his children—playing with them, wrestling with them, talking with them, praying with them, and tucking them in bed at night. So here, too, was the model of a great father that I needed to see.

Watching Doug Barram relate to his family, I was like a giant sponge, soaking it all in. This was the family life for which I had yearned and about which I had only heard before.

I loved being around them so much that I cut his grass every week just to have an excuse to be there. (I would have painted his house and put on a new roof, too, if it had needed them.)

In this model, my mom's words about what marriage should be came to life. She had provided a vision; Doug and his family put flesh on the dream. Between the two, I formed my expectations for the kind of marriage relationship that I would one day build.

WHAT A MODEL PROVIDES

If you're an ACOD, just what are the benefits you could gain from finding a good marriage model (or model couple)—benefits great enough to make the search worth your time and effort? My models gave me four things primarily, and they summarize the benefits pretty well.

First, they gave me hope that marital commitment can *endure for a lifetime.* If your only family experience has been that marriage doesn't last, that conflicts lead inevitably to the death of the relationship, you need hope. You need some reason to believe that things can be different in the future, different for you and your spouse.

Without an example of marital success to look at regularly, however, such hope will be hard to come by. Your frame of reference will still be confined to scenes of failure.

A model like Doug Barram expanded my frame of reference. I saw that failed marriages aren't the only kind. That marriage can not only survive but even be great. That what my mom had said about how marital commitment is supposed to last a lifetime is true.

Second, my models gave me the expectation that commitment will *endure for a lifetime.* Once you have the hope that marriage *can* endure, you need to progress to the expectation that it *will* endure. Though you've previously seen only marital failure, marital health and thriving need to become your new idea of normal.

The impact of parental divorce on the expectations of ACODs is so powerful that one researcher was led to observe that young people today tend to enter marriage "in a profound state of cluelessness."

Again, however, the encouragement and example of my mom, plus the strong relationship of Doug Barram and his wife, eventually developed a realistically positive expectation in me. I went from hoping that surely I could somehow be more successful at marriage than my parents to firmly believing that this *would* be the case. Despite living under the curse of parental divorce, I could and would have a solid marriage.

Third, my models gave me examples of healthful ways to relate—daily habits that build up a marriage. Relationships often founder because, for various reasons, the people in them simply stop doing the positive things that keep the tie strong—

things like helping each other. Saying "I love you." Putting an encouraging arm around a discouraged loved one's shoulder. Deferring to the other's desires as often as possible.

"We are mesmerized by the romantic idea of marriage and blinded to the reality," wrote Gen X author Pamela Paul. "We are sold on Cinderella, not on how uncomfortable wearing glass slippers for the next 50 years might be."[1]

In other words, we forget how much hard and consistent work it takes to live "happily ever after."

We are sold on Cinderella, not on how uncomfortable wearing glass slippers for the next 50 years might be.

Here again, though, my mom and Doug Barram came through for me. Over years of watching Doug and his wife, Loretta, I saw love put into action. I saw my mom regularly putting her children's needs ahead of her own. And I saw Doug helping his wife around the house and with their children and telling her "I love you" in various ways. Even when making a request at dinner like "Please pass the carrots," his love and respect for her shone through.

Fourth, my models gave me examples of how to resolve conflicts without destroying the relationship. Conflict is inevitable, and ACODs tend to think it inevitably leads to divorce. But in healthy marriages, husband and wife find ways to work out their differences and grow even closer together as a result.

In these four significant ways, my mom and Doug Barram showed me, despite my handicaps as an ACOD, that I could have a good marriage. They shaped my hopes and expectations, and they gave me the practical skills for building strong, lasting relationships. Their examples have played a key part in the making of my marriage.

Finding a Good Model

If you're an ACOD and you haven't been blessed with positive examples like the two I enjoyed, where can you find them? Here are some possibilities:

First, ask God to bring individuals and couples into your life who will model healthy marriage for you. He cares so much for you, and He wants to provide for your every need, including this one (see 1 Peter 5:7).

Second, look around you. Perhaps among your relatives there's a couple who stand out as having a strong, stable marriage. You might also find such a person or couple in your circle of friends, among your neighbors, or even at your place of work. The good news is that though your experience has led you to think of marriage as a relationship that's likely to fail, there are, in fact, many solid marriages all around you.

Third, one of the best places to look is in your local church. Although Christian or other religiously based marriages aren't perfect, they are typically among the strongest you'll find.

The next few times you're in church, look around you before and after the service. You may well see some couples who demonstrate obvious love and respect for each other and might be good to observe further. Talk to your pastor and explain what you need; he might even be able to recommend a couple who would invite you to spend time with them, watch how they relate, and ask whatever questions you might have.

In short, you're looking for another Doug Barram family. You want a couple who will mentor you in how to have a healthy marriage.

GOOD MODELS—DON'T LEAVE HOME WITHOUT THEM

As an ACOD, you face tough odds in trying to experience a strong, lasting marriage. You'll recall that at the start of this book, I compared it to being asked to paint a scene (of a desert in bloom) that you'd never observed, in person or in picture. Next to impossible, right?

Well, what good models can do for you is provide the picture. They can show you what the scene is supposed to look like. They can prove that this scene is not just a pleasant figment of someone's imagination, not just a nice fantasy that's far removed from the realities of daily life.

Good and even great marriages do exist. Find one or two and soak in what they look like and how they work. And let the conviction begin to grow in your heart that you, too, can experience such a lasting and fulfilling relationship.

Questions for Reflection and Application

1. Do you already have at least one positive model of commitment and unconditional love in your life?

2. If you still need such an example, where might you find it?

3. Which of the benefits of a strong role model might prove most helpful to you? Why?

Chapter Seven

Stepping Out of the Trailer

*If I say I'm going to do something,
and I know that my accountability partner
is going to ask me about it soon, and he's not
going to accept any excuses for failing to do it,
I'm a lot more motivated to follow through.*

In chapter 5, I wrote of the fact that we have the power of choice, a power that we have to exercise for good if we're to break the cycle of divorce. That principle is so important that I want to expand on it in this chapter.

The reason this is such a big deal is that making the right choice *and acting on it,* when we've been used to making the wrong choice, takes us way out of our comfort zone. And we human beings just *hate* to move out of our comfort zones. But we have to be willing to do that, consistently, for the rest of our lives, if we're going to build and maintain healthy marriages.

Let me tell you the story of a woman who was willing to move way out of her comfort zone and, in the process, helped to break the cycle of divorce for her three sons.

My Mom, My Hero

After my father deserted our family, leaving my mom as the single parent to three boys, she pushed herself out of her comfort zone in so many ways to meet our needs and bless us that I can't begin to count them. But one in particular stands out in my memory.

My mom was not the outdoorsy type. In fact, that statement would draw peals of laughter from most members of my family. Given the choice, she would prefer the amenities of city life any day. Furthermore, she didn't have much money in those years to feed and care for a family of four. No one would have blamed her if, when she got a little extra cash, she spent it on her own comfort and pleasure.

I tell you those things so you can appreciate what happened one weekend day early in my childhood. Mom had gone out that morning in our pathetic, old Ford Falcon. She hadn't told us where she was going. When she came home a little later, the Falcon was towing a tired, worn, teardrop trailer. Inside, we soon discovered there were some of the basic tools of camping: a lamp, a propane stove, a tent, and some flashlights—all well used.

We were going camping! We boys were thrilled at the prospect. Mom tried hard to convince us she was, too, and we believed her at the time. She'd managed to save a few extra dollars, and rather than spend them on herself, she had spent them on something she knew we'd love.

Off we went, that same day, to Rocky Point, Mexico, for our first camping adventure. Now, understand that Mom knew nothing about camping, and of course neither did us boys. But that didn't stop us or even diminish our enthusiasm.

Once we got to our campsite on the Mexican coast, however, reality set in. We couldn't get the stove to work. Ditto for the lamp. We were clueless about setting up a tent. Even the flashlights were dying. We went to sleep a little cold and a little hungry. The next morning found us huddled together in the trailer, second-guessing just how great camping was supposed to be. I can only imagine what Mom was thinking, but I imagine it included a longing for her soft, warm bed back in Phoenix.

It all began with a mom who made a choice to do something that would help her sons to cope with the curse of divorce—something that required her willingness to step way *out of her comfort zone.*

Then the Cholla Bay Camping Club showed up. This was a group of kindred spirits who loved camping together and did so regularly. They quickly set up camp and got a nice, warm fire going—something we had been unable to do. Soon one of the men came over and invited us to join them for coffee and hot chocolate. They didn't have to ask twice!

After we were warmed up, those pro campers showed us how to fire up the stove and cook on it. How to light the lantern. How to pitch a tent. They even scrounged up replacement batteries for our flashlights.

At the finish of that weekend, as our time there drew to a close and everyone prepared to go home, the members of Cholla Bay Camping invited us—the only single-parent family in the group—to join their club. For the rest of my growing-up years, we went with them once a month to Rocky Point. It was great fun, great learning, with plenty of positive male role models for us boys.

And it all began with a mom who made a choice to do something that would help her sons to cope with the curse of divorce—something that required her willingness to step way *out of her comfort zone.*

You might say that she was willing to step out of the trailer to break the curse.

Why It's So Tough

All human beings are creatures of habit. We take comfort in the familiar. Even when we know change would probably be good for us, we still struggle to take that first step out of the trailer. We're leaving the known for the unknown, and that's scary.

In my book *Heart Shift*, I describe nine reasons why all people struggle to take that first step out of the trailer. These range from lack of time to fear of failure to fear of losing what we already have, and so on. And these are understandable reasons for hesitating to initiate change.

For ACODs, the difficulty in taking that first step is magnified. We're even more fearful, more suspicious, less optimistic, and less trusting than the norm. Even when we know what we're leaving behind is bad, it's still so hard to step into the unknown.

Let's suppose, for instance, that you have the habit—a manifestation of the curse—of blaming others for everything that goes wrong. This book has brought home to you the reality that that's just not the case. You need to start accepting responsibility for—at the very least—your *response* to the bad things that have happened to you.

Even when we know what we're leaving behind is bad, it's still so hard to step into the unknown.

Again, any normal person will struggle to step out of the trailer and start accepting that responsibility. It's uncomfortable. It's nice to deflect blame to a scapegoat. But for you as an ACOD, it's even harder than usual to accept blame.

For one thing, it will require admitting that you've been wrong about some important things, like how much of your current unhappiness is the fault of the parent who "caused" the divorce or who left the home after the breakup. It will also require forgiving the parent who hurt you the most—and believe me, I know how tough that can be. You might even need to ask for his forgiveness for blaming him unjustly all these years.

If all that weren't hard enough, stepping out of the trailer to stop blaming others will require you to look honestly at your own shortcomings. How much of your pain have you brought on yourself through your attitudes, words, and actions? Which of your own habits make it difficult for you to build healthy relationships?

Answering such questions won't be easy. But it will be necessary.

Two-Degree Changes, Part II

The good news, as I first explained in chapter 5, is that you don't need to—and shouldn't try to—make huge changes overnight. Small changes in the right direction can add up over time to major course corrections.

This point was made hilariously in the film *What About Bob?*, starring Bill Murray as the title character—a man with some serious psychological issues. His therapist, played by Richard Dreyfuss, advocated an approach that he called "baby steps," which was very much akin to the idea of two-degree changes. (In fact, the therapist had written a book called *Baby Steps*. He gave Bob a copy and added the cost to his bill.)

The film's humor comes from Bob's naïve, bumbling attempts to make those baby steps of progress. The situation gets even funnier when lovable but annoying Bob invites himself into the middle of the therapist's family summer vacation.

Though the movie plays Bob's efforts for laughs, he does make a certain amount of progress over the course of the film. And as we've already seen, the concept itself is entirely valid. So the question then becomes, what might it look like to step out of the trailer, to make the first two-degree change in overcoming whichever of the manifestations of the curse is causing you the most trouble? Let's take a look at some possibilities.

Suppose you have a tendency to isolate yourself. Your first step might be to ask your spouse out for a date. If you withdraw physically in your own home, you might make a point of sitting with your spouse one evening while you both read or watch TV together.

If you struggle with false guilt, your first step might be to simply write on a note card, "I am not to blame for my parents' divorce." Then carry that card with you and look at it several times throughout the day. Reading it aloud to yourself would be another small step in the right direction.

If you've been keeping unhealthy family secrets, a safe first step would be to write them out on a piece of paper. Then destroy the paper if you feel you must, but write them out again the next day and the next. (Eventually, as you ask God to give you the strength, you'll want to show that paper to someone you can trust.)

If you're prone to fear-based procrastination, your first step could be to break down some task you need to do into small, manageable pieces. Just write out the stages. A simple example could be paying your bills. You might write, "Gather bills, checkbook, and pen. Open first bill, see how much is owed, and write the check. Put the check and return portion of the bill into the return envelope, close and seal. Attach stamp." And so on. (Next you'll tackle that first stage, which may give you the momentum to go on to the second.)

If you've been making poor choices, your first step might be to ask yourself, "What lessons should I have learned from my previous mistakes?" Or you might ask, "What mistakes have I made that I definitely do *not* want to repeat?"

Likewise if you're in the habit of making false starts, you might ask yourself, "Why did those attempts to do something good end so badly? What lessons have I learned?"

If breaking commitments is a problem for you, you might start asking God to give you wisdom about which commitments you should and shouldn't make, which promises you can and can't keep. To encourage yourself, you might also write out and review regularly, "I am a person of integrity. I make wise commitments and keep my promises."

If you've tended to blame others for everything bad in your life, your first step could be to make a list of the people you blame most often and the things for which you blame them. (Your next step might then be to analyze, as best you can, how much of the problem is what each of those people said or did and how much is the way in which you've chosen to respond to those words or actions.)

If you struggle with smoldering anger, you might start by identifying some way in which you give evidence of that anger—like me pointing my finger at my daughters. (Then, also like me, you could think of some way to make yourself vividly aware of what you're doing and begin to get control of that behavior.)

Is not really listening to others your problem? Your first step out of the trailer could be to force yourself to wait until the other person finishes speaking a thought before you reply. In other words, no more cutting off the other person in mid-sentence. Or you might start briefly repeating back to the other person what you understood her to say, before you give your response. ("If I heard you correctly, Joan, you're concerned about . . .")

Suppose you're prone to launch into an argument at the drop of a hat. You could start forcing yourself—again, asking for God's help—to monitor your feelings in a given conversation or situation. As you do this, you'll probably begin to notice what triggers your emotions, your feeling of defensiveness, or your sense of needing to disagree. Another first step might be to ask yourself, before you respond, "*Why* does this other person think or feel that way?"

Finally, if your struggle is with seeing God only as impersonal and unconcerned about you and your pain, a great first step would be to turn back to those scriptures in the last section of chapter 5—the ones that speak of His love and care for you. Then write them out on small cards that you can carry and review throughout the day. Another first step would be to write out a list of all the *good* things God has put in your life. Go back and add to it over a period of several days. Then review it every day. It isn't difficult to start making small but important changes. (Please see my book *The Two-Degree Difference* if this idea of two-degree changes has grabbed your heart.)

The Value of Making Yourself Accountable

Earlier in this book, I spoke of the value of making yourself accountable to a trusted person for the changes you're trying to accomplish. But the message bears repeating here.

As I said earlier in this chapter, even small, first steps in the right direction can be hard to pull off. But the task can be made immensely easier if you're not trying to do it alone. Your spouse, a sibling, a close friend, a counselor—someone you can trust to have your best interests at heart and to respect your privacy—can be a great asset in taking the baby steps that eventually lead to major improvements in your life.

Such an ally can provide encouragement when you're frustrated or disappointed. He or she can also help you analyze situations more objectively than you can on your own. And, if you'll allow it, this person can hold you accountable for making your two-degree course corrections along the way.

I'll say it again: There's great power that comes from knowing that in a day or two or three, somebody you trust and respect is going to ask you the tough questions. "Did you stop to ask *why* your wife was saying something you found irritating before launching into an argument?" "Did you look at your schedule and analyze what you could realistically do before making any new commitments this week?" "Did you point in anger at your girls this week? If you did, did you pay them a dollar on the spot?" "Did you take that first step toward preparing your tax returns this week—did you make your list of all the documentation you'll need to gather?"

You get the picture. If I say I'm going to do something, and I know that my accountability partner is going to ask me about it soon, and he's not going to accept any excuses for my failing to do it, I'm a lot more motivated to follow through.

Knowing you'll be called to account for something you know you ought to do may not be the most noble reason to do it, but it works.

I urge you, therefore, to find yourself a good accountability partner even before you step out of the trailer to start overcoming those tendencies that weaken your ability to sustain a strong marriage. Finding such a person is itself not a small step, but it will greatly enhance your chances of making all your subsequent steps successful.

Trusting That God Will "Show Up"

Back in chapter 5, I referred to that time in ancient history when the people of Israel were moving from slavery in Egypt into the land that God had promised to give them. Well, in another part of the story, those people were about to take a *big* step; they were about to cross the Jordan River from east to west, into that land flowing with milk and honey.

Life and health imply movement. When we make the choice to move, God shows up.

Moses, their leader, knew he was about to die and would not cross the river with the rest of the nation. So to prepare the people for going on without him, he reminded them of all that God had done for them and of the laws He had provided to guide them in daily living. Then, near the end of his lengthy message, he spoke these words: "This day I call heaven and earth as witnesses against you that I have set before you life and death, blessings and curses. Now choose life . . ."[1]

In the Hebrew language in which that biblical book of Deuteronomy was originally written, the word translated *life* means "movement." That's one of the ways that we check on whether something is alive, isn't it—whether or not it's moving under its own power. Life and health imply movement.

In the same manner as God through Moses challenged Israel to choose life—to move forward into that land of promise, obeying His laws—He also challenges us ACODs today. He calls us to choose life, to start moving in small but steady steps to break the cycle of divorce in our lives.

When we make that choice, day by day and even moment by moment, the amazing thing is that God "shows up" on our behalf. He strengthens us to do those things that we need to do, whether it's looking at ourselves and our lives more honestly, speaking words of blessing rather than blasting, taking that next small step in the right direction, or whatever the need of the moment may be.

What's more, God does those things that we need but that we can't do for ourselves. In Israel's case, He parted the waters of the Jordan at flood stage so the people could cross over on dry land. He gave them victory after victory over superior forces. He made the thick and fortified walls of a mighty city fall to the ground. Scripture tells us that on one occasion, He even made the sun stand still long enough for Israel to bring a late-day battle to a successful conclusion!

In our case, God can change hearts. For example, I don't know about you, but I simply can't find it in myself to fully forgive someone who has hurt me badly. God, however, has worked that willingness in my heart many times.

He can also strengthen and enable an arthritis-crippled single mom named Zoa Trent, who wanted to model commitment to her sons, to be there for them 24/7, taking them camping in their formative years and speaking calmly and lovingly to them in their rebellious teen years. (*Zoa*, by the way, is Greek for *life*, and no one was ever better named.) She chose life for herself and her boys, and her attitude in spite of her physical pain was always "Let's get moving!"

God can also open doors to overcoming the curse in our lives. I wrote in chapter 6 about Doug Barram, the man who introduced me to God in my high school years and who showed me what it means to be a husband and a father. I wasn't looking for such a man; I didn't even know I needed that kind of loving example. But God knew what I needed and brought Doug into my life.

After I had gotten to know Doug, and I had also finally met my dad—who had lived no more than 20 miles away all those years while I was growing up and had never made contact of any kind—I took a close look at the two examples they provided of how to live a life. And I chose life and I chose blessing. I vowed that when the time came, with God's help, I would be Doug Barram and not my father to my own wife and children.

Whatever it is that you need to overcome the curse and break the cycle of divorce in your life, I encourage you to choose life. To step out of the trailer. To call on God for His help. And to look expectantly for Him to show up, empowering you to do your part and to do *for* you those things that are beyond your grasp.

He's a big God. A miracle-working God. And He loves *you.*

Questions for Reflection and Application

1. What will be required of you if you're to step out of the trailer and deal with your most troublesome manifestation of the curse?

2. What might be your first two-degree change in addressing that manifestation?

3. To whom could you make yourself accountable for taking your first steps in the right direction?

4. What do you need God to do for you that you can't do for yourself?

Chapter Eight

Touching Future Generations

Children may not ask you tough questions about how you're living (but then again, they might), but never forget that they're watching you, listening to you, and learning from your every move, every day.

As human beings caught up in the daily routines of life, we tend to wonder sometimes if what we're doing really makes much difference. In the working world, are we just cogs in the business machine? If we have children, do they recognize all that we do for them, much less appreciate it? Will all of our hopes and efforts have any lasting impact?

Well, I'm living proof that (a) divorce is a generational curse and, therefore, (b) if you can break the cycle of divorce, you do so not only for yourself, but also for your children, your grandchildren, and generations even in the distant future.

How's that for lasting impact?

The reason I'm evidence of both *a* and *b* is that I had a terrific mom who broke the cycle of divorce for my brothers and me. By all accounts, our marriages and our lives generally should have been deeply troubled. That we've fared so well is tribute to the fact that our mother chose life and blessing and passed these on to us.

The principle she taught was that marriage is supposed to be a permanent, lifetime commitment.

Let me remind you, through the words of Elizabeth Marquardt (herself an ACOD) in her book *Between Two Worlds*, of the common experience of many of our fellow ACODs: "Our parents' divorce is linked to our higher rates of depression, suicidal attempts and thoughts, health problems, childhood sexual abuse, school dropout, failure to attend college, arrests, addiction, teen pregnancy, and more. . . . Some of us continue to struggle with the scars left from our parents' divorce: we have a harder time finishing school, getting and keeping jobs, maintaining relationships, and having lasting marriages."[1]

Again, the fact that my brothers and I avoided most of that heartache is a credit to our mom. Let me tell you more about her.

A Single Mom's Legacy

My mom was divorced twice before she discovered and embraced God's love for her. After that, as she read the Bible and learned more of His principles for living, she not only applied them to her own life but also taught them to her sons. And one of those was that marriage is supposed to be a permanent, lifetime commitment.

As I pointed out earlier, it might have sounded strange to hear a twice-divorced woman teaching the permanence of marriage. But her commitment to us was so rock-solid, so clearly unconditional, that we never doubted the truth of what she was saying or the fact that such a relationship was possible. After all, she modeled that kind of love every day.

She went to all our football games, baseball games, and wrestling matches. She washed sweat, blood, and grass stains out of our uniforms, even with severely arthritic hands. She took us to the library, where we roamed free while she looked for books to help her in forging a career and fighting a crippling illness. She prayed for us every day, often with tears in her eyes during Jeff's and my turbulent teen years.

She taught us how to be men, and not just men but *gentlemen*. She always expected the best of us and forgave us the worst. She couldn't tie a necktie or button a coat—she couldn't even spank us when we misbehaved. But when she put her hand gently on mine and spoke her concern for my conduct, her eyes pierced my soul and I wanted desperately never to disappoint her again. (Of course, I often did.)

She never spoke negatively of our father, either. She never

blamed him for deserting us, never bad-mouthed him for our financial struggles.

Do you begin to see how we beat the odds?

We've seen the kinds of attitudes, words, and behaviors that destroy a marriage. We're struggling even now to overcome those same tendencies.

Far from dropping out of school, my twin brother, Jeff, and I both earned Ph.D.'s. He became a cancer researcher; I became a counselor, speaker, and writer. Our older brother, Joe, trains Realtors to be outstanding at serving others.

As for our marriages, I've been married for 26 years and counting to Cindy, the finest woman I've ever known besides my mom. Jeff's wife, Dee, struggles with multiple sclerosis, yet they've loved each other dearly for more than 30 years. Joe did get divorced (after 20 years), but he has grown both spiritually and in general maturity since then. He's now 10 years and counting into a solid second marriage, applying what Mom taught us all.

THE IMPACT WE CAN HAVE

When we break the cycle of divorce and build strong and stable marriages, we spare our own children from the heartache and pain of divorce, and we greatly improve the chances that their children will likewise be spared. We pass on blessings rather than a curse. We help them to be much more healthy and happy than children of divorce.

As ACODs, because we've experienced the curse and are choosing every day to reverse it, we can also give our children the benefit of our own painful past. We've seen the kinds of attitudes, words, and behaviors that destroy a marriage. We're struggling even now to overcome those same tendencies. With age-appropriate, loving candor, we can guide our children in building healthy relationships and avoiding destructive habits.

By the way we treat our spouses and children, we can also be for them the kind of model that my mom and Doug Barram were for me. We can show them:

- how to communicate openly and honestly.
- how to be proactive and take initiative.
- how to make good choices.
- how to put the needs of others before our own.
- how to make and keep commitments.
- how to ask for and offer forgiveness.
- and how to relate to, and draw strength from, a loving God.

Besides providing this kind of example to our own children and other family members (e.g., nieces and nephews), we might also look for other children of divorce who, like me with

Doug, would benefit from such a living illustration of healthy adulthood. These might be friends of our children, children on the same sports teams as our children, or children in our places of worship.

The Goal

Elizabeth Marquardt captures the goal well here: "Many of us dream of a whole family, unbroken by divorce—a family where our children never even think about the concept of home because they blessedly take it for granted. . . . In my early twenties I wasn't able to imagine a future for myself, but now I see a future bright with hope.

"[I]t's not enough to love our children. As hard as I know it can be, we parents must also do our best to love and forgive *each other*, every day. . . . We do this so that we can sustain unbroken families that last a lifetime, not just for the sake of our own happiness, but for theirs."[2]

Ask yourself every day, "What kind of legacy will I leave to my children?"

To that perspective I would only add that our own power to love and forgive is limited; the real power comes from God. But the well-being of our children and of theirs *is* the ultimate goal.

Let me encourage you, then, to ask yourself every day, "What kind of legacy am I leaving to my children?" Or, if you don't have children, "Based on how I'm currently dealing with the effects of being an adult child of divorce, what impact am I having on those around me? If nieces, nephews, or other young people are observing me, what lessons are they learning from my example?"

When you think about it, this is another form of accountability. Children may not ask you tough questions about how you're living (but then again, they might), but never forget that they're watching you, listening to you, and learning from your every move, every day.

In short, your life and how you handle the tough realities of being an ACOD *will* have an impact on future generations. The only question is what kind of impact it will be.

And the answer to that is up to you.

Questions for Reflection and Application

1. Besides yourself and your spouse, whose future might be most affected by the success or failure of your marriage? Your own child? A sibling? Future children?

2. What does my mom's story tell you about the potential impact of a parent, even a single parent, on a child of divorce?

3. In your own words, what do you hope will be your legacy in the area of personal relationships?

Chapter Nine

If You've Already Been Divorced

We need to learn from the past, but we must not become slaves to it. It's today and tomorrow that we can make positive changes, today and tomorrow that God has given us to do those things that will build a strong marriage.

Perhaps you've read to this point—or you skipped ahead when you saw this chapter on the contents page—and you're thinking, *This idea of breaking the cycle of divorce sounds well and good, but I'm already divorced. Realistically, isn't it too late for me? I'm right in the middle of the cycle of divorce, just like my parents before me.*

The resounding answer is that *no*, it's not too late for you. And *yes*, you can still break the cycle of divorce.

Whatever has happened to you in the past, or whatever poor choices you have made yourself, you can start fresh today. With God's help, you can put the past behind you and start taking wise, healthful steps in the right direction. It has become a cliché, but today truly is the first day of the rest of your life, and your future can be so much brighter than your past.

The God of Second Chances

The biblical book of Luke, chapter 15, includes one of the most remarkable stories in all of Scripture. It's a story that Jesus told and that seems to be aimed straight at people who need a second chance—people just like you and me.

Whatever has happened to you in the past, or whatever poor choices you have made yourself, you can start fresh today.

The story centers on a young man, his older brother, and, in the middle of it all, their father. The young man—let's call him Tom—was feeling frisky, as our parents used to say—eager to get out and "see the world," to indulge every appetite. To finance his adventure, he went to his dad and said, "Father, give me my share of the estate."[1]

Now, since a family estate didn't normally get divided up until the patriarch died, Tom was essentially saying, "Dad, I wish you were dead. But give me my share of the family money without making me wait for that."

When the father graciously granted his request in spite of the disrespect, "the younger son got together all he had."[2] He packed up all his possessions, because he was leaving and had no intention of ever coming back. He was making a total break with his dad (and the rest of the family).

Then Tom "set off for a distant country."[3] His goal: Put as much distance as possible between himself and his father. That was not only true physically, but it was also true morally and spiritually. As soon as this reckless jet-setter landed in that faraway land, he began to spend his money as if there were no tomorrow, on "wild living" (booze, fast women, and who knows what else).

Much to the young man's disappointment, however, tomorrow did come, and quickly. Soon all the money was gone, along with all his new, good-time friends. Now Tom was penniless, homeless, friendless, and still clueless.

It didn't help that his adopted homeland went into a severe economic depression at the same time. Jobs were hard to come by. The only work Tom could land was tending a herd of pigs—and even the pigs were eating better than him!

What was he to do? He had cut all ties with his family, made a mockery of his father's values. The dictionary of the day could have put his photo next to the entry for "poor choices." At this point, he didn't deserve anything from his dad except contempt and condemnation.

And yet . . .

Our young playboy knew enough about his father to have a glimmer of hope that maybe, just maybe, Dad would show enough mercy to let him be a household servant. To be reinstated as a son—that was beyond comprehension. But the servants ate pretty well in his father's home, and that looked good compared to sharing seed pods with the sows.

So off young Tom went, heading toward Dad's estate, rehearsing the speech that he hoped would gain him admittance to the servants' quarters. Desperate for some kind of second chance. No other options if he caught his father in a bad mood.

Now here's where the story starts to get interesting for those of us who need a second chance.

While Tom was still some distance from the home spread, just a speck on the horizon, his father saw him. Which means that Dad was *looking* for him. A glance in the right direction wouldn't have done the trick; Dad was *straining* to see the young man. Maybe he had climbed the tallest hill on the estate; maybe he had built a tower on that tallest hill. He *longed* to see his son again, and he refused to give up hope that the young man would return someday.

So when he saw Tom, Dad took off running toward him. When he got to him, he threw his arms around Tom and kissed him. Tom started into his humble-pie speech, but Dad cut him off. "Quick! Bring the best robe and put it on him," he told the servants. "Put a ring on his finger and sandals on his feet. Bring the fattened calf and kill it. Let's have a feast and celebrate."[4]

And then came words that had to have struck Tom to the core of his being. "For this son of mine was dead and is alive again," Dad said. "He was lost and is found."[5]

The father said so much with those few words. He said that

despite Tom's rebellion, despite his despising all that his dad stood for, and despite his throwing away half the family fortune, all was forgiven. And regardless of what the young man deserved—a servant's position at best—Dad was restoring him to the full status and privileges of "son-hood."

Tom was back in the family, being given a clean slate and a fresh start. Not only that, but Dad was even throwing a party in his honor to welcome him home!

The great news for us is that Jesus, in telling this story, was clearly saying that this gracious, loving, forgiving, second-chance-providing father is a true picture of God, the heavenly Father. God, Jesus said, loves us, longs to be with us, and forgives us just like the dad in the story.

And no matter how badly we may have blown it in life, even turning our backs on Him, He's ready to run in our direction and offer us that second chance as soon as He sees us turn toward Him.

That's good news, indeed. And if you've already been divorced, I encourage you to thank God and embrace that hope. The God of the universe is eager to give you a second chance.

They Did It, and So Can You

Just as many ACODs have broken the cycle of divorce started by their parents and grandparents, so it's also true that many who have experienced divorce themselves have taken advantage of a second chance and built strong marriages. You can do the same.

Having gone through divorce by no means dooms you to permanent marital failure.

I've already mentioned my mom, who got divorced twice before she learned to trust in God and let His love satisfy her soul. She modeled unconditional love, forgiveness, and commitment to my brothers and me. She held us accountable, but always in the context of complete acceptance. She gave us the foundation for believing, despite her own history of broken marriages, that we could succeed in matrimony.

A good friend of mine, married while still in college, came home one day to the news that his wife had fallen in love with his friend and was leaving him for good. Understandably, he was devastated by the divorce that followed.

Later, though, he was given a second chance at marriage. He met a great young woman, and they fell in love and wed. They're now more than 30 years into one of the best marriages I've ever seen, with four great, now-adult children and a growing number of grandchildren to add zest to their middle and later years.

I also mentioned earlier my brother Joe, who—since getting serious with God later in life as our mom did—recovered from his divorce and is now more than 10 years into a strong and vibrant marriage.

Even in the notoriously-unhealthy-for-marriage world of professional entertainers, we can find examples of people who went through divorce but then built lasting unions. Paul Newman, for instance, divorced once before marrying Joanne Woodward, his wife now of almost 50 years at the time of this writing. Actor and later President Ronald Reagan went through a divorce before marrying Nancy, his loving wife of 52 years at the time of his death. And singer Johnny Cash also went through a divorce before marrying June Carter, his beloved wife for 35 years before her death in 2003.

My point is that having gone through divorce, while it makes a second marriage even harder to maintain, by no means dooms you to permanent marital failure. Like many before you, you can succeed.

Pressing into the Future

There's another scripture that applies well to those of us who need a second chance, whether it's because of divorce or some other regrettable circumstance. It's a statement from the apostle Paul, who wrote, "One thing I do: Forgetting what is behind and straining toward what is ahead, I press on toward the goal."[6] Though Paul wrote in the context of serving God, the principle applies as well to us ACODs who are trying to build lasting marriages.

And the principle is simply this: We need to put past mistakes and past poor choices behind us, and we need to focus on the future.

This doesn't mean, of course, that we completely forget the past. That's not possible. But we don't allow it, no matter how difficult or even painful, to dominate our thinking. We choose instead to focus on the present and the future. We concentrate on those attitudes and those practices that we now know make for success in marriage and in life generally.

So, for example, if we've come to realize that we have a problem with blaming others for our shortcomings, we don't dwell on past instances of that and wallow in guilt. Instead, we ask, "What two-degree change can I make *today* to start overcoming that tendency?" And we can also consider, "If I keep repeating this small change day after day, what kind of progress might I see in a month's time? In six months? In a year?"

As another, more specific example, if we've been prone to starting arguments at the drop of a hat, we might focus on the thought, *Today I'm going to make a point of focusing on the things I appreciate about my spouse and give him or her five sincere compliments. And if I catch myself starting to argue, I will literally bite my tongue (gently) as a reminder to stop immediately and get control of myself.*

We need to learn from the past, but we must not become slaves to it. It's today and tomorrow that we can make positive changes, today and tomorrow that God has given us to do those things that will build a strong marriage.

Commit to the Permanence of Marriage

A part of pressing positively into the future is committing ourselves to the permanence of marriage. Our parents didn't model this for us. If we've already been divorced, we have further reason to question whether lifetime marriage really exists.

Don't lower your standards. Don't be satisfied with less. Make the commitment and live like you believe it.

Nonetheless, in our hearts, we know that marriage is meant to last. We know that this is right and that it's what's best for us and our children. So we determine that despite past failures, we believe in the permanence of marriage. It's what we want, and with God's help we're going to strive for that with everything we've got. We won't lower our standards. We won't be satisfied with less.

Then, having made that commitment, we live as if we believe it and mean it. When issues or problems arise in our marriages, we don't look for a way out of the relationship. Instead, we look for ways to work through the issues—preferably, together.

We banish the word *divorce* from our vocabulary in times of disagreement. We refuse to dwell on the notion that we would be better off alone or with someone else. We remind ourselves, *My spouse is my life-mate, not my enemy*. And we take action consistent with our commitment.

A woman once told me candidly, "When my husband does something that really bugs me, it's easy to 'go negative'—to start reciting in my mind all his habits that irritate me. To review all the times that he's ever disappointed or hurt me. Even to start thinking about how much better off I might be without him."

That's dwelling on the past and letting it enslave you.

But this woman continued, "I eventually came to realize that such thinking is useless at best. And at worst, it was really poisoning my attitude toward my husband. So I started praying about it, and God impressed upon me the thought that in such times, I needed to turn my thoughts in an entirely different direction.

"That's when I began to catch myself as quickly as I could in that thought cycle and tell myself, *These thoughts aren't right, and they don't please God*. And then I would start to recite all the things I *admire* about my husband—his hard work, his thoughtfulness (most of the time!), his warm smile, his devotion to me and our children, and so on. And I would ask God to forgive me and to help me forgive and respect my husband."

That's putting the past behind you and taking action consistent with a commitment to your marriage.

Get Help

Finally, if you've already been divorced, you may need help from others even more than other ACODs. I talked in chapter 6 about the benefits of finding examples to give you hope, to encourage you, and to show you the way to resolve conflict and build healthy relationships. Those benefits apply even more when you've been through marital failure before.

Some good models of unconditional love, acceptance, and successful marriage could make a huge difference in your prospects.

Let's face it. You've had at least one bad experience with the sad and painful end of a marriage. Whatever your exact circumstances, things didn't work out. Statistics say that second marriages fail even more often than first unions. You likely have more concerns and anxieties about your ability to sustain a marriage than someone getting wed for the first time. For all these reasons, some good models of unconditional love, acceptance, and successful marriage could make a huge difference in your prospects.

Besides examples, you might also want to look for a mentor—someone older than you, of your same gender, who shares your commitments both to God and to the permanence of marriage, and who has been in a good marriage for a long time. This could be a relative, a friend, a person at your house of worship, or even a counselor. Wherever you find this individual, he or she could be a tremendous asset to you.

When you have questions, your mentor can help you find answers. When you face temptations, your mentor can hold you accountable for making good decisions and taking healthful actions. When you're discouraged, your mentor can provide the encouragement to hang in there, keep taking the right actions, and trust that things can work out.

Obviously, for such a relationship to work, your mentor needs to be someone you can trust and someone who will have your best interests at heart. You'll need to be honest and candid in describing your thoughts, feelings, and actions, as well as the state of your marriage. And you'll need to be willing to follow your mentor's counsel.

Again, though, if you can find such a person, he or she can be a wonderful help in making your marriage successful.

Remember, too, that the God who gives us second chances

also wants to be actively involved in helping us take advantage of those opportunities. If we're trying to conduct our marriages in a way that honors Him, we can ask for His wisdom and strength in our daily living, like my friend whom I quoted above.

Likewise, we can turn to Scripture for encouragement and wisdom. There we can find assurance of His love and forgiveness. (You might want to read the story of that prodigal young man in Luke 15 every now and then.)

We can also find reminders of His desire to be a consistent, helping presence in our lives. "Never will I leave you," we read; "never will I forsake you."[7]

And there, too, we will find His wisdom for healthy relationships. For example, on the strength to be found in learning from models and mentors, we read, "Two are better than one . . . . If one falls down, his friend can help him up. . . . A cord of three strands is not quickly broken."[8]

The God who observed that "it is not good for the man to be alone," and who declared that "for this reason a man will leave his father and mother and be united to his wife, and they will become one flesh,"[9] wants very much to see your marriage succeed. More than anyone else, He wants to guide, encourage, and empower you to that end.

At any time of day or night, no matter where we are, our heavenly Father is as close as a prayer. Let Him become an active part of your life and your prospects for marital success will increase exponentially.

You Can Succeed

If you've already been divorced, I hope that this entire chapter has been a big dose of encouragement and inspiration for you. Yes, the statistics say that your odds of marital success are slim. But you can beat those odds. With God's help in applying the principles in this chapter and this book, you *can* succeed.

Are you in need of a second chance today? There's a God who's just waiting for you to turn in His direction.

Questions for Reflection and Application

1. If you've been divorced already, what does it mean to you that God stands ready to give you a second chance?

2. What past mistakes do you need to put behind you in order to press ahead into a positive future?

3. If you need additional help in overcoming the effects of a divorce, where might that help come from? If an answer doesn't come readily to mind, where could you start looking?

Chapter Ten

From a Curse to a Blessing

The great truth that can more than conquer the curse is that through your power of choice and God's power to help you carry out what you know to be right thoughts, words, and actions, you can begin today to move in a positive direction.

At the beginning of this book, I wrote that the biblical picture of being "under a curse" is that of a stream that has been dammed up. Consequently, no life-giving water is flowing. And that's a vivid picture of the curse under which we've grown up—you and I—when we've grown up in homes of divorce.

As we've seen in the pages of this book, however, we don't have to stay under that curse. Or, to return to our imagery, by following the principles we've explored here, we can poke holes in that dam and see it gradually break down completely, releasing the flow of clean, fresh water we so desperately need.

In the desert, we can see lush and fragrant and riotously colorful flowers bloom.

Let me tell you the story of a woman we'll call Kelly. Talk about growing up under a curse! If there has ever been anyone the odds were stacked up against for building and sustaining a strong and healthy marriage, it was Kelly. Kelly's situation makes her the perfect poster child for just how difficult some children of divorce can have it.

Kelly grew up in a family in which her grandparents were divorced. Then Kelly's own parents divorced.

Not only that, but both her mom and her dad were from families of six children, and in both cases, three of the six siblings divorced. One of Kelly's uncles, by himself, kept a law firm's worth of attorneys busy—he was married *eight* times!

Kelly herself was one of eight children in her parents' family. All those children are grown now, and all got married. But only three are still married to their original spouses. Some have been married numerous times.

Over the years, as you might imagine, a number of children were born to Kelly's siblings. Many of those nieces and nephews are now grown, too—and many of them are already divorced as well.

You can see, then, why I call Kelly an icon for "child of divorce." Clearly, unfortunately, marriage as a lifetime commitment, "till death do us part," is not the norm in her family. It's not what she saw modeled. No one could blame her for wondering if such a relationship is truly possible.

And yet . . .

Despite growing up in such circumstances, at the time of

this writing, Kelly and her husband have been married for 31 years and counting.

Has their relationship had its lows as well as its highs? Sure. Is it hassle-free and conflict-free? Of course not. But do they love each other deeply? And are they committed to each other and to the relationship, to working out their "issues" and facing life and its challenges *together*? Absolutely.

I call Kelly an icon for "child of divorce." And yet as of this writing, she and her husband have been married for 31 years and counting.

They are, if you will, a magnificent red rosebush in a mostly barren landscape.

How did this happen?

GROWING . . . TOGETHER

Kelly and her husband have built and sustained a strong marriage the same way you can, using the principles and strategies discussed in this book.

Through commitment to each other and to the relationship, they have grown closer together over the years rather than letting Kelly's curse of being an ACOD tear them apart.

Like you, they have the power to choose how they will respond to whatever life throws at them. They choose, day by day, to love, to resolve differences, to forgive and reconcile when necessary, and to put the needs of the other above their own when *that's* needed.

Kelly has been known to joke, "If I weren't so stubborn, determined to make my own marriage work, we might have been divorced several times by now!"

As you need to do, Kelly has faced her fears and "stepped out of the trailer" to deal with her issues growing out of being an ACOD—to move toward health. She'll tell you that she still struggles with the manifestations of the curse. It's not easy, and even having a good spouse doesn't make those problems just go away. Again, it's a daily—sometimes moment-by-moment—choice.

When all they can manage, even with His help, is a step or two "out of the trailer" and in the right direction, they trust that God is going to show up, honor their good intentions, and do for them those things that only He can do.

Furthermore, Kelly and her husband have found models to learn from, examples of unconditional love, of healthy marital relationship, and of commitment. They've seen successful marriages in action. They know it can be done, despite the negative track record in Kelly's family.

Most especially, Kelly and her spouse have crafted a marriage of more than 31 years by drawing on the love and power of God. When they need wisdom beyond their own to solve a problem or overcome some obstacle, they seek it first in prayer.

When they know the life-giving thing to say or do but they just can't summon the strength from within to follow through, they ask God for His power.

And when all they can manage, even with His help, is a step or two "out of the trailer" and in the right direction, they trust that God is going to show up, honor their good intentions, and do for them those things that only He can do.

The sad truth is that being an adult child of divorce has put you under a curse. But the great truth that can more than conquer the curse is that through your power of choice and God's power to help you carry out what you know to be right thoughts, words, and actions, you can begin today to move in a positive direction.

Today, you can start to reverse the curse.

Today, you can take those first steps, initiate that first two-degree change, to overcome the manifestations of the curse in your life.

Today, you can begin to break the cycle of divorce in which you and your family have been trapped. In so doing, you will not only make a far better life for yourself, but you will also bless future generations—your own children and grandchildren, and many generations yet to come.

The choice is yours.

Notes

Introduction

1. Judith S. Wallerstein, Julia M. Lewis, and Sandra Blakeslee, *The Unexpected Legacy of Divorce* (New York: Hyperion, 2000), p. xiii.
2. Beverly and Tom Rodgers, "Pain and Triumph for Children of Divorce," on www.soulhealinglove.com, 1/13/05, citing The Heritage Foundation's report "The Effects of Divorce on America," 6/5/00.
3. "Children of Divorce Getting Divorced Themselves; Becoming Teen Moms, Single Moms, Battered Wives," on http://divorcereform.org/teenmoms.html, 7/15/04.

Chapter 1

1. Toby Green, "Custody and Safekeeping," Body & Soul, 11/18/01, on www.tobygreen.com, 1/13/05.
2. Beverly and Tom Rodgers, "Pain and Triumph for Children of Divorce," on www.soulhealinglove.com, 1/13/05, citing The Heritage Foundation's report "The Effects of Divorce on America," 6/5/00.
3. "Divorce Statistics" on www.co.midland.mi.us, 1/14/05.
4. Leslie Carbone, "The Divorce Caste," on www.pfm.org, 1/14/05.

5. Cara Williams in "Survey suggests parental breakup may affect child's marriage prospects in adulthood," Canadian Press, 9/11/01, on www.fact.on.ca, 1/14/05.
6. Gary A. Sprague, "Breaking the Cycle," *Single-Parent Family*, Focus on the Family, 01/96.

Chapter 2

1. Peg Tyre, "Trend Toward Solitary Confinement Worries Experts," www.cnn.com/US/9801/09/solitary.confinement/#1.
2. Ecclesiastes 4:9-10

Chapter 3

1. 1 Corinthians 15:33
2. Cohabitors 46% more likely to divorce (Andrew Herrmann, "20-somethings who have witnessed ugly divorces in no rush to repeat error," *Chicago Sun-Times*, 6/10/03, on www.suntimes.com/special-sections/marriage, 1/13/05).
3. Proverbs 13:12

Chapter 4

1. 1 John 2:11

Chapter 5

1. Everett L. Worthington, Jr., and R. Kirby Worthington, "No Excuses," www.christianitytoday.com, 1/13/05.
2. 2 Kings 21:5-6
3. 2 Kings 21:20-21
4. 2 Kings 22:2
5. Karen L. Maudlin, "Children of Divorce," www.christianitytoday.com, 1/14/05.
6. See *The Two-Degree Difference* and *Heart Shift* (Broadman & Holman).
7. Proverbs 11:14, NASB.
8. Matthew 10:29-31
9. 1 Peter 5:7
10. Ephesians 2:4
11. 1 John 4:16
12. Psalm 69:16
13. Psalm 86:5
14. Psalm 100:5
15. John 3:16
16. Deuteronomy 23:4-5 (emphasis added)
17. Philippians 2:13
18. Philippians 4:13

Chapter 6

1. Pamela Paul, *The Starter Marriage and the Future of Matrimony* (New York: Random House, 2002) as

quoted in Karen S. Peterson, "Starter Marriage: A new term for early divorce," *USA Today*, 1/29/02, p. 8D.

Chapter 7

1. Deuteronomy 30:19

Chapter 8

1. Elizabeth Marquardt, *Between Two Worlds* (New York: Crown, 2005), p. 189.
2. Ibid., p. 191.

Chapter 9

1. Luke 15:12
2. Luke 15:13
3. Ibid.
4. Luke 15:22-23
5. Luke 15:24
6. Philippians 3:13-14
7. Hebrews 13:5
8. Ecclesiastes 4:9, 10, 12
9. Genesis 2:18, 24

Recommended Resources

General

Ron L. Deal, *The Smart Stepfamily* (Minneapolis: Bethany House, 2006)

Elizabeth Marquardt, *Between Two Worlds* (New York: Crown, 2005)

John Trent, *Choosing to Live the Blessing* (Colorado Springs, Colo.: WaterBrook, 1997)

Judith S. Wallerstein, Julia M. Lewis, and Sandra Blakeslee, *The Unexpected Legacy of Divorce* (New York: Hyperion, 2000)

Feeling isolated

Randy Carlson, *Starved for Affection* (Carol Stream, Ill.: Tyndale/Focus on the Family, 2005)

Sharon Hersh, *Bravehearts: Unlocking the Courage to Love with Abandon* (Colorado Springs, Colo.: WaterBrook, 2000)—for women

False guilt

Henry Cloud, *Changes That Heal: How to Understand Your Past to Ensure a Healthier Future* (Grand Rapids, Mich.: Zondervan, 1997)

James C. Dobson, *Emotions: Can You Trust Them?* (Ventura, Calif.: Regal, 2003)

Unhealthy family secrets

Dave Carder, Earl Henslin, John Townsend, Henry Cloud, and Alice Brawand, *Secrets of Your Family Tree: Healing for Adult Children of Dysfunctional Families* (Chicago: Moody, 1995)

Henry Cloud, *Changes That Heal: How to Understand Your Past to Ensure a Healthier Future* (Grand Rapids, Mich.: Zondervan, 1997)

Marsha Means, *Living with Your Husband's Secret Wars* (Grand Rapids, Mich.: Revell, 1999)

Patrick Means, *Men's Secret Wars* (Grand Rapids, Mich.: Revell, 1999)

Fear-based procrastination

Carol Kent, *Tame Your Fears and Transform Them into Faith, Confidence, and Action* (Colorado Springs, Colo.: NavPress, 2003)—for women

John C. Maxwell, *Failing Forward: Turning Mistakes into Stepping Stones for Success* (Nashville: Nelson, 2000)

Making poor choices

Dave Carder, Earl Henslin, John Townsend, Henry Cloud, and Alice Brawand, *Secrets of Your Family Tree: Healing for*

Adult Children of Dysfunctional Families (Chicago: Moody, 1995)

Henry Cloud, *Changes That Heal: How to Understand Your Past to Ensure a Healthier Future* (Grand Rapids, Mich.: Zondervan, 1997)

Henry Cloud and John Townsend, *Boundaries in Marriage* (Grand Rapids, Mich.: Zondervan, 2002)

James C. Dobson, *Emotions: Can You Trust Them?* (Ventura, Calif.: Regal, 2003)

A habit of making false starts

Gary and Barbara Rosberg, *Divorce-Proof Your Marriage* (Carol Stream, Ill.: Tyndale, 2003)

Breaking commitments

Alistair Begg, *Lasting Love: How to Avoid Marital Failure* (Chicago: Moody, 2002)

Al Janssen, *The Marriage Masterpiece* (Carol Stream, Ill.: Tyndale/Focus on the Family, 2001)

Les and Leslie Parrott, *When Bad Things Happen to Good Marriages: How to Stay Together When Life Pulls You Apart* (Grand Rapids, Mich.: Zondervan, 2001)—referring to marital commitments

Jim Talley, *Reconcilable Differences* (Nashville: Nelson, 1991)—referring to marital commitments

Blaming others

Alistair Begg, *Lasting Love: How to Avoid Marital Failure* (Chicago: Moody, 2002)

Henry Cloud and John Townsend, *Boundaries in Marriage* (Grand Rapids, Mich.: Zondervan, 2002)

Gary Smalley, *The DNA of Relationships: How You Are Designed for Satisfying Relationships* (Carol Stream, Ill.: Tyndale, 2004)

Smoldering anger/inability to forgive

Archibald Hart, "Resentment: The Cancer of Emotions," Focus on the Family broadcast CD

R. T. Kendall, *Total Forgiveness* (Lake Mary, Fla.: Charisma, 2002)

Grace Ketterman and David Hazard, *When You Can't Say "I Forgive You": Breaking the Bonds of Anger and Hurt* (Colorado Springs, Colo.: NavPress, 2000)

Gary Rosberg, *Healing the Hurt in Your Marriage* (Carol Stream, Ill.: Tyndale/Focus on the Family, 2004)

Gary Smalley, "Overcoming Anger," Focus on the Family broadcast cassette

Neil Clark Warren, *Make Anger Your Ally* (Carol Stream, Ill.: Tyndale/Focus on the Family, 1990)

Not really listening to others

Gary Chapman, *Covenant Marriage: Building Communication & Intimacy* (Nashville: Broadman & Holman, 2003)

James C. Dobson, *Five Essentials for Lifelong Intimacy* (Sisters, Ore.: Multnomah, 2005)

Archibald D. Hart and Sharon Hart Morris, *Safe Haven Marriage: Building a Relationship You Want to Come Home To* (Nashville: W Publishing Group, 2003)

Les and Leslie Parrott, *Love Talk: Speak Each Other's Language Like You Never Have Before* (Grand Rapids, Mich.: Zondervan, 2004)

Gary Rosberg, *Healing the Hurt in Your Marriage* (Carol Stream, Ill.: Tyndale/Focus on the Family, 2004)

Seeing God only as an impersonal, uncaring being

Steve and Dee Brestin, *Building Your House on the Lord: A Firm Foundation for Family Life* (Colorado Springs, Colo.: Shaw, 2003)

Les Carter and Frank Minirth, *The Freedom from Depression Workbook* (Nashville: Nelson, 1995)

Max Lucado, *He Still Moves Stones* (Nashville: W Publishing Group, 1999)

Lysa Terkeurst, *Who Holds the Key to Your Heart?* (Chicago: Moody/Focus on the Family, 2002)—for women

Gary Thomas, *Sacred Marriage* (Grand Rapids, Mich.: Zondervan, 2002)

The value of mentors/accountability when trying to make positive choices

Henry Cloud, *Changes That Heal: How to Understand Your Past to Ensure a Healthier Future* (Grand Rapids, Mich.: Zondervan, 1997)

How to have a successful marriage when you've already been divorced

Joseph Warren Kniskern, *Making a New Vow: A Christian's Guide to Remarrying After Divorce* (Nashville: Broadman & Holman, 2003)

Kevin Leman, *Becoming a Couple of Promise* (Colorado Springs, Colo.: NavPress, 1999)

Gary Smalley, *FOF Marriage Series: The Blended Marriage* (Ventura, Calif.: Gospel Light, 2004)

How to overcome your fears when trying to make positive changes

Henry Cloud, *Changes That Heal: How to Understand Your Past to Ensure a Healthier Future* (Grand Rapids, Mich.: Zondervan, 1997)

Carol Kent, *Tame Your Fears and Transform Them into Faith, Confidence, and Action* (Colorado Springs, Colo.: NavPress, 2003)—for women

The wisdom in making a series of small, positive changes rather than trying to make huge changes all at once

John Trent, *Heart Shift* (Nashville: Broadman & Holman, 2004)

John Trent, *The Two-Degree Difference* (Nashville: Broadman & Holman, 2006)

Dr. John Trent is president and founder of Strong Families.com. He is also a best-selling author and sought-after speaker at retreats, conferences, churches, and seminars across the country.

Dr. Trent has launched The Blessing Challenge, a seven-year initiative with the goal of seeing one million people choose to change the life of one child. (Find out more at www.TheBlessing.com.)

In addition to his StrongFamilies in Stressful Times Seminar, Dr. Trent has spoken regularly to corporate America on work/life balance and Leading from Your Strengths. He's addressed organizations such as Chick-fil-A, Northwestern Insurance, The Walt Disney Corporation, Universal Studios, The United States Army, The United States Coast Guard Academy, and many others.

Dr. Trent has been a featured guest on television and radio programs such as the *Oprah Winfrey Show, Focus on the Family, Insight for Living,* the *Billy Graham Evangelistic Association, The 700 Club, Chapel of the Air, Talk to the Doctors, Life Perspectives,* Moody Broadcasting's *Prime Time, Parent Talk, Family Radio,* and many more.

Dr. Trent is the author or co-author of more than a dozen best-selling, award-winning books, including *The Blessing* and *The Two-Degree Difference.* For more information, visit his Web site at www.StrongFamilies.com.

Dr. Trent has been married to his wife, Cindy, for 31 years. They live in Scottsdale, Arizona, and have two grown daughters.

Larry Weeden serves as director of book development and curriculum for Focus on the Family. A veteran of more than 30 years in Christian publishing, he has worked with authors including Chuck Colson, John Maxwell, Gary Smalley, Jerry Jenkins, Lisa Whelchel, and many others. He's also an active freelance writer, with more than 20 books to his credit, including *Feeling Guilty, Finding Grace* and *Wired by God* (co-authored with Joe White).

FOCUS ON THE FAMILY®

Welcome to the Family

Whether you purchased this book, borrowed it, or received it as a gift, thanks for reading it! This is just one of many insightful, biblically based resources that Focus on the Family produces for people in all stages of life.

Focus is a global Christian ministry dedicated to helping families thrive as they celebrate and cultivate God's design for marriage and experience the adventure of parenthood. Our outreach exists to support individuals and families in the joys and challenges they face, and to equip and empower them to be the best they can be.

Through our many media outlets, we offer help and hope, promote moral values and share the life-changing message of Jesus Christ with people around the world.

Focus on the Family MAGAZINES

These faith-building, character-developing publications address the interests, issues, concerns, and challenges faced by every member of your family from preschool through the senior years.

THRIVING FAMILY®
Marriage & Parenting

FOCUS ON THE FAMILY CLUBHOUSE JR.®
Ages 4 to 8

FOCUS ON THE FAMILY CLUBHOUSE®
Ages 8 to 12

FOCUS ON THE FAMILY CITIZEN®
U.S. news issues

For More INFORMATION

ONLINE:
Log on to
FocusOnTheFamily.com
In Canada, log on to
FocusOnTheFamily.ca

PHONE:
Call toll-free:
800-A-FAMILY (232-6459)
In Canada, call toll-free:
800-661-9800

Rev. 3/11

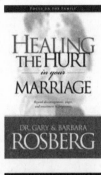

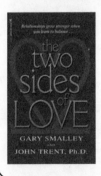